ESSENTIALS OF RADIO

ESSENTIALS OF RADIO

By

MORRIS SLURZBERG, B.S., M.A.,

Instructor of Electricity, Radio and Television,
Henry Snyder High School,
Jersey City, New Jersey

and

WILLIAM OSTERHELD, B.S., M.A.,

Instructor of Electricity and Radio
Wm. L. Dickinson High School, Jersey City

NEW YORK   TORONTO   LONDON

McGRAW-HILL BOOK COMPANY, INC.

ESSENTIALS OF RADIO

THE MAPLE PRESS COMPANY, YORK, PA.

PREFACE

In the past few years the field of electronics has expanded at a phenomenal pace, and predictions are that it will continue to grow at an accelerated rate for some time to come. Although the field of electronics was already quite large before the war, the enormous development program carried on during the war years has produced many new applications of electronics and has opened this field to possibilities of astounding proportions. Electronic principles are employed in all branches of communications, such as telephone, telegraph, radio, television, facsimile, radar, shoran, loran, teleran, and sonar. Applications of electronic principles are also found in various branches of scientific research, many branches of therapeutics, and a wide variety of industrial manufacturing processes. There is scarcely an industry that does not today employ some electronic device as a process control or safety device in the manufacture of its products.

Although the circuits used in the many applications of electronics are quite diversified and complex they all have two points in common: (1) They employ the basic circuit elements such as resistors, inductors, capacitors, and vacuum tubes. (2) They employ one or more of the basic circuit applications of these basic circuit elements. Therefore, in order to understand the many complex circuits used in electronics, it is necessary to have a thorough knowledge of the basic circuit elements and their basic circuit applications. With this knowledge as a background it is then only necessary to study the new circuit element and its circuit applications in order to understand the operation of any complex circuit that may be used in television, radar, industrial control, etc.

The purpose of this text is to present, at an intermediate level, a comprehensive study of the principles of operation of vacuum tubes, their basic circuits, and the application of these circuits to low-frequency radio-receiver applications. A chapter on test equipment and test procedures as applied to receiver circuits and a chapter on transmitters are also included in the text to provide an introductory knowledge to these subjects. A review of the operating characteristics and circuit applications of resistors, inductors, and capacitors as used in electronic circuits is presented in Chap. II. For a more thorough treatment of the subject

v

matter covered in Chap. II, the reader is referred to the authors' text "Electrical Essentials of Radio."

This book is intended for: (1) students studying radio or electronics in a high school, trade school, vocational school, technical school, or junior college; (2) persons not attending any regular school but who wish to study the subject on an intermediate level. This book is also intended to provide the background necessary for further study of electronics in fields such as the high-frequency and ultrahigh-frequency circuit applications which require as a prerequisite a knowledge of the basic detector, amplifier, oscillator, and rectifier circuits for low-frequency applications as presented in this text.

The following features, not ordinarily found in any one book, have been incorporated in this text.

1. A minimum knowledge of mathematics is required. Most of the mathematics involves the use of only addition, subtraction, multiplication, division, and square root. The use of equations and vectors and plotting and interpretation of curves are explained in the text.

2. Examples are used throughout the book to illustrate the applications of the equations and principles discussed in the text. All except a few minor equations are followed by an illustrative example. The values used in the examples have been carefully selected and represent actual practical values. Examples of complex as well as simple circuits are illustrated for d-c circuits, a-c circuits, and vacuum-tube circuits.

3. Letter symbols, abbreviations, and drawing symbols used for circuit diagrams have been selected wherever possible to conform to those adopted or recommended by the IRE, RMA, or ASA.

4. The principle of operation of the various circuit elements and the analysis of the operation of electric and vacuum-tube circuits are explained according to the electron theory except in a few instances where it is more practical to refer to current flow.

5. In recognition of the value of visual instruction, drawings are used to illustrate each principle as it is presented. As many of the important features of the parts used in electricity and radio cannot be readily shown by diagrams, numerous photographs of actual commercial products appear throughout the text.

6. The operation of the circuits used to perform each of the basic functions of a vacuum tube, namely, detection, amplification, oscillation, and rectification, is explained in great detail in order to illustrate the purpose and action of each circuit element in the composite circuit. In the explanation of the operation of these circuits a wide variety of tube types has been employed so that the tube types for specific applications conform to those used in practical circuits.

CONTENTS

CHAPTER I

INTRODUCTION TO RADIO

Much of the progress in civilization may be attributed to man's ability to communicate with his fellow men and thereby transmit his thoughts to them. The progress of civilization and the means of communication quite naturally have advanced at about the same pace. Radio is the newest and most modern means of communication, and in one manner or another it affects the lives of hundreds of millions of people.

Radio is a branch of a new field of science called *electronics*. Electronics has enabled scientists to develop means of examining the germ structure of bacteria and to see through fog and the utter blackness of night. It is used to detect poisons, to guarantee food values, to control manufacturing processes, and to protect life and property. Electronics has opened a new field to science and should result in many developments that will contribute to a better world.

1-1. Forms of Communication. Man's chief means of communication are the senses of sight and hearing. These are commonly referred to as the *audible* and *visible* means of communication. Each method has been used since the early stages of civilization and each is still used extensively.

Visual Means of Communication. The sense of sight has long been useful to man, first as a means of warning him of approaching dangers and later to enable him to receive messages in written form. There are numerous examples illustrating the progress of the visible methods of communication, such as the hieroglyphics of the ancient Egyptians, the smoke signals of the American Indians, printed matter such as newspapers, books, etc., photography, motion pictures, and television.

Audible Means of Communication. The sense of hearing also has been used for communication through many stages of civilization. It, too, served to warn man of approaching dangers long before the development of modern communication systems. As civilization progressed, the audible methods of communication went through numerous stages as illustrated by the development of languages to convey thoughts, the development of devices such as the telegraph, telephone, wireless, and radio to transmit messages over greater distances, and the development

1

of devices such as the phonograph and sound motion pictures to make it possible to keep a record of the message.

1-2. History of Radio Communication. *Basic Electrical Principles.* Through consistent research and experimentation many scientists have contributed to the development of radio communication. Credit for the invention of radio can go to no one person as was given Morse for the telegraph, Bell for the telephone, and Marconi for wireless telegraphy. Its development has taken years, and many men have made important contributions. A brief history of radio progress can, therefore, be outlined by presenting the names of these scientists and the contributions they have made.

In 1865, James Clerk Maxwell, utilizing the electrical and magnetic experiments developed by Michael Faraday and Hans Christian Oersted, proposed the following theories: (1) that light waves were electromagnetic in character; (2) that a charge of electricity moving through space constituted an electric current as well as a charge moving in the wires of an electric circuit; (3) that a magnet moving in space generated an electromotive force in the space around it.

In 1888, Heinrich Hertz proved by direct experiments that the predictions made by Maxwell were true. Hertz made a very careful study of electric waves and found not only that they move with the same speed as light, but that they behave in the same manner as do light waves in every way except that they cannot be seen by the human eye. While the waves of visible light are so short that from 30,000 to 60,000 are required to equal the space of one inch, the electric waves were discovered by Hertz to have lengths ranging from several inches to several miles.

Wireless. In 1895, Marconi invented the aerial, and he was able to increase the distance by which electric waves could be projected into space. To increase the energy of transmission, antenna structures were made very large and high voltages were used. The early commercial transmitters were of the spark type, utilizing the charge and discharge of a capacitor through an oscillator circuit containing a spark gap, which was inductively coupled to the antenna circuit and in resonance with it. The principle of inductive coupling and the resonance between various parts of the transmitting circuit was discovered by Sir Oliver Lodge. Following the spark system of transmission the continuous-wave method was used, and during this time the Poulsen arc and the Alexanderson and Goldschmidt alternators came into use. For detection at the receiving end of the radio system, the coherer and the crystal detector were generally used.

Radio. The transmission of voice, music, etc., through space was

originally referred to as *radiotelephony* but it is now called *radio*. Its
development and advancement are due largely to the introduction and
development of the vacuum tube. Engineers working on transcontinen-
tal wired-telephone systems began using vacuum tubes in these telephone
circuits about 1912. Use of these tubes resulted in rapid developments,
and by 1915 engineers of the Bell System were able to transmit voice
messages by wireless telephone from Washington to Paris, and from

Fig. 1-1.—Evolution from the early DeForest tube to the modern vacuum tubes of more
complex structure. (*Courtesy of RCA Manufacturing Co., Inc.*)

Washington to Hawaii nearly 5,000 miles away. Several radio broadcasting stations were operated on an experimental basis before 1920, but
it was not until 1920 that broadcast of regularly scheduled programs was
introduced by station KDKA of Pittsburgh. Commercial broadcast radio
receivers were first introduced in 1921. By 1922 radio had advanced to
the stage of broadcasting events originating outside of the studio, such
as band concerts, football games, etc. Continuous improvements in the
quality of broadcasting and the introduction of station networks have
aided in the further development of radio.

1-3. Development of the Vacuum Tube. *Development of Basic Principles.* Although much of the progress in the development and applications of vacuum tubes has been made during the past twenty years, the basic principles upon which all vacuum tubes operate were established during the latter half of the nineteenth century. A study of the electrical conductivity of gases was started in 1853 by Alexander Becquerel. From his experiments he came to certain conclusions as to the conductivity of gases. Although these conclusions were later refuted by Gustav Wiedemann, they were confirmed in 1881 by René Blondlot.

Thomas Edison used these principles to develop his incandescent lamp. His first commercially practical lamp was made in 1879. Four years later, while conducting experiments to perfect the lamp, he noticed that, if a second electrode, in the form of a wire or plate, was placed inside the lamp and this electrode made positive with respect to one end of the filament, a small current flowed to this electrode when the filament was heated. This effect is called the *Edison effect.* Apparently the only use that Edison could imagine for such a device was as an indicator of voltage variations in a lighting circuit; hence in his application for a patent in 1883 he refers to the lamp as an *electrical indicator.*

The Fleming Valve. The news of the Edison effect aroused interest throughout the scientific world. Sir William Preece, who was particularly interested in this phenomenon, persuaded Edison to give him one of these experimental lamps and proceeded to make quantitative measurements of the Edison effect. Experiments with the incandescent lamp were also being conducted at this time by Prof. J. A. Fleming, an electrical adviser to the Edison Electric Light Company of London. In one of his earlier experiments Fleming showed that if the cold electrode is heated to incandescence an electric current may be made to flow through the vacuum by use of an external battery. In continuing the quantitative measurements made by Sir William Preece, Fleming produced a curve showing the relation between the voltage across the lamp and the current flowing through the vacuum. He also proved that a unidirectional current would flow in the cold electrode circuit even if an alternating current were used to heat the filament.

In his search for a means of rectifying high-frequency alternating currents, Fleming utilized the principles of the Edison effect and developed what he referred to as an *oscillation valve.* In England, vacuum tubes are still referred to as valves. In the application for a United States patent, he calls this device an instrument for converting alternating electric currents into continuous currents.

Factors Affecting the Electron Emission. Between 1899 and 1901 Prof. J. J. Thomson, the discoverer of the electron, and Prof. O. W.

Richardson carried on scientific research to determine the relation between the amount of heat, material used, and the electron emission resulting when a material was heated in vacuum. From these experiments Prof. Richardson was able to formulate the fundamental laws of electron emission from heated materials in vacuum. These laws have

Fig. 1-2.—Dr. Irving Langmuir, Sir Joseph John Thomson, and Dr. William D. Coolidge at the General Electric laboratories when Thomson, the famous discoverer of the electron, visited America in 1923. (*Courtesy of General Electric Company.*)

served as a basis for determining the materials to be used as the electron emitter and the temperature required to obtain the desired electron flow.

The Audion. As the Fleming valve served to rectify high-frequency alternating currents, and therefore could be used as a detector, it provided the means needed for further advancement in wireless communication. This valve acted only as a rectifier and could not be used as an amplifying device, which is one of the most important uses of vacuum tubes. About 1906, Dr. Lee De Forest introduced a new vacuum tube, to which he added a third electrode, called a *grid*. By means of this grid he was able to control the amount of electron flow; thus the tube could now be used as either a detector or an amplifier. This tube was called an *audion* and constituted a considerable advance over earlier forms of radio detectors.

The exact manner in which this tube functioned was not known until about 1912, when Dr. Irving Langmuir demonstrated that the output of a vacuum tube was dependent on the following factors: (1) the electron emission, which is controlled by the current flowing in the filament; (2) the voltage applied to the plate; (3) the grid voltage; (4) the spacing between the electrodes.

Modern Vacuum Tubes. Improvements to the vacuum tube were accelerated by further study and experimentation carried on by numerous scientists and led to the modern vacuum tube. Some of the improvements are: (1) high-vacuum tubes, which permit high voltages to be applied to the plate; (2) better materials for the electron emitter; (3) heaters for a-c operation; (4) the beam power tube, for control of direction of the flow of electrons; (5) new elements, such as the screen grid and the suppressor grid; (6) multi-purpose tubes, which makes it possible for one tube to take the place of two or more tubes; (7) new types of construction, such as metal, single-end, loktal, bantam, miniature, and acorn tubes; (8) special-purpose tubes, such as voltage regulators, electron-ray indicators, controls for relay and sweep circuits, cathode-ray tubes, photo tubes, and television tubes.

1-4. Development of the Radio Circuit. In addition to the improvement of the vacuum tube, many other changes, additions, and methods of connecting the various parts of radio transmitters and receivers have taken place during the past thirty years.

Radio Circuits. In 1914, Maj. E. H. Armstrong obtained a patent on the *regenerative circuit,* also known as a *feedback* or *self-heterodyning circuit.* In 1924, Louis Alton Hazeltine gave the world his tuned-radio-frequency method of amplification and the principle of neutralization of the capacitance of coils. Hartley, Colpitts, and Meissner made variations in the oscillator circuit that is used in all superheterodyne receivers and in all transmitter circuits. The constant-current system of plate modulation as developed by Heising is the method most commonly used by transmitting stations.

The circuits developed by these men constituted a considerable advancement in radio design and were quite complex when compared to the simple crystal-detector circuits. In comparison to the radio circuit as used in modern receivers, however, they are simple. Although most commercial receivers use either the superheterodyne or tuned-radio-frequency circuit, their only resemblance to the fundamental circuits as developed by Armstrong and Hazeltine is in the basic principle involved. Numerous changes and additions to these circuits, such as ganged tuning, band switching, automatic volume control, power detectors, filter circuits, etc., were contributed by a countless number of men, and these changes are responsible for the great difference between the basic and modern circuits.

Circuit Elements. During the time all these changes were being made in the vacuum-tube and radio-circuit design, constant improvements were also being made in the resistors, capacitors, and inductors used in the radio circuits in order to improve their operating efficiency. Electrolytic capacitors, carbon-type variable controls, powdered-iron-core radio-frequency coils, ganged variable capacitors, and midget variable capacitors are but a few of these improvements. As in the case of the vacuum tube and the radio circuit, these improvements represent the efforts of many individuals in the various industries and research laboratories throughout the world.

Further Circuit Improvements. In the early stages of radio, all transmitters used what is known as *amplitude modulation.* With this method undesired noises, such as static, were amplified in the same proportion as were the desired signals. If the original strength of the undesired signals represented a moderate proportion of the signal strength of a desired station, the reception of signals from this station would be very noisy.

Major Armstrong, in seeking a way to eliminate static, decided that some method of modulating the signal must be used for which nature had no duplicate. His method of f-m, or *frequency modulation,* is the result, and it has revolutionized the field of radio communication. It is now possible to hear entertainment over the radio without being disturbed by the annoying noises made by static.

1-5. Other Applications of Electronics. The principles of electronics and vacuum tubes are used for applications other than those of radio communication. These uses may be divided into the following four classifications: (1) television; (2) industry; (3) instruments; (4) therapeutics. These four subjects represent large fields of application and books can be written about each field. For this reason these subjects will be treated very briefly in this text.

Television. This branch of communication deals with the transmission and reception of visual images at a distance. As the word *radio* has become synonymous with the communication of audible sounds, *television* is used to represent the communication of visual signals. This subject deals with the study of lenses, light, electronic scanning, the iconoscope or electric eye of the television camera, and the kinescope.

corresponding to the loudspeaker of a radio receiver. In addition, all the basic principles of electric circuits—resonance, amplification, etc.— that are used in radio receivers and transmitters are also used in television apparatus.

Industrial Applications. The applications of electronics and vacuum tubes to industry are many and varied. The basic circuits of many of these applications are similar to those used in radio, the only difference being the use to which they are put. For example, the principles of

Fig. 1-3.—View of a television program being televised. (*Courtesy of General Electric Company.*)

resonance are used to control the thickness, quality, weight, and moisture content of a material. Amplifier circuits are used to increase the intensity of weak current impulses produced by phototubes and cause them to operate relays controlling circuits of door openers, lighting systems, power systems, safety devices, etc.

Principles other than those common to radio are also used, such as stroboscopic lighting, which can cause fast-moving objects to appear motionless or make their movements appear similar to the slow motion of motion pictures. By means of this principle it is possible to study the movements of various parts of a machine under their operating conditions. It is also used for high-speed photography applications in order to arrest the motion of fast-moving objects.   Phototubes and photo cells are used to control lighting, open doors, operate protective devices, etc.

These are but a few of the many applications of the principles of electronics to industry.   Further developments indicate that many new applications of electronics will result in numerous additional uses.

Instruments.   The principles of electronics have made it possible to measure quantities that up to now have been impossible to measure.

Fig. 1-4.—Photoelectric safety control.   The light is reflected across the front and returned to the phototube by means of two mirrors shown in the foreground of the equipment.   (*Courtesy of RCA Manufacturing Co., Inc.*)

The vacuum-tube voltmeter, cathode-ray oscillograph, resonant circuit checkers, and signal generators are but a few of the many new types of instruments that have become synonymous with radio and electronics. The use of these instruments has become as valuable for checking electronic circuits as the ammeter and voltmeter are for checking electric circuits.

Therapeutics.   Medical doctors and scientists in the field of therapeutics, which is the treatment of diseases, are constantly finding new uses for the principles of electronics to aid in treating and preventing physical ailments.   Their instruments include: (1) X rays, which are used for treatment of skin disorders and acute infections as well as for taking pictures of internal structures; (2) ultraviolet lamps for arresting harmful mold and bacteria; (3) short-wave diathermy units for healing sprains and fractures; (4) electro-cardiographs for measuring heartbeats; (5) inductotherm units used to generate artificial fever; (6) oscillographs for illustrating muscle actions.   These are but a few of the many applications of electronics that are being used in the field of therapeutics.

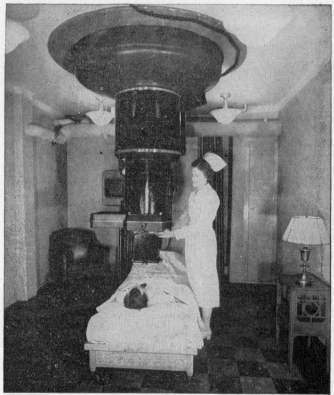

FIG. 1-5.—A patient under treatment with the 1,000,000-volt X-ray therapy unit in one of the nation's large hospitals.   (*Courtesy of General Electric Company.*)

1-6. Sound.   Radio is a means of sending information through space from one point to another.   The information may be either a sound wave produced by the voice or some musical instrument, or a wave so interrupted that it is broken into a combination of long and short groups that correspond to the characters of the Morse code.   Therefore, radio is nothing more than the sending out or receiving of sound through space from one point to another, without any wires connecting the two points.

It is therefore essential to know something about sound and sound waves before studying the principles of radio.

Sound is the sensation produced in the brain by sound waves. It makes use of one of our five fundamental senses, namely, that of hearing. The air in a room in which no sound is present is in a static condition; in other words, it is motionless. If a sound is made by a person, by a musical instrument, or by any other means, the air about it is set into vibration. When these vibrations strike the eardrum of any person, the eardrum too will vibrate in a similar manner. The auditory nerves will be stimulated and will communicate the sensation of sound to the brain. These air vibrations are called *sound waves*. Sound waves are produced

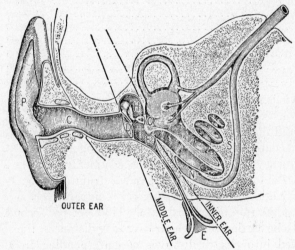

OUTER EAR   MIDDLE EAR   INNER EAR

Fig. 1-6.—Internal structure of the human ear. (*Reprinted by permission from the Bell Laboratories Record.*)

by the mechanical vibration of any material in an elastic medium. For example, the vibration of the reeds in a harmonica, the skin on a drum, the strings on a violin, or the cone of a radio loudspeaker will all send out various sound waves. These waves will produce different sounds, depending on the number of vibrations that the wave makes per second. The number of complete waves or vibrations created per second is known as the *frequency* of the sound and is generally expressed as the number of cycles per second. For example, a sound wave making 2000 vibrations per second would be the same as 2000 cycles per second, and it is said that the sound wave is producing 2000 cycles.

If the sound is loud enough to be heard by the human ear, it is said to be *audible*. Its pitch will vary with the frequency. High frequencies produce sounds having a high pitch and low frequencies produce sounds of low pitch.

1-7. Frequency Ranges of Sound Waves. The range of frequencies that the human ear is capable of hearing will vary with the individual, the lower limit being approximately 20 cycles and the upper limit 20,000 cycles. Some persons are able to hear the low-pitch sounds but cannot hear those of high pitch, while others can hear the high-pitch sounds but cannot hear those of low pitch, and there are people who are able to hear sounds covering a wide range of frequencies.

Below is a list of a few common audible sounds and their approximate frequency range.

Human voice	75–3000 cycles
Piano	25–8000 cycles
Violin	200–3000 cycles
Trombone	100– 500 cycles
Clarinet	150–1500 cycles
Flute	250–2300 cycles
Piccolo	500–4500 cycles

Code signals may be sent at any audio frequency, but experience has shown that a signal having a frequency of 1000 cycles will produce a pleasing sound that can be continually listened to easily and that will permit each dit, dah, or space to be quickly distinguished.

The frequency range of sound waves, commonly taken as 20 to 20,000 cycles, is at the lower end of the wave spectrum (see Fig. 1-9). Sound waves usually are capable of traveling only comparatively short distances and travel at the rate of approximately 1130 feet per second. In order for sounds to be carried through air over long distances, the sound waves are converted into electrical waves of corresponding frequencies and applied to a high-frequency carrier wave by modern radio transmitting stations.

Sound waves may also be referred to in terms of the length of a wave. Figure 1-8 illustrates a tuning fork producing sound waves whose frequency is 256 cycles per second. At this frequency one cycle is completed in $\frac{1}{256}$ second, and, since sound waves travel at approximately 1130 feet per second, the length of one wave may easily be calculated.

Example 1-1. The frequency range of a piano is from 25 to 8000 cycles. (a) What is the range of wavelengths in feet? (b) In meters? (c) If the sound waves are converted to electrical waves by a microphone, what is the frequency range of the electric currents?

Given: Find:
    Sound waves = 25–8000 cycles   (a) Wavelengths, feet = ?
                                     (b) Wavelengths, meters = ?
                                     (c) Frequency range of electric currents = ?

Solution:

(a)   Wavelength, 25 cycles $= \dfrac{\text{feet per second}}{\text{cycles per second}} = \dfrac{1130}{25} = 45.2$ feet

     Wavelength, 8000 cycles $= \dfrac{\text{feet per second}}{\text{cycles per second}} = \dfrac{1130}{8000} = 0.14125$ foot

(b)   NOTE: 1 meter = 39.37 inches = 3.28 feet

     Wavelength, 25 cycles $= \dfrac{\text{wavelength, feet}}{3.28} = \dfrac{45.2}{3.28} = 13.7$ meters

     Wavelength, 8000 cycles $= \dfrac{\text{wavelength, feet}}{3.28} = \dfrac{0.14125}{3.28} = 0.043$ meter

(c)   25 to 8000 cycles (same frequencies as the sound waves)

1-8. Radio Waves. Radio transmitting stations convert sound waves to electrical impulses. The electrical impulses that represent the original sound waves are sent out by the use of high-frequency alternating currents. These currents produce magnetic and electric fields that radiate in all directions over long distances without losing much of their original strength. The magnetic and electric fields produced by this means are called *radio waves*. The strength and frequency of the radio wave is dependent on the high-frequency alternating current producing it, and, therefore, it will vary in the same manner as the alternating current.

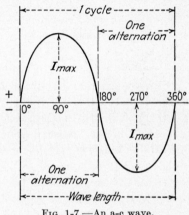

FIG. 1-7.—An a-c wave.

An a-c wave (see Fig. 1-7) reverses its direction at fixed intervals, and during each interval the current will rise from zero to its maximum value, then diminish to zero. By referring to this figure it can be seen that an a-c wave completes one cycle after it has made two alternations, one in the positive direction and one in the negative direction. The fixed interval required for each alternation is 180 degrees, and for one cycle or two alternations it would be 360 degrees. I is a symbol used to denote current and *max* an abbreviation of the word maximum. I_{max} would, therefore, mean the maximum amount of current flow; from Fig. 1-7 this would occur at every 90- and 270-degree instant of an alternating-current cycle.

1-9. Wavelength, Frequency. *Speed of Radio Waves.* Radio waves travel at the same speed as light waves, or 186,000 miles per second. In radio calculations the metric system is used, and it is desirable to express the speed of radio waves in meters per second.

Example 1-2. If radio waves travel at the rate of 186,000 miles per second, what is their rate in meters per second? Note: One meter is equal to 39.37 inches; also, one mile is equal to 5280 feet.

Given:
  Miles per second = 186,000
  Feet per mile = 5280
  Inches per meter = 39.37

Find:
  Meters per second = ?

Solution:

$$\text{Meters per second} = \frac{\text{inches per second}}{39.37}$$

$$= \frac{186,000 \times 5280 \times 12}{39.37}$$

$$\cong 300,000,000$$

Note: $\cong$ means *is approximately equal to* (see Appendix II).

Wavelength and Frequency Definitions. WAVELENGTH. The distance that the radio wave travels in one cycle is called its *wavelength;* it is

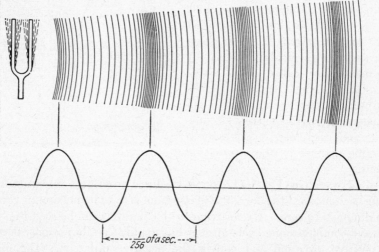

Fig. 1-8.—Propagation of sound waves.

expressed in meters and is often represented by the symbol λ, a letter of the Greek alphabet pronounced lambda.

FREQUENCY. The number of cycles per second of a radio wave is called its *frequency* and is generally represented by the letter *f*. In radio work it is common practice to refer to the frequency as its number of cycles instead of cycles per second. This is merely an abbreviation and it should be remembered that it really means cycles per second.

Wavelength and Frequency Calculations. WAVELENGTH. If the frequency of a wave is known, it is possible to calculate the distance traveled in one cycle by means of the equation

$$\lambda = \frac{300,000,000}{f} \tag{1-1}$$

where λ = wavelength, meters
f = frequency, cycles per second

Example 1-3. What is the length of a radio wave whose frequency is 570,000 cycles?

Given: Find:
f = 570,000 cycles λ = ?

Solution:

$$\lambda = \frac{300,000,000}{f} = \frac{300,000,000}{570,000} = 526.3 \text{ meters}$$

KILOCYCLES. The frequencies of the common radio waves are of high values, that is, in the hundreds of thousands or millions of cycles per second. For convenience these frequencies are generally expressed in kilocycles or megacycles and abbreviated as kc and mc respectively. *Kilo-* is a prefix meaning thousand; hence a kilocycle is equal to 1000 cycles. Recalling the abbreviation referred to above, one kilocycle actually means 1000 cycles per second. *Mega-* is a prefix meaning million; hence a megacycle is equal to 1,000,000 cycles. Additional information on multiple units and the use of exponents is given in Appendixes III and IV.

When radio frequencies are expressed in kilocycles, Eq. (1-1) becomes

$$\lambda = \frac{300,000}{f} \tag{1-2}$$

where λ = wavelength, meters
f = frequency, kilocycles

Example 1-4. What is the wavelength of radio station WMCA, which operates on a frequency of 570 kc?

Given: Find:
f = 570 kc λ = ?

Solution:

$$\lambda = \frac{300,000}{f} = \frac{300,000}{570} = 526.3 \text{ meters}$$

FREQUENCY. Equation (1-2) can be transposed to solve for frequency instead of wavelength, and becomes

$$f = \frac{300,000}{\lambda} \tag{1-3}$$

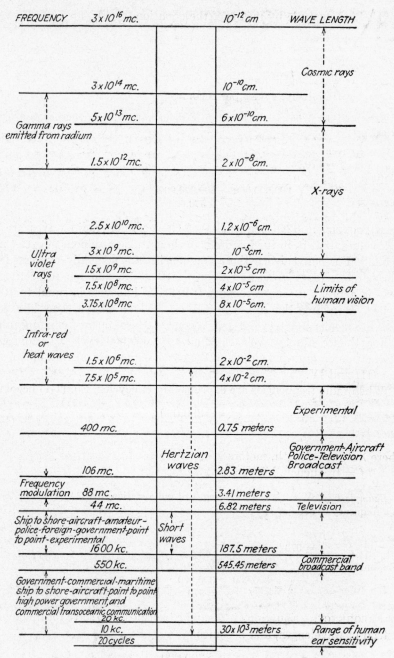

FIG. 1-9.—Relation of frequency and wavelength of various waves.

Example 1-5. If by definition a short radio wave is one whose wavelength does not exceed 200 meters, what is the lowest frequency at which a short-wave radio receiver may operate?

Given: Find:
$\lambda = 200$ meters $f = ?$

Solution:

$$f = \frac{300,000}{\lambda} = \frac{300,000}{200} = 1500 \text{ kc}$$

From Eq. (1-3) it can be seen that the greater the length of the radio wave the lower its frequency will be, and conversely the shorter a radio wave is the higher its frequency will be. By applying this thought to Example 1-5 it becomes evident that the frequency of short-wave radio transmitters will be 1500 kc and higher.

In order to get an idea of the length of a radio wave, it is necessary only to change the wavelength to our common units of feet or miles.

Example 1-6. What is the length in feet of one radio wave of the broadcast station referred to in Example 1-4?

Given: Find:
$\lambda = 526.3$ meters   Feet $= ?$

Solution:

$$\text{Feet} = \frac{\text{meters} \times 39.37}{12} = \frac{526.3 \times 39.37}{12} = 1726 \text{ feet}$$

The solution of Example 1-6 indicates that each wave transmitted by station WMCA is 1726 feet long, or approximately one-third of a mile.

Knowing that radio waves travel 186,000 miles per second, the time required for a radio wave to get from one place to another can be readily calculated.

Example 1-7. How long does it take a radio wave to travel from New York to San Francisco, a distance of approximately 2600 miles?

Given: Find:
Miles $= 2600$ Time $= ?$
Miles per second $= 186,000$

Solution:

$$t = \frac{\text{miles}}{186,000} = \frac{2600}{186,000} = 0.0139 \text{ second}$$

The solution of Example 1-7 indicates that it takes only about 0.014 second for a person's voice broadcast on a radio program to travel from New York to San Francisco.

1-10. Simple Explanation of Radio Transmission and Reception. Have you ever asked the question, "How is it possible for a person to sing, talk, or play a musical instrument, in fact to make any audible

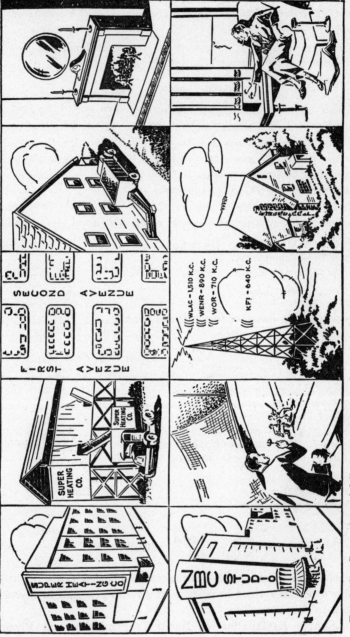

Fig. 1-10.—Comparison of delivery, receiving, and use of coal (top) with sending, receiving, and use of sound waves (below).

sound, and be heard almost instantly by people thousands of miles away?" To answer this question the sending and receiving of sound waves will be compared with the delivery and receiving of a ton of coal.

If a person orders a ton of coal from a coalyard, the coal is loaded on a truck, which carries it to his home. The driver stops the truck at the person's home because he ordered the coal. The buyer does not want the truck—he wants the coal; so the driver and his helpers unload the coal into the bin and drive away with the truck to deliver the rest of the load.

In a similar manner, if an audible sound wave is made at some transmitting station, this audible sound gets to the listener's home only if a means of carrying it there is provided. In place of a coal truck, transmitting stations use a *carrier wave*. Just as the coal had to be put on the truck, the audible sound wave must be put on the carrier wave. A *modulator* is used for this purpose. The modulator takes the audible sound wave that has been changed to electrical impulses by the microphone and superimposes it on the carrier wave. The resultant is called a *modulated wave*.

This modulated wave is now sent out by a *transmitting antenna*, just as the coal truck was sent from the coalyard. During the day any number of coal trucks pass the door of the buyer mentioned above, but the only truck that stops is the one that is to deliver the coal to his home. In the same manner any number of modulated waves pass the antenna of the listener's radio. He turns a dial on his receiver and selects the station he wants to listen to. This is actually selecting the desired modulated wave.

Next the ton of coal was separated from the truck placed in the bin, and the truck then continued on its way to make other deliveries. In radio, part of the energy of the modulated wave enters the receiver; the remainder is available for other receivers. At the receiver the audible sound wave is separated from the modulated wave by the *detector*, which may also be called the *demodulator*.

No heat is obtained from the coal unless it is burned, and similarly no sound is obtained from the audio wave unless it causes some material to vibrate. The amount of energy output of the detector (audio wave) is so small that it is sufficient only to operate a set of earphones. If it is desired to fill a room with the sound wave, it becomes necessary to use a *loudspeaker*. In order to obtain sufficient energy to operate a loudspeaker an *audio amplifier*, inserted after the detector, is included in radio receivers.

Just as there are numerous trucks carrying coal, so too there are numerous carrier waves carrying audio waves. Also, just as the trucks must be controlled to prevent interference between them, so too the modulated waves must be controlled. To prevent interference among modulated waves, the Federal Communications Commission assigns definite frequencies to the transmitting or broadcasting stations. For example, the frequency of the carrier wave of station KFI, Los Angeles, is 640 kc; WLAC, Nashville, 1510 kc; and WENR, Chicago, 890 kc. By setting the dial of a receiver to 710 kc, a person in New York will be able to hear the program being broadcast by station WOR any time of the day, any day of the week, month, or year.

1-11. General Picture of Radio Transmission and Reception. The chart shown as Fig. 1-11 presents a simple picture of the various operations required to send a sound wave out into space and to have it received many miles away.

The top line is a block diagram illustrating the essential portions of a radio transmitter and receiver. It is called a *block diagram* because each section is represented by merely drawing a block and labeling it to conform with the portion it represents. The first unit is the *microphone*, where the audible sound waves are picked up and changed into electrical impulses. The electrical impulses from the microphone are too weak to be sent through space on the carrier wave and, therefore, must be amplified. This is accomplished by sending the wave from the microphone to the *speech amplifier*. The next block is called the *oscillator*, which is the portion that sets up the carrier wave of the transmitter, in this example, 550 kc. This is followed by the *modulator*, which receives energy from both the oscillator and the speech amplifier. At the modulator the audio waves of the speech amplifier are superimposed on the *carrier wave*, and this modulated carrier wave is then sent out into space by the *transmitting antenna*.

The *receiving antenna* is affected by the magnetic and electric fields set up in space by the transmitting antenna, and if the *selector* or tuning portion of the receiver is set for the proper frequency (in this example 550 kc), a workable amount of electrical energy enters the receiver. The amount of energy is small and must be increased in strength at this point by the *radio-frequency amplifier*. The selector and the r-f amplifier are shown in a single block because these two operations are generally combined. The next block, labeled *detector*, might also be called the *demodulator* because at this point the audio waves are separated from the carrier wave. The audio waves coming from the detector are too weak to operate a loudspeaker and therefore must be sent through an *audio-frequency amplifier* before going on to the *loudspeaker*.

The second line indicates the frequency of the wave as it enters and leaves the various parts of the transmitter and receiver operated at a frequency assumed to be 550 kc. The third line is a diagrammatic

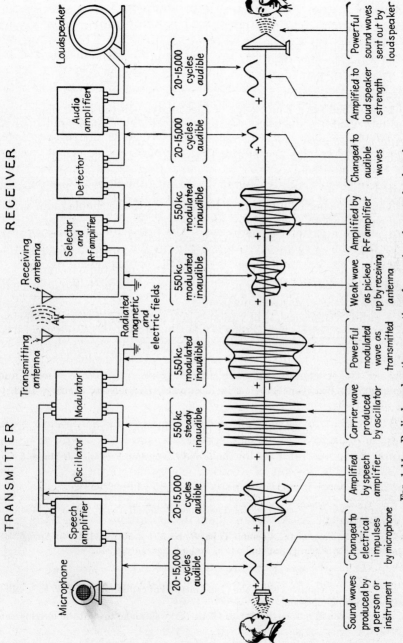

Fig. 1-11.—Radio-broadcasting operations from microphone to loudspeaker.

representation of these frequencies. A careful examination of the figure will show that every step performed in the transmitter is also performed in the receiver but in reversed order, starting with the sound waves entering the microphone at the transmitter and ending with similar sound waves leaving the loudspeaker of the receiver.

The fourth line summarizes the purpose of each part of the radio transmitter and receiver.

1-12. Need for a Knowledge of Electricity. In the block diagram of Fig. 1-11, each function is represented merely as a square and called an *oscillator, modulator, amplifier,* or *detector.* Each one of these parts is made up of various electrical devices such as resistors, inductors, capacitors, and tubes, all properly connected in order to perform the function desired.

There have been a number of changes made to the simple radio circuit used years ago to give us the modern radio receiver and transmitter. Where the broadcast band formerly extended from 500 to 1500 kc, its higher frequencies now extend into megacycles. Of the various circuits used in the development of radio only two, the tuned radio frequency and the superheterodyne, are in general use today, the superheterodyne being practically the standard circuit used.

A radio circuit consists of various kinds and types of electrical devices properly connected. In order to understand these circuits, one must have a broad and thorough knowledge of electrical and radio theory.

BIBLIOGRAPHY

EICHBERG, R., War Time Progress in Electronics, *Radio News*, January, 1943, to May, 1943.

Encyclopaedia Britannica.

FLETCHER, G. L., MOSBACHER, I., and LEHMAN, S., *Unified Physics*, McGraw-Hill Book Company, Inc., New York.

MANLY, H. P., *Drake's Cyclopedia of Radio and Electronics*, Frederick J. Drake & Co., Chicago.

MOODY, W., New Devices for Industry, *Radio News*, February, 1943.

PRATER, C. D., Fundamental Atomic Physics, Electron Control Methods, Gas Discharge Device, Photo Electric Phenomena, *Radio News*, February, 1943, to July, 1943.

TYNE, G. F. J., Saga of the Vacuum Tube, *Radio News*, March, 1943, to April, 1946.

WINTERS, S. R., Therapeutic Radionics, *Radio News*, July, 1943.

QUESTIONS

1. Name six examples of (*a*) the visual method of communication, (*b*) the audible method of communication.

2. What contributions did James Clerk Maxwell make toward the development of radio?

3. What contribution did Heinrich Hertz make toward the development of radio?

4. What was Marconi's contribution to the development of radio?

5. What device contributed largely to the development and advancement of radio?

6. What is meant by the Edison effect?

7. What was Fleming's contribution to the development of the vacuum tube?

8. What was De Forest's contribution to the development of the vacuum tube?

9. What was Langmuir's contribution to the development of the vacuum tube?

10. Name some of the developments in vacuum-tube design that resulted in the modern tubes.

11. Name five men generally associated with the early development of radio circuits and describe the contribution made by each of them.

12. Why is Armstrong's name associated with frequency modulation?

13. Name four types of applications, other than radio, that use the principles of electronics and vacuum tubes. List some specific applications in each.

14. Define (a) sound, (b) sound waves, (c) frequency of sound waves, (d) pitch.

15. Explain what occurs when sound waves strike the human ear and produce the sensation of sound.

16. What frequency is commonly used for the audio wave of code signals? Why?

17. How are radio waves produced?

18. What two factors make up radio waves?

19. How does the speed of radio waves compare with (a) light waves? (b) Electricity? (c) Sound?

20. Define (a) wavelength, (b) frequency, (c) cycle, (d) kilocycle, (e) megacycle.

21. What are the essential functions of a transmitter?

22. What purpose does each function of the transmitter serve?

23. What are the essential functions of a receiver?

24. What purpose does each function of the receiver serve?

25. Describe a simple analogy of radio transmission and reception.

26. Prepare a block diagram of a simple radio receiver. Label each block and state its function.

27. Name two types of radio circuits used in modern receivers.

28. Why is a knowledge of electricity necessary in order to study radio?

PROBLEMS

1. The frequency of the sound waves produced by middle C on a piano is 256 cycles. (a) What is the wavelength of the sound in feet? (b) In meters?

2. A musical note of 256 cycles (Prob. 1) is picked up by a microphone and changes from sound waves to electrical impulses. (a) What is the wavelength of the electrical impulses in feet? (b) In meters? (NOTE.—Electricity and radio waves travel at the rate of 186,000 miles per second.)

3. Radio programs are often presented to studio audiences as well as to the radio audience. (a) How long does it take the sound waves to reach a listener in the studio audience seated 200 feet away? (b) How long does it take the program to reach a listener at the loudspeaker of a radio receiver 500 miles away? (c) Which listener hears the program first?

4. How far would a sound wave travel in the time that it takes a radio wave to travel 500 miles?

5. If the musical notes of a violin range from 200 to 3000 cycles (vibrations) per second, what is its range of wavelength?

6. If the musical notes of a base viol range from 36 to 240 cycles (vibrations) per second, what is its range of wavelength?

7. If the shrill sound of an insect has a frequency of 12,000 cycles, what is the wavelength in feet?

8. If the sound of a creaking door has a frequency of 15,000 cycles, what is its wavelength in feet?

9. What is the frequency of the carrier wave of a transmitter whose wavelength is 526 meters?

10. What is the frequency of the carrier wave of a transmitter whose wavelength is 206.8 meters?

11. What are the wavelengths of a television transmitter whose frequencies are 61.25 and 65.75 mc?

12. What are the wavelengths of a television transmitter whose frequencies are 45.25 and 49.75 mc?

13. A certain short-wave transmitter operates on a wavelength of 38.4 meters. What is its frequency?

14. A certain f-m station operates on an assigned frequency of 95.3 mc. (a) What is its wavelength in meters? (b) What is its wavelength in feet?

15. A certain f-m station operates on an assigned frequency of 99.3 mc. (a) What is its wavelength in meters? (b) What is its wavelength in feet?

16. A certain radio station operating on an assigned frequency of 1050 kc is transmitting a violin solo. (a) If the notes of the violin range from 200 to 3000 vibrations per second, what is the range of the audio-frequency electrical current impulses? (b) How many cycles does the carrier-wave current make for each cycle of the lowest frequency note? (c) How many cycles does the carrier-wave current make for each cycle of the highest frequency note?

17. How many cycles does the current of a 46.7-mc carrier wave make in the time that it takes a 5000-cycle audio-frequency current to complete one cycle?

18. How many cycles does the current of a 550-kc carrier wave make in the time that it takes a 5000-cycle audio-frequency current to complete one cycle?

19. How many cycles does the current of the 550-kc carrier wave (Prob. 18) make in the time that it takes a 50-cycle audio-frequency current to complete one cycle?

20. How long does it take the radio waves of a transmitter located at Chicago to reach San Francisco, a distance of approximately 1600 miles?

21. How long does it take the radio waves of a transmitter located at San Francisco to reach Honolulu, Hawaii (approximately 2500 miles away)?

22. How long does it take the radio waves of a transmitter located at New York to reach Melbourne, Australia, approximately 10,000 miles away?

23. How far would a sound wave travel in the time that it takes the radio waves of Prob. 22 to travel 10,000 miles?

24. Complete the following table of frequency and wavelength ratings of the stations listed as follows.

Station	Location	Kilocycles	Meters	Station	Location	Megacycles	Meters
WIOD	Miami	610		WNBC-FM	New York		3.083
KSL	Salt Lake City		258.62	WCBS-FM	New York	96.9	
KDKA	Pittsburgh		294.11	WLWK	Cincinnati		49.34
KOA	Denver	850		KWID	San Francisco		19.62
WLAC	Nashville	1510		WGEA	Schenectady	9.53	
KIRO	Seattle		422.53	WRUW	Boston	11.73	

25. Add four of your favorite stations to the list of Prob. 24 and fill in their frequencies and wavelengths in the table.

CHAPTER II

CIRCUIT ANALYSIS

In order to understand the essentials of radio it is necessary that the reader possess a good foundation of basic electrical theory, circuit analysis, and a knowledge of the various circuit elements involved. To those who have studied the authors' book, *Electrical Essentials of Radio*, this chapter should serve as a brief résumé of circuit elements and circuit analysis. To those who have obtained the knowledge of basic electricity from some other source, it presents a brief treatment of those electrical essentials that are important to the study of radio but are omitted in electrical texts that treat electricity from the power and machinery standpoint.

2-1. Resistors. A resistor is a device used in an electric circuit because of its resistance. When used in a circuit to provide a required amount of resistance it is considered as being a circuit element.

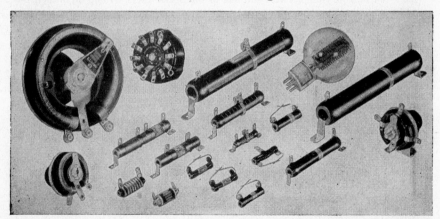

Fig. 2-1.—Some of the various types of resistors used in radio. (*Courtesy of Ohmite Manufacturing Company.*)

Resistors are generally used to limit the amount of current flowing in a circuit or to obtain a desired amount of voltage for a certain part of a circuit. Resistors are rated in both their ohmic value and the amount of power that they can dissipate. The power rating is also a measure of its current rating because the power dissipated by a resistor is equal to I^2R. Standard resistors range from a fraction of an ohm to several megohms and from a fraction of a watt to several hundred watts.

Classification of Resistors According to Material.　Two general types of materials are used in the manufacture of resistors, namely, carbon and metal.　Resistors may therefore be classified according to the material used and are generally referred to as being either carbon or wire-wound.

The metallic or *wire-wound resistors* consist of a wire or ribbon, usually an alloy of two or more elements such as copper, iron, nickel, chromium, zinc, manganese, etc., wound around a supporting form made of an insulating material.

The nonmetallic or *carbon resistors* consist of either carbon or graphite powder held together by a suitable binding substance.　It is formed into rods and cut into short pieces to make up the resistor.　Because of the high specific resistance of carbon and graphite, carbon resistors of high ohmic values can be made much smaller than wire-wound resistors.

Classification of Resistors According to Control.　Resistors may be further classified as: (1) fixed; (2) variable; (3) adjustable; (4) tapped; (5) automatic resistance control.

A *fixed resistor* is one whose value cannot be changed by any mechanical means.　Fixed resistors may be of either the wire-wound or carbon type.　Low-power wire-wound fixed resistors are made by winding the wire on a Bakelite or fiber strip and attaching suitable connecting lugs at each end.　A flexible low-power wire-wound resistor is made by winding a fine nichrome wire on a specially treated silk cord and then covering it with impregnated fiber.　High-power wire-wound resistors are made by winding the wire on large threaded porcelain tubes and attaching terminals at each end; the entire unit is then dipped in an enamel or a porcelain solution and baked.　Fixed resistors of the carbon type are used extensively for low-power applications.　They are generally used where a low-power high resistance is required.　Their ohmic values range from 5 ohms to 10 megohms and are indicated by a color code adopted by the Radio Manufacturers' Association (see Appendix VIII).

A *variable resistor* is one whose value of resistance at its terminals may be varied.　Two commonly used types of variable resistors are called the *rheostat* and the *potentiometer*.　The rheostat and potentiometer are similar in appearance and method of operation but differ in the manner in which they are connected in a circuit.

An *adjustable resistor* is one that may be adjusted to a desired value and then set at that value.　It differs from the variable resistor in that once it is adjusted to the desired value it is kept at that value.　Adjustable resistors are of the metallic type and are generally wound on porcelain forms.　They are provided with one or more movable collars, which may be clamped in a definite position after they have been adjusted to the desired value.

A *tapped resistor*, sometimes called a *voltage divider*, is one that provides two or more definite values of resistance on a single unit. Tapped resistors are similar to adjustable resistors except that the collars are not made movable but are set at fixed positions along the resistor to give definite values of resistance. Tapped resistors are of the metallic type and may be of the low-power wire-wound variety that uses a fiber or Bakelite form or may be of the high-power wire-wound type that uses a porcelain form.

An *automatic resistance-control resistor* is one whose resistance value changes automatically with a change in current or temperature. A nickel or iron wire is placed inside a glass tube filled with an inert gas such as hydrogen, or inside an air-cooled metal case. When the current flowing through this unit increases it causes an increase in the temperature of the wire. The increase in temperature causes an increase in resistance that regulates the current and prevents it from rising excessively.

Fig. 2-2.—An automatic ballast-regulating tube that may be used as an automatic resistance-control resistor. (*Courtesy of Amperite Company.*)

Uses of Resistors. Resistors are used to adjust the current and voltage of electrical circuits. In radio circuits they are used as voltage dividers (see Chap. XI), loads for the output of a vacuum tube, resistance to provide the proper grid bias, current regulators in filament circuits, filter networks, grid leaks, etc. The use to which a resistor is applied determines how it is to be constructed and how accurately its resistance value must be maintained. The accuracy of resistors varies with the kind of materials used and the care exercised in their manufacture. High-quality wire-wound commercial resistors can be obtained with values of resistance that are accurate within 1 per cent of their rated values.

In selecting a resistor its power rating as well as its resistance value must be taken into consideration. The power rating may be found by

$$P = I^2R \tag{2-1}$$

where P = power, watts

I = current, amperes

R = resistance, ohms

Example 2-1. What is the power rating of a 1000-ohm resistor that will safely withstand a maximum current of 100 ma?

Given: Find:

R = 1000 ohms P = ?

I = 100 ma = 0.1 amp

Solution:

$$P = I^2R = 0.1^2 \times 1000 = 10 \text{ watts}$$

Example 2-2.   How much current can a 10,000-ohm, 5-watt resistor safely withstand?

Given: Find:
    $R = 10,000$ ohms $I = ?$
    $P = 5$ watts

Solution:

$$I = \sqrt{\frac{P}{R}} = \sqrt{\frac{5}{10,000}} = 0.0223 \text{ amp or } 22.3 \text{ ma}$$

2-2. Rheostats and Potentiometers.   *Rheostats.*   A rheostat is a variable resistor whose value of resistance at its terminals may be varied by means of a sliding contact arm.   A rheostat is generally used to control the amount of current flowing in the load to which it is connected.

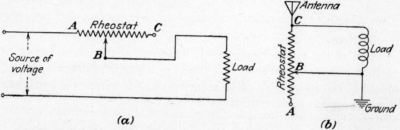

FIG. 2-3.—Circuits illustrating uses of rheostats.   (a) Rheostat in series with a load, (b) rheostat in parallel with a load.

Two types of circuits illustrating the use of rheostats are shown in Fig. 2-3.

Figure 2-3*a* shows a rheostat connected in series with the load and Fig. 2-3*b* shows a rheostat connected in parallel with the load.   It should be noted that only two of the three terminals (marked *A*, *B*, *C* on the diagram) are used and that current flows through only that part of the resistance actually between the sliding contact arm and the end of the resistor being used as a terminal.   Use of terminals *A* and *B* in the series circuit of Fig. 2-3*a* and terminals *B* and *C* in the parallel circuit of Fig. 2-3*b* results in obtaining an increase in current flowing through the load by rotating the sliding contact arm of the rheostat in a clockwise direction (see Fig. 2-6).

Potentiometers.   A potentiometer is a variable resistor (similar to a rheostat) connected so that it may be used for subdividing a voltage by means of a sliding contact arm.   Figure 2-4 shows how a potentiometer may be connected to the line and load.   It should be observed that all three terminals are used and that, by varying the position of the sliding contact arm *B*, it is possible to obtain any voltage from zero to line voltage at the load. The potentiometer selected must nave the section AB large enough to carry the current taken by the load plus the amount taken by the potentiometer itself. As the power consumed by a potentiometer is all lost, its current should be kept at a minimum. This can be accomplished by increasing the resistance between A and C to a very high value in order to keep the current in BC at a minimum.

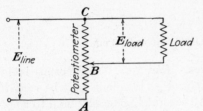

Fig. 2-4.—Circuit illustrating the use of a potentiometer.

Uses of Rheostats and Potentiometers. Rheostats and potentiometers are used to control various types of circuits used in radio, such as volume, tone, antenna, plate voltage, and audio. As the amount of current flowing in these circuits is very small, carbon resistors can be used (see Fig. 2-5).

When higher currents are required, metallic or wire-wound resistors are used (see Fig. 2-6). An objection to metallic resistors is that noisy operation of the receiver may result when the contact arm moves from one turn of wire to another. This occurs when there is an appreciable amount of voltage drop between adjacent turns of wire. Carbon controls do not present such conditions as the resistance change progresses smoothly and not in steps as in the wire-wound controls.

Taper. Rheostats and potentiometers used for control circuits may vary in direct ratio, or they may taper. In a direct-ratio potentiometer, the resistance value varies directly with the degree of rotation. That is, at quarter rotation the resistance value is one-quarter of the total resistance, and similarly at half rotation it is one-half of the total resistance. When a potentiometer is tapered, the resistance does not vary directly with the rotation. The potentiometer shown in

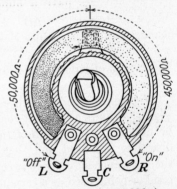

Fig. 2-5.—A carbon-type potentiometer with left-hand taper.

Fig. 2-5 has a total resistance of 500,000 ohms. At half rotation the resistance is only 50,000 ohms, and at quarter rotation it will be less than 25,000 ohms as the resistance is tapered and not uniform between the *off* position and the mid-point. In a similar manner, the resistance at three-quarter rotation would not be equal to one-half of 450,000 plus 50,000 (or 275,000) because the resistance between the mid-point and the *on* position is not uniform but is tapered.

It is necessary to taper the resistance of a control in order to obtain an apparently uniform control of the signal. When the control is turned to the halfway position, it is generally expected that the signal volume will be one-half that obtained at the full or *on* position of the control.

In order to double a given volume of sound, an increase of approximately ten times the original intensity is required. At one-half full volume, only one-tenth of the full volume voltage is required, and therefore one-tenth of the total resistance is all that is needed.

Potentiometers are either left-hand or right-hand tapered, depending on which side is tapered out. In Figs. 2-5 and 2-6 the left hand of the control is tapered out; therefore each is a left-hand taper.

Comparison of Wire-wound and Carbon Controls. Wire-wound and carbon controls have a number of

Fig. 2-6.—A wire-wound potentiometer with left-hand taper. (*Courtesy of Ohmite Manufacturing Company.*)

advantages and disadvantages, which, for purposes of comparison, are listed below. The choice of a control will depend on the use to which it is to be put.

ADVANTAGES

Wire-wound	Carbon
1. Absolute accuracy of the resistance value	1. Ease of obtaining taper
2. High current-carrying ability	2. Silent operation
3. Low resistance values easily obtained ($\frac{1}{2}$ ohm)	3. High resistance values easily obtained (2 or more megohms)

DISADVANTAGES

Wire-wound	Carbon
1. More difficult to obtain a taper	1. Resistance will vary with heat, humidity, wear, etc.
2. Noisy operation	2. Low current-carrying ability
3. Limited high resistance value that can be obtained (150,000 ohms)	3. Limited low resistance value obtainable (500 ohms)

2-3. Inductors. Inductance must be considered wherever a current of varying magnitude is flowing in a circuit. In radio, the principles of inductance are useful in understanding the action of *inductance coils,* or *choke coils* as they are generally called, and of the various types of *transformers* used.

Characteristics of Inductance. Three of the characteristics of inductance that are important to the study of radio are: (1) inductance opposes any change in the amount of current flowing in its circuit; (2) the changing current in an inductance coil will cause a voltage to be induced in that coil in the case of self-inductance or in an adjacent coil or conductor in the case of mutual inductance; (3) energy may be transferred from one circuit to another.

Unit of Inductance. The unit of inductance is the henry and its symbol is L. A circuit is said to have an inductance of one henry when a current changing at the rate of one ampere per second induces an emf of one volt. Low values of inductance are expressed in millihenries (10^{-3} henries) or microhenries (10^{-6} henries). These subunits are generally abbreviated and appear as mh and μh respectively. Additional information on subunits and the use of exponents is given in Appendixes III and IV.

Inductance may be expressed in terms of flux linkages and current as

$$L = \frac{\phi}{10^8 I} \tag{2-2}$$

where L = inductance, henries

ϕ = flux linkages, maxwells

I = current, amperes

10^8 is a constant and is necessary in order to express the equation in our practical units of volts, amperes, etc.

Energy must be provided by the source of power in order to establish the magnetic field. This energy may be stored in the field as potential energy or, as in a-c circuits, may be returned to the circuit. The amount of energy stored by the magnetic field is dependent upon the current and the inductance as expressed by

$$W = \frac{LI^2}{2} \tag{2-3}$$

where W = energy of the field, watt-seconds (or joules)

L = inductance, henries

I = current, amperes

Self-inductance. Self-inductance is the property of a single circuit that opposes any change in the amount of current in that circuit. The unit of self-inductance is the *henry* and a circuit is said to have a self-inductance of one henry when a current changing at the rate of one ampere per second induces an average emf of one volt.

The induced voltage in an inductor is proportional to the number of turns and the rate at which the flux (and current) is changing; this is expressed by the equation

$$E_{ave} = \frac{N\phi}{t10^8} \qquad (2\text{-}4)$$

where E_{ave} = average induced emf, volts

N = number of turns

ϕ = total change in the number of lines of flux linking the turns N, maxwells (one maxwell = one magnetic line of force)

t = time required to produce the change, seconds

Example 2-3.   A flux of 1,800,000 lines links a coil having 300 turns.   The flux in the coil decreases from maximum value to zero in 0.18 second.   (a) What is the value of the induced voltage?   (b) What is the inductance of the coil if a current of 1 amp is required to reduce the flux of 1,800,000 lines?   (c) How much energy is stored in the magnetic field?   (d) If upon opening the circuit the current decreases to zero in 0.18 second, what is the average value of the power expended by the magnetic field during this time?

Given:

N = 300 turns

ϕ = 1,800,000 lines

t = 0.18 second

I = 1 amp

Find:

(a) E_{ave} = ?

(b) L = ?

(c) W = ?

(d) P = ?

Solution:

(a) $E_{ave} = \dfrac{N\phi}{t10^8} = \dfrac{300 \times 1,800,000}{0.18 \times 10^8} = 30$ volts

(b) $L = \dfrac{N\phi}{10^8 I} = \dfrac{300 \times 1,800,000}{10^8 \times 1} = 5.4$ henries

(c) $W = \dfrac{LI^2}{2} = \dfrac{5.4 \times 1 \times 1}{2} = 2.7$ watt-seconds

(d) $P = \dfrac{\text{watt-seconds}}{\text{seconds}} = \dfrac{2.7}{0.18} = 15$ watts

Although inductance is generally associated with coils, practically all circuits have some inductance.   When a coil is used expressly for its property of inductance, it is called an *inductor*.   The self-inductance of a coil depends upon its physical characteristics, that is, its dimensions, number of turns, and the magnetic qualities of its core.   One of the three following equations will provide a means of calculating the self-inductance of air-core coils.   Figure 2-7 shows three classifications of coil shapes for which the three equations are used.   The coil shown in Fig. 2-7*a* is called a *multilayer coil*, and its inductance may be found by use of the equation

$$L = \frac{0.8a^2N^2}{6a + 9b + 10c} \qquad (2\text{-}5)$$

Figure 2-7*b* shows a flat or *pancake coil* whose inductance may be calculated by the equation

$$L = \frac{a^2N^2}{8a + 11c} \qquad (2\text{-}5a)$$

Figure 2-7c shows a form of *solenoid* in which the length does not exceed the diameter by any great amount. The inductance of such a coil may be found by the equation

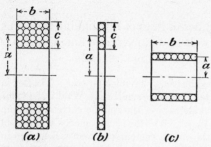

$$L = \frac{a^2N^2}{9a + 10b} \qquad (2\text{-}5b)$$

where L = inductance of the coil, microhenries

N = number of turns

a, b, c = dimensions, inches (Fig. 2-7)

Fig. 2-7.—Types of inductance coils. (a) Multilayer, (b) flat or pancake, (c) solenoid.

Example 2-4. What is the inductance of a multilayer coil that has 1200 turns and whose dimensions are $a = 1\frac{1}{2}$, $b = \frac{3}{4}$, and $c = 1\frac{1}{2}$ inches?

Given:
N = 1200 turns
a = 1.5 in.
b = 0.75 in.
c = 1.5 in.

Find:
L = ?

Solution:

$$L = \frac{0.8a^2N^2}{6a + 9b + 10c} = \frac{0.8 \times 1.5^2 \times 1200^2}{6 \times 1.5 + 9 \times 0.75 + 10 \times 1.5} = 84{,}292 \ \mu h$$

The above equations will give reasonably accurate results for coils without iron cores as may be found in radio-frequency circuits.

Mutual Inductance. When two windings are placed so that a change of current in one will cause its changing magnetic field to cut the turns of the other, an induced emf will be set up in the second coil. The two circuits are then said to possess *mutual inductance.*

Unit of Mutual Inductance. Two circuits have a mutual inductance of one henry when a current in one circuit, changing at the rate of one ampere per second, induces an average emf of one volt in the second circuit.

Primary and Secondary. The winding that receives the energy from the power source is called the *primary* and the winding that delivers the energy to the load is called the *secondary.* Each winding has a self-inductance of its own that may be calculated by Eqs. (2-5), (2-5a), or (2-5b). The self-inductance of the primary is designated as L_P and that of the secondary as L_S.

Coefficient of Coupling. When two circuits are arranged so that energy from one circuit may be transferred to the other, the circuits are said to be *coupled.* Mutual inductance is an example of coupled circuits.

In the case of mutual inductance, if all the magnetic lines set up by the current in the first circuit cut all the turns of the second circuit, the circuits would be coupled perfectly. If only half of the lines set up in the first circuit cut the turns of the second circuit, the coupling is only 50 per cent. The per cent of coupling is usually referred to as the *coefficient of coupling* and designated by the letter K. It is expressed mathematically by the equation

$$K = \frac{M}{\sqrt{L_1 L_2}} \tag{2-6}$$

where K = the coefficient of coupling (expressed as a decimal)
M = the mutual inductance of the two circuits
L_1 = the self-inductance of the first coil
L_2 = the self-inductance of the second coil

Example 2-5.   What is the coefficient of coupling of two coils whose mutual inductance is 1.0 henry and whose self-inductances are 1.2 and 2.0 henries?

Given: Find:
   M = 1.0 henry K = ?
   L_1 = 1.2 henries
   L_2 = 2.0 henries

Solution:

$$K = \frac{M}{\sqrt{L_1 L_2}} = \frac{1.0}{\sqrt{1.2 \times 2.0}} = 0.645$$

The coefficient of coupling depends upon the construction of the coils and also largely upon whether the coils are wound on an iron core or on an air core. The highest possible value is one and the lowest is zero. Iron-core transformers often achieve the high value of 0.98, which is considered excellent. The coefficient of coupling for air-core transformers used in radio circuits is very low and will vary considerably, depending upon the design of the coils and the frequency of the circuits in which they are used. In radio circuits a low value of coefficient of coupling is often desired, as it aids sharpness of tuning.

Calculation of Voltage Induced in the Secondary. The voltage induced in the second circuit by a change of current in the first may be expressed by the equation

$$E_{\text{ave}\cdot 2} = \frac{N_2 K \phi}{t 10^8} \tag{2-7}$$

where $E_{ave \cdot 2}$ = average induced emf in the second circuit, volts

N_2 = number of turns on the coil in the second circuit

ϕ = total change in the number of lines linking the turns N_1, maxwells

Example 2-6.   Two coils, the first having 200 turns and the second 350 turns, are placed so that only 40 per cent of the lines set up by coil 1 link coil 2.   If 600,000 lines are set up when 3 amperes flow through coil 1, what voltage will be induced in coil 2 if the current decreases from 3 amperes to zero in 0.10 second?

Given:

N_2 = 350 turns

$K = 0.40$

ϕ = 600,000 lines

$t = 0.10$ sec

Find:

$E_{ave \cdot 2} = ?$

Solution:

$$E_{ave \cdot 2} = \frac{N_2 K \phi}{t 10^8} = \frac{350 \times 0.40 \times 600,000}{0.10 \times 10^8} = 8.40 \text{ volts}$$

2-4. Inductive Reactance and Angle of Lag.   Inductance is the property of a circuit that opposes any *change* in the amount of *current* flowing in the circuit.   As the current in an a-c circuit is continually changing in amount, it follows that the effect of inductance must be considered in alternating-current circuits.   The effects of inductance upon the current flowing in an a-c circuit are twofold; namely, (1) that it sets up an opposition to the flow of current, and (2) that it causes a delay or lag in the current.

Inductive Reactance.   A current flowing through a wire always sets up a magnetic field about the wire.   If the current varies in strength the magnetic field too will vary in strength.   When an alternating current flows through a coil, the resulting varying magnetic field about each turn will induce a voltage in its adjacent turns.   This induced voltage opposes the *change* in amount of *current* and results in a lower current than if inductance were not present.   Inductance therefore introduces an opposition to the flow of alternating current.   This opposition is called *inductive reactance* and is expressed in ohms; its symbol is X_L.   The value of the inductive reactance is affected by two factors, (1) the inductance of the circuit, and (2) the rate or speed at which the current is changing, which is proportional to the frequency.   The effects of these two factors upon the inductive reactance are shown by the equation

$$X_L = 2\pi f L \tag{2-8}$$

where X_L = inductive reactance, ohms

π = constant, 3.14

f = frequency, cycles per second

L = inductance, henries

If a circuit were assumed to consist of inductance only, the amount of current flowing in such a circuit would be

$$I_L = \frac{E_L}{X_L} \tag{2-9}$$

where I_L = current flowing in the inductor, amperes
  E_L = voltage across the inductor, volts
  X_L = reactance of the inductor, ohms

In actual practice it is impossible to have a circuit containing inductance only because the wire of which the inductor is wound has some resistance. However, the resistance is usually so small compared with the inductive reactance that it is ignored and the circuit is assumed to contain inductance only.

If the resistance of an inductor is to be considered, its ohmic effect must be combined with the inductive reactance. The combined ohmic effect is called the *impedance* and is represented by the symbol Z_L. Mathematically it is equal to

$$Z_L = \sqrt{R_L{}^2 + X_L{}^2} \tag{2-10}$$

where Z_L = impedance of the inductor, ohms
  R_L = resistance of the inductor, ohms
  X_L = reactance of the inductor, ohms

When both the resistance and inductive reactance of an inductor are taken into consideration, the current flowing in the inductor will be

$$I_L = \frac{E_L}{Z_L} \tag{2-11}$$

Example 2-7. The choke coil of a filter circuit has an inductance of 30 henries and a resistance of 400 ohms. Find: (*a*) the inductive reactance at 60 cycles; (*b*) the impedance at 60 cycles; (*c*) the current when the voltage across the coil is 250 volts at 60 cycles.

Given:	Find:
L = 30 henries	X_L = ?
R_L = 400 ohms	Z_L = ?
f = 60 cycles	I_L = ?
E_L = 250 volts	

Solution:

(*a*) $X_L = 2\pi fL = 2 \times 3.14 \times 60 \times 30 = 11{,}304$ ohms
(*b*) $Z_L = \sqrt{R_L{}^2 + X_L{}^2} = \sqrt{400^2 + 11{,}304^2} = 11{,}311$ ohms
(*c*) $I_L = \dfrac{E_L}{Z_L} = \dfrac{250}{11{,}311} = 0.0221$ amp = 22.1 ma

The results of the above example show that the impedance and the inductive reactance are practically equal and that the current will be practically the same whether the resistance is considered or neglected. This is always the case when the inductive reactance is five or more times as great as the resistance.

Angle of Lag. When an a-c circuit contains inductance only, the changes in current take place 90 electrical degrees later than the changes in the voltage. This is more commonly expressed as, the current lags

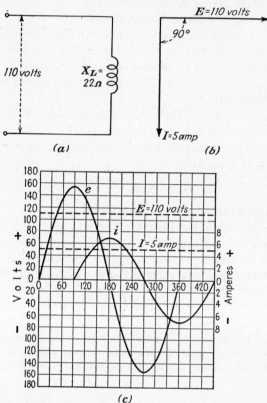

Fig. 2-8.—Methods of illustrating the lagging current caused by inductance. (a) The circuit, (b) vector diagram, (c) sine-wave diagram.

the voltage by 90 degrees. This effect may be shown by the sine-wave diagram of Fig. 2-8c or by the vector diagram of Fig. 2-8b.

If the resistance of the inductor is to be considered, the angle of lag will decrease as the resistance increases. The angle of lag can be determined by the equations

$$\cos \theta_L = \frac{R_L}{Z_L} \tag{2-12}$$

$$\cos \theta_L = \frac{R_L}{\sqrt{R_L{}^2 + X_L{}^2}} \tag{2-12a}$$

where θ_L = angle of lag, degrees

cos θ_L = cosine of the angle θ, from table of cosines, Appendix XII

Example 2-8.   By what angle does the current lag the voltage in the coil of Example 2-7?

Given: Find:
    R_L = 400 ohms θ_L = ?
    Z_L = 11,311 ohms

Solution:

$$\cos \theta_L = \frac{R_L}{Z_L} = \frac{400}{11{,}311} = 0.0353$$

$$\theta_L = 88° \text{ (from Appendix XII)}$$

2-5. Inductors Connected in Series or Parallel.   When two or more inductors are connected in series and placed so that no coupling exists between them, the inductance of the circuit will be

$$L_T = L_1 + L_2 + L_3 \cdots \tag{2-13}$$

When two or more inductors are connected in parallel and placed so that no coupling exists between them, the inductance of the circuit will be

$$L_T = \frac{1}{\dfrac{1}{L_1} + \dfrac{1}{L_2} + \dfrac{1}{L_3} \cdots} \tag{2-14}$$

When two coils are connected in series and coupling exists between them, the inductance of the circuit will be

$$L_T = L_1 + L_2 \pm 2K \sqrt{L_1 L_2} \tag{2-15}$$

where L_T = inductance of the circuit

NOTE: $\pm 2K \sqrt{L_1 L_2}$; use + when the magnetic fields of the two coils are aiding and − when the fields are opposing.

Example 2-9.   Two coils, each with an inductance of 4 henries are arranged so that they may be connected in the various ways shown in Fig. 2-9.   What is the inductance of the circuit when the two coils are connected in series so that they are: (*a*) aiding and the coupling is 100 per cent; (*b*) opposing and the coupling is 100 per cent; (*c*) in a position that produces zero coupling; (*d*) aiding and the coupling is 50 per cent?

Given: Find:
    L_1 = 4 henries L_T = ?
    L_2 = 4 henries

Solutions:

(*a*) $L_T = L_1 + L_2 \pm 2K \sqrt{L_1 L_2} = 4 + 4 + (2 \times 1 \sqrt{4 \times 4}) = 16$ henries
(*b*) $L_T = L_1 + L_2 \pm 2K \sqrt{L_1 L_2} = 4 + 4 - (2 \times 1 \sqrt{4 \times 4}) = 0$ henries
(*c*) $L_T = L_1 + L_2 \pm 2K \sqrt{L_1 L_2} = 4 + 4 \pm (2 \times 0 \sqrt{4 \times 4}) = 8$ henries
(*d*) $L_T = L_1 + L_2 \pm 2K \sqrt{L_1 L_2} = 4 + 4 + (2 \times 0.5 \sqrt{4 \times 4}) = 12$ henries

2-6. Neutralizing Inductance.   When it is desired that a coil of wire have the lowest amount of inductance that is possible, the coil is wound so that each turn of wire with a current flowing in one direction has its inductive effect neutralized by a turn with its current flowing in the opposite direction.   The coil is then said to be *noninductively wound*.

If a coil requires only a few turns it may be noninductively wound by first looping the wire as shown in Figure 2-10a and winding the loop

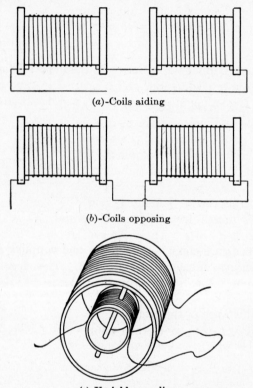

(a)-Coils aiding

(b)-Coils opposing

(c)-Variable coupling

Fig. 2-9.—Two coupled inductors connected in series.

around the core.   The completed coil will be as shown in Fig. 2-10b. When the coil requires a large number of turns, it would be difficult to loop the wire first.   In this case the coil is usually wound in two sections, each having two leads.   When completed, the two winding sections are connected in series in such a manner that the currents in each section set up magnetic fields of opposite directions, which will neutralize one another.

The wires used to connect various parts of a receiver sometimes cause unwanted inductance. This is usually true of filament or heater circuits in a-c-operated sets, especially if the wires are spaced some distance apart and are parallel to one another. The inductive effect may be reduced to a negligible amount by twisting the wires as shown in Fig. 2-11a, or even by running the wires parallel to each other but right alongside one another as shown in Fig. 2-11b.

2-7. Chokes. Inductance coils used in the filter circuits of radio power-supply systems and in the audio-frequency and radio-frequency circuits are commonly referred to as *chokes*.

Power-supply Chokes. These chokes are used to aid in converting the pulsating-current output of a rectifier into the direct current that is needed for radio-tube circuits. As the rectifier pulsating currents are usually in the order of 60 or 120 pulsations per second, high values of inductance are required. In order to obtain high values of inductance, the coils have a large number of turns and are wound on iron cores. Common values of these chokes range from 5 to 30 henries.

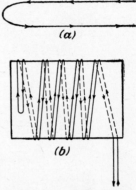

Fig. 2-10.—Noninductive winding. (a) A loop of wire, (b) a noninductively wound coil.

Audio-frequency Chokes. These chokes are used in some types of amplifier circuits to keep out (or to filter) certain parts of the current from the amplifier to improve its operation. This type of coil has a high value of inductance, generally in the order of 100 henries. Audio

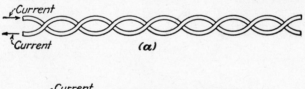

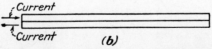

Fig. 2-11.—Noninductive wiring. (a) Wires twisted to reduce the inductance, (b) wires placed parallel to one another to reduce the inductance.

chokes offer a high impedance to the a-f currents and a low resistance to the direct current, thereby choking off the a-f currents and causing them to take another path, but permitting the direct current to flow through freely. In order to obtain high values of inductance, the coils have a large number of turns and are wound on iron cores.

FIG. 2-12.—Typical power chokes and a-f transformers.   (*Courtesy of Thordarson Electric Manufacturing Division, Maguire Industries, Inc.*)

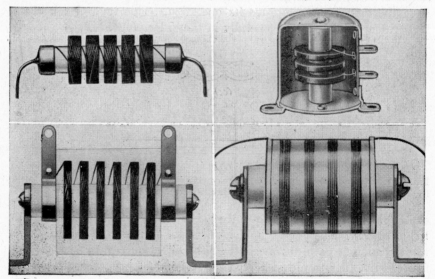

FIG. 2-13.—R-f chokes.   (*Courtesy of Hammarlund Manufacturing Company, Inc.*)

Radio-frequency Chokes. These coils are used in r-f circuits to provide a high impedance to the r-f currents and a low resistance to direct current. Because they operate on high frequencies, a high impedance can be obtained with relatively low values of inductance as compared with a-f chokes and power-supply chokes. Commonly used r-f chokes range from 2.5 to 125 millihenries.

Many of the r-f coils are wound on nonmagnetic cores and are referred to as *air-core coils.* Another type of r-f coil is wound on a specially prepared magnetic core consisting of finely powdered iron particles held

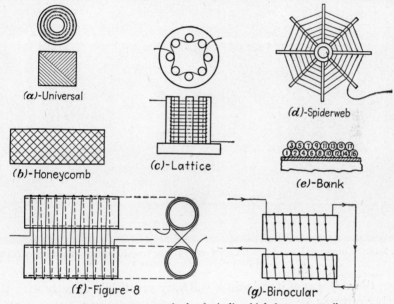

(a)-Universal

(b)-Honeycomb

(c)-Lattice

(d)-Spiderweb

(e)-Bank

(f)-Figure-8

(g)-Binocular

FIG. 2-14.—Various methods of winding high-frequency coils.

together with a magnetic insulating binding substance. Because of this special type of iron core, the desired value of inductance can be obtained with a smaller number of turns, resulting in a lower resistance, a smaller coil, and a higher value of Q. This value Q is the ratio of inductive reactance to resistance (see Art. 2-23).

Another construction feature of r-f coils is that special methods are used in winding the coils in order to reduce the distributed capacitance (see Art. 2-15) of the coil. Among the methods used are the universal, honeycomb, lattice, spider-web, bank, figure-of-eight and the binocular types of windings shown in Fig. 2-14.

2-8. Transformers. When two or more coils are arranged so that energy may be transferred from one circuit to another, the combination is generally referred to as a *transformer.*

Power-supply Transformers. These transformers are used to supply voltages, both above and below the value of the line voltage, to the various circuits in radio apparatus. Power transformers can be used only on a-c-operated units and therefore cannot be used with battery-operated portable radios or with a-c/d-c receivers. These transformers have two or more windings wound on a laminated iron core. The number of windings and the turns per winding depend upon the voltages that the transformer is to supply. As the coefficient of coupling is generally 0.95 or

Fig. 2-15.—Cutaway views of two types of radio power transformers. (*Courtesy of Standard Transformer Corporation.*)

more, the voltages of its windings will vary practically directly with the number of turns, or

$$\frac{E_P}{E_S} = \frac{N_P}{N_S} \tag{2-16}$$

where E_P = primary voltage
E_S = secondary voltage
N_P = turns, primary winding
N_S = turns, secondary winding

Figure 2-15 illustrates typical power transformers. Figure 2-16 is a schematic diagram of a transformer's windings.

Example 2-10. A radio power transformer is to supply a receiver with voltages of 2.5, 6.3, and 750 volts center tapped as shown in Fig. 2-16. The primary line voltage is 115 volts and the primary winding has 184 turns. Find: (*a*) the number of turns on section *cd*; (*b*) the number of turns on section *ef*; (*c*) the number of turns on section *gh* and *hi*; (*d*) the number of turns on section *gi*.

Given:

$$E_P = 115 \text{ volts}$$
$$E_{cd} = 2.5 \text{ volts}$$
$$E_{ef} = 6.3 \text{ volts}$$
$$E_{gi} = 750 \text{ volts}$$
$$N_P = 184 \text{ turns}$$

Find:

(a) $N_{cd} = ?$
(b) $N_{ef} = ?$
(c) $N_{gh}, N_{hi} = ?$
(d) $N_{gi} = ?$

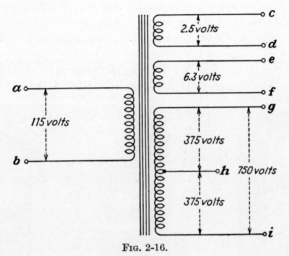

Fig. 2-16.

Solution:

(a) $N_S = N_P \dfrac{E_S}{E_P} = 184 \times \dfrac{2.5}{115} = 4 \text{ turns}$

(b) $N_S = N_P \dfrac{E_S}{E_P} = 184 \times \dfrac{6.3}{115} = 10 \text{ turns}$

(c) $N_S = N_P \dfrac{E_S}{E_P} = 184 \times \dfrac{375}{115} = 600 \text{ turns}$

(d) $N_S = N_P \dfrac{E_S}{E_P} = 184 \times \dfrac{750}{115} = 1200 \text{ turns}$

Audio-frequency Transformers. These transformers, Fig. 2-12, are used in a-f circuits as coupling devices and operate at frequencies ranging between 100 and 5000 cycles. They consist of a primary and secondary winding wound on a laminated iron or steel core. Because of the higher frequencies, special grades of steel such as silicon steel or several kinds of alloys that have very low losses should be used. These transformers usually have a greater number of turns on the secondary winding, common ratios being between 2 to 1 and 4 to 1. However, the impedance of the primary and secondary windings is of perhaps even greater importance than the ratio of turns, as the transformer selected should have its impedance match those of the circuits to which they are connected.

Impedance matching is described fully in the chapters on vacuum-tube amplifier circuits.

Radio-frequency Transformers. These transformers are used to couple one stage of r-f amplification to the next stage. The windings are usually of the universal type and may be wound on either an air core or on the special powdered-iron core. Often they are wound with a special type of wire called *litz wire* and the windings are given special treatment to help them withstand varying temperature and humidity. These transformers have a low number of turns, and the primary is of a lower number than the secondary. The r-f transformers operate at the frequency range of the receiver, such as the broadcast band 530 to 1550 kc, short

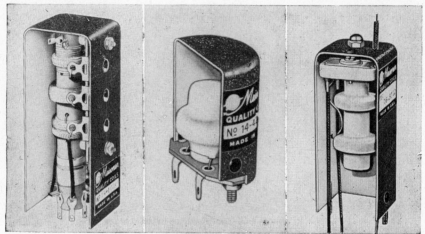

Fig. 2-17.—Typical r-f transformers. (*Courtesy of Meissner Manufacturing Division, Maguire Industries, Inc.*)

wave 5.8 to 19 mc, etc. When a receiver is to operate on several frequency ranges, a group of coils may be mounted in a single container, or several separate coils of the plug-in type may be used.

Intermediate-frequency transformers are r-f transformers designed for operation at a definite frequency. Standard i-f transformers can be obtained for frequencies of 175, 262, 370, 456, and 1500 kc. Of these the 175 and the 456 kc are the most commonly used.

2-9. Special Considerations of High-frequency Coils. *Shielding.* High-frequency circuits, such as the r-f and i-f circuits using the chokes and transformers just described, often have undesired coupling between adjacent circuits owing to their electrostatic and magnetic fields. High-frequency coils are generally enclosed in a metal shield, Fig. 2-17, in order to reduce the coupling effect caused by the electrostatic and magnetic fields. When any stray electrostatic lines of force reach the metallic shield they are short-circuited by the conducting material of the shield and are then grounded. When a magnetic field passes through such a shield an emf is induced in it, and, as the shield forms a closed circuit, a current will flow in the shield. This current will set up its own magnetic field, which, according to Lenz's law, will oppose the original magnetic field and tend to keep it from spreading beyond the shield.

Shields should be carefully designed as to size because the currents set up in them act as a loss that must be subtracted from the power in the coil circuit. This has a tendency to increase the resistance and also to reduce the inductance. Both of these effects result in a lower Q and hence reduce the effectiveness of the coil. The shield should be of a heavy material that is a good conductor, such as copper, brass, or aluminum, and should be large enough so that it is not too close to the coil. Copper shields are seldom used because of the corroding effect that air has on copper. Aluminum is used extensively because of its mechanical strength, low cost, and good conductivity.

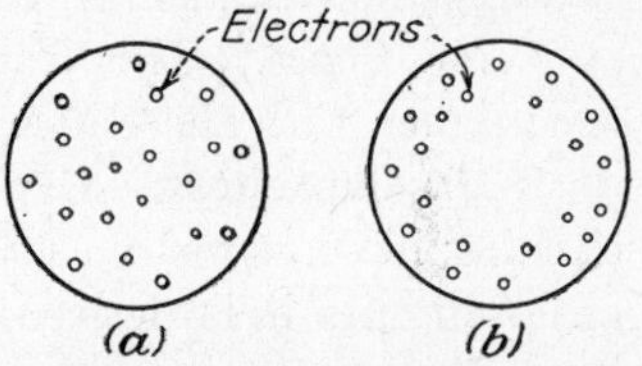

Fig. 2-18.—Distribution of the electrons over the area of a conductor carrying a current. (a) For direct current and low-frequency alternating current, (b) for high-frequency currents.

Alternating-current Resistance of Coils. When coils are used in high-frequency circuits, the resistance to the high-frequency currents is much greater than the d-c resistance of the coils.

Skin effect, which is one cause for this increased resistance, is explained in the following manner. With direct current, the electrons constituting the current flow are distributed evenly throughout the entire cross-section area of the conductor, as shown in Fig. 2-18a, while with high-frequency current the electrons are concentrated near the surface of the wire and practically no electrons flow at the center of the wire, as is shown in Fig. 2-18b. This reduces the effective area of the conductor and thereby increases its effective resistance.

Another cause of the increased effective resistance at high frequencies is the *eddy currents* that are set up by voltages induced in the conductor. These voltages are induced by the concentric magnetic fields of varying strength that are set up around the conductor. These eddy currents do no useful work but they cause additional heating of the conductor and are considered as a loss. Therefore, eddy currents produce the same effect as an increase in resistance.

At high frequency, it is common practice to combine all the resistance effects, that is, the d-c or ohmic resistance, the skin effect, and the eddy-current effect, into a single value called the *a-c resistance* of the coil. This a-c resistance of a coil increases as the frequency at which the coil is operated is increased. The skin effect, and hence the a-c resistance, increases at a greater rate for large conductors than for small ones. In order to reduce the value of the a-c resistance, a special type of conductor called *litz wire* is made by weaving a large number of small insulated wires to form the conductor. As the individual wires are insulated, they act as separate conductors and will result in a fairly uniform distribution of current at broadcast and even at short-wave frequencies but are not highly effective for ultrahigh frequencies. Another method used to reduce the value of the a-c resistance is to use hollow conductors or thin, flat, strip conductors. The litz wire is used mostly for receivers, while the hollow conductor is used mostly for transmitters.

Distributed Capacitance. The distributed capacitance effect is described in Art. 2-15, and its effect is minimized by special methods of winding the coils, as has been explained in Art. 2-7.

Color Codes. The leads of transformers are generally marked in accordance with the RMA color code as shown in Appendix X.

2-10. Capacitors. Capacitance is present in practically all a-c circuits; in some instances it is desired, while in others it is not. In many radio circuits it is desired, and in such cases a special device called a *capacitor* is used to obtain the amount of capacitance desired. The capacitor is also known as a *condenser*, but even though the name condenser is used considerably, capacitor is the better name and is rapidly becoming the more popular.

Characteristics of Capacitance. Two of the characteristics of capacitance that are important to the study of radio are: (1) capacitance opposes any *change* in the amount of *voltage* of its circuit; (2) when a voltage is applied to a capacitor, a quantity of electricity is stored in the capacitor, which may later be discharged.

A Simple Capacitor. A capacitor is formed when two conductors are placed close to one another but separated by an insulator. The *conductors* are generally made of thin *plates* in order to obtain sufficient area, and the *insulator*, also called the *dielectric*, is a thin piece of insulating material.

This device is capable of storing an electrical charge when a difference of potential is applied to its terminals. The amount of charge stored in the capacitor is a measure of its capacitance and is expressed by

$$C = \frac{Q}{E} \qquad (2\text{-}17)$$

When a capacitor is charged, an electrostatic field will exist about its conductors. The energy in a capacitor is stored in this electrostatic field; the amount of energy stored is dependent upon the capacitance and the charging potential and is expressed by

$$W = \frac{CE^2}{2} \tag{2-18}$$

where C = capacitance, farads

Q = charge in the capacitor, coulombs (ampere-seconds)

E = charging potential, volts

W = energy of the electrostatic field, watt-seconds (joules)

Unit of Capacitance. Capacitance is the property of a circuit that opposes any *change* in the amount of *voltage*. The unit of capacitance is the *farad* and a circuit is said to have a capacitance of one farad when a voltage changing at the rate of one volt per second causes an average current of one ampere to flow. The farad, however, is too large a unit for practical purposes and the *microfarad* (10^{-6} farad) and *micro-microfarad* (10^{-12} farad) are commonly used. These subunits are generally abbreviated and appear as μf and $\mu\mu f$ respectively.

Factors Affecting the Capacitance. The capacitance depends upon the area of the plates, the kind of material used as the dielectric, and the thickness of the dielectric. Their relation to the capacitance is expressed by the equation

$$C = \frac{22.45KA(N-1)}{10^8 t} \tag{2-19}$$

where C = capacitance, microfarads

K = dielectric constant (see Appendix VII)

A = area of one plate, square inches

t = thickness of the dielectric, inches

N = number of plates

Example 2-11. A capacitor is made up of 103 plates of lead foil, each 2 inches square, and separated by layers of mica 0.01 inch thick. (*a*) What is its capacitance? (*b*) What charge is produced in the capacitor when it is connected across a 300-volt d-c source of power? (*c*) If the charging current could be maintained at 5 ma, how long would it take to charge the capacitor? (*d*) How much energy is stored in the capacitor?

Given:

$K = 5.5$

$A = 2 \times 2$ square inches

$N = 103$ plates

$t = 0.01$ inch

$E = 300$ volts

$I = 5$ ma

Find:

(*a*) $C = ?$

(*b*) $Q = ?$

(*c*) Time $= ?$

(*d*) $W = ?$

Solution:

(a) $C = \dfrac{22.45KA(N-1)}{10^8t} = \dfrac{22.45 \times 5.5 \times 2 \times 2 \times 102}{10^8 \times 0.01} = 0.050 \ \mu f$

(b) $Q = CE = 0.050 \times 10^{-6} \times 300 = 0.000015$ coulomb (amp-sec)

(c) Time $= \dfrac{\text{ampere-seconds}}{\text{amperes}} = \dfrac{0.000015}{0.005} = 0.003$ second

(d) $W = \dfrac{CE^2}{2} = \dfrac{0.050 \times 10^{-6} \times 300 \times 300}{2} = 0.00225$ watt-second

2-11. Capacitive Reactance and Angle of Lead. When a voltage is applied to the plates of a capacitor, a current will flow momentarily and cause the plates to become *charged*, one *negative* and the other *positive*. The negative plate will have an excess of electrons, and if a higher voltage of the same polarity is applied to the capacitor, the effect will be to tend to increase the number of electrons on that plate. Since the plate already has an excess of electrons, its action will tend to oppose the increase. This corresponds with the definition that capacitance opposes any change in the amount of voltage. However, if the increased voltage is maintained, it will in a short time cause additional electrons to be transferred from one plate to the other. From this it can be seen that capacitance offers an opposition to the flow of current and also delays the change in voltage.

Capacitive Reactance. The opposition to the flow of alternating current offered by a capacitor is called *capacitive reactance*. It is expressed in *ohms* and its symbol is X_C. The value of the capacitive reactance is affected by two factors, (1) the capacitance of the circuit and (2) the rate or speed at which the voltage is changing, which is proportional to the frequency. The effect of these two factors upon the capacitive reactance is shown by the equation

$$X_c = \frac{10^6}{2\pi fC} \tag{2-20}$$

or

$$X_c = \frac{159,000}{fC} \tag{2-20a}$$

where X_c = capacitive reactance, ohms

f = frequency, cycles per second

C = capacitance, microfarads

If an a-c circuit were assumed to consist of capacitance only, the amount of current flowing in such a circuit would be

$$I_c = \frac{E_c}{X_c} \tag{2-21}$$

where I_c = current in the capacitor circuit, amperes

E_c = voltage across the capacitor, volts

X_c = reactance of the capacitor, ohms

In actual practice, capacitors always have some resistance which, in most cases, is so small compared to the capacitive reactance that it is ignored.   However, if the resistance of the capacitor is to be considered,

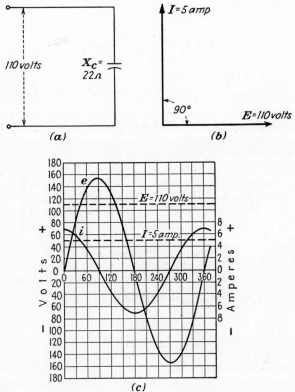

FIG. 2-19.—Methods of illustrating the leading current caused by capacitance.   (*a*) The circuit, (*b*) vector diagram, (*c*) sine-wave diagram.

its ohmic effect must be combined with the capacitive reactance; the combined effect is called the *impedance*.   Mathematically, it is equal to

$$Z_C = \sqrt{R_c{}^2 + X_c{}^2} \qquad (2\text{-}22)$$

where Z_C = impedance of the capacitor, ohms

R_c = equivalent series resistance of the capacitor, ohms

X_c = reactance of the capacitor, ohms

Angle of Lead.   When an a-c circuit contains capacitance only, the voltage lags the current by 90 electrical degrees.   This may also be stated as, the current leads the voltage by 90 electrical degrees.   This effect may be shown by the sine-wave diagram of Fig. 2-19*c* or by the vector diagram of Fig. 2-19*b*.

If the resistance of the circuit is to be considered, the angle of lead will decrease as the resistance increases. The angle of lead can be determined by the equation

$$\cos \theta_C = \frac{R_C}{Z_C} \qquad (2\text{-}23)$$

or

$$\cos \theta_C = \frac{R_C}{\sqrt{R_C^2 + X_C^2}} \qquad (2\text{-}23a)$$

where θ_C = angle of lead, degrees

$\cos \theta_C$ = cosine of the angle θ, from table of cosines Appendix XII

Example 2-12. What is the reactance, impedance, current, and phase angle of a 10-μf capacitor when connected to a 110-volt, 60-cycle line? Note that the capacitor is not a perfect one and that its resistance has the same effect as a 10-ohm resistor connected in series with the capacitor.

Given:	Find:
$C = 10 \ \mu\text{f}$	$X_C = ?$
$E_C = 110\text{-volts}$	$Z_C = ?$
$f = 60 \text{ cycles}$	$I_C = ?$
$R_C = 10 \text{ ohms}$	$\theta_C = ?$

Solution:

$$X_C = \frac{159,000}{fC} = \frac{159,000}{60 \times 10} = 265 \text{ ohms}$$

$$Z_C = \sqrt{R_C^2 + X_C^2} = \sqrt{10^2 + 265^2} = 265.2 \text{ ohms}$$

$$I_C = \frac{E_C}{Z_C} = \frac{110}{265.2} = 0.414 \text{ amp}$$

$$\cos \theta_C = \frac{R_C}{Z_C} = \frac{10}{265.2} = 0.0377$$

$$\theta_C = 88° \text{ (from Appendix XII)}$$

2-12. Capacitors Connected in Series or Parallel. When two or more capacitors are connected in series, the capacitance of the circuit will be

$$C_T = \frac{1}{\dfrac{1}{C_1} + \dfrac{1}{C_2} + \dfrac{1}{C_3} \cdots} \qquad (2\text{-}24)$$

This equation is often used in a simplified form for circuits containing only two capacitors connected in series, as

$$C_T = \frac{C_1 C_2}{C_1 + C_2} \qquad (2\text{-}24a)$$

$$C_2 = \frac{C_T C_1}{C_1 - C_T} \qquad (2\text{-}24b)$$

When two or more capacitors are connected in parallel, the capacitance of the circuit will be

$$C_T = C_1 + C_2 + C_3 \cdots \qquad (2\text{-}25)$$

Example 2-13. It is desired to increase the capacitance of a circuit containing one 10-μf capacitor so that the circuit will have a capacitance of 15 μf. This is to be done by adding a capacitor to the circuit. (*a*) Should the added capacitor be connected in series or in parallel with the original capacitor? (*b*) What value should the added capacitor have? (*c*) If the capacitor had been connected in series instead of parallel or vice versa what would be the capacitance of the circuit? (*d*) What kind of circuit would be required if the desired capacitance were 8 μf? (*e*) What value of capacitor would have to be added to obtain the capacitance desired in part (*d*)?

Given:

$C_1 = 10 \ \mu\text{f}$

(*b*) $C_T = 15 \ \mu\text{f}$

(*e*) $C_T = 8 \ \mu\text{f}$

Find:

(*a*) Connection $= ?$

(*b*) $C_2 = ?$

(*c*) $C_T = ?$

(*d*) Connection $= ?$

(*e*) $C_2 = ?$

Solution:

(*a*) Parallel

(*b*) $C_2 = C_T - C_1 = 15 - 10 = 5 \ \mu\text{f}$

(*c*) $C_T = \dfrac{C_1 C_2}{C_1 + C_2} = \dfrac{10 \times 5}{10 + 5} = 3.33 \ \mu\text{f}$

(*d*) Series

(*e*) $C_2 = \dfrac{C_T C_1}{C_1 - C_T} = \dfrac{8 \times 10}{10 - 8} = 40 \ \mu\text{f}$

2-13. Commercial Capacitors. *Classification of Capacitors.* Capacitors are manufactured in various forms and may be divided into two fundamental classes, namely, *fixed capacitors* and *variable capacitors*. The fixed capacitors may be further classified as to the type of material used for the dielectric, such as mica, paper, oil, and electrolytes.

Mica Capacitors. Mica capacitors are made by stacking a number of thin tin-foil (or aluminum-foil) plates and sheets of mica in alternate layers. As mica can be split into thin sheets, it is an excellent material for use as the dielectric. Mica capacitors have low losses and will withstand higher voltages than paper capacitors. Commonly used sizes range from 0.00005 to 0.02 microfarad and are usually enclosed in a molded Bakelite container to keep out moisture. Their capacitance and voltage rating are generally indicated on the capacitor by the RMA color code (Appendix IX).

Paper-dielectric Capacitors. Paper-dielectric capacitors are usually made with tin-foil conductors or plates and some form of specially treated paper for the dielectric. The tin foil and paper are cut in long narrow strips and are then rolled together to form a more compact unit. As even high-quality paper may contain tiny holes, it is common practice to use several layers of thin paper as the dielectric. The leads of this type of capacitor are usually soldered in such a manner that each turn of a conductor (plate) is connected to its lead in order to reduce the inductive effect of the various turns.

Paper capacitors are used extensively in radio work because they are smaller and less expensive than mica capacitors; however, they have higher losses than mica capacitors. Commonly used sizes range from 0.0002 to several microfarads and they are generally placed in a metal or cardboard container and sealed with wax or pitch to keep out moisture.

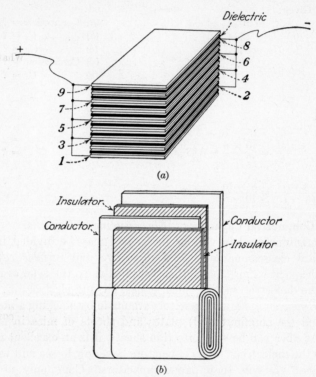

FIG. 2-20.—Typical construction of capacitors. (a) Mica-dielectric capacitors, (b) paper-dielectric capacitors.

Oil-dielectric Capacitors. In radio transmitter circuits it is not unusual to have voltages above 600 volts, and under such conditions paper capacitors will not have a very long life. In such cases, special capacitors are used, with oil or oil-impregnated paper as the dielectric. These capacitors are more expensive and are used mostly in transmitters.

Electrolytic Capacitors. An electrolytic capacitor consists of two metallic plates separated by an electrolyte. From the description of the action and construction of capacitors, it might seem that the purpose of the electrolyte is to act as the dielectric or insulator. This supposition

(a)

(b)

FIG. 2-21.—Commercial types of capacitors. (a) Mica-dielectric, (b) paper-dielectric. (*Courtesy of Solar Manufacturing Corporation.*)

is inaccurate in that the *electrolyte* is not the actual dielectric material but is the *negative electrode*. The *dielectric* consists of an extremely thin *oxide film* that is formed on the surface of the positive plate of the capacitor. This is due to the peculiar characteristic of aluminum and a few other metals that causes a nonconducting film to be formed on their surfaces when they are immersed in certain electrolytic solutions and a current is passed through the metal and the electrolyte.

Electrolytic capacitors have the advantage of being small in size and low in cost and of possessing certain self-healing qualities. A disadvantage is that most electrolytic capacitors must be connected to a constant polarity and hence can be used with direct current or intermittent direct current (rectified alternating current) only. Electrolytic capacitors may be of either the wet or dry type and are commonly used in sizes ranging from 1 to 50 microfarads.

Wet Electrolytic Capacitors. The electrolyte used in wet electrolytic capacitors is always in liquid form, and the container must therefore be made leakproof. In most wet-type capacitors, the container also serves as the negative electrode, since it makes direct contact with the electrolyte. The positive electrode is generally made of a thin aluminum sheet arranged in some special manner to obtain a large surface area. The electrolytic solution is generally a concentrate of a borate, phosphate, citrate, silicate, etc., of sodium or ammonia dissolved in water. Wet electrolytic capacitors are generally cylindrical in shape and should always be mounted in a vertical position.

Dry Electrolytic Capacitors. By using a jellylike electrolyte, electrolytic capacitors can be constructed in a dry form. They are considered dry in the same sense that dry cells are considered dry, that is, because the electrolyte cannot be spilled or poured from its container. Dry electrolytic capacitors provide high values of capacitance in relatively small dimensions and are the most economical type for many applications. Most of the electrolytic capacitors used in radio are of the dry type. In general, a dry electrolytic capacitor consists of a positive foil, a negative foil, and a separator containing an electrolyte, which are all wound into a roll and provided with means for electrical connection, housing, and mounting.

The positive foil, usually made of aluminum, is subjected to a special electrochemical forming process, which completely covers it with an extremely thin oxide film. The nature and thickness of this film will govern its voltage and capacitance per unit area. The separator is made of some absorbent material, usually gauze, paper, nonfibrous cellulose, or various combinations of these. It serves to hold the electrolyte in position and also keeps the positive and negative foils from making physical contact. The electrolyte consists of a chemical solution essentially similar to a dry paste and serves as the negative electrode. In addition, it tends to maintain the film on the positive electrode. The negative foil, generally aluminum, is usually unformed and acts merely

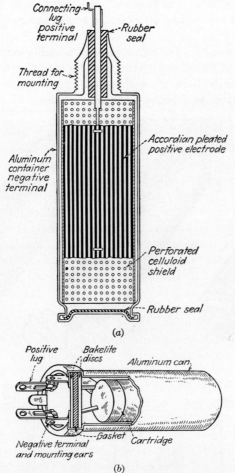

(a)

(b)

Fig. 2-22.—Cross-section view showing the construction of electrolytic capacitors.   (a) Wet electrolytic, (b) dry electrolytic.

as a means of making contact with the electrolyte, which is the negative electrode of the capacitor.

Dry electrolytic capacitors may be housed in cardboard tubes, cardboard cartons, and round or rectangular metal cans. Various types of mounting features are available, and either soldering lugs, screw terminals, or flexible leads are provided for external connections. As there is no danger of the electrolyte leaking out, dry electrolytic capacitors may be mounted in any position.

Capacitor Blocks.   Radio receivers generally require a number of capacitors and, in order to conserve space and to reduce cost, it has been found advantageous to build several capacitors in a single container. The unit is then referred to as a dual, a triple, or a multiple unit, or as a *capacitor block.*

Variable Capacitors.   In certain parts of a radio circuit it is necessary to use a capacitor whose capacitance can be varied or adjusted to meet the needs of the circuit in which it is used.   A variable capacitor or an adjustable capacitor may be used for this purpose.

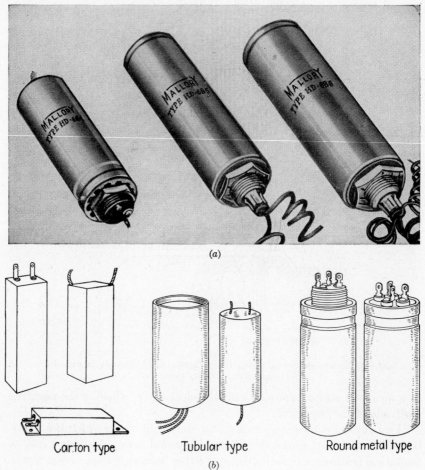

(a)

Carton type   Tubular type   Round metal type

(b)

Fig. 2-23.—Typical electrolytic capacitors.   (a) Wet electrolytic, (b) dry

A variable capacitor consists of two sets of plates, a rotating set called the *rotor*, and a stationary set called the *stator*. The capacitor is so constructed that the rotor plates will move freely in between the stator plates, thus causing the value of capacitance to be varied. The capacitance is affected by the area of the plates actually in mesh and by the air space (dielectric) between the plates. The thickness of the plates has no effect on the capacitance, and the thickness used is determined largely for the strength and ruggedness of the capacitor.

Ranges of Variable Capacitors. For ordinary broadcast reception, the capacitors used will range from 250 to 500 $\mu\mu$f (maximum values when all of the rotor plates are in mesh with the stator). For short-wave reception, the capacitance is generally 150 $\mu\mu$f or less. For high frequencies and ultrahigh frequencies, midget capacitors, whose maximum values range from 25 to 150 $\mu\mu$f, are used. When a smaller capacitance is required, microcapacitors are used. Microcapacitors have a maximum capacitance as low as 5 $\mu\mu$f.

Other Variable Capacitors. MULTIPLE or GANG CAPACITORS are used when it is desired to vary the capacitance in several circuits by means of a single dial. They consist of two or more capacitors mounted on a single shaft.

SPLIT-STATOR CAPACITORS are used when it is necessary that the capacitance of a circuit be perfectly balanced. The stator of this type of capacitor is separated into two equal parts, each half being electrically insulated from the other.

Capacitors with a large number of plates may be constructed with

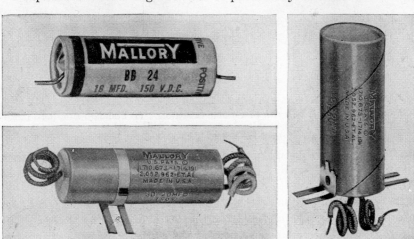

(c)

electrolytic, (c) dry electrolytic. (*Courtesy of P. R. Mallory & Co., Inc.*)

half of the stator and rotor plates mounted 180 degrees mechanically from the other half in order to achieve mechanical balance.

Transmitting capacitors are generally constructed with a larger air gap because the voltage between plates is considerable higher than that used in receivers.

Adjustable capacitors consist of two plates separated by a mica sheet and are so constructed that the distance separating the two plates

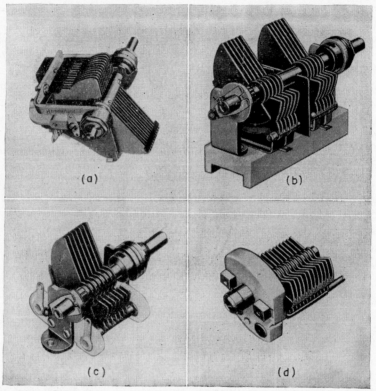

Fig. 2-24.—Commercial types of variable capacitors. (a) Standard-size single broadcast capacitor, (b) midget split-stator capacitor, (c) midget single capacitor, (d) micro capacitor. (*Courtesy of Hammarlund Manufacturing Company, Inc.*)

can be varied by adjusting a small setscrew. They can be obtained with a minimum capacitance as low as 0.5 $\mu\mu f$ and maximum capacitances as high as 10 $\mu\mu f$.

2-14. Operating Characteristics of Capacitors. *Losses.* The losses in a capacitor consist of *leakage*, *dielectric*, and *resistance* losses. The three are usually combined and called the *capacitor losses*. At low frequencies the effect of the losses are so small that they are usually neglected. At high frequencies the losses are often considered in circuit analysis and the circuit is then considered as a capacitor and resistor connected either in series or parallel, depending upon the type of circuit (Art. 2-25).

Voltage Ratings of Capacitors.   Capacitors are rated for the maximum voltage at which they may be safely operated as well as for their capacitance.   The voltage rating is usually specified for two conditions: (1) *the d-c working voltage;* (2) *the a-c working voltage.*   The d-c working voltage rating is 1.414 times as great as the a-c working voltage.   For example, a capacitor rated at 450 volts d-c will have an a-c rating of 318 volts.

Polarized Capacitors.   In radio applications, electrolytic capacitors are limited to circuits that are polarized, although the circuits may also contain small a-c components. For this reason, most electrolytic capacitors are usually *polarized,* that is, one terminal is marked positive and the other negative.   Polarized capacitors should not be subjected to reversed polarity, as a heavy current will pass through the capacitor under this condition and may cause serious damage to the unit.

Fig.   2-25.—Commercial   types   of adjustable capacitors.   (*Courtesy of Hammarlund Manufacturing Company, Inc.*)

Nonpolarized Capacitors.   Certain types of dry electrolytic capacitors are so constructed that they operate equally well on either polarity of a d-c line.   However, they are not designed for alternating currents and therefore should not be used on a-c circuits.   Nonpolarized capacitors are used wherever the supply voltage may become reversed and remain so indefinitely.

2-15. Distributed Capacitance.   Two conductors separated by an insulator form a capacitor, and, if an alternating current is impressed across these two conductors, capacitor action will result.   Because of this, any inductance coil will have capacitances between adjacent turns, capacitances between nonadjacent turns, capacitances between terminal leads, and capacitances between the ground and each turn.   The total effect produced by these capacitances can usually be represented by a single capacitance of the equivalent value.   This is generally called the *distributed capacitance* of the coil.

Effects of Distributed Capacitance.   One effect of distributed capacitance is to by-pass a certain amount of the radio-frequency currents. The amount of r-f current that is by-passed increases directly with the frequency.   At low frequencies, the effect is negligible and can be ignored. At high frequencies, the distributed capacitance causes a loss of energy, which also increases directly with the frequency.   This loss in energy is equivalent to a resistance loss and produces the same effect as if the effective resistance of the coil was increased.

Another effect of distributed capacitance is the manner in which it affects the tuning circuit.   The distributed capacitance acts as a capacitor connected in parallel with the variable tuning capacitor, thus increasing the effective capacitance of the circuit.

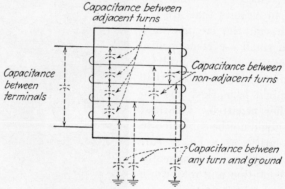

Fig. 2-26.—Distributed capacitances of a coil.

Distributed capacitance sometimes produces another effect since the distributed capacitance and coil form a parallel resonant circuit that will be resonant at some rather high frequency.   At this frequency, oscillating currents will circulate in the winding and the distributed capacitance, thereby causing unstable operation of the circuit.

2-16. Electric Circuits.   An electric circuit is the path taken by an electric current from its source through all of the components of the circuit and back to the source.

Classification of Circuits.   When a circuit contains only one circuit element, it is called a *simple circuit*.   When a circuit contains two or more circuit elements, it may be either a series, parallel, series-parallel, or parallel-series circuit.

A *series circuit* consists of two or more elements connected end to end so that the current will pass from one circuit element on to the next, etc., until the path has been completed (see Fig. 2-27).

A *parallel circuit* consists of two or more elements connected so that the current will have as many paths as there are circuit elements (see Fig. 2-28).

A *series-parallel circuit* consists of one or more parallel groups connected as part of a series circuit.

A *parallel-series circuit* consists of one or more series groups connected as part of a parallel circuit.

In addition to the above classifications, circuits may also be classified according to the kind of current applied to the circuit, that is, as either direct-current or alternating-current circuits.

2-17. Direct-current Circuit Calculations. The most important characteristics of a d-c circuit are the resistance, current, voltage, and power of its various parts and of the complete circuit. A definite relation exists between the current, voltage, and resistance. This relation is commonly called *Ohm's law* and is stated as: the current flowing through

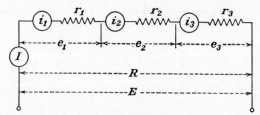

FIG. 2-27.—Typical series circuit.

any resistance will be equal to the voltage across that resistance divided by the ohms of that resistance. This is expressed mathematically as

$$I = \frac{E}{R} \tag{2-26}$$

The power may be expressed in terms of voltage, current, and resistance in the following forms:

$$P = EI \quad \text{or} \quad P = I^2R \quad \text{or} \quad P = \frac{E^2}{R} \tag{2-27}$$

Simple Circuit. As the simple circuit has only one circuit element, all the circuit characteristics can be obtained by use of Eqs. (2-26) and (2-27).

Series Circuit. The equations used to express the relation between the current, voltage, resistance, and power of the simple circuit may be used for the series circuit in the following manner:

$$I = \frac{E}{R} \tag{2-26}$$

$$i_1 = \frac{e_1}{r_1}, \quad i_2 = \frac{e_2}{r_2}, \quad i_3 = \frac{e_3}{r_3}, \cdots \tag{2-26a}$$

$$P = EI \quad \text{or} \quad P = I^2R \quad \text{or} \quad P = \frac{E^2}{R} \quad (2\text{-}27)$$

$$p_1 = e_1 i_1 \quad \text{or} \quad p_1 = i_1{}^2 r_1 \quad \text{or} \quad p_1 = \frac{e_1{}^2}{r_1} \quad (2\text{-}27a)$$

In the above equations the capital-letter symbols refer to the values of the complete circuit and the small-letter symbols refer to the values of the individual circuit elements.

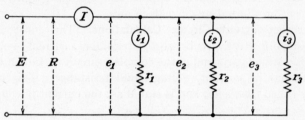

FIG. 2-28.—Typical parallel circuit.

The relation between the values for the complete circuit and for the individual circuit elements for each of the various quantities is expressed by the following equations.

$$R = r_1 + r_2 + r_3 \cdots \qquad (2\text{-}28)$$
$$E = e_1 + e_2 + e_3 \cdots \qquad (2\text{-}29)$$
$$I = i_1 = i_2 = i_3 \cdots \qquad (2\text{-}30)$$
$$P = p_1 + p_2 + p_3 \cdots \qquad (2\text{-}31)$$

Parallel Circuit. The relation between the various quantities of the parallel circuit is expressed by the following equations.

$$I = \frac{E}{R} \qquad (2\text{-}26)$$

$$i_1 = \frac{e_1}{r_1}, \qquad i_2 = \frac{e_2}{r_2}, \qquad i_3 = \frac{e_3}{r_3} \cdots \qquad (2\text{-}26a)$$

$$P = EI \quad \text{or} \quad P = I^2R \quad \text{or} \quad P = \frac{E^2}{R} \quad (2\text{-}27)$$

$$p_1 = e_1 i_1 \quad \text{or} \quad p_1 = i_1{}^2 r_1 \quad \text{or} \quad p_1 = \frac{e_1{}^2}{r_1} \quad (2\text{-}27a)$$

The relation between the values for the complete circuit and for the individual circuit elements is expressed by the following equations.

$$R = \frac{1}{\dfrac{1}{r_1} + \dfrac{1}{r_2} + \dfrac{1}{r_3} \cdots} \qquad (2\text{-}32)$$

$$E = e_1 = e_2 = e_3 \cdots \qquad (2\text{-}33)$$

$$I = i_1 + i_2 + i_3 \cdots \qquad (2\text{-}34)$$
$$P = p_1 + p_2 + p_3 \cdots \qquad (2\text{-}31)$$

When the parallel circuit contains only two circuit elements, Eq. (2-32) may be expressed as,

$$R = \frac{r_1 r_2}{r_1 + r_2} \qquad (2\text{-}32a)$$

$$r_2 = \frac{R r_1}{r_1 - R} \qquad (2\text{-}32b)$$

Series-parallel Circuit. As this type of circuit is a combination of both the series and the parallel circuits, its solution involves both series and parallel principles. The first step is to calculate the combined resistance value of each parallel group. The circuit may then be considered as a series circuit. When the voltage across each parallel group has been found, it will then be possible to calculate the current and the power for each element in the parallel groups.

As the variety of series-parallel circuits is innumerable and as no single set of equations will satisfy all cases, the following example is presented to illustrate the general procedure of solution which may be applied to any series-parallel circuit.

Example 2-14. Calculate the resistance, current, and power of the circuit shown in Fig. 2-29. Also calculate the current in each resistor and the power consumed by each.

Given:

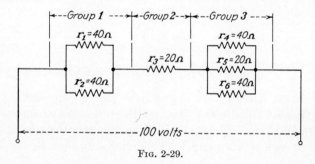

Fig. 2-29.

Solution:

$$R_{GR\cdot1} = \frac{r_1 r_2}{r_1 + r_2} = \frac{40 \times 40}{40 + 40} = 20 \text{ ohms}$$

$$R_{GR\cdot2} = r_3 = 20 \text{ ohms}$$

$$R_{GR\cdot3} = \frac{1}{\dfrac{1}{r_4} + \dfrac{1}{r_5} + \dfrac{1}{r_6}} = \frac{1}{\dfrac{1}{40} + \dfrac{1}{20} + \dfrac{1}{40}} = 10 \text{ ohms}$$

The circuit may now be represented by an equivalent series circuit as shown in Fig. 2-30.

$$\text{Fig. 2-30.}$$

$$R = R_{GR \cdot 1} + R_{GR \cdot 2} + R_{GR \cdot 3} = 20 + 20 + 10 = 50 \text{ ohms}$$
$$I = \frac{E}{R} = \frac{100}{50} = 2 \text{ amp}$$
$$P = EI = 100 \times 2 = 200 \text{ watts}$$
$$E_{GR \cdot 1} = IR_{GR \cdot 1} = 2 \times 20 = 40 \text{ volts}$$
$$E_{GR \cdot 2} = IR_{GR \cdot 2} = 2 \times 20 = 40 \text{ volts}$$
$$E_{GR \cdot 3} = IR_{GR \cdot 3} = 2 \times 10 = 20 \text{ volts}$$
$$i_1 = \frac{e_1}{r_1} = \frac{40}{40} = 1 \text{ amp}$$
$$i_2 = \frac{e_2}{r_2} = \frac{40}{40} = 1 \text{ amp}$$
$$i_3 = \frac{e_3}{r_3} = \frac{40}{20} = 2 \text{ amp}$$
$$i_4 = \frac{e_4}{r_4} = \frac{20}{40} = 0.5 \text{ amp}$$
$$i_5 = \frac{e_5}{r_5} = \frac{20}{20} = 1 \text{ amp}$$
$$i_6 = \frac{e_6}{r_6} = \frac{20}{40} = 0.5 \text{ amp}$$
$$p_1 = e_1 i_1 = 40 \times 1 = 40 \text{ watts}$$
$$p_2 = e_2 i_2 = 40 \times 1 = 40 \text{ watts}$$
$$p_3 = e_3 i_3 = 40 \times 2 = 80 \text{ watts}$$
$$p_4 = e_4 i_4 = 20 \times 0.5 = 10 \text{ watts}$$
$$p_5 = e_5 i_5 = 20 \times 1 = 20 \text{ watts}$$
$$p_6 = e_6 i_6 = 20 \times 0.5 = 10 \text{ watts}$$

Parallel-series Circuit. This circuit is also a combination of both series and parallel circuits and involves the principles of each in solving for its characteristics. The first step is to calculate the combined resistance value of each series group. The circuit may then be considered as a parallel circuit.

As the variety of parallel-series circuits is innumerable and as no single set of equations will satisfy all cases, the following example is presented to illustrate the general procedure of solution which may be applied to any parallel-series circuit.

Example 2-15. Calculate the resistance, current, and power of the circuit shown in Fig. 2-31a. Also calculate the current, voltage, and power of each resistor.

Given:

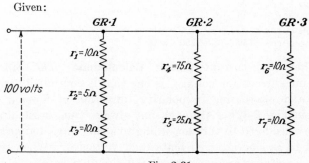

Fig. 2-31a

Solution:

$$R_{GR\cdot1} = r_1 + r_2 + r_3 = 10 + 5 + 10 = 25 \text{ ohms}$$
$$R_{GR\cdot2} = r_4 + r_5 = 75 + 25 = 100 \text{ ohms}$$
$$R_{GR\cdot3} = r_6 + r_7 = 10 + 10 = 20 \text{ ohms}$$

The circuit may now be represented by an equivalent parallel circuit as shown in Fig. 2-31b.

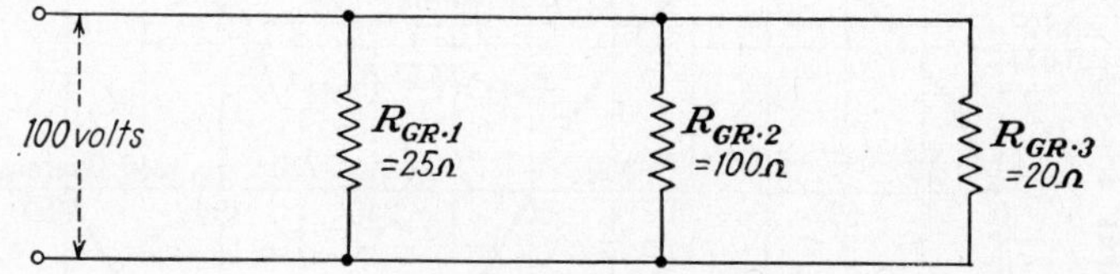

FIG. 2-31b

$$R = \frac{1}{\frac{1}{R_{GR\cdot1}} + \frac{1}{R_{GR\cdot2}} + \frac{1}{R_{GR\cdot3}}} = \frac{1}{\frac{1}{25} + \frac{1}{100} + \frac{1}{20}} = 10 \text{ ohms}$$

$$I = \frac{E}{R} = \frac{100}{10} = 10 \text{ amp}$$

$$P = EI = 100 \times 10 = 1000 \text{ watts}$$

$$i_1 = i_2 = i_3 = \frac{E}{R_{GR\cdot1}} = \frac{100}{25} = 4 \text{ amp}$$

$$i_4 = i_5 = \frac{E}{R_{GR\cdot2}} = \frac{100}{100} = 1 \text{ amp}$$

$$i_6 = i_7 = \frac{E}{R_{GR\cdot3}} = \frac{100}{20} = 5 \text{ amp}$$

$$e_1 = i_1 r_1 = 4 \times 10 = 40 \text{ volts}$$
$$e_2 = i_2 r_2 = 4 \times 5 = 20 \text{ volts}$$
$$e_3 = i_3 r_3 = 4 \times 10 = 40 \text{ volts}$$
$$e_4 = i_4 r_4 = 1 \times 75 = 75 \text{ volts}$$
$$e_5 = i_5 r_5 = 1 \times 25 = 25 \text{ volts}$$
$$e_6 = i_6 r_6 = 5 \times 10 = 50 \text{ volts}$$
$$e_7 = i_7 r_7 = 5 \times 10 = 50 \text{ volts}$$
$$p_1 = e_1 i_1 = 40 \times 4 = 160 \text{ watts}$$
$$p_2 = e_2 i_2 = 20 \times 4 = 80 \text{ watts}$$
$$p_3 = e_3 i_3 = 40 \times 4 = 160 \text{ watts}$$

$$p_4 = e_4 i_4 = 75 \times 1 = 75 \text{ watts}$$
$$p_5 = e_5 i_5 = 25 \times 1 = 25 \text{ watts}$$
$$p_6 = e_6 i_6 = 50 \times 5 = 250 \text{ watts}$$
$$p_7 = e_7 i_7 = 50 \times 5 = 250 \text{ watts}$$

2-18. Alternating-current Circuit Calculations. *The Sine Wave.*
An alternating current (or voltage) is one that is continually varying in magnitude and alternating in polarity (direction of flow) at regular intervals (see Fig. 2-32). Although not always true, most alternating currents are considered to vary according to a sine wave and accordingly are referred to as sine-wave currents (and voltages). When sine-wave currents and voltages are considered, the circuit calculations are most generally based on the effective value, although occasionally the maximum or the average value may be used. The numerical relationship between the maximum, effective, and average values is shown in Fig.

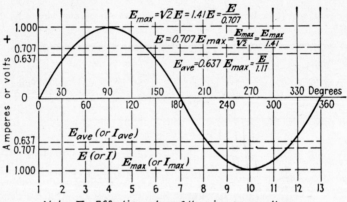

Note: E = Effective value of the sine-wave voltage
I = Effective value of the sine-wave current

Fig. 2-32.—Relative values of an alternating sine-wave voltage (or current).

2-32. The development of these relationships can be found in the authors' *Electrical Essentials of Radio.*

Circuit Characteristics. The important characteristics of a-c circuits are the resistance, inductance, capacitance, impedance, current, voltage, frequency, power, power factor, and phase angle of its various parts and of the complete circuit. A definite relation exists between the current, voltage, and impedance. This relation is commonly referred to as *Ohm's law for a-c circuits* and may be stated as: the current flowing through any impedance will be equal to the voltage across that impedance divided by the ohms of that impedance. This may be expressed mathematically as

$$I = \frac{E}{Z} \tag{2-35}$$

The power may be expressed in terms of the current and resistance as

$$P = I^2R \qquad (2\text{-}27)$$

As resistance is the only kind of circuit element that consumes power, only the value of R can be used in this equation, and care should be exercised that it is not confused with X_L, X_c, or Z, which are also expressed in ohms.

The power may also be expressed in terms of voltage, current, and power factor as

$$P = E \times I \times \text{P-F} \qquad (2\text{-}36)$$

The power factor may be expressed in terms of power, voltage, and current as

$$\text{P-F} = \frac{P}{E \times I} \qquad (2\text{-}37)$$

The power factor may also be expressed in terms of resistance and impedance as

$$\text{P-F} = \frac{R}{Z} \qquad (2\text{-}37a)$$

The power factor may also be found from the phase angle, as

$$\text{P-F} = \cos \theta \qquad (2\text{-}37b)$$

The phase angle may be obtained by reference to the cosine tables (Appendix XII). When the power factor, which is equal to the cosine of the phase angle, is known, the angle corresponding to that value may be obtained from the cosine table.

Simple Circuit. As the simple circuit has only one circuit element, the current can be obtained by use of Eq. (2-9), (2-21), or (2-26):

$$I_L = \frac{E_L}{X_L} \qquad (2\text{-}9)$$

$$I_c = \frac{E_c}{X_c} \qquad (2\text{-}21)$$

$$I_R = \frac{E}{R} \qquad (2\text{-}26)$$

The power may be found by

$$P = I^2R \qquad (2\text{-}27)$$
$$P = E \times I \times \text{P-F} \qquad (2\text{-}36)$$

The power factor may be found by

$$\text{P-F} = \frac{P}{E \times I} \tag{2-37}$$

$$\text{P-F} = \frac{R}{Z} \tag{2-37a}$$

The phase angle may be found from the power factor value and the cosine tables (Appendix XII).

Series Circuit. Most of the equations used for the solution of the simple circuit also apply to the series circuit, as may be seen in the following list of equations for the series circuit.

$$I = \frac{E}{Z} \tag{2-35}$$

$$i = \frac{e}{r} \qquad i = \frac{e}{x_L} \qquad i = \frac{e}{x_C} \tag{2-38}$$

$$P = I^2 R \tag{2-27}$$

$$P = E \times I \times \text{P-F} \tag{2-36}$$

$$\text{P-F} = \frac{P}{E \times I} \tag{2-37}$$

$$\text{P-F} = \frac{R}{Z} \tag{2-37a}$$

In the above equations the capital-letter symbols indicate the values of the complete circuit and the small-letter symbols indicate the values of the individual circuit elements.

The relation between the various quantities for the complete circuit and for the individual circuit elements is expressed by the following equations.

$$R = r_1 + r_2 + r_3 \cdots \tag{2-28}$$

$$X_L = x_{L1} + x_{L2} + x_{L3} \cdots \tag{2-39}$$

$$X_C = x_{C1} + x_{C2} + x_{C3} \cdots \tag{2-40}$$

$$Z = \sqrt{R^2 + (X_L - X_C)^2} \tag{2-41}$$

$$E = e_1 + e_2 + e_3 \cdots \text{ (added vectorially)} \tag{2-42}$$

$$I = i_1 = i_2 = i_3 \cdots \tag{2-30}$$

$$P = p_1 + p_2 + p_3 \cdots \tag{2-31}$$

Example 2-16. The series circuit shown in Fig. 2-33 is connected to a 150-volt, 60-cycle power line. Find: (*a*) the resistance of the circuit; (*b*) the inductive reactance of the circuit; (*c*) the capacitive reactance of the circuit; (*d*) the impedance of the circuit; (*e*) the line current and the current in each circuit element; (*f*) the voltage across each circuit element; (*g*) the line voltage from the voltages across each circuit element; (*h*) the power consumed by each circuit element; (*i*) the line power; (*j*) the power factor of each circuit element; (*k*) the power factor of the line; (*l*) the phase angle between the line current and line voltage.

Given:

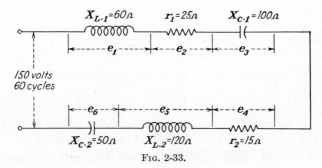

Fig. 2-33.

Solution:

(a) $R = r_1 + r_2 = 25 + 15 = 40$ ohms

(b) $X_L = x_{L1} + x_{L2} = 60 + 120 = 180$ ohms

(c) $X_C = x_{C1} + x_{C2} = 100 + 50 = 150$ ohms

(d) $Z = \sqrt{R^2 + (X_L - X_C)^2} = \sqrt{40^2 + (180 - 150)^2} = 50$ ohms

(e) $I = \dfrac{E}{Z} = \dfrac{150}{50} = 3$ amp

$i_1 = i_2 = i_3 = i_4 = i_5 = i_6 = I = 3$ amp

(f) $e_1 = i_1 X_{L1} = 3 \times 60 = 180$ volts

$e_2 = i_2 r_1 = 3 \times 25 = 75$ volts

$e_3 = i_3 X_{C1} = 3 \times 100 = 300$ volts

$e_4 = i_4 r_2 = 3 \times 15 = 45$ volts

$e_5 = i_5 X_{L2} = 3 \times 120 = 360$ volts

$e_6 = i_6 X_{C2} = 3 \times 50 = 150$ volts

(g) $E = \sqrt{E_R{}^2 + (E_{XL} - E_{XC})^2} = \sqrt{(e_2 + e_4)^2 + (e_1 + e_5 - e_3 - e_6)^2}$

$= \sqrt{(75 + 45)^2 + (180 + 360 - 300 - 150)^2}$

$= \sqrt{120^2 + 90^2} = 150$ volts

(h) $p_1 = i_1{}^2 r_{L1} = 3^2 \times 0 = 0$ watts

$p_2 = i_2{}^2 r_1 = 3^2 \times 25 = 225$ watts

$p_3 = i_3{}^2 r_{C1} = 3^2 \times 0 = 0$ watts

$p_4 = i_4{}^2 r_2 = 3^2 \times 15 = 135$ watts

$p_5 = i_5{}^2 r_{L2} = 3^2 \times 0 = 0$ watts

$p_6 = i_6{}^2 r_{C2} = 3^2 \times 0 = 0$ watts

(i) $P = p_1 + p_2 + p_3 + p_4 + p_5 + p_6$

$= 0 + 225 + 0 + 135 + 0 + 0 = 360$ watts

(j) p-f$_1 = \dfrac{r_1}{z_1} = \dfrac{0}{60} = 0$

p-f$_2 = \dfrac{r_2}{z_2} = \dfrac{25}{25} = 1$

p-f$_3 = \dfrac{r_3}{z_3} = \dfrac{0}{100} = 0$

p-f$_4 = \dfrac{r_4}{z_4} = \dfrac{15}{15} = 1$

p-f$_5 = \dfrac{r_5}{z_5} = \dfrac{0}{120} = 0$

$$\text{p-f}_6 = \frac{r_6}{z_6} = \frac{0}{50} = 0$$

(k) $\text{P-F} = \dfrac{R}{Z} = \dfrac{40}{50} = 0.800$

(l) θ = the angle whose cosine is equal to the power factor.

  = $\cos^{-1} 0.800 = 37°$ lagging current (Appendix XII)

(Note: The current lags the voltage because X_L is greater than X_C.)

The above example illustrates all the series-circuit calculations. In practical problems it is usually only necessary to find several of these calculated values, and those not required may be omitted.

Parallel Circuit. The relation between the various quantities for the parallel circuit is expressed by the following equations.

$$I = i_1 + i_2 + i_3 \cdots \text{ (added vectorially)} \tag{2-43}$$

$$i = \frac{e}{r}, \qquad i = \frac{e}{x_L}, \qquad i = \frac{e}{x_C} \tag{2-38}$$

$$P = p_1 + p_2 + p_3 \cdots \tag{2-31}$$

$$P = E \times I \times \text{P-F} \tag{2-36}$$

$$\text{P-F} = \frac{P}{E \times I} \tag{2-37}$$

$$Z = \frac{E}{I} \tag{2-44}$$

The relation between the various quantities for the complete circuit and for the individual circuit elements is expressed by the following equations.

$$R = \frac{1}{\dfrac{1}{r_1} + \dfrac{1}{r_2} + \dfrac{1}{r_3} \cdots} \tag{2-32}$$

$$X_L = \frac{1}{\dfrac{1}{x_{L1}} + \dfrac{1}{x_{L2}} + \dfrac{1}{x_{L3}} \cdots} \tag{2-45}$$

$$X_C = \frac{1}{\dfrac{1}{x_{C1}} + \dfrac{1}{x_{C2}} + \dfrac{1}{x_{C3}} \cdots} \tag{2-46}$$

$$E = e_1 = e_2 = e_3 \cdots \tag{2-33}$$

Example 2-17. The parallel circuit shown in Fig. 2-34 is connected to a 200-volt, 60-cycle power line. Find: (a) the current flowing in each branch of the parallel circuit; (b) the line current; (c) the power taken by each branch; (d) the power taken by the whole circuit; (e) the power factor of the circuit; (f) the impedance of the circuit.

Given:

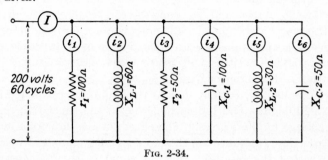

Fig. 2-34.

Solution:

(a) $i_1 = \dfrac{e_1}{r_1} = \dfrac{200}{100} = 2$ amp

$i_2 = \dfrac{e_2}{x_{L1}} = \dfrac{200}{60} = 3.33$ amp

$i_3 = \dfrac{e_3}{r_2} = \dfrac{200}{50} = 4$ amp

$i_4 = \dfrac{e_4}{x_{C1}} = \dfrac{200}{100} = 2$ amp

$i_5 = \dfrac{e_5}{x_{L2}} = \dfrac{200}{30} = 6.67$ amp

$i_6 = \dfrac{e_6}{x_{C2}} = \dfrac{200}{50} = 4$ amp

(b) $I = \sqrt{(i_1 + i_3)^2 + (i_2 + i_5 - i_4 - i_6)^2}$

$= \sqrt{(2 + 4)^2 + (3.33 + 6.67 - 2 - 4)^2}$

$= \sqrt{6^2 + 4^2} = 7.21$ amp

(c) $p_1 = i_1{}^2 r_1 = 2^2 \times 100 = 400$ watts

$p_3 = i_3{}^2 r_2 = 4^2 \times 50 = 800$ watts

$p_2 = p_4 = p_5 = p_6 = 0$ watts (pure inductances and pure capacitances)

(d) $P = p_1 + p_2 + p_3 + p_4 + p_5 + p_6$

$= 400 + 0 + 800 + 0 + 0 + 0 = 1200$ watts

(e) $\text{P-F} = \dfrac{P}{E \times I} = \dfrac{1200}{200 \times 7.21} = 0.832$

(f) $Z = \dfrac{E}{I} = \dfrac{200}{7.21} = 27.74$ ohms

Combination Circuits. The series-parallel and the parallel-series circuits are generally referred to as *combination circuits.* The presentation of the method of solution of these circuits is too lengthy to include in this résumé, but if the solution of such circuits becomes necessary the method may be obtained from Chap. X of the authors' *Electrical Essentials of Radio.*

Since the parallel resonant circuit, actually a simple combination circuit, is used in many radio circuits, some of the important calculations for this circuit are included in Art. 2-21.

2-19. Resonant Circuits. Resonance is a condition that exists when the inductive reactance and the capacitive reactance of a circuit are equal. Therefore, a resonant circuit must contain both inductance and capacitance; it also contains at least a small amount of resistance because all inductors and capacitors have some resistance. Resonant circuits may be either of the series or parallel type.

In a-c circuits, the current due to the inductive reactance lags its voltage by 90 degrees and the current due to the capacitive reactance leads its voltage by 90 degrees. The effects of the inductive reactance and the capacitive reactance are therefore 180 degrees out of phase with one another and the resultant effect is equal to their algebraic sum. If either the capacitor or the inductor of a resonant circuit is adjusted so

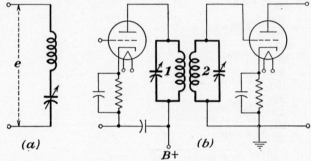

Fig. 2-35.—Typical resonant circuits. (*a*) Series resonant circuit, (*b*) 1–parallel resonant circuit 2–series resonant circuit.

that the individual reactances are equal at some frequency, the circuit is said to be in resonance.

Classification of Resonant Circuits as Series or Parallel. Because resonant circuits form only a part of a complete radio circuit, it is sometimes very difficult to determine whether the resonant circuit is to be considered as a series or a parallel type. Several resonant circuits (drawn in heavy lines) are shown in Fig. 2-35. The circuit shown in (*a*) is very readily recognized as being a series resonant circuit. The two resonant circuits of (*b*) appear to be parallel resonant circuits but actually circuit 1 is considered as a parallel resonant circuit and circuit 2 as a series resonant circuit.

Circuit 1 is considered a parallel resonant circuit because it receives its electrical energy from the plate circuit of the tube to which it is connected. Circuit 2 is considered a series resonant circuit because no separate voltage is applied to the inductor and capacitor, but instead a voltage is induced in the inductor (secondary of an r-f transformer), which is then considered as a voltage connected in series with the inductor and the capacitor. The following procedure will help to determine whether a circuit should be classed as parallel or series: (1) locate the inductive and capacitive components forming the resonant circuit; (2) locate the source of the alternating (or signal) voltage for these components; (3) determine whether the components are in series or parallel with the source of voltage. In radio circuits the signal voltage may be derived from any one of the following sources: antenna, output of a vacuum tube, or the induced voltage from other circuits.

2-20. Series Resonant Circuits. A series resonant circuit generally consists of a fixed inductor and a variable or an adjustable capacitor connected in series with a source of alternating voltage. Typical series

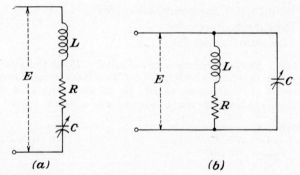

(a)   *(b)*

Fig. 2-36.—Equivalent circuits of typical resonant circuits. (a) Series, (b) parallel.

resonant circuits are illustrated in Fig. 2-35a and circuit 2 of Fig. 2-35b. The diagram shown in Fig. 2-36a is the equivalent circuit used to represent either of the typical series resonant circuits of Fig. 2-35. The resistance R is not necessarily a separate resistor but generally represents the total resistance of the coil, the capacitor, and the conductors of the circuit.

Relation between f, L, and C at Resonance. At resonance the inductive reactance is equal to the capacitive reactance; therefore from Eqs. (2-8) and (2-20) this may be expressed mathematically as

$$2\pi f_r L = \frac{10^6}{2\pi f_r C} \qquad (2\text{-}47)$$

where f_r = frequency of resonance, cycles
L = inductance, henries
C = capacitance, microfarads

At radio frequencies, f is generally expressed in kilocycles, L in microhenries, and C in microfarads. The commonly used equations for f_r, L, and C are derived by substituting these units in Eq. (2-47), as

$$2\pi f_r 10^3 L 10^{-6} = \frac{10^6}{2\pi f_r 10^3 C} \tag{2-47a}$$

or
$$f_r^2 = \frac{10^6}{(2\pi)^2 10^3 \times 10^{-6} \times 10^3 LC} = \frac{10^6}{(2\pi)^2 LC} \tag{2-47b}$$

and
$$f_r = \frac{10^3}{2\pi \sqrt{LC}} = \frac{159}{\sqrt{LC}} \tag{2-48}$$

From Eq. (2-48)

$$L = \frac{25,300}{f_r^2 C} \tag{2-49}$$

$$C = \frac{25,300}{f_r^2 L} \tag{2-50}$$

where f_r = frequency of resonance, kilocycles
L = inductance, microhenries
C = capacitance, microfarads

Example 2-18.   A series circuit has a fixed inductor of 250 μh and a variable capacitor whose maximum capacitance is 350 $\mu\mu$f.   (a) What is the resonant frequency when the capacitor is set at its maximum value?   (b) To what value must the capacitor be adjusted in order to make the circuit resonant with a 1000-kc signal?

Given:

$L = 250\ \mu h$
$C_{max} = 350\ \mu\mu f$
(a) $C = 350\ \mu\mu f$
(b) $f_r = 1000$ kc

Find:

(a) $f_r = ?$
(b) $C = ?$

Solution:

(a) $f_r = \dfrac{159}{\sqrt{LC}} = \dfrac{159}{\sqrt{250 \times 350 \times 10^{-6}}} = 538$ kc

(b) $C = \dfrac{25,300}{f_r^2 L} = \dfrac{25,300}{1000^2 \times 250} = 101\ \mu\mu f$

Impedance, Current, and Voltage Characteristics at Resonance.   The impedance of the series circuit is expressed by Eq. (2-41), as

$$Z = \sqrt{R^2 + (X_L - X_c)^2} \tag{2-41}$$

Since resonance is a condition that exists only when X_L and X_c are equal, it becomes apparent that the impedance of a series circuit is at its minimum value when the series circuit is at resonance.

The current flowing in the circuit is equal to the voltage divided by the impedance, and when the impedance is at the minimum value the current will be at the maximum value.

The voltage drop across the various parts of a series circuit is proportional to the resistance or the reactance of the individual parts.   Since the inductive reactance and the capacitive reactance are equal, their voltage drops are also equal and as they have a 180-degree phase difference, their vector sum will be zero.   Under this condition the resistance voltage drop must be equal to the line voltage.   As the resistance of the series resonant circuit is generally very low compared to the reactance values it is evident that the reactance voltages will be higher than the resistance voltage and hence higher than the line voltage.   The reactance voltage drops will be greater than the line voltage by the ratio of the reactances to the resistance and may be expressed as

$$E_L = E \frac{X_L}{R} \tag{2-51}$$

$$E_c = E \frac{X_c}{R} \tag{2-52}$$

As the ratio of X_L to R is generally referred to as the circuit Q, Eq. (2-51) may be expressed as

$$E_L = EQ \tag{2-53}$$

The value of Q for series resonant circuits often exceeds 100, hence such a circuit can develop high reactive voltages from low values of signal voltage.

Example 2-19.   A series resonant circuit has a resistance of 10 ohms and an inductive reactance of 500 ohms at its resonant frequency.   What is the voltage across the inductor, capacitor, and resistor if the applied voltage is 5 volts at a frequency equal to the resonant frequency of the circuit?

Given: Find:
$\quad R = 10$ ohms $\quad E_L = ?$
$\quad X_L = 500$ ohms $\quad E_c = ?$
$\quad E = 5$ volts $\quad E_R = ?$
Solution:

$$E_L = E \frac{X_L}{R} = 5 \times \frac{500}{10} = 250 \text{ volts}$$
$$E_C = E_L \text{ (at resonance)} = 250 \text{ volts}$$
$$E_R = E \text{ (at resonance)} = 5 \text{ volts}$$

2-21. Parallel Resonant Circuits.   *The Circuit.*   A parallel resonant circuit generally consists of an inductor and a capacitor connected in parallel across a source of alternating voltage.   A typical parallel resonant circuit is illustrated by circuit 1 of Fig. 2-35*b*.   The equivalent circuit diagram is given in Fig. 2-36*b*.   Generally, most of the resistance of the circuit is in the inductor; the resistance of the capacitor is so small that it may be neglected.   On this basis the circuit is considered as an inductor with a small amount of series resistance in one branch and a perfect capacitor in the other branch, as is shown in Fig. 2-36*b*.

Relation between f, L, and C at Resonance. The relation between f, L, and C for a parallel resonant circuit is the same as for the series resonant circuit. These relationships have been expressed by Eqs. (2-48), (2-49), and (2-50).

Impedance, Current, and Voltage Characteristics at Resonance. The parallel resonant circuit (Fig. 2-36b) is actually a parallel-series circuit and its impedance may be expressed as

$$Z_T = \frac{Z_1 Z_2}{Z_1 + Z_2} \tag{2-54}$$

where Z_T = impedance of the parallel circuit

Z_1 = impedance of branch 1

Z_2 = impedance of branch 2

$Z_1 + Z_2$ = vector sum, or series impedance of the circuit.

As the resistance of the circuit is generally very low compared to the reactance (high circuit Q), the resistance may be neglected in the calculation of Z_1 and Z_2 for the numerator of Eq. (2-54); Z_1 then becomes approximately equal to X_L, and Z_2 becomes nearly equal to X_C. The resistance must, however, be included in the denominator, for $Z_1 + Z_2$ is equal to the impedance that the circuit would have if it were connected as a series circuit: [Eq. (2-41)] $Z = \sqrt{R^2 + (X_L - X_C)^2}$. The impedance of the parallel resonant circuit may therefore be expressed as

$$Z_{T \cdot r} = \frac{X_L X_C}{\sqrt{R^2 + (X_L - X_C)^2}} \tag{2-55}$$

At resonance, $X_L = X_C$; therefore Eq. (2-55) may be expressed as

$$Z_{T \cdot r} = \frac{X_L X_L}{R} = Q X_L \tag{2-56}$$

Example 2-20. A parallel resonant circuit (Fig. 2-36b), is resonant at a frequency of 1500 kc. The inductive reactance and the capacitive reactance at the resonant frequency are each 1000 ohms, and the resistance of the inductor is 10 ohms. (a) What is the impedance at resonant frequency? (b) What is the impedance at 1485 kc if the inductive reactance is then 990 ohms and the capacitive reactance is 1010 ohms?

Given:
              $R = 10$ ohms

(a) $X_L = 1000$ ohms

      $X_C = 1000$ ohms

(b) $X_L = 990$ ohms

      $X_C = 1010$ ohms

Find:

(a) $Z_{T \cdot r} = ?$

(b) $Z_{1485} = ?$

Solution:

(a) $Z_{T\cdot r} = \dfrac{X_L X_L}{R} = \dfrac{1000 \times 1000}{10} = 100,000$ ohms

(b) $Z_{1485} = \dfrac{X_L X_C}{\sqrt{R^2 + (X_L - X_C)^2}} = \dfrac{990 \times 1010}{\sqrt{10^2 + (990 + 1010)^2}} = 44,718$ ohms

A careful study of Eq. (2-55) will show that the impedance will be at the maximum value when the circuit is resonant. This may be further observed from the results of Example 2-20.

The current of a parallel resonant circuit is at its minimum value when the circuit is resonant because the circuit impedance is then at its maximum value. The current in each reactance, which is called the *circulating current*, will be greater than the line current by the ratio of the reactance to the resistance and may be expressed as

$$I_L = I_C = I\frac{X_L}{R} = IQ \tag{2-57}$$

The apparently unusual condition of the current in each reactance being higher than the line current is due to the fact that the two currents are equal in amount and differ in phase by nearly 180 degrees. The line current is the vector sum of the currents in the two branches and hence will be very low.

The voltage across each branch of the parallel resonant circuit will be equal to the line voltage.

2-22. Resonance Curves. *Need for the Curves.* In order to understand the characteristics of resonant circuits it is necessary to know how

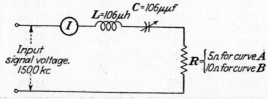

Fig. 2-37.—Series resonant circuit used to illustrate the characteristics of a series resonant circuit as indicated by Table II-I and the curves of Fig. 2-38.

the circuit acts at frequencies above and below the frequency of resonance as well as at the resonant frequency. These characteristics may be understood when they are seen in the form of graphs or *resonance curves*, as they are commonly called.

Curves of the Series Resonant Circuit. Series resonant circuits are used when the maximum current is desired for a definite frequency or band of frequencies. A curve showing the variation of the current over a band of frequencies will show how the current varies with the frequency.

Figure 2-37 shows a series resonant circuit with all of its values indicated on the diagram.   The circuit is resonant at 1500 kc, as may be calculated by Eq. (2-48).   The values listed in Table II-I have been calculated by use of Eqs. (2-8), (2-20), 2-41), and (2-35).

Table II-I

Frequency, kc	X_L	X_C	R	Z	I ma when $E = 0.5$
1470	980	1020	5	40.31	12.4
1475	983.5	1016.5	5	33.37	14.98
1480	987	1013	5	26.47	18.8
1485	990	1010	5	20.61	24.2
1490	993	1007	5	14.86	33.6
1495	997	1003	5	7.81	64.02
1500	1000	1000	5	5.0	100
1505	1003	997	5	7.81	64.02
1510	1007	993	5	14.86	33.6
1515	1010	990	5	20.61	24.2
1520	1013	987	5	26.47	18.8
1525	1016.5	983.5	5	33.37	14.98
1530	1020	980	5	40.31	12.4
1470	980	1020	10	41.23	12.1
1475	983.5	1016.5	10	34.48	14.5
1480	987	1013	10	27.85	17.9
1485	990	1010	10	22.36	22.3
1490	993	1007	10	17.20	29.1
1495	997	1003	10	11.68	42.8
1500	1000	1000	10	10.0	50.0
1505	1003	997	10	11.68	42.8
1510	1007	993	10	17.20	29.1
1515	1010	990	10	22.36	22.3
1520	1013	987	10	27.85	17.9
1525	1016.5	983.5	10	34.48	14.5
1530	1020	980	10	41.23	12.1

Curve *A* of Fig. 2-38 is plotted from the values listed in Table II-I. Examination of the curves shows that no appreciable current flows until the frequency is approximately 1470 kc.   The current increases slowly with increases of frequency until the frequency is very close to the resonant frequency.   Then the current increases very rapidly until the maximum current is reached at the frequency of resonance.   As the frequency is increased beyond resonance, the current decreases very rapidly at first and then decreases more slowly until no appreciable current flows at approximately 1530 kc.   In radio, a circuit that is or can be adjusted so that it is resonant for a definite frequency is referred to as a *tuned circuit*.

Curve *B* is the resonance curve for a circuit similar to that of Fig. 2-37 but with a resistance value of 10 ohms in place of the original resist-

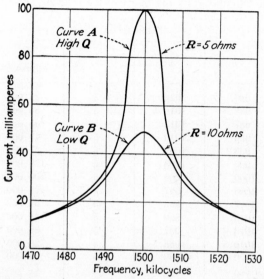

FIG. 2-38.—Resonance curves of the series circuit shown in Fig. 2-37.

ance value of 5 ohms.   Comparison of the two curves shows that as the resistance of the circuit is increased the maximum current is reduced. Therefore, in order to produce maximum current the resistance of the series resonant circuit should be as low as possible.   The resistance value also affects the slope of the resonance curves, and this important characteristic will be discussed in the following article.

Curves of the Parallel Resonant Circuit. Parallel resonant circuits are used: (1) when the signal current of a definite frequency or band of frequencies is to be reduced to a minimum; (2) when it is desired to obtain a higher signal voltage across the resonant circuit at a definite frequency or band of frequencies.   Par-

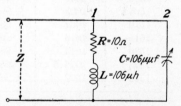

FIG. 2-39.—Parallel resonant circuit used to illustrate the characteristics of a parallel resonant circuit as indicated by Table II-II and the curves of Fig. 2-40.

allel resonance curves are generally drawn to show how the impedance of the circuit varies over a band of frequencies close to the frequency of resonance, as is illustrated by Fig. 2-40.   Curves may also be drawn to show the variation of current over the frequency band.

Figure 2-39 shows a parallel resonant circuit with all of its values indicated on the diagram. It should be noted that these values are the same as those used for the series circuit of Fig. 2-37. The circuit is resonant at 1500 kc, as may be calculated by Eq. (2-48). The values listed in Table II-II have been calculated by use of Eqs. (2-8), (2-20), (2-55), and (2-35).

TABLE II-II

Frequency, kc	X_L	X_C	R	Z (approx.)	I ma when $E = 100$
1470	980	1020	5	25,000	4.00
1475	983.5	1016.5	5	30,000	3.33
1480	987	1013	5	38,000	2.63
1485	990	1010	5	48,000	2.08
1490	993	1007	5	67,000	1.49
1495	997	1003	5	128,000	0.78
1500	1000	1000	5	200,000	0.50
1505	1003	997	5	128,000	0.78
1510	1007	993	5	67,000	1.49
1515	1010	990	5	48,000	2.08
1520	1013	987	5	38,000	2.63
1525	1016.5	983.5	5	30,000	3.33
1530	1020	980	5	25,000	4.00
1470	980	1020	10	24,250	4.12
1475	983.5	1016.5	10	29,000	3.44
1480	987	1013	10	36,000	2.78
1485	990	1010	10	44,500	2.25
1490	993	1007	10	58,000	1.72
1495	997	1003	10	85,500	1.17
1500	1000	1000	10	100,000	1.00
1505	1003	997	10	85,500	1.17
1510	1007	993	10	58,000	1.72
1515	1010	990	10	44,500	2.25
1520	1013	987	10	36,000	2.78
1525	1016.5	983.5	10	29,000	3.44
1530	1020	980	10	24,250	4.12

Curve *A* of Fig. 2-40 is plotted from the values listed in Table II-II. Examination of the curve shows that the impedance is maximum at the resonant frequency (1500 kc) and that the impedance decreases sharply when the frequency is varied slightly above and below resonance. As the deviation from resonant frequency is increased, the amount of decrease in impedance tapers off.

Curve *B* is the resonance curve for a circuit similar to that of Fig. 2-39 but with a resistance value of 10 ohms in place of the original resistance

value of 5 ohms.   Comparison of the two curves shows that as the resistance of the circuit is decreased the value of the impedance is increased. As parallel resonant circuits are used to reduce the current at a definite frequency to the minimum value, the impedance of the circuit should be at the maximum value.   Furthermore, in order to obtain the maximum current the resistance of the parallel resonant circuit should be as low as possible.

2-23. Circuit Q. *Definition of Circuit Q.*   The ratio of the inductive reactance of a tuned circuit to the resistance of the circuit is referred to as the Q of the circuit. Expressed mathematically

$$Q = \frac{X_L}{R} \qquad (2\text{-}58)$$

As R is the resistance of the entire circuit, its value will be slightly higher than the resistance of the coil, and therefore the circuit Q will be slightly lower than the coil Q.   The difference between the values of the circuit Q and the coil Q is normally small because the resistance of the capacitor and

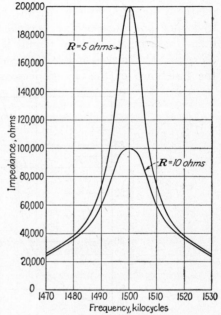

FIG. 2-40.—Resonance curves of the parallel circuit shown in Fig. 2-39.

the connecting wires of the circuit is low compared to the resistance of the coil.   Furthermore, as R is practically equal to the effective high-frequency resistance of the coil, and as this high-frequency resistance varies almost directly with the frequency, the circuit Q remains practically constant for normal ranges of frequency.

Relation between Circuit Q and the Slope of the Resonance Curves. The slope of the resonance curves is dependent on the Q of the tuned circuit.   This can be seen from the slopes of the curves of Figs. 2-38 and 2-40.   As the inductance and the inductive reactance have the same values for both of the curves, the circuit Q will vary with the value of R. Examination of these curves will show that low values of R (high values of Q) produce resonance curves with very steep slope and high values of R (low values of Q) produce flatter curves.

Relation between the Slope of the Curves and Selectivity.   The selectivity of a series tuned circuit may be defined as its ability to admit the maximum amount of current of a desired frequency (or band of frequencies) and to exclude all appreciable amounts of currents for any other frequencies. The slope of the resonance curve is therefore an indication of the selectivity of a circuit.

A series tuned circuit that produces a steep resonance curve allows a relatively high current flow only for those frequencies close to the resonant frequency and opposes any appreciable amount of current flow for all other frequencies. Such a circuit is very selective and is said to *tune sharply*. The curves of Fig. 2-38 show that the selectivity increases as the resistance of the circuit decreases. As a decrease in R causes an

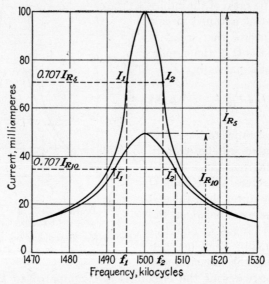

Fig. 2-41.—Resonance curves with the width of the band ($f_2 - f_1$) indicated.

increase in Q, it may be said that the selectivity of the series tuned circuit increases with an increase in Q.

If the curve is too steep, the variation in current, generally called the *response*, will be too great even for only slight deviations from the resonant frequency. The curves of Figs. 2-38 and 2-40 show that increasing the resistance will broaden the response curve. A circuit with a flat response curve is said to *tune broadly*.

Usually the resistance of the coil, capacitor, and conductors is sufficient to produce the desired response, and it is therefore seldom necessary to include a resistor in tuned circuits.

Relation between the Width of the Resonance Curve and the Circuit Q. The purpose of the series tuned circuit is to pass the currents of a desired frequency or band of frequencies and to exclude all others. The purpose of the parallel tuned circuit is to exclude the current of a desired frequency or band of frequencies and to pass all others. It is therefore apparent that the range of frequencies should be definitely defined.

The width of the frequency band is measured at the points on the response curves where the current (in the case of series tuned circuits) is equal to 0.707 times the current at resonance. The width of the curve at this point is equal to $f_2 - f_1$ (see Fig. 2-41) and is generally referred to as the width of the band. Examination of the curves (Fig. 2-41) will show that the width of the frequency band is affected by the value of the circuit Q. This may be expressed mathematically as

$$f_2 - f_1 = \frac{f_r}{Q} \tag{2-59}$$

Example 2-21. The curves of Fig. 2-41 are for a series resonant circuit whose inductive reactance is 1000 ohms at the resonant frequency of 1500 kc. (a) Calculate the width of the band if the resistance of the circuit is 5 ohms. (b) Calculate the width of the band if the resistance of the circuit is 10 ohms.

Given: Find:
$$f_r = 1500 \text{ kc}$$ (a) $f_2 - f_1 = ?$
$$X_L = 1000 \text{ ohms}$$ (b) $f_2 - f_1 = ?$
(a) $R = 5 \text{ ohms}$
(b) $R = 10 \text{ ohms}$

Solution:

(a) $f_2 - f_1 = \dfrac{f_r}{Q} = \dfrac{f_r}{\dfrac{X_L}{R}} = \dfrac{1500}{\dfrac{1000}{5}} = 7.5 \text{ kc}$

(b) $f_2 - f_1 = \dfrac{f_r}{Q} = \dfrac{f_r}{\dfrac{X_L}{R}} = \dfrac{1500}{\dfrac{1000}{10}} = 15 \text{ kc}$

Effect of the LC Ratio on Selectivity. Observation of the equation for finding the resonant frequency of a tuned circuit, Eq. (2-48), indicates that there is only one value of L times C for each value of resonant frequency. A table of the LC products for commonly used values of frequency is given in Appendix XIV.

As the frequency of resonance of a tuned circuit is only dependent on its LC product, it can be seen that any number of combinations of L and C can be used to obtain the same resonant frequency. The value of the inductance (in microhenries) may be made greater, less than, or equal to the value of the capacitance (in micromicrofarads). The manner in which the tuned circuit is to be used will determine the LC ratio that should be used. For series tuned circuits it is desirable to have a high LC ratio, since this produces resonance curves with steep slopes. As the LC ratio is reduced the slope of the curve decreases and the circuit selectivity decreases.   The curves of Fig. 2-42 show the effect of the LC ratio upon the slope of the resonance curves of a series tuned circuit.

The effect of the LC ratio on the parallel tuned circuits is opposite to that of the series circuit.   In other words, increasing the LC ratio increases the selectivity of the series tuned circuit and decreases the selectivity of the parallel tuned circuit.   For this reason the expression is reversed for the parallel circuit and is referred to as the CL ratio.

2-24. Uses of Resonant Circuits.   Resonant circuits are one of the most important types of circuits used in radio receivers, radio transmitters, and electronic devices.

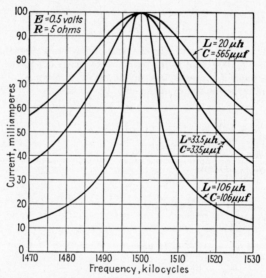

Fig. 2-42.—Resonance curves of a series tuned circuit showing the effect of the LC ratio on the slope of the curve.

The principles of resonance are used in tuning a radio so that it will receive a desired program.   This may be done by adjusting a series tuned circuit to resonance at the frequency corresponding to the carrier-wave frequency of the broadcasting station transmitting the desired program. According to the principles of resonance, this causes the current from the desired station to have the greatest effect in the receiver and reduces the effect of the signals of all other stations to a negligible amount.

Parallel resonant circuits may be used as the output load of a tube when it is necessary for the circuit to have a high impedance in addition to having high selectivity.

These are only two of the many uses of resonant circuits as applied to radio and electronics.   The application of these circuits to radio and electronics is described in the following chapters.   That there are numerous uses possible for resonant circuits may be seen from the characteristics of series and parallel resonant circuits.   Table II-III is a tabular arrangement of the characteristics of resonant circuits.

Table II-III

Quantity	Series circuit	Parallel circuit
At Resonance:		
Reactance; $(X_L - X_C)$	Zero; (because $X_L = X_C$)	Zero; (because $X_L = X_C$)
Frequency of resonance	$\dfrac{159}{\sqrt{LC}}$	$\dfrac{159}{\sqrt{LC}}$
Impedance	Minimum value; $Z = R$	Maximum value; $Z = QX_L$
I_{line}	Maximum value	Minimum value
I_L	I_{line}	Q times I_{line}
I_C	I_{line}	Q times I_{line}
E_L	Q times E_{line}	E_{line}
E_C	Q times E_{line}	E_{line}
Phase angle between I_{line} and E_{line}.	0°	0°
Angle between E_L and E_C	180°	0°
Angle between I_L and I_C	0°	180°
Desired value of Q	High	High
Desired value of R	Low	Low
Highest selectivity	High Q; low R; high LC ratio	High Q; low R; high CL ratio
When f is greater than f_r Reactance; $(X_L - X_C)$	Inductive	Capacitive
Phase angle between I_{line} and E_{line}	Lagging current	Leading current
When f is less than f_r Reactance; $(X_L - X_C)$	Capacitive	Inductive
Phase angle between I_{line} and E_{line}	Leading current	Lagging current

2-25. Electric Circuits Applied to Radio.   Radio circuits are quite intricate and complex, and when a circuit diagram is examined as a whole it may seem very confusing.   In order for the complete circuit to be understood, the individual circuits should be analyzed separately and their effects in relation to the other circuits should be studied.

Every electric circuit must contain at least one circuit element, either a resistor, an inductor, or a capacitor. Practical circuits that contain only resistance, inductance, or capacitance usually cannot be obtained because: (1) wire-wound resistors have inductance and capacitance in addition to resistance; (2) inductors have resistance and distributed capacitance in addition to inductance; (3) capacitors have resistance, and in some cases inductance, in addition to capacitance.

Equivalent Circuits. The extraneous resistance, inductance, or capacitance that exist in resistors, inductors, and capacitors have practically no effect at low frequencies but have to be taken into consideration at higher frequencies.

The inductance of a resistor can be considered as an inductor connected in series with the resistor. The capacitance can be considered as

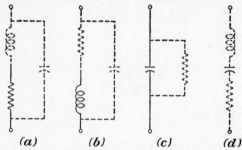

(a)   (b)   (c)   (d)

Fig. 2-43.—Equivalent circuits for the three kinds of circuit elements.   (a) A resistor, (b) an inductor, (c) a capacitor used on direct current, (d) a capacitor used on alternating current.

a capacitor connected in parallel with the resistor. The equivalent circuit for the resistor is then as shown in Fig. 2-43a.

The resistance of an inductor can be considered as a resistor connected in series with the inductor. The distributed capacitances can be considered as a single lumped capacitance connected in parallel with the inductor. The equivalent circuit for the inductor is then as shown in Fig. 2-43b.

Capacitors are used in both direct and alternating current circuits. When used in d-c circuits there is no inductive effect and the resistance can be considered as a resistor connected in parallel with the capacitor as shown in Fig. 2-43c.   When a capacitor is used in a-c circuits, the equivalent circuit can be considered as either series or parallel.   The series equivalent circuit (Fig. 2-43d) is usually the more useful.   Often the inductance is negligible, and, if the capacitor's losses are also negligible, the equivalent series resistance value approaches zero.

Example 2-22.   A 2000-ohm 50-watt resistor has an inductance of 3 μh and a distributed capacitance of 2 $\mu\mu$f.   (a) What is its impedance at 1000 kc?   (b) What is its impedance at 60 mc?

Given: Find:
$$R = 2000 \text{ ohms}$$ $$Z = ?$$
$$L = 3 \ \mu\text{h}$$
$$C = 2 \ \mu\mu\text{f}$$

Solution:

(a) $X_L = 2\pi f L = 6.28 \times 1000 \times 10^3 \times 3 \times 10^{-6} = 18.84$ ohms

$X_C = \dfrac{159,000}{fC} = \dfrac{159,000}{1000 \times 10^3 \times 2 \times 10^{-6}} = 79,500$ ohms

$Z = X_C \sqrt{\dfrac{R^2 + X_L{}^2}{R^2 + (X_L - X_C)^2}}$ (From Appendix V)

$ = 79,500 \sqrt{\dfrac{2000^2 + 18.84^2}{2000^2 + (18.84 - 79,500)^2}}$

$ = 1999$ ohms

(b) $X_L = 6.28 \times 60 \times 10^6 \times 3 \times 10^{-6} = 1130$ ohms

$X_C = \dfrac{159,000}{60 \times 10^6 \times 2 \times 10^{-6}} = 1325$ ohms

$Z = 1325 \sqrt{\dfrac{2000^2 + 1130^2}{2000^2 + (1130 - 1325)^2}} = 1514$ ohms

Combined Circuits. When two or more individual circuits become part of a complex circuit the following two factors should be taken into consideration: (1) the means used to transfer energy from one circuit to another, generally called *coupling of the circuits;* and (2) the means used to separate the different types of currents so that they will flow through the proper circuits, generally called *filter action.*

2-26. Filter Circuits. *Purpose of a Filter.* When two or more individual circuits are combined they form a complex circuit through which the following kinds of currents may flow: (1) direct, (2) low-frequency (60 cycles), (3) audio-frequency, (4) radio-frequency. The purpose of a filter is to separate these currents at any desired point of the circuit and to direct each of them into the conductor or circuit through which it is desired to have them flow.

Filter Action. A filter circuit consists of a combination of capacitors, inductors, and resistors connected so that it will separate alternating currents from direct currents, low-frequency currents from high-frequency currents, or alternating currents within a band of frequencies from alternating currents outside of this band. The action of any filter depends upon the following principles of alternating current circuits:

1. The opposition offered to the flow of alternating currents by inductance varies directly with the frequency. Therefore inductance offers comparatively little opposition to direct, pulsating, or low-frequency alternating currents and great opposition to radio-frequency currents.

2. The opposition offered to the flow of alternating currents by capacitance varies inversely with the frequency. Therefore capacitance offers

comparatively great opposition to low-frequency currents and little opposition to radio-frequency currents. It also will block the flow of direct current.

3. A series resonant circuit has a low impedance at resonance and offers little opposition to the flow of all currents whose frequencies lie within a narrow band above and below the resonant frequency. Such a circuit will offer a comparatively great opposition to the flow of currents of all other frequencies.

4. A parallel resonant circuit has a high impedance at resonance and will offer a comparatively great opposition to the flow of all currents whose frequencies lie within a narrow band above and below the resonant frequency. Such a circuit will offer little opposition to the flow of currents of all other frequencies.

5. Resistors do not provide any filtering action when used alone, since they oppose the flow of all currents to the same extent. When connected in series with a capacitor, inductor, or both, they increase the impedance of the circuit. Increasing the resistance of a resonant circuit reduces the value of the peak of the resonance curve and decreases the slope of the curves, which indicates that the circuit will be less selective.

Filter Circuit Terms. CLASSIFICATION OF FILTERS. There are four general classifications of filter circuits, namely, low-pass, high-pass, band-pass, and band-stop, each of which is considered in the next article.

ATTENUATION CURVES are graphs of current plotted against frequency and are used to show the attenuation (reduction) of current as the frequency varies.

CUTOFF is the term used to indicate the point at which a small change in frequency results in considerable attenuation of the current.

SHARPNESS OF ATTENUATION is the term used to indicate the steepness of the slope of the attenuation curve. A curve that is quite steep is generally preferred, and the circuit is said to possess sharp attenuation.

A T-TYPE FILTER is a basic filter circuit containing a number of inductors and capacitors connected in a manner resembling the letter T.

A PI-TYPE FILTER is a basic filter circuit containing a number of inductors and capacitors connected in a manner resembling the Greek letter π.

An M-DERIVED FILTER is merely a variation of either one of the basic type filters arranged to provide certain desired characteristics.

A MULTIPLE-SECTION FILTER is one that contains two or more units of a basic-type filter. Its purpose is to achieve sharper attenuation.

The SOURCE IMPEDANCE is the impedance of the circuit leading into the filter.

The LOAD IMPEDANCE is the impedance of the circuit into which the filter feeds.

The CHARACTERISTIC IMPEDANCE is the impedance of the filter circuit and is dependent upon the values of the inductance and capacitance. The impedance of the filter, the source, and the load should have equal values.

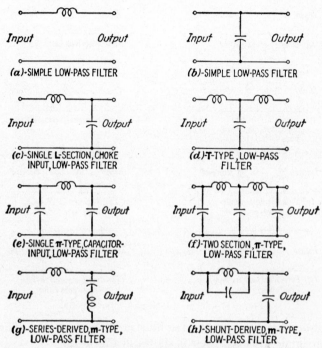

(a)-SIMPLE LOW-PASS FILTER

(b)-SIMPLE LOW-PASS FILTER

(c)-SINGLE L-SECTION, CHOKE INPUT, LOW-PASS FILTER

(d)-T-TYPE, LOW-PASS FILTER

(e)-SINGLE π-TYPE, CAPACITOR-INPUT, LOW-PASS FILTER

(f)-TWO SECTION, π-TYPE, LOW-PASS FILTER

(g)-SERIES-DERIVED, m-TYPE, LOW-PASS FILTER

(h)-SHUNT-DERIVED, m-TYPE, LOW-PASS FILTER

FIG. 2-44.—Typical low-pass filter circuits.

2-27. Types of Filter Circuit. *Low-pass Filter.* A low-pass filter is one which allows all currents of frequencies below the cutoff frequency to pass on to the desired circuit and opposes and thereby diverts the flow of all currents of frequencies above this value.

The simplest low-pass filter is either an inductor in series with the load (Fig. 2-44a), which attenuates the current as the frequency increases, or a capacitor in parallel with the load (Fig. 2-44b), which diverts a greater amount of current from the load as the frequency increases. Neither of these, when used alone, produces very sharp attenu-

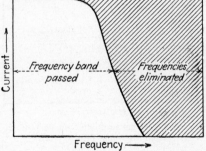

FIG. 2-45.—Characteristic curve for a simple low-pass filter circuit.

ation, and in order to obtain sharper attenuation both the series connected inductor and the parallel connected capacitor are used (see Fig. 2-44c). In order further to improve the sharpness of attenuation, additional

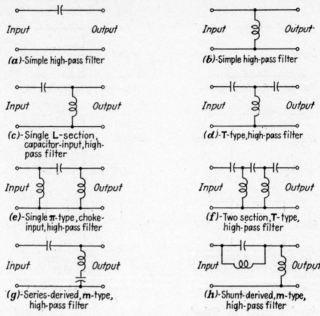

(a)-Simple high-pass filter

(b)-Simple high-pass filter

(c)-Single L-section, capacitor-input, high-pass filter

(d)-T-type,high-pass filter

(e)-Single π-type, choke-input, high-pass filter

(f)-Two section,T-type, high-pass filter

(g)-Series-derived, m-type, high-pass filter

(h)-Shunt-derived, m-type, high-pass filter

Fig. 2-46.—Typical high-pass filter circuits.

capacitors and inductors are used as illustrated in Fig. 2-44. The attenuation of a simple low-pass filter is shown in Fig. 2-45.

High-pass Filter. A high-pass filter is one which allows all currents of frequencies above a certain value to pass on to the desired circuit and opposes or diverts the flow of all currents of frequencies below this value.

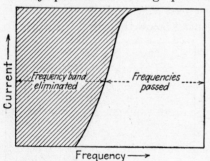

Fig. 2-47.—Characteristic curve for a simple high-pass filter circuit.

The simplest high-pass filter is either a capacitor in series with the load (Fig. 2-46a), which opposes the flow of low-frequency currents and passes the high-frequency currents, or an inductor in parallel with the load (Fig. 2-46b), which diverts most of the low-frequency currents from the load but diverts very little of the high-frequency currents. Neither of these, when used alone, produces very sharp attenuation, and in order to attain sharper attenuation both the series connected capacitor and the parallel connected inductor are used (see Fig. 2-46c). In order further to improve the sharpness of attenuation, additional capacitors and inductors are used as shown in Fig. 2-46. The attenuation of a simple high-pass filter is shown in Fig. 2-47.

Band-pass Filter. A band-pass filter is one which allows the currents of a narrow band of frequencies to pass on to a desired circuit and opposes or diverts all currents whose frequencies are above or below this band.

The simplest band-pass filter is either a series resonant circuit connected in series with the load (Fig. 2-48a) or a parallel resonant circuit

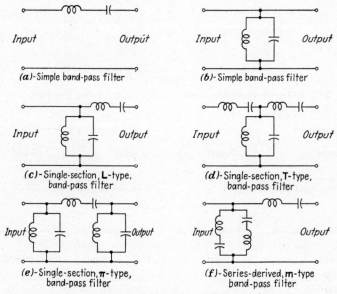

(a)-Simple band-pass filter

(b)-Simple band-pass filter

(c)-Single-section, L-type, band-pass filter

(d)-Single-section, T-type, band-pass filter

(e)-Single-section, π-type, band-pass filter

(f)-Series-derived, m-type band-pass filter

Fig. 2-48.—Typical band-pass filter circuits.

connected across the load (Fig. 2-48b). The series resonant circuit (Fig. 2-48a) passes all currents of frequencies within the band for which it is tuned and opposes the currents of all frequencies outside of the band. The parallel resonant circuit (Fig. 2-48b) diverts very little of the current of the frequencies within the band for which it is tuned and diverts all currents of those frequencies outside of the band. Combinations of two or more series resonant circuits and parallel resonant circuits are used as shown in Fig. 2-48 in order to attain better response (attenuation) curves. The response curve of a simple band-pass filter is shown in Fig. 2-49.

Band-stop Filter. A band-stop filter, also called a *band-suppression* or *band-exclusion filter*, is one which opposes or diverts the currents of a narrow band of frequencies from flowing in a certain circuit and passes the currents of all frequencies outside of this band.

The simplest band-stop filter is either a parallel resonant circuit connected in series with the load (Fig. 2-50a) or a series resonant circuit connected across the load (Fig. 2-50b). The parallel resonant circuit (Fig. 2-50a) opposes all currents of those frequencies within the band

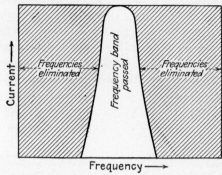

Fig. 2-49.—Characteristic curve for a simple band-pass filter circuit.

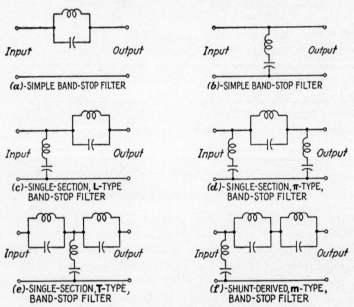

Fig. 2-50.—Typical band-stop filter circuits.

for which it is tuned and passes the currents of all frequencies outside of the band. The series resonant circuit (Fig. 2-50b) diverts all currents of those frequencies within the band for which it is tuned and diverts very little of the current for the frequencies outside of this band. Combinations of two or more parallel resonant circuits and series resonant circuits are used as shown in Fig. 2-50 in order to attain better response curves. The response curve of a simple band-stop filter is shown in Fig. 2-51.

M-derived Filters. These circuits are derived from the basic filters, and their purpose is to achieve a sharper attenuation. Additional impedances are inserted into the basic circuits to form either a shunt-

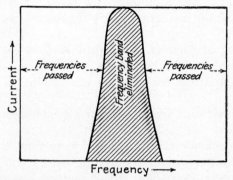

Fig. 2-51.—Characteristic curve for a simple band-stop filter circuit.

derived or series-derived type of filter. If the additional impedances are added to the shunt arm of the section, the filter is series-derived, and if the additional impedances are added to the series arm of the section, the filter is shunt-derived.

Resistor-capacitor Filter Circuits. When it is necessary to separate the direct current and alternating current that may be flowing in a circuit, this may be accomplished by using a capacitor to provide a path for the alternating current and a resistor to provide a path for the direct current.

The circuit of Fig. 2-52a illustrates a capacitor used to allow the passage of the alternating signal current from the screen-grid circuit of a tube to the ground. The resistor keeps the alternating current from getting into the B supply, where it may cause trouble.

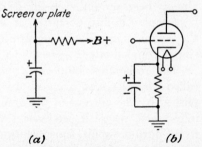

Fig. 2-52.—Resistor-capacitor filter circuits. (a) Filter action in the plate or screen-grid circuit, (b) cathode bias circuit.

The resistor is also used to provide the correct voltage for the screen grid by acting as a dropping resistor.

The circuit of Fig. 2-52b shows a resistor connected between the cathode and ground; its purpose is to supply a negative voltage for the grid of the tube. This resistor, usually of several thousand ohms, offers a high impedance to the flow of the signal current, which would reduce the current to a critical value. A large reduction in signal current at this point in a circuit would cause degeneration, an action that should be avoided except in circuits where degeneration serves a desired purpose. If a capacitor is connected across the resistor as shown in the illustration, it will provide a low-impedance path for the alternating signal current. Diverting the signal current through the capacitor will not affect the voltage drop across the resistor necessary to produce the correct negative grid voltage.

2-28. Coupling of Circuits. *Principles of Coupling.* Two circuits are said to be coupled when they have a *common impedance* that permits the transfer of electrical energy from one circuit to another. This common impedance is called the *coupling element* and it may be a resistor, an inductor, a capacitor, a transformer, or a combination of two or more of these elements.

Coupling elements are usually required to perform some filter action in addition to the function of transferring energy from one circuit to another. Conversely, every filter circuit contains a section that acts as a coupling device. In some instances, coupling circuits and filter circuits are much alike, and it may be difficult to state whether they should be called filters or coupling units. The choice of name, which is really unimportant, may be governed by that function which is considered of major importance. The type of impedance used will be determined by the kinds of current flowing in the input circuit and the kind desired in the output circuit. The characteristics of each type of impedance have already been presented in the study of filters.

Simple Coupled Circuits. A simple coupled circuit is one in which the common impedance consists of only a single element. A group of simple coupled circuits are shown in Fig. 2-53.

The resistance, inductive, and capacitive-coupled circuits are also called *direct-coupled circuits.* In these circuits the coupling is accomplished by the current of the input circuit flowing through the common impedance, where it produces a voltage drop. This voltage is applied to the output circuit, thus resulting in a transfer of electrical energy from the input to the output circuit. The output voltage is equal to the product of the current in the coupling element and its impedance.

The transformer-coupled circuit shown in Fig. 2-53d is also referred to as *indirect coupling, magnetic coupling,* or *mutual-inductive coupling.* In this type of coupling the transfer of energy is accomplished by the alternating current of the input circuit flowing through the primary winding and setting up an alternating magnetic field. The magnetic lines of this field link the turns of the secondary winding and induce the voltage that supplies the energy for the output circuit.

In some applications of coupling devices the input circuit may have both alternating and direct current flowing, and it is desired that the coupling unit transfer only the alternating current to the output circuit. The transformer-coupled unit will serve this purpose satisfactorily as it will pass only the alternating current. The other simple coupled circuits (Fig. 2-53a, b, and c) can be modified by inserting a capacitor in series with the output side, so that no direct current can reach the load. This is illustrated by the circuit of Fig. 2-53f.

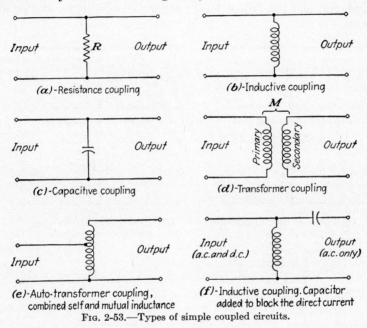

Fig. 2-53.—Types of simple coupled circuits.

Complex-coupled Circuits. A complex-coupled circuit is one in which the common impedance consists of two or more circuit elements. A few of the numerous types of complex coupling are shown in Fig. 2-54.

The proportion of energy transferred in a simple inductive-coupled circuit increases as the frequency increases, while with simple capacitive coupling the proportion of energy transferred decreases as the frequency increases. Using combinations of two or more elements in the coupling unit makes it possible to obtain various proportions of energy transfer for inputs of varying frequency. For example, the coupling element of Fig. 2-54a is really a series-tuned circuit and hence will have a minimum impedance at its resonant frequency. The proportion of energy transfer, too, will be at a minimum value when the frequency of the input circuit is equal to the resonant frequency of the coupling unit. At frequencies above resonance the proportion of energy transfer will increase and will be inductive. At frequencies below resonance the proportion of energy transfer will also increase but will be capacitive. The fact that the energy transfer is minimum at the resonant frequency may be more clearly understood when it is stated that the input side of the filter is generally a part of a series circuit, for example, the plate circuit of a tube, as shown in Fig. 2-54e. It can now be seen that at resonance, when the impedance of the coupling unit is minimum, its voltage drop will be at its minimum, and the proportion of energy transfer must also be at its minimum.

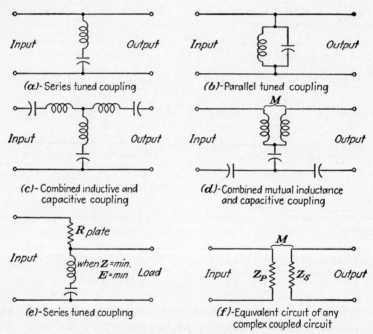

(a)- Series tuned coupling

(b)-Parallel tuned coupling

(c)- Combined inductive and capacitive coupling

(d)-Combined mutual inductance and capacitive coupling

(e)-Series tuned coupling

(f)-Equivalent circuit of any complex coupled circuit

Fig. 2-54.—Typical complex-coupled circuits.

In general, the amount of energy transferred will be proportional to the current flowing through the coupling unit and to the impedance of the unit. For purpose of analysis, complex-coupled circuits may be represented by a simple equivalent circuit, as shown in Fig. 2-54f.

Coefficient of Coupling. The ratio of the energy of the output circuit to the energy of the input circuit is called the *coefficient of coupling*. *Critical, tight,* and *loose coupling* are terms used to express the relative value of the coefficient of coupling for mutual-inductive (transformer)-coupled circuits.

Figure 2-55 shows the response curves for tight, critical, and loose coupling. *When the maximum amount of energy is transferred from one circuit to another, the circuits are said to possess critical coupling;* this is also referred to occasionally as *optimum coupling.* If the coefficient of coupling is higher than that necessary to produce critical coupling, it is referred to as being *tight,* and if it is lower than that required for critical coupling, it is referred to as being *loose.*

The effect of varying the coupling between two circuits may be seen from the response curves of Figs. 2-55 and 2-60. When two circuits are very tightly coupled, resonance will be obtained at two new frequencies, one below and the other above the normal frequency of resonance for the capacitor and inductor used. As the coupling is decreased, the two peaks come closer together until critical coupling is reached and a single

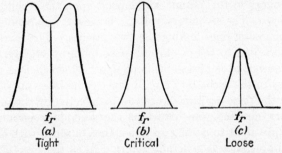

f_r f_r f_r
(a)   *(b)*   *(c)*
Tight   Critical   Loose

Fig. 2-55.—Response curves showing the effects of various amounts of coupling.

peak of maximum height is obtained. If the coupling is decreased below the critical value, a single peak of reduced height is obtained.

Air-core transformers, commonly used in radio circuits, illustrate the importance of the amount of coupling between the primary and the secondary windings. Since it is difficult to design an air-core transformer in which a large portion of the magnetic lines set up by the primary winding will link the turns of the secondary winding, the coefficient of coupling is generally low. A low value for the coefficient of coupling is not objectionable in some circuits, as it provides certain desirable characteristics, which will be presented in the following article.

2-29. Characteristics of Mutual-inductive-coupled Circuits. Inductive coupling, particularly mutual inductance as provided by the transformer, is the means most commonly used to transfer energy from one circuit to another. The characteristics of these circuits depend upon the type of circuit, that is, whether a capacitor is connected to the primary, to the secondary, or to both. The characteristics are also dependent upon the amount of coupling between the two circuits.

Coupled Impedance. The primary and the secondary circuits of a transformer are separate electrical circuits that are magnetically coupled.

Each circuit has an impedance of its own, generally designated as Z_P and Z_S. The impedance of the primary winding, when no load is applied to the secondary, consists of the resistance and inductance of the primary winding. The impedance of the secondary circuit consists of the resistance and inductance of the secondary winding plus the impedance of any load connected to the circuit. When the secondary circuit is left open, that is, when no load is applied to its terminals, the impedance of the secondary will be infinity, or so large that it is immeasurable. Under this condition the presence of the secondary will have no effect upon the primary circuit.

When a load is applied to the secondary, the impedance will have a significant value and a current will flow in the secondary circuit. The amount of energy in this circuit will depend upon the secondary voltage and impedance. The secondary voltage, however, is dependent upon the number of magnetic lines linking the two circuits. The number of linkages is proportional to the coefficient of coupling; therefore the amount of energy transferred is also dependent upon the coefficient of coupling. As the energy in the secondary circuit must come from the primary, it is evident that the primary impedance will be affected by the impedance of the secondary circuit. The effect of the secondary circuit upon the primary is equivalent to adding an impedance in series with the primary. This added impedance is generally referred to as the *coupled impedance*.

The numerical value of the coupled impedance of a mutual-inductive-coupled circuit may be found by the equation

$$Z_{P-S'} = \frac{(2\pi f M)^2}{Z_S} \qquad (2\text{-}60)$$

where $Z_{P-S'}$ = impedance coupled into the primary by the secondary, ohms

f = frequency of the power source, cycles per second

M = mutual inductance, henries

Z_S = secondary impedance, ohms

The derivation of this equation is explained in the following steps:

1. From the definition two circuits have a mutual inductance of one henry when a current in one circuit, changing at the rate of one ampere per second, induces an average emf of one volt in the second circuit. The induced voltage in the second circuit may be expressed as

$$E_{ave \cdot S} = M \frac{I_{P2} - I_{P1}}{t_2 - t_1} \qquad (2\text{-}61)$$

This equation indicates that when the mutual inductance M is one henry and the rate of current change $\dfrac{I_{P2} - I_{P1}}{t_2 - t_1}$ is one ampere per second, the average value of the induced voltage $E_{\text{ave.}S}$ will be one volt. In other words, this equation is derived from the definition of the unit of mutual inductance.

2. When an alternating current I_P is flowing, the current is continually changing from a maximum value to zero in a positive and negative direction and at a rate proportional to the frequency. As the alternating current I_P is an effective value, the maximum current will be I_P divided by 0.707. Also, a change in current from the maximum value to zero occurs in a period of time corresponding to one-quarter of a cycle. Therefore

$$\frac{I_{P2} - I_{P1}}{t_2 - t_1} = \frac{I_{\max} - I_o}{\dfrac{1}{4f}} = \frac{I_{\max}}{\dfrac{1}{4f}} = \frac{\dfrac{I_P}{0.707}}{\dfrac{1}{4f}} = \frac{4fI_P}{0.707} \qquad (2\text{-}62)$$

Applying Eq. (2-62) to Eq. (2-61), then

$$E_{\text{ave.}S} = M \frac{4fI_P}{0.707} \qquad (2\text{-}63)$$

3. The induced secondary voltage $E_{\text{ave.}S}$ is expressed as an average value, and in practical work it is desired to have it expressed as the effective value E. As the average value is equal to $2/\pi$ (or 0.637) times the maximum value and the effective value is equal to 0.707 times the maximum value, then the effective value may be expressed as

$$E_S = \frac{E_{\text{ave.}S}}{\dfrac{2}{\pi}} \times 0.707 = \frac{0.707\pi E_{\text{ave.}S}}{2} \qquad (2\text{-}64)$$

or

$$E_{\text{ave.}S} = \frac{2E_S}{0.707\pi} \qquad (2\text{-}64a)$$

substituting Eq. (2-64a) in Eq. (2-63)

$$\frac{2E_S}{0.707\pi} = M \frac{4fI_P}{0.707}$$

or

$$E_S = 2\pi fMI_P \qquad (2\text{-}65)$$

4. The secondary current I_S will, therefore, be

$$I_S = \frac{E_S}{Z_S} = \frac{2\pi fMI_P}{Z_S} \qquad (2\text{-}66)$$

5. This secondary current upon flowing through the secondary winding sets up a magnetic field of its own that induces a voltage in the primary. This induced voltage will be 180 degrees out of phase with the primary impressed voltage and is referred to as a *counter,* or *back voltage.* By the same reasoning as was used to derive the secondary induced voltage, it may be shown that this counter voltage induced in the primary will be

$$E_{counter} = 2\pi f M I_S \qquad (2\text{-}67)$$

Substituting Eq. (2-66) for I_S in Eq. (2-67)

$$E_{counter} = (2\pi f M)\frac{(2\pi f M)I_P}{Z_S} = \frac{(2\pi f M)^2}{Z_S} I_P \qquad (2\text{-}68)$$

6. As this voltage represents the effect that the secondary has upon the primary and is equal to the product of impedance and current, it may be stated from Eq. (2-68) that the effect of the secondary impedance upon the primary is

$$Z_{P-S'} = \frac{(2\pi f M)^2}{Z_S} \qquad (2\text{-}60)$$

The coupled impedance expressed by Eq. (2-60) may be represented by an equivalent resistance and an equivalent reactance connected in series with the primary circuit. The numerical values of the equivalent resistance and equivalent reactance are expressed by the following equations,

$$R_{P-S'} = \frac{(2\pi f M)^2 R_S}{Z_S^2} \qquad (2\text{-}69)$$

$$X_{P-S'} = \frac{(2\pi f M)^2 X_S}{Z_S^2} \qquad (2\text{-}70)$$

where $R_{P-S'}$ = resistance coupled into the primary by the secondary, ohms

$X_{P-S'}$ = reactance coupled into the primary by the secondary, ohms

f = frequency of the power source, cycles per second

M = mutual inductance, henries

R_S = resistance of the secondary circuit, ohms

Z_S = impedance of the secondary circuit, ohms

X_S = reactance of the secondary circuit, ohms

NOTE: When X_S is inductive, then $X_{P-S'}$ has a negative sign, and when X_S is capacitive, $X_{P-S'}$ has a positive sign.

Example 2-23. A mutual-inductance-coupled circuit is shown in Fig. 2-56, together with the circuit values. (a) What coupled impedance does the secondary

present to the primary?   (b) What is the value of the equivalent resistance component
of the coupled impedance?   (c) What is the value of the reactance component of the
coupled impedance?   (d) Draw the equivalent-circuit diagram.   (e) What is the
effective impedance of the primary circuit?   (f) What is the primary circuit current if the voltage of the 175-kc signal is 10 volts?   (g) What is the secondary voltage?   (h) What is the secondary current?

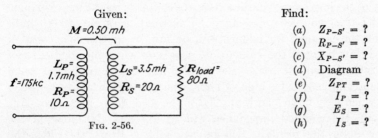

Given:

$M = 0.50$ mh

$f = 175kc$ $L_P = 1.7mh$ $L_S = 3.5mh$ $R_{load} = 80\Omega$
        $R_P = 10\Omega$ $R_S = 20\Omega$

FIG. 2-56.

Find:

(a) $Z_{P-S'} = ?$
(b) $R_{P-S'} = ?$
(c) $X_{P-S'} = ?$
(d)   Diagram
(e) $Z_{PT} = ?$
(f) $I_P = ?$
(g) $E_S = ?$
(h) $I_S = ?$

Solution:

(a) $Z_{P-S'} = \dfrac{(2\pi f M)^2}{Z_S} = \dfrac{(2\pi f M)^2}{\sqrt{(R_S + R_{load})^2 + (2\pi f L_S)^2}}$

$= \dfrac{(6.28 \times 175 \times 10^3 \times 0.50 \times 10^{-3})^2}{\sqrt{(20 + 80)^2 + (6.28 \times 175 \times 10^3 \times 3.5 \times 10^{-3})^2}}$

$= \dfrac{301,950}{3847} = 78.5$ ohms

(b) $R_{P-S'} = \dfrac{(2\pi f M)^2 R_S}{Z_S{}^2} = \dfrac{301,950 \times 100}{(3847)^2} = 2.04$ ohms

(c) $X_{P-S'} = \dfrac{(2\pi f M)^2 X_S}{Z_S{}^2} = \dfrac{301,950 \times 3846}{(3847)^2} = 78.5$ ohms

(d)

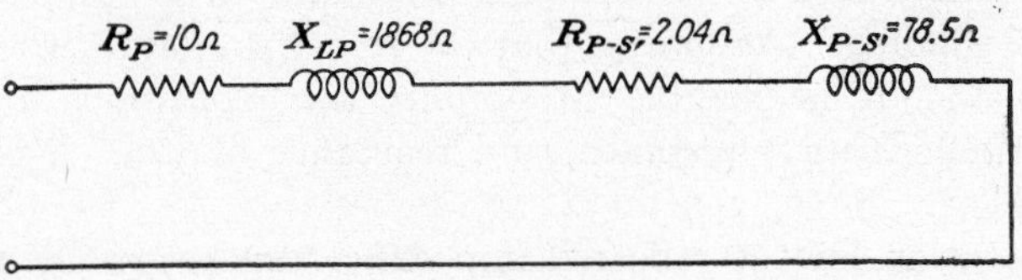

$R_P = 10\Omega$ $X_{LP} = 1868\Omega$ $R_{P-S} = 2.04\Omega$ $X_{P-S} = 78.5\Omega$

FIG. 2-57.

(e) $Z_{PT} = \sqrt{(R_P + R_{P-S'})^2 + (X_P - X_{P-S'})^2}$

$= \sqrt{(10 + 2.04)^2 + (1868 - 78.5)^2} = 1789.6$ ohms

(f) $I_P = \dfrac{E}{Z_{PT}} = \dfrac{10}{1789.6} = 0.00558$ amp $= 5.58$ ma

(g) $E_S = 2\pi f M I_P = 549.5 \times 0.00558 = 3.06$ volts

(h) $I_S = \dfrac{E_S}{Z_S} = \dfrac{3.06}{3847} = 0.000795$ amp $= 0.795$ ma

Examining the results of this example, it can be seen that the effect
of the coupled equivalent resistance is to increase the effective resistance
of the primary circuit. The equivalent reactance that is coupled into
the primary by a secondary whose reactance is inductive is opposite in

phase to the primary reactance and hence reduces the effective reactance of the primary circuit. The net result is a reduction in the effective primary impedance, more current thereby being allowed to flow in the primary circuit, thus making possible the transfer of more energy to the secondary circuit.

Many of the important characteristics of coupled circuits are explained by the effects of coupled impedance. Examination of Eq. (2-60) indicates that the coupled impedance will be low when the coefficient of coupling is low because the value of M decreases when the coefficient of coupling is decreased. Further, the coupled impedance will be low when the secondary impedance is high. Thus, when the coefficient of coupling is low or when very little load is applied to the secondary (high secondary impedance), the coupled impedance will be low and the effect of the secondary upon the primary will be negligible. However, when the coefficient of coupling is high or when the secondary carries considerable amounts of load (low secondary impedance), the coupled impedance will be high and the secondary will produce considerable effect upon the primary circuit.

Coupled Impedance when the Coefficient of Coupling Approaches Unity. Iron-core transformers, such as the audio transformers used in radio receivers, generally have a coefficient of coupling of nearly unity. Furthermore, in well-designed audio transformers, the total reactance of the secondary winding is so high in comparison with the resistance of the secondary winding and the load impedance that the secondary impedance may be assumed to be approximately equal to the reactance of the secondary winding. Assuming that $M = \sqrt{L_P L_S}$ (true when $K = 1$) and $Z_S = X_{LS}$, it is possible to simplify the expressions for reflected (coupled) impedance, resistance, and reactance of Eqs. (2-60), (2-69), and (2-70).

The equation for the reflected impedance can be simplified by substituting $\sqrt{L_P L_S}$ for M and X_{LS} for Z_S in Eq. (2-60); then

$$Z_{P-S'} = \frac{(2\pi f \sqrt{L_P L_S})^2}{X_{LS}} = \frac{(2\pi f L_P)(2\pi f L_S)}{2\pi f L_S} \qquad (2\text{-}71)$$

$$Z_{P-S'} = \frac{L_P}{L_S} Z_S \qquad (2\text{-}71a)$$

As the primary and secondary windings are linked by the same flux when $K = 1$ and as they will have approximately equal dimensions, their inductances will vary as the square of their respective number of turns (Art. 2-3), or

$$\frac{L_P}{L_S} = \frac{N_P^2}{N_S^2} \qquad (2\text{-}72)$$

and
$$\frac{L_P}{L_S} = \frac{1}{n^2} \qquad (2\text{-}72a)$$

where $n = \dfrac{N_S}{N_P}$

Substituting Eq. (2-72a) in (2-71a)

$$Z_{P-S'} = \frac{Z_S}{n^2} \qquad (2\text{-}73)$$

It is sometimes desired to determine the impedance reflected to the secondary by the primary. By a similar procedure, it can be shown that

$$Z_{S-P'} = n^2 Z_P \qquad (2\text{-}74)$$

With the same assumptions, the equation for the reflected resistance and reactance can also be simplified. Substituting $\sqrt{L_P L_S}$ for M and X_{LS} for Z_S in Eq. (2-69)

$$R_{P-S'} = \frac{(2\pi f L_P)(2\pi f L_S)R_S}{(2\pi f L_S)(2\pi f L_S)} = \frac{L_P}{L_S}R_S \qquad (2\text{-}75)$$

and
$$R_{P-S'} = \frac{R_S}{n^2} \qquad (2\text{-}76)$$

By similar reasoning

$$R_{S-P'} = n^2 R_P \qquad (2\text{-}77)$$

Applying the same method to Eq. (2-70), it can be shown that

$$X_{P-S'} = \frac{X_S}{n^2} \qquad (2\text{-}78)$$

and
$$X_{S-P'} = n^2 X_P \qquad (2\text{-}79)$$

From Eqs. (2-78) and (2-79), it can be shown that

$$L_{P-S'} = \frac{L_S}{n^2} \qquad (2\text{-}80)$$

$$L_{S-P'} = n^2 L_P \qquad (2\text{-}81)$$

$$C_{P-S'} = n^2 C_S \qquad (2\text{-}82)$$

$$C_{S-P'} = \frac{C_P}{n^2} \qquad (2\text{-}83)$$

Circuit with Untuned Primary and Untuned Secondary. The simplest type of transformer coupling would be a circuit having an untuned primary and an untuned secondary with a resistance or inductance load. Such a circuit is shown in Fig. 2-58a. This circuit is often used as an equivalent circuit to represent the effects produced by a shield, metal panel, or other metal object located near a coil. The effect of the shield or panel upon the coil would be the same as that of a secondary winding

consisting of inductance and resistance in series.   The coupled impedance
of such a circuit will increase the effective resistance of the primary and
reduce its effective reactance.   It also indicates that the losses of the
coil circuit are increased by an amount proportional to the resistance
coupled into the primary by the secondary, which is actually the shield
or near-by metal panel.

Circuit with Untuned Primary and Tuned Secondary.   The circuit
shown in Fig. 2-58*b* differs from the one in Fig. 2-58*a* in that a capacitor
is used in place of the resistor in the secondary circuit.   The commonly
used tuned-radio-frequency amplifier circuit, or its equivalent circuit,
is similar to this fundamental circuit.

The secondary is similar to the series tuned circuit studied in Arts.
2-19 to 2-22.   Its characteristics will be the same as those of the series
tuned circuit.   At resonant frequency the impedance will be at its
minimum and the current at its maximum.   The impedance coupled

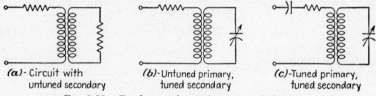

(a)- Circuit with   (b)-Untuned primary,   (c)-Tuned primary,
    untuned secondary   tuned secondary   tuned secondary

FIG. 2-58.—Fundamental transformer-coupled circuits.

into the primary will be large and will have a critical effect upon the
primary current.   At frequencies above or below resonance the secondary
impedance increases and its current decreases.   The impedance coupled
into the primary decreases, and the effect on the primary circuit is
decreased.

Circuit with Tuned Primary and Tuned Secondary.   This type of
circuit (Fig. 2-58*c*) is used extensively in radio receivers.   A common
example of this circuit is the intermediate-frequency amplifier of the
superheterodyne receiver.   This circuit is very useful for amplifiers
because it can be designed to provide an approximately uniform secondary
current response over the range of frequencies that are normally applied
to the primary.

2-30. Band-pass Amplifier Circuits. *Ideal Response Curve.*   The
ideal response curve for the tuning or i-f amplifier circuits would be one
having a flat top and very steep sides.   The flat top should be approximately 10 kc wide.   This band of 10 kc is not arbitrarily chosen but
represents a 5-kc side band above and below the carrier frequency
of any transmitting station.   These side bands are a part of every
modulated carrier wave, and the width of the side band varies with the

frequency of the audio signal. The frequency of audible signals varies from 20 cycles to more than 20,000 cycles. However, most radio receivers are capable only of reproducing sounds up to 5000 cycles. Many broadcasting stations can transmit with a 10-kc side band but operate with only a 5- to 6-kc side band because of the limitations of the average receivers. A circuit with a flat-top response curve will produce currents of equal strength for all audio signals. A circuit that produces a response curve with steep sides will be very selective.

This ideal can be most nearly achieved by use of two resonant circuits (Fig. 2-59) tuned to the same frequency and possessing a very definite value of coupling. Such circuits are known as *band-pass filters*, *band-pass amplifiers*, or *band-pass circuits*.

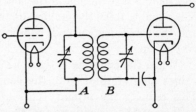

Fig. 2-59.—Band-pass amplifier circuit.

Effect of the Coefficient of Coupling on the Band-pass Circuits. The important characteristic of the band-pass circuit is the manner in which the secondary current varies with the frequency when a constant-voltage

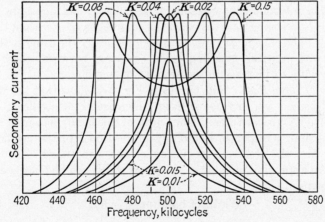

Fig. 2-60.—Response curves showing the effect of the coefficient of coupling between two resonant circuits tuned to the same frequency.

variable-frequency wave is applied to the primary. Since the amount of current in the secondary varies directly with the amount of coupling between the primary and secondary windings, the shape of the response curve will be affected by the coefficient of coupling.

The effect of the coefficient of coupling upon the shape of the response curves is shown in Fig. 2-60. These curves represent the response of a circuit similar to that shown in Fig. 2-59 when both resonant circuits are tuned to 500 kc. When the coefficient of coupling is low ($K = 0.01$), the secondary current will be low and the curve will be quite peaked. When the coupling is increased to 0.015, the secondary current increases and there is a reduction in the sharpness of the peak of the curve. When K is equal to 0.02, the maximum amount of secondary current is obtained and the resonance curve is comparatively flat at the top and its sides are very steep.

When the coupling is tight, as is the case for the three curves with K values greater than 0.02, the coupled impedance at resonance is high. This reduces the primary current, which in turn reduces the induced voltage at the secondary and thereby causes a lower secondary current. This accounts for the decrease in secondary currents at resonance for coefficients of coupling greater than the critical value. At frequencies below resonance the reactance coupled into the primary is inductive and for frequencies above resonance it is capacitive. The coupled reactance is opposite to that of the primary circuit and therefore reduces the effective primary impedance. The lower primary impedance causes an increase in primary current, which in turn causes an increase in the secondary voltage and consequently increases the secondary current. This action introduces new resonant frequencies and accounts for the humps in the resonance curves when the coupling is greater than the critical value. The current at these peaks is practically the same as the peak current with critical coupling. The spacing between these peaks increases with an increase in the amount of coupling.

Width of Band Pass. The curves of Fig. 2-60 show that the width of the band passed will increase with any increase in the coefficient of coupling above its critical value. The width of this band, measured at 0.707 of the maximum response, is directly proportional to the coefficient of coupling and the resonant frequency of the two tuned circuits (Fig. 2-59). An approximate value of this band width can be obtained by use of the equation

$$\text{Width of band pass} = Kf_r \qquad (2\text{-}84)$$

Example 2-24. What is the approximate width of the frequency band of a band-pass filter circuit having a resonant frequency of 456 kc and a coefficient of coupling of 0.02?

Given: Find:
  $K = 0.02$ Width of band pass = ?
  $f_r = 456$ kc

Solution:

  Width of band pass = Kf_r = 0.02×456 = 9.12 kc = 9120 cycles

The most important characteristics of a band-pass circuit are the width of the band of frequencies it allows to pass and the uniformity of response within this band. From the curves of Fig. 2-60 it can be seen that at critical coupling ($K = 0.02$) the response is fairly uniform for a band of frequencies between 495 and 505 kc. As the coefficient of coupling is increased ($K = 0.04, 0.08, 0.15$), it can be seen that the band becomes wider and the response is less uniform.

The coefficient of coupling of band-pass circuits is usually adjusted to such a value that uniform response is obtained for a band of 10 kc. The uniformity of the response, however, is also dependent upon the

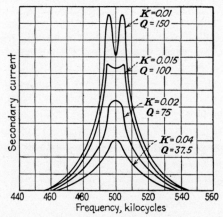

FIG. 2-61.—Characteristics of a band-pass amplifier showing the effect of circuit Q on the uniformity of response within the band being passed.

circuit Q (Art. 2-23). The effect of circuit Q upon the uniformity of response is illustrated by the curves of Fig. 2-61. When Q is too high pronounced double humps occur, and if Q is too low the response curve is round instead of flat. Apparently the best value of Q would be such that it will produce the maximum transfer of energy, or critical coupling. The value of critical coupling may be determined by

$$K_c = \frac{1}{\sqrt{Q_P Q_s}} \qquad (2\text{-}85)$$

where K_c = critical coupling
Q_P = Q of the primary circuit
Q_s = Q of the secondary circuit
$\sqrt{Q_P Q_s}$ = Q of the complete circuit

However, experiments have shown that the best value of Q is approximately 50 per cent more than that required to produce critical coupling, hence the equation for practical circuits is

$$K_c = \frac{1.5}{\sqrt{Q_P Q_S}} \qquad (2\text{-}86)$$

or

$$Q_P Q_S = \frac{2.25}{K_c^2} \qquad (2\text{-}87)$$

From Eq. (2-84) it can be seen that the coefficient of coupling would be equal to the width of the band pass divided by the frequency of resonance. As the width of the band pass is usually about 10 kc and the resonant frequency of the r-f and i-f circuits is generally 175 kc or more, the coefficient of coupling must therefore be less than 0.057. Substituting this value of K in Eq. (2-87), it can be seen that the values of the circuit Q's will be 25 or more if Q_P and Q_S are approximately equal.

Example 2-25. A band-pass filter circuit is tuned to a resonant frequency of 456 kc. If Q_P and Q_S are equal, what values of Q are required to produce an 8-kc band?

Given: Find:
    f_r = 456 kc Q_P = ?
    Width of band pass = 8 kc Q_S = ?

Solution:

$$K = \frac{\text{Width of band pass}}{f_r} = \frac{8}{456} = 0.0175$$

$$Q_P Q_S = \frac{2.25}{K^2} = \frac{2.25}{(0.0175)^2} = 7346$$

$$Q_P = Q_S = \sqrt{7346} = 85.7$$

2-31. Delayed-action Circuits. Inductors or capacitors may be used in electric, radio, and electronic circuits to control the time required for the current or voltage to reach a certain value. The operation of these circuits is based on the time constant of the resistance-inductance or the resistance-capacitance combination. These circuits are generally referred to as *R-L* and *R-C* circuits.

Time Constant of Resistance-inductance Circuits. Inductance, by definition (Art. 2-3), is the property of a circuit that opposes any change in the amount of current flowing in that circuit. The opposition to a change in the amount of current is caused by the induced voltage due to the self-inductance of the circuit. This induced emf will be in a direction opposite to that of the impressed voltage whenever the current is increasing in amount and in the direction of the impressed voltage when the current is decreasing in amount.

If an inductor, which may be considered as a resistance and inductance in series, is connected to a direct current power source, a current will flow in the circuit. The amount of current that will flow will be its Ohm's law value, namely, the voltage applied to the circuit divided by the resistance of the circuit. In a circuit having only resistance (Fig. 2-62a) the current will rise to its Ohm's law value practically instantaneously, as indicated in Fig. 2-62b. However, as the inductor has the effect of a resistance and inductance connected in series (Fig. 2-63a), the current will require an appreciable amount of time to reach its Ohm's law value, as is shown in Fig. 2-63b. This is explained by the fact that in order for the current to reach its final value of 5 amperes, it must progressively pass through its lesser values such as 1, 2, 3, and 4 amperes. Under these conditions, the current is changing in amount, and the circuit will have an emf induced in it owing to the self-inductance of the circuit. This induced emf will oppose the impressed voltage and thus will prevent the current from reaching its Ohm's law value as long as the induced emf is present. The current will, however, eventually reach its Ohm's law value, the time required to accomplish this depending upon the relative values of the inductance and resistance. The current increases in a manner indicated by the graph shown in Fig. 2-63b and will rise to 63.2 per cent of its final value in a period of time, expressed in seconds, equal to the inductance of the circuit divided by the resistance of the circuit. This is called the *time constant* of the circuit and is expressed mathematically as

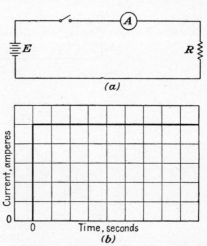

FIG. 2-62.—Characteristics of current vs time for a circuit containing only resistance. (a) The circuit, (b) current vs time characteristics.

$$t = \frac{L}{R} \tag{2-88}$$

where t = time, seconds, for the current to reach 63.2 per cent of its final value
L = inductance of the circuit, henries
R = resistance of the circuit, ohms

Example 2-26. An *R-L* circuit is used to control the time of closing a relay. The relay closes when the current reaches 63.2 per cent of its final value and the circuit resistance and inductance are 12 ohms and 2.4 henries respectively. What is the time interval between the closing of the line switch and the operation of the relay?

Given: Find:
    $R = 12$ ohms $t = ?$
    $L = 2.4$ henries

Solution:

$$t = \frac{L}{R} = \frac{2.4}{12} = 0.2 \text{ second}$$

The time required for the current to reach values other than 63.2 per cent of the final value follows a curve known mathematically as an

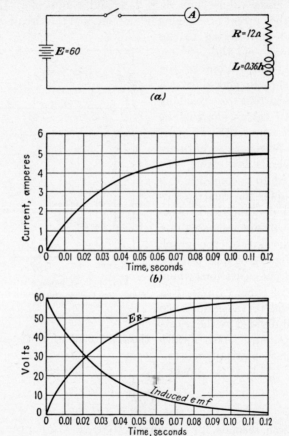

(a)

(b)

(c)

Fig. 2-63.—Characteristics of current and voltage vs time for a circuit containing resistance and inductance. (*a*) The circuit, (*b*) current vs time characteristics, (*c*) voltage vs time characteristics.

exponential curve. The universal time-constant curves of Fig. 2-67 provide a simple means of finding the current at any instant of time.

Further analysis of the *R-L* circuit will show that, when the current is increasing, the voltage drop across the resistance will increase at the same time rate as the current. This is so because the voltage drop across the resistance at any instant of time is equal to the product of the current and the resistance. Furthermore, as the sum of the voltages around the circuit must be equal to the applied voltage, the induced emf due to the inductance must at any instant of time be equal to the applied

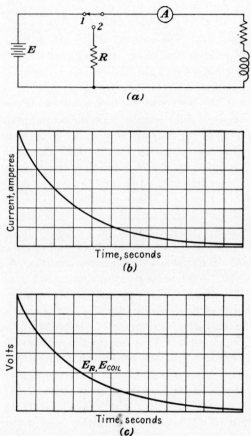

Fig. 2-64.—Characteristics of current and voltage vs time. (*a*) The circuit, (*b*) current vs time characteristics with switch in position 2, (*c*) voltage vs time characteristics with switch in position 2.

voltage less the *IR* drop. Figure 2-63*c* shows the voltage characteristics of the circuit when the current is building up.

The circuit shown in Fig. 2-64*a* is arranged so that the *R-L* circuit may either be connected to the direct current power source or connected so that the inductance will be short-circuited through the resistance. If the circuit is connected to the direct current power source, a current will flow in the circuit and will rise to its Ohm's law value according to the current-time curve already described. When a current is flowing in the circuit, energy is transferred to the magnetic field. If the switch (Fig. 2-64a) is changed from position 1 to position 2, so that the inductance is disconnected from the power source and then instantaneously short-circuited across the resistance, the energy in the collapsing magnetic field will induce a voltage in the turns of the coil and will cause a current to flow in the circuit. The current will decrease as the energy is dissipated in the resistance. The rate at which the current decreases will depend upon the relative values of the inductance and the resistance. The current-time changes will also follow an exponential curve but will be a descending curve. As the inductance is now actually in parallel with the resistance, the resistance voltage drop and the induced emf will be equal in value and will decrease according to an exponential curve. The current-time characteristics are shown in Fig. 2-64b and the voltage-time characteristics are shown in Fig. 2-64c. The time in seconds as determined by L divided by R now represents the time in which the current (and voltage) decreases 63.2 per cent; hence the current and voltage will drop to 36.8 per cent of their maximum values in L/R seconds. The time required for the current and voltage to decrease to values other than 36.8 per cent of their maximum values can be found by use of the universal exponential curves presented at the end of this article.

Time Constant of Resistance-capacitance Circuits. Capacitance, by definition (Art. 2-10), is the property of a circuit that opposes any change in the amount of voltage. The opposition to a change in the voltage across a capacitor may be explained by the fact that in order to accomplish a change in voltage the number of electrons at the plates of the capacitor must be changed. This requires a passage of electrons from one plate of the capacitor to the other and hence a current must flow before there can be a change in voltage. If the voltage across the capacitor is increased, electrons will flow from the positive plate to the negative; if the voltage across the capacitor is decreased, electrons will flow from the negative plate to the positive. In either case a current flow must precede a change in voltage at the plates of the capacitor.

If a perfect capacitor, that is, one having no resistance, is connected to a direct-current power source, a high current surge will flow instantly and will charge the capacitor. As the capacitor becomes charged almost instantaneously, the amount of current flow will decrease rapidly. The capacitor will charge to the value of the impressed voltage and the current flow will diminish to zero practically instantaneously.

If the capacitor, or its circuit, contains resistance in addition to the capacitance (Fig. 2-65a), the capacitor will become charged to the same value of voltage but will require a longer period of time to reach its final

value.   The voltage increases in a manner indicated by the graph shown
in Fig. 2-65b and will rise to 63.2 per cent of its final value in a period of
time, expressed in seconds, equal to the product of the capacitance and

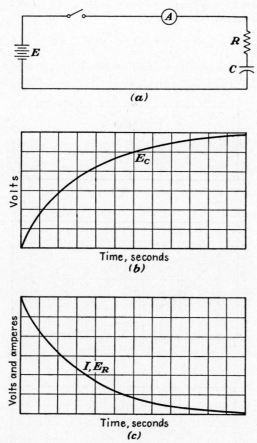

(a)

(b)

(c)

Fig. 2-65.—Characteristics of current and voltage vs time for a circuit containing
resistance and capacitance. (a) The circuit, (b) capacitor volts vs time characteristics,
(c) current and resistance volts vs time characteristics.

resistance of the circuit.   This is called the *time constant* of the circuit
and is expressed mathematically as

$$t = CR \qquad \qquad (2\text{-}89)$$

where t = time, seconds, for the voltage across the capacitor to reach
63.2 per cent of its final value
  C = capacitance of the circuit, farads
  R = resistance of the circuit, ohms

Example 2-27.   What is the time constant of an automatic-volume-control filter circuit that uses a 1.25-megohm resistor and a 0.25 μf capacitor?

Given: Find:
    R = 1.25 megohms t = ?
    C = 0.25 μf

Solution:
$$t = CR = 0.25 \times 10^{-6} \times 1.25 \times 10^{6} = 0.3125 \text{ second}$$

The time required for the voltage to reach values other than 63.2 per cent of the final value follows an exponential curve.   The universal time-

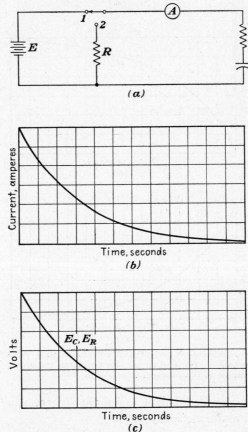

FIG. 2-66.—Characteristics of current and voltage vs time.   (*a*) The circuit, (*b*) current vs time characteristics with switch in position 2, (*c*) voltage vs time characteristics with switch in position 2.

constant curves of Fig. 2-67 provide a simple means of finding the voltage at any instant of time.

If the switch in the circuit of Fig. 2-66*a* is closed to position 1, the voltage and current characteristics of the circuit will conform to the voltage-time and current-time curves shown in Fig. 2-65. While a current is flowing in the circuit energy is being stored in the capacitor. If the switch (Fig. 2-66a) is changed from position 1 to position 2, the energy stored in the capacitor will cause a current to flow in the resistor and the capacitor will discharge through the resistor. At the instant of

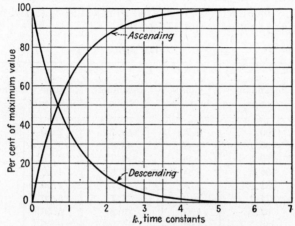

FIG. 2-67.—Universal time-constant curves.

closing the switch the current will be at its highest value (Ohm's law value) and will decrease exponentially, as shown in Fig. 2-66b. The voltage across the capacitor and resistor will be equal in amount and will also decrease exponentially with time, as is shown in Fig. 2-66c.

Universal Time-constant Curves. The time required for the current of an *R-L* circuit or the voltage across the capacitor of an *R-C* circuit to

TABLE II-IV.—ASCENDING CURVE

k time constants	Per cent of maximum value	k time constants	Per cent of maximum value	k time constants	Per cent of maximum value
0.00	0.000	0.70	50.3	2.50	91.8
0.05	4.9	0.80	55.1	3.00	95.0
0.10	9.5	0.90	59.3	3.50	97.0
0.15	14.0	1.00	63.2	4.00	98.2
0.20	18.1	1.20	69.9	4.50	98.9
0.30	25.9	1.40	75.3	5.00	99.3
0.40	33.0	1.60	79.8	5.50	99.6
0.50	39.3	1.80	83.5	6.00	99.8
0.60	45.1	2.00	86.5	7.00	99.9

reach values other than 63.2 per cent of their final values may be determined mathematically by use of suitable equations. The mathematics involved is beyond the scope planned for this text. A shorter and more convenient method of determining the time required to attain any percentage of the final value is by use of time-constant curves. As all of the current-time and voltage-time relations vary exponentially, it is possible to represent these variations by the two general exponential curves shown in Fig. 2-67. These curves are plotted from values obtained mathematically and listed in Tables II-IV and II-V.

TABLE II-V.—DESCENDING CURVE

k time constants	Per cent of maximum value	k time constants	Per cent of maximum value	k time constants	Per cent of maximum value
0.00	100	0.70	49.7	2.50	8.2
0.05	95.1	0.80	44.9	3.00	5.0
0.10	90.5	0.90	40.7	3.50	3.0
0.15	86.0	1.00	36.8	4.00	1.8
0.20	81.9	1.20	30.1	4.50	1.1
0.30	74.1	1.40	24.7	5.00	0.7
0.40	67.0	1.60	20.2	5.50	0.4
0.50	60.7	1.80	16.5	6.00	0.2
0.60	54.9	2.00	13.5	7.00	0.1

Example 2-28. An *R-L* circuit used to control the action of a switch has a resistance of 12 ohms and an inductance of 0.5 henry and is connected to a 6-volt battery. (*a*) If the switch operates when the current attains 63.2 per cent of its final value, what time is required to operate the switch? (*b*) If the switch requires 400 ma to operate, what is the time between the start of current flow and the closing of the switch?

Given: Find:
  $R = 12$ ohms   (*a*) $t = ?$
  $L = 0.5$ henry   (*b*) $t = ?$
Solution:

(*a*) $t = \dfrac{L}{R} = \dfrac{0.5}{12} = 0.0416$ second

(*b*)   maximum current value $= \dfrac{E}{R} = \dfrac{6}{12} = 0.5$ amp

Per cent of maximum current required to operate the switch $= \dfrac{400}{500} \times 100 = 80$ per cent

From curve, Fig. 2-67, $k = 1.6$

$t = k\dfrac{L}{R} = \dfrac{1.6 \times 0.5}{12} = 0.0666$ second

Example 2-29. A 0.005-μf capacitor and a 2-megohm resistor are connected to form an *R-C* circuit. If the *R-C* combination is connected to a 300-volt source of d-c power, what time is required for the voltage across the capacitor to reach (*a*) 100 volts, (*b*) 200 volts, (*c*) 270 volts? If the capacitor becomes fully charged (300 volts) and is then discharged through the 2-megohm resistor, what time is required to discharge the capacitor to (*d*) 250 volts, (*e*) 200 volts, (*f*) 110 volts, (*g*) 50 volts?

Given: Find:
R = 2 megohms t = ?
C = 0.005 μf

Solution:

(*a*) Per cent of maximum value = $\dfrac{100}{300} \times 100$ = 33.3 per cent

k (from Fig. 2-67) = 0.40
$t = kCR = 0.40 \times 0.005 \times 10^{-6} \times 2 \times 10^6$ = 0.004 second

(*b*) Per cent of maximum value = $\dfrac{200}{300} \times 100$ = 66.6 per cent

k (from Fig. 2-67) = 1.1
$t = kCR = 1.1 \times 0.005 \times 10^{-6} \times 2 \times 10^6$ = 0.011 second

(*c*) Per cent of maximum value = $\dfrac{270}{300} \times 100$ = 90 per cent

k (from Fig. 2-67) = 2.27
$t = kCR = 2.27 \times 0.005 \times 10^{-6} \times 2 \times 10^6$ = 0.0227 second

(*d*) Per cent of maximum value = $\dfrac{250}{300} \times 100$ = 83.3 per cent

k (from Fig. 2-67) = 0.19
$t = kCR = 0.19 \times 0.005 \times 10^{-6} \times 2 \times 10^6$ = 0.0019 second

(*e*) Per cent of maximum value = $\dfrac{200}{300} \times 100$ = 66.6 per cent

k = (from Fig. 2-67) = 0.40
$t = kCR = 0.40 \times 0.005 \times 10^{-6} \times 2 \times 10^6$ = 0.004 second

(*f*) Per cent of maximum value = $\dfrac{110}{300} \times 100$ = 36.6 per cent

k = (from Fig. 2-67) = 1
$t = kCR = 1 \times 0.005 \times 10^{-6} \times 2 \times 10^6$ = 0.01 second

(*g*) Per cent of maximum value = $\dfrac{50}{300} \times 100$ = 16.6 per cent

k = (from Fig. 2-67) = 1.8
$t = kCR = 1.8 \times 0.005 \times 10^{-6} \times 2 \times 10^6$ = 0.018 second

Uses of Delayed-action Circuits. There are numerous applications of *R-C* and *R-L* circuits both in radio and in industrial electronics. A few of the applications are as follows.

A grid-leak detector circuit (see Chap. V) uses a capacitor and a resistor connected in parallel in the grid circuit of the detector tube. Actually this *R-C* combination is a time-constant circuit and the values of *R* and *C* are chosen to produce a time constant of sufficient duration that the charge on the capacitor gained during the positive half cycles does not have time to completely discharge through the resistor during the negative half cycles. Other examples of time-constant circuits in radio apparatus include automatic volume control, relaxation oscillator, and trigger circuits.

Industrial applications of time-constant circuits include controlling the length of time for a specific manufacturing operation, timing of electric welders, timing the exposure of photofinishing processes, timing of instruments, producing repeated action for life tests, and motor control.

BIBLIOGRAPHY

ALBERT, A. L., *The Electrical Fundamentals of Communication*, McGraw-Hill Book Company, Inc., New York.

DAWES, C. L., *Course in Electrical Engineering*, Vols. I and II, McGraw-Hill Book Company, Inc., New York.

DEELEY, P. M., *Electrolytic Capacitors*, The Cornell-Dubilier Electric Corporation, South Plainfield, N. J.

FLETCHER, G. L., MOSBACHER, I., and LEHMAN, S., *Unified Physics*, McGraw-Hill Book Company, Inc., New York.

GHIRARDI, A. A., *Radio Physics Course*, Murray Hill Books, Inc., New York.

GILBERT, N. E., *Electricity and Magnetism*, The Macmillan Company, New York.

HENNEY, K., *Principles of Radio*, John Wiley & Sons, Inc., New York.

MAGNUSSON, C. E., *Electric Transients*, McGraw-Hill Book Company, Inc., New York.

Mallory-Yaxley Radio Service Encyclopedia, P. R. Mallory & Co., Inc., Indianapolis, Ind.

MANLY, H. P., *Drake's Cyclopedia of Radio and Electronics*, Frederick J. Drake & Co., Chicago.

SLURZBERG, M., and OSTERHELD, W., *Electrical Essentials of Radio*, McGraw-Hill Book Company, Inc., New York.

TERMAN, F. E., *Fundamentals of Radio*, McGraw-Hill Book Company, Inc., New York.

TIMBIE, W. H., *Elements of Electricity*, John Wiley & Sons, Inc., New York.

TURNER, R. P., Methods of Measuring Radio Frequencies, *Radio News*, January, 1943.

TURNER, R. P., Delay and Timing Circuits, *Radio News*, August, 1943.

WATSON, H. M., WELCH, H. E., EBY, G. S., *Understanding Radio*, McGraw-Hill Book Company, Inc., New York.

QUESTIONS

1. Name and describe the various types of resistors (*a*) when classified according to material used, (*b*) when classified according to their control.

2. Give four applications of resistors to radio circuits.

3. Why must the power rating of a resistor be taken into consideration?

4. Explain the use of (*a*) a rheostat, (*b*) a potentiometer.

5. What is meant by taper? Why is taper necessary?

6. Describe three characteristics of inductance that are important to the study of radio.

7. What is meant by (*a*) self-inductance? (*b*) Mutual inductance?

8. What is the relation between mutual inductance and the coefficient of coupling?

9. Explain two effects that inductance has upon the current flowing in an a-c circuit.

10. What is meant by inductive reactance? What factors of the circuit determine its value?

11. What is meant by the impedance of an inductance coil? How do the values of impedance and inductive reactance compare for coils generally used in radio circuits?

12. Why does the current lag the voltage in an a-c circuit that contains inductance?

13. Describe three methods of neutralizing the effects of inductance.

14. Explain the characteristics and uses of each of the following types of chokes: (a) power supply, (b) audio frequency, (c) radio frequency.

15. Explain the characteristics and uses of each of the following types of transformers: (a) power supply, (b) audio frequency, (c) radio frequency, (d) intermediate frequency.

16. Why is it necessary to shield high-frequency coils? What precautions should be taken in the construction of a shield?

17. Describe each of the three resistance effects that are combined in the a-c resistance of a coil.

18. Describe two characteristics of capacitance that are important to the study of radio.

19. What factors affect the capacitance of a capacitor?

20. Why does the voltage lag the current in an a-c circuit that contains capacitance?

21. What is meant by the impedance of a capacitor? How does the value of impedance and capacitive reactance compare for capacitors generally used in a-c circuits?

22. Describe the characteristics for each of the following types of capacitor: (a) mica dielectric, (b) paper dielectric, (c) oil dielectric.

23. Describe the construction of (a) a wet electrolytic capacitor, (b) a dry electrolytic capacitor.

24. State three advantages of electrolytic capacitors. State a disadvantage of electrolytic capacitors.

25. Describe the constructional features of each of the following types of variable capacitors: (a) broadcast, (b) midget, (c) micro, (d) split-stator, (e) transmitting, (f) adjustable.

26. How are capacitors generally rated in regards to voltage?

27. Describe three effects of distributed capacitance.

28. Describe five classifications of electric circuits in regards to the manner in which the circuit elements are connected.

29. What is meant by Ohm's law for a-c circuits?

30. In a series a-c circuit, what is the relation between the complete circuit and the individual circuit elements in regards to (a) current, (b) voltage, (c) resistance, (d) inductive reactance, (e) capacitive reactance?

31. In a parallel a-c circuit, what is the relation between the complete circuit and the individual circuit elements in regards to (a) current, (b) voltage, (c) resistance, (d) inductive reactance, (e) capacitive reactance?

32. What is meant by resonance?

33. What is the recommended procedure to be followed in order to determine the classification of a resonant circuit?

34. What is the relation between the line voltage and the reactive voltages for a series resonant circuit?

35. Describe the impedance and current characteristics of a series resonant circuit.

36. What is the relation between the line current and the reactive currents for a parallel resonant circuit?

37. What are the impedance and line-current characteristics of a parallel resonant circuit?

38. What is the purpose of resonance curves?

39. How do the resonance curves for a series resonant circuit compare with those for a parallel resonant circuit?

40. What is meant by circuit Q? How does the circuit Q of a tuned circuit compare with the coil Q?

41. What is the relation between the circuit Q of a tuned circuit and (a) the selectivity, (b) the width of the resonance curve?

42. How does the LC ratio affect the selectivity of (a) a series tuned circuit, (b) a parallel tuned circuit?

43. What is meant by filter action? What are the five principles of a-c circuits upon which the action of any filter circuit depends?

44. Describe each of the following types of filters: (a) low-pass filter, (b) high-pass filter, (c) band-pass filter, (d) band-stop filter.

45. What is the purpose of m-derived filters? How are m-derived filters constructed?

46. Why is it necessary to couple circuits?

47. How is coupling accomplished in (a) a simple direct-coupled circuit? (b) A simple indirect-coupled circuit?

48. What is meant by a complex-coupled circuit? Where are complex-coupled circuits used?

49. Explain what is meant by the following terms: (a) coefficient of coupling, (b) critical coupling, (c) tight coupling, (d) loose coupling, (e) optimum coupling.

50. What is meant by coupled impedance? How does coupled impedance affect the primary circuit?

51. Explain the relation between coupled impedance and the coefficient of coupling.

52. Explain the effects of coupled impedance on the primary circuit in a circuit having (a) an untuned primary and an untuned secondary, (b) a circuit with an untuned primary and a tuned secondary, (c) a circuit with a tuned primary and a tuned secondary.

53. What is meant by a band-pass amplifier circuit? What are its circuit characteristics?

54. How does the shape of the response curve of a band-pass circuit vary with the coefficient of coupling?

55. In a band-pass circuit, what effect has the coefficient of coupling on the width of band pass?

56. In a band-pass circuit, what is the relation between the circuit Q and the coefficient of coupling?

57. What is the essential purpose of time-delay circuits?

58. Explain the operation of a delayed-action (a) R-L circuit, (b) R-C circuit.

59. What is meant by the time constant of a delayed-action (a) R-L circuit, (b) R-C circuit?

60. What is the purpose of the universal time-constant curves? How are they used in the solution of time-delay circuits?

61. Name four applications of time-delay circuits. Explain the circuit actions of one of these applications.

PROBLEMS

1. What is the power rating of the following resistors: (*a*) a 50-ohm resistor that can carry 200 ma, (*b*) a 10,000-ohm resistor that can carry 10 ma, (*c*) a 250,000-ohm resistor that can carry 2 ma, (*d*) a 50-ohm resistor that can carry 1000 ma?

2. What is the current rating of the following resistors: (*a*) a 50,000-ohm 10-watt resistor, (*b*) a 25-watt 1500-ohm resistor, (*c*) a ½-watt 2-megohm resistor, (*d*) a 5-watt 750-ohm resistor, (*e*) a ¼-watt 3-megohm resistor?

3. A 25,000-ohm potentiometer having a uniform resistance is used to obtain 30 volts across a load; the power source is rated at 90 volts. (*a*) What is the current in each part of the potentiometer (see Fig. 2-4) if the load resistance is 5000 ohms? (*b*) What is the current in each part of the potentiometer if the load resistance is 10,000 ohms?

4. A flux of 20,000 lines links the turns of a coil having 200 turns. (*a*) What is the value of the induced voltage if the flux decreases to zero in 0.025 second? (*b*) What is the inductance of the coil if a current of 50 ma is required to produce the flux of 20,000 lines? (*c*) How much energy is stored in the magnetic field?

5. A flux of 20 lines links a coil having 30 turns. The flux in the coil is varying in accordance with an alternating current and therefore varies from zero to maximum value (and vice versa) in one-quarter of a cycle. What is the value of the induced voltage at the following values of frequency: (*a*) 500 cycles? (*b*) 500 kc? (*c*) 1500 kc? (*d*) 30 mc?

6. What is the inductance of each of the following coils: (*a*) a 400-turn multilayer coil whose dimensions are $a = \frac{3}{4}$ inch, $b = 2$ inches, $c = \frac{1}{2}$ inch? (*b*) A 40-turn flat coil whose dimensions are $a = 1\frac{1}{4}$ inches, $c = 1\frac{1}{2}$ inches? (*c*) A 200-turn solenoid whose dimensions are $a = \frac{3}{4}$ inch, $b = 3$ inches?

7. What is the inductance of each of the following coils: (*a*) a 32-turn flat coil whose dimensions are $a = 1\frac{1}{8}$ inches, $c = 1\frac{1}{4}$ inches? (*b*) A 320-turn solenoid whose dimensions are $a = \frac{5}{8}$ inch, $b = 5$ inches? (*c*) A 1000-turn multilayer coil whose dimensions are $a = 1$ inch, $b = 2$ inches, $c = \frac{3}{4}$ inch?

8. What is the mutual inductance of two coils wound adjacent to one another? Assume that all the magnetic lines set up in the first coil cut all the turns of the second coil. The primary coil consists of 800 turns wound on a cardboard core 1 inch in diameter and 4 inches long. The secondary coil consists of 1600 turns wound on a cardboard core $1\frac{1}{4}$ inches in diameter and 4 inches long.

9. Find the coefficient of coupling for each of the following combinations: (*a*) two coils whose self-inductances are 0.05 and 0.08 mh and whose mutual inductance is 0.015 mh, (*b*) two coils whose self-inductances are 40 and 62.5 μh and whose mutual inductance is 16 μh, (*c*) two coils whose self-inductances are 4 and 9 mh and whose mutual inductance is 240 μh.

10. Two coils, the first having 50 turns and the second 100 turns, are placed so that only 5 per cent of the lines set up by coil 1 link coil 2. If 800 lines are set up when 5 ma flow through coil 1, what voltage will be induced across coil 2 if the current decreases from its maximum value to zero in 0.00005 second?

11. What is the inductive reactance of a 2.5-mh choke coil at (*a*) 550 kc? (*b*) 1000 kc? (*c*) 1500 kc? (*d*) 4.25 mc?

12. A 15-henry choke coil that has a resistance of 375 ohms is connected to a 110-volt 60-cycle power supply. Find (*a*) the inductive reactance, (*b*) the impedance, (*c*) the current, (*d*) the angle of lag.

13. It is desired to calculate the inductance of a choke coil from the readings obtained with the coil connected to an a-c power source. The following are the readings obtained: voltmeter, 120 volts; milliammeter, 80 ma; wattmeter, 1.6 watts; frequency meter, 60 cycles. (*a*) What is the impedance of the coil? (*b*) What is the resistance of the coil (determined from the wattmeter and ammeter readings)? (*c*) What is the inductive reactance of the coil? (*d*) What is the inductance of the coil?

14. Two coils, one having an inductance of 150 μh and the second of 600 μh, are arranged so that they may be connected in series in the various ways shown in Fig. 2-9. What is the inductance of the circuit when the two coils are connected in series so that they are (*a*) aiding and the coupling is 100 per cent? (*b*) Opposing and the coupling is 100 per cent? (*c*) In a position that produces zero coupling? (*d*) Aiding and the coupling is 50 per cent?

15. The transformer shown in Fig. 2-68 has 460 turns on its primary winding. (*a*) How many turns are there on the winding section *cd*? (*b*) Section *ef*? (*c*) Section *gh*? (*d*) Section *ik*? (*e*) Sections *ij* and *jk*?

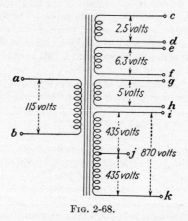

Fig. 2-68.

16. A fixed capacitor is made of 720 plates of lead foil, each 2 by 3 inches, separated by a beeswaxed paper dielectric 0.006 inch thick. (*a*) What is its capacitance? (*b*) What charge is produced in the capacitor when it is connected across a 250-volt d-c power supply? (*c*) How much energy is stored in the capacitor?

17. How many plates must be used to make a fixed capacitor of 0.0005 μf if the plates are ¾ inch square and the dielectric is made of mica sheets 0.007 inch thick?

18. What is the capacitance of a rolled-type fixed capacitor consisting of two plates, each 1 inch wide and 162 inches long, separated by paraffined paper 0.005 inch thick?

19. What is the maximum capacitance of a 21-plate variable capacitor if each plate has an area of 2.75 square inches and the air gap is 0.025 inch?

20. What is the capacitance of a 15-plate midget variable capacitor if the area of each rotor plate is 0.80 square inch and the air gap is 0.025 inch?

21. What is the capacitance of a 14-plate micro variable capacitor if the area of each plate is 0.35 square inch and the air gap is 0.0205 inch?

22. What is the capacitive reactance of a 0.001-μf capacitor when connected in a circuit of the following high-frequency currents: (*a*) 550 kc? (*b*) 1000 kc? (*c*) 1500 kc? (*d*) 4.25 mc?

23. An 8-μf fixed capacitor that has a resistance of 10 ohms is connected to a 110-volt 60-cycle power supply. Find: (a) the capacitive reactance, (b) the impedance, (c) the current, (d) the power factor, (e) the phase angle, (f) the power.

24. What is the capacitance of the following circuits: (a) An 8-, a 4-, and two 2-μf capacitors connected in parallel? (b) An 8-, a 4-, and two 2-μf capacitors connected in series?

25. What is the capacitance of the circuit shown in Fig. 2-69?

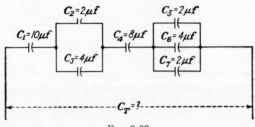

Fig. 2-69.

26. A four-tube radio set has its heaters connected in series. The rated voltages are 25, 6.3, 6.3, and 12.6 volts, and they all draw 0.3 ampere. (a) What value of resistance must be connected in series with these heaters in order to operate them directly from a 110-volt line? (b) How much power is consumed by the dropping resistor?

27. A 500-, a 400-, and a 600-ohm resistor are connected in parallel across a 300-volt power line. Find (a) the total resistance of the circuit, (b) the current in each resistor, (c) the line current, (d) the power taken by each resistor, (e) the power taken by the circuit.

28. A radio receiver has five tubes whose heaters each draw 0.3 ampere. The heaters are connected in parallel to a 2.5-volt tap of the power transformer. (a) What is the resistance of each heater? (b) What is the resistance of the heater circuit? (c) What is the total current taken from the power transformer by this heater circuit?

29. Find the following quantities for the circuit shown in Fig. 2-70: (a) the resistance of each group, (b) the resistance of the complete circuit, (c) the line current, (d)

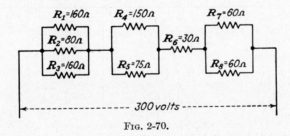

Fig. 2-70.

the power consumed by the complete circuit, (e) the voltage across each resistor, (f) the current in each resistor, (g) the power consumed by each resistor.

30. Find the following quantities for the circuit shown in Fig. 2-71: (a) the resistance of each group, (b) the resistance of the complete circuit, (c) the line current, (d) the power consumed by the complete circuit, (e) the current in each resistor, (f) the voltage across each resistor, (g) the power consumed by each resistor.

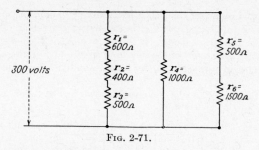

Fig. 2-71.

31. The series circuit shown in Fig. 2-72 is connected to a 100-volt 60-cycle power line. Find: (a) the resistance of the circuit, (b) the inductive reactance of the circuit, (c) the capacitive reactance of the circuit, (d) the impedance of the circuit, (e) the line current and the current in each circuit element, (f) the impedance of each circuit element, (g) the voltage across each circuit element, (h) the power consumed by each circuit element, (i) the power taken from the line, (j) the power factor of each circuit

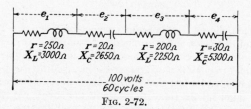

Fig. 2-72.

element, (k) the power factor angle of each circuit element, (l) the power factor of the complete circuit, (m) the power factor angle of the complete circuit.

32. The parallel circuit shown in Fig. 2-73 is connected to a 100-volt 60-cycle power line. Find: (a) the current flowing in each branch of the parallel circuit, (b) the line current, (c) the power taken by each branch, (d) the power taken by the whole circuit, (e) the power factor of the circuit, (f) the phase angle between the line current and the line voltage, (g) the impedance of the circuit.

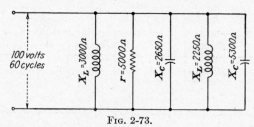

Fig. 2-73.

33. A series tuned circuit has an inductance of 725 μh. At what value of capacitance must its variable capacitor be adjusted in order to obtain resonance for the following frequencies: (a) 500 kc?   (b) 880 kc?   (c) 1600 kc?

34. A series tuned circuit has an inductance of 316 μh and a variable capacitor whose maximum capacitance is 320 $\mu\mu$f.   (a) What is the resonant frequency when the capacitor is set for the maximum value?   (b) At what value must the capacitor be set in order to make the circuit resonant at 1070 kc?   (c) What is the highest resonant frequency that can be obtained if the minimum value of the variable capacitor is 15 $\mu\mu$f?

35. A variable capacitor having a maximum capacitance of 350 $\mu\mu$f is used for tuning a broadcast receiver. (*a*) What inductance is required to make the circuit resonant at 500 kc when the capacitor is set at its maximum value? (*b*) What is the highest resonant frequency that can be obtained with this coil if the minimum value of the capacitor is 15 $\mu\mu$f?

36. If the coil of Prob. 35, together with the circuit wiring, has a distributed capacitance of 15 $\mu\mu$f, what will the frequency range of the circuit be? NOTE: The distributed capacitance is considered as a capacitor connected in parallel with the variable capacitor.

37. It is desired to cover a short-wave band whose lowest frequency is to be 1700 kc by the use of a fixed capacitor C_S connected in series with the tuning capacitor C_T as shown in Fig. 2-74. The maximum and minimum capacitance of the tuning

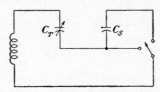

FIG. 2-74.

capacitor are 350 $\mu\mu$f and 15 $\mu\mu$f, respectively, the inductance of the secondary is 290 μh, and the distributed circuit capacitance is 15 $\mu\mu$f. (*a*) Find the capacitance of the series capacitor C_S. (*b*) What is the highest frequency to which the circuit may be tuned if the distributed circuit capacitance is to be taken into consideration and the series capacitor is used as determined in part *a*? (*c*) What is the highest frequency to which the circuit may be tuned if the distributed circuit capacitance is ignored? (*d*) What is the highest frequency to which the circuit may be tuned if the distributed circuit capacitance is ignored and the minimum value of the variable capacitor is 10 $\mu\mu$f?

38. A series resonant circuit has a resistance of 12 ohms and an inductive reactance of 300 ohms at its resonant frequency. (*a*) What is the value of the circuit Q? (*b*) What is the voltage across the inductor, the capacitor, and the resistor at resonance if the applied voltage is 10 volts? (*c*) What is the impedance of the circuit at resonance? (*d*) What is the value of the current at resonance if the applied voltage is 10 volts?

39. A 70- to 140-$\mu\mu$f adjustable capacitor and an inductance coil are connected in parallel to form the primary side of an i-f transformer whose resonant frequency is to be 460 kc. (*a*) What inductance must the coil have if the circuit is to be resonant at 460 kc when the adjustable capacitor is set at its mid-value of 105 $\mu\mu$f? (*b*) What is the Q of the primary winding if its resistance is 12 ohms? (*c*) What is the impedance of the circuit at resonance? (*d*) What is the line current at resonance if the voltage across the tuned circuit is 50 volts? (*e*) What is the current in the inductor circuit at resonance? (*f*) What is the current in the capacitor circuit at resonance?

40. A 2.5-mh coil and a 25- to 80-$\mu\mu$f adjustable capacitor are connected in parallel to form the primary of an i-f transformer whose resonant frequency is 460 kc. (*a*) At what value must the capacitor be set in order to obtain resonance at 460 kc? (*b*) What is the Q of the winding if its resistance is 13.75 ohms? (*c*) What is the impedance of the circuit at resonance? (*d*) What is the line current at resonance if the voltage across the tuned circuit is 90 volts?   (*e*) What is the current in the inductor circuit at resonance?   (*f*) What is the current in the capacitor circuit at resonance?

41. A parallel resonant circuit is to be used as a wave trap to eliminate the effects of a 1300-kc signal.   The circuit has a resistance of 1.5 ohms and a capacitance (distributed and wiring) of 10 $\mu\mu$f.   (*a*) What value of inductance must be used with a capacitor whose value is 65 $\mu\mu$f?   (*b*) What is the circuit Q?   (*c*) What is the width of the band being eliminated?

42. What is the band width of a tuned circuit at a resonant frequency of 456 kc if the circuit Q is 45.6?

43. What is the band width of a tuned circuit at a resonant frequency of 262 kc if the circuit Q is 25?

44. Plot the series resonance curves (Q vs. f_r) for a circuit having a capacitance of 100 $\mu\mu$f and an inductance of 253 μh.   Assume the impressed voltage to be 500 mv and plot curves for the conditions when R equals 5 ohms and when R equals 10 ohms.

45. Plot the parallel resonance curves (Z vs. f_r) for a circuit having a capacitance of 100 $\mu\mu$f and an inductance of 253 μh.   Plot two curves, one for the condition when R equals 5 ohms and the other when R equals 10 ohms.

46. A 2000-ohm 50-watt resistor has an inductance of 3 μh.   What is the impedance of the resistor at (*a*) 500 cycles?   (*b*) 500 kc?   (*c*) 1500 kc?   (*d*) 4 mc?   (*e*) 15 mc?   (*f*) 65 mc?

47. The 2000-ohm 50-watt resistor of Prob. 46 has a distributed capacitance of 2 $\mu\mu$f.   If the inductance is neglected and only the resistance and distributed capacitance are considered, what is its impedance at (*a*) 500 cycles?   (*b*) 500 kc?   (*c*) 1500 kc?   (*d*) 4 mc?   (*e*) 15 mc?   (*f*) 65 mc?

48. The 2000-ohm 50-watt resistor referred to in Probs. 46 and 47 has an inductance of 3 μh and a distributed capacitance of 2 $\mu\mu$f.   Considering all three effects, what is its impedance at (*a*) 500 cycles?   (*b*) 500 kc?   (*c*) 1500 kc?   (*d*) 4 mc?   (*e*) 15 mc?   (*f*) 65 mc?

49. A 2.5-mh choke has a resistance of 70 ohms.   If its distributed capacitance is ignored, what is its impedance at (*a*) 460 kc?   (*b*) 1600 kc?   (*c*) 4 mc?   (*d*) 15 mc?

50. If the choke coil of Prob. 49 has a distributed capacitance of 1 $\mu\mu$f, what is its impedance at (*a*) 460 kc?   (*b*) 1600 kc?   (*c*) 4 mc?   (*d*) 15 mc?

51. It is desired that a filter choke having a resistance of 80 ohms oppose the flow of a 60-cycle current with twenty times the opposition that it offers to direct current. What is the inductance of the coil?

52. (*a*) To which type of current will a 0.05-μf capacitor offer the greater opposition, a 4000-cycle a-f signal or a 1600-kc r-f signal?   (*b*) How many times greater is the larger impedance than the smaller impedance?   (*c*) Which type of current is blocked by this capacitor?

53. A 20-mh choke coil and a 500-$\mu\mu$f capacitor are connected as shown in Fig. 2-44*c* to form a low-pass filter circuit.   What opposition is offered by the capacitor (*a*) to the highest frequency audio signal usually obtained in a radio receiver (5000 cycles)?   (*b*) To the lowest frequency carrier wave usually obtained in a radio receiver (500 kc)?   What opposition is offered by the inductor (*c*) to a 5000-cycle signal? (*d*) To a 500-kc signal?

54. A 4-henry choke coil and a 0.1-μf capacitor are connected as shown in Fig. 2-46*c* to form a high-pass filter circuit.   What opposition is offered by the capacitor (*a*) to 60 cycles (power disturbances)?   (*b*) To a 1200-cycle a-f signal?   What opposition is offered by the inductor (*c*) to 60 cycles?   (*d*) To a 1200-cycle a-f signal?

55. A 5000-ohm resistor and a 0.5-μf capacitor are connected in parallel to form a resistor-capacitor filter circuit.   (*a*) What impedance does the capacitor offer to a

5000-cycle current?   (b) Which path will the major portion of the 5000-cycle current take?

56. A circuit similar to the one shown in Fig. 2-52a is to be used in the r-f stage of a receiver.   It is desired that the capacitor offer an impedance of one hundred times that of the resistor, whose value is 7500 ohms.   What size capacitor is required if the signal is 1500 kc?

57. A 7200-ohm resistor and a 20-μf capacitor are connected as shown in Fig. 2-52b.   (a) What impedance does the capacitor offer to a 100-cycle a-f signal?   (b) Will the a-f signal take the path of the capacitor or of the resistor?

58. A mutual-inductive-coupled circuit is shown in Fig. 2-75, together with the circuit values.   Find (a) the impedance coupled into the primary by the secondary, (b) the equivalent resistance component of the coupled impedance, (c) the equivalent

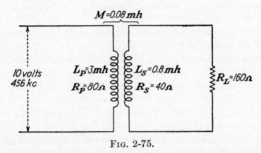

F$_{IG}$. 2-75.

reactance component of the coupled impedance, (d) the equivalent circuit diagram, (e) the effective impedance of the primary, (f) the primary current, (g) the secondary voltage, (h) the secondary current.

59. An audio transformer with a 3 to 1 step-up ratio has an inductance of 80 henries and a resistance of 100 ohms on its primary side.   The inductance of the secondary winding is 720 henries and its resistance is 1000 ohms.   (a) What value of inductance is reflected to the primary by the secondary?   (b) What value of resistance is reflected to the primary by the secondary?   (c) If a load impedance of 7200 ohms is connected across the secondary, what value of impedance is reflected to the primary by the secondary?   (d) What value of inductance does the primary reflect to the secondary?   (e) What value of resistance does the primary reflect to the secondary?

60. An audio transformer with a 2.5 to 1 step-up ratio has an inductance of 50 henries and a resistance of 80 ohms on its primary side.   The inductance of the secondary winding is 312.5 henries and its resistance is 500 ohms.   (a) What value of inductance is reflected by the primary to the secondary?   (b) What value of resistance is reflected by the primary to the secondary?   (c) What value of inductance is reflected by the secondary to the primary?   (d) What value of resistance is reflected by the secondary to the primary?   (e) If the load on the secondary has a capacitance of 200 $\mu\mu$f, what is the reflected capacitance at the primary side?

61. (a) What is the approximate width of the frequency band passed by a band-pass amplifier circuit having a resonant frequency of 260 kc and a coefficient of coupling of 0.03?   (b) What value of coefficient of coupling is required to produce a band width of 10 kc?   (c) If the primary and secondary Q's are equal, what is their value for the condition of coupling in (a)?   (d) If the primary and secondary Q's are equal, what is their value for the condition of coupling in (b)?

62. A band-pass filter to be used in the i-f amplifier of a radio receiver is to pass a band 10 kc wide centering about a frequency of 465 kc.   (a) What is the coefficient of coupling? (*b*) What is the circuit Q? (*c*) What is the capacitance of the tuning capacitors if the primary and secondary inductances are both 2 mh?

63. It is desired that a band-pass circuit used in the i-f amplifier of a radio receiver pass a band 10 kc wide. The circuit Q is equal to 40. (*a*) What value of coefficient of coupling is required? (*b*) What are the extreme limits of the frequency band passed? (*c*) What is the capacitance of the tuning capacitors if the inductance of the primary and secondary windings are 6 mh each?

64. A low-current d-c relay that has an inductance of 25 henries is connected in series with a 1000-ohm resistor to form an R-L time-delay control circuit operated on a 110-volt d-c circuit. (*a*) What is the time constant of the circuit? (*b*) If the relay closes when the current reaches 88 ma, what time elapses between closing the line switch and operation of the relay?

65. A low-current d-c relay having an inductance of 10 henries is to close 0.02 second after the line switch is closed. What value resistor should be connected in series with the relay if it closes when the current reaches (*a*) 63.2 per cent of its final value? (*b*) 80 per cent of its final value?

66. A broadcast-band receiver is to have an R-C circuit with a time constant of 0.2 second for its avc circuit. (*a*) What value resistor is required if a 0.1-μf capacitor is used? (*b*) What value resistor is required if a 0.15-μf capacitor is used? (*c*) What value capacitor is required if a 1-megohm resistor is used?

67. A grid-leak detector circuit contains a 250-$\mu\mu$f capacitor shunted by a 1-megohm resistor. (*a*) What is the time constant of this circuit? (*b*) If the highest a-f signal to be applied to the circuit is 5000 cycles, what is the time required to complete one of these cycles? (*c*) Under the conditions of (*a*) and (*b*) will the capacitor ever become completely discharged? (*d*) Explain answer to (*c*).

68. A 0.05-μf capacitor and a 0.5-megohm resistor are connected to form an R-C circuit. The R-C combination is connected to a 250-volt, d-c source. (*a*) What time is required for the voltage across the capacitor to reach 50 volts, 100 volts, 200 volts? (*b*) What current flows when the switch is closed? (*c*) What current flows when the voltage across the capacitor reaches 200 volts? (*d*) If the capacitor is fully charged and is then discharged through the 0.5-megohm resistor, what is the current at the instant it starts to discharge? (*e*) What is the value of the voltage RC seconds after the capacitor starts to discharge? (*f*) At what time will the capacitor be discharged to half voltage?

CHAPTER III

SIMPLE RECEIVING CIRCUITS

Radio transmitters throughout the world are simultaneously sending out their modulated radio waves in all directions. A modulated wave is produced by properly combining the audio signal to be transmitted with the carrier wave of the transmitter. A carrier wave, an audio signal, and the resulting modulated carrier wave are shown in Fig. 3-1. A radio receiver makes it possible to listen to the audio signals sent out from any one of the transmitters within the range of the receiver. The basic operations are the same for a simple crystal receiver as for a complex

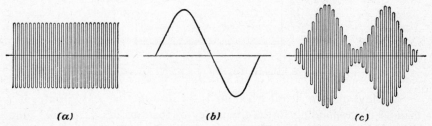

(a)   (b)   (c)

Fig. 3-1.—Wave forms of currents used in radio transmission. (a) High-frequency carrier wave, (b) audio signal wave, (c) modulated carrier wave.

modern receiver using vacuum tubes. Through the study of the operations of the crystal receiver the basic functions can easily be understood; the inclusion of vacuum tubes at this time would only complicate the subject. Once the fundamental operations of a radio receiver are thoroughly understood, they can then be applied to vacuum-tube receivers.

3-1. Functions of a Receiver. The essential functions of a receiver are: (1) to *receive* the various waves sent out by radio transmitters; (2) to *select* the desired radio wave and to exclude all others; (3) to *separate* the audio signal wave from the modulated carrier wave; (4) to *convert* the audio signal to sound waves. Observation of Fig. 1-11 will show that the fundamental operations of a receiver and transmitter are similar but are used in reverse order.

When a radio wave cuts through a conductor it induces a voltage, or electrical pressure, in that conductor. This electrical pressure causes the free electrons in the conductor to be drawn toward the positive

131

terminal of the antenna circuit, thus setting up an electric current in
that conductor.   In a radio receiver this conductor is called the *antenna*.

At any instant, a number of different radio waves are cutting through
the receiving antenna, and each induces a voltage in the antenna.   Since
the signal of only one station should be heard at one time, some provision
must be made for separating the desired signal from the others.   The
part of the receiver performing this function is called the *selector* or the
tuner.   When a receiver is properly tuned, the modulated carrier wave
of only the desired station is utilized.   The next function of the receiver
is to separate the audio signal wave from the modulated carrier wave.
This function is called *detection* and the part of the receiver doing this
work is called the *detector*.

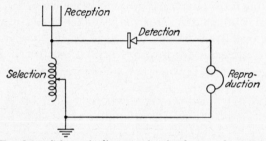

Fig. 3-2.—Schematic diagram of a simple crystal receiver.

A sound may be heard when air is set into motion and vibrates in a
manner corresponding to the frequency of that sound.   The final function of the receiver therefore is to convert the audio-frequency signals
from electrical impulses to sound waves.   This is accomplished by causing
a diaphragm to vibrate in accordance with the variations in strength
and frequency of the audio signals.   The unit that performs this function
is known as the *audible device* and may be either a set of *earphones* or a
loudspeaker.

These four functions are performed by the simple receiving circuit
shown in Fig. 3-2, in the following manner: (1) the antenna receives the
radio waves; (2) the desired signal is selected by adjusting the slide-wire
tuning coil; (3) the crystal detector allows only the audio component of
the modulated wave to flow through it; (4) the earphones change the
electrical impulses of the audio signals into sound waves.

3-2. Reception.   *Types of Receiving Antennas.*   An antenna is a wire
or system of wires made up in one of several forms and installed at
sufficient height above the ground so that it is free from any surrounding
objects.   Throughout the development of radio numerous types of
receiving antennas have been used.   Some of these are still being used,

while others have become obsolete. | Three simple types of antennas are shown in Fig. 3-4; these forms were used in the early stages of radio development and some are still being used.

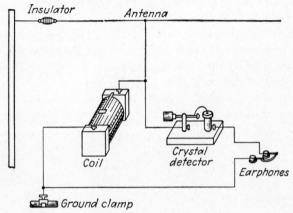

Fig. 3-3.—Illustration of the parts and circuit of the simple crystal receiver shown in Fig. 3-2.

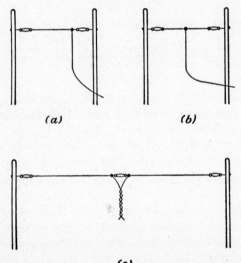

Fig. 3-4.—Three types of simple antennas. (a) Inverted *L* with end connected lead-in, (b) *T* type with center connected lead-in, (c) doublet type with center connected lead-in.

Purpose of the Antenna.   The purpose of the antenna is to intercept as much of the radio-frequency power radiated by the transmitting station as is possible.   This is true for all receiving antennas regardless of type or construction.   The amount of voltage induced in an antenna will depend on the power and frequency of the transmitter, the distance from the transmitter to the receiver, and the length, location, and direction of the receiving and transmitting antennas.

Although the power of a transmitter may be 50,000 watts or more and the antenna voltage may be as high as 50,000 volts, only a few microwatts of power are picked up by the receiving antenna and the value of the induced voltage is only in microvolts. The voltage induced in a receiving antenna decreases as the distance from the transmitting antenna increases. Because of this, the signal from a low-power station cannot be heard over great distances.

Factors Affecting the Manner of Construction of an Antenna. In order to obtain the maximum signal input for a receiver, it is necessary that the antenna intercept the maximum amount of energy possible from the

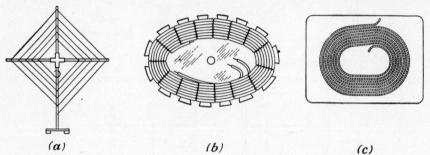

(a)   *(b)*   *(c)*

FIG. 3-5.—Three types of loop antennas. (a) Early loop antenna, (b) loop antenna used in modern receivers, (c) loop antenna used in modern receivers.

transmitted wave. This is accomplished by constructing the receiving antenna in such a manner that its flat top will be in the direction that will enable it to intercept the maximum amount of energy from the transmitted wave.

It is not possible to have a receiving antenna pick up the maximum energy of the signal transmitted by each broadcasting station. In the early days of radio, the antenna was generally installed so that it would pick up the maximum amount of energy from the weakest station. The direction of the receiving antenna is no longer as important a factor as in the past because of the increased power of the modern transmitters, and because of the increased over-all sensitivity of the modern receivers.

In early radio sets, a loop antenna was mounted on the top of the receiver. These loop antennas (see Fig. 3-5) could be rotated so that the maximum signal input could be obtained for all stations. The modern midget and portable receivers are constructed with a loop antenna mounted in the receiver. The effect of the relative directions of the receiving and transmitting antennas on these receivers can sometimes be observed by changing the position of the receiver, thus changing the relative position of the receiving and transmitting antennas. It may be observed that although the maximum signal input is received from one station for a certain position of the receiver, the signal from another station may be very weak for the same position.

The antenna should be mounted higher than the buildings surrounding it; otherwise some of the radio waves may be prevented from cutting through the antenna. Its length is generally determined by the building on which it is to be mounted. If the antenna becomes too long, it may become necessary to connect a capacitor in series with it. This is discussed in greater detail in the article on tuning.

The best operation of a radio receiver can only be obtained when it is used with a properly constructed antenna. In a simple receiver, eith~~ a crystal type or a one-tube set, successful operation depends upon the strength and the quality of the input signal, since there is little or no

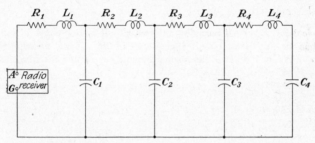

Fig. 3-6.—Electrical characteristics of the antenna circuit.

provision made for amplification. The greater efficiency of the modern complex multitube superheterodyne receivers cannot be obtained unless the input signal strength is much greater than that of the undesirable noises that are also picked up.

3-3. Electrical Characteristics of the Antenna. *Equivalent Circuit of the Antenna.* If a receiving antenna is divided into a number of equal lengths, each division can be represented by a resistor, an inductor, and a capacitor. Electrically this circuit can be represented as shown in Fig. 3-6. The effect of the inductances $L_1, L_2, L_3, L_4, \ldots$ is produced by the high-frequency currents induced in the antenna. The capacitors C_1, C_2 $C_3, C_4, \ldots$ represent the capacitances existing between the antenna acting as one plate of a capacitor, the ground as the other plate, and the air as the dielectric. The resistance of the wire and the resistance of the ground are represented by the resistors R_1, R_2, R_3, R_4, etc. Applying the rules for adding resistors in series, inductors in series, and capacitors in parallel, the total resistance, inductance, and capacitance of the antenna circuit may be calculated as follows:

$$R_A = R_1 + R_2 + R_3 + R_4 \cdots \qquad (3\text{-}1)$$
$$L_A = L_1 + L_2 + L_3 + L_4 \cdots \qquad (3\text{-}2)$$
$$C_A = C_1 + C_2 + C_3 + C_4 \cdots \qquad (3\text{-}3)$$

The equivalent circuit may be represented as a series resonant circuit, as shown in Fig. 3-7. As resistance impedes the flow of electric current, the amount of signal current will vary inversely with the total resistance of the circuit. It is therefore essential that the resistance should be as low as practicable.

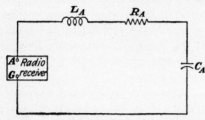

FIG. 3-7.—Equivalent circuit of the antenna.

By substituting the values of L_A and C_A in Eq. (2-48), the resonant frequency of the antenna circuit may be determined.

Example 3-1.   A typical receiving antenna circuit whose length is approximately 100 feet has an equivalent circuit capacitance of 200 $\mu\mu$f and an equivalent circuit inductance of 50 μh.   What is the resonant frequency of this antenna circuit?

Given: Find:
   $C_A = 200 \ \mu\mu$f $f_r = ?$
   $L_A = 50 \ \mu$h
Solution:

$$f_r = \frac{159}{\sqrt{L_A C_A}} = \frac{159}{\sqrt{50 \times 200 \times 10^{-6}}} = 1590 \text{ kc}$$

Fundamental Frequency of the Antenna.   If the antenna of Example 3-1 is connected to a crystal detector, a pair of earphones, and the ground as shown in Fig. 3-8a, the audible signals sent out by a transmitting station having a carrier frequency of 1590 kc will be heard in the earphones.   The frequency of resonance of an antenna circuit is called the *fundamental frequency of the antenna.*   The value of the fundamental frequency will vary with the length and height of the antenna and should be of such a value that it corresponds to the frequency range of the radio waves to be received.   For best results, the electrical characteristics of an antenna circuit, whether it be used for broadcast, short-wave, or ultra-high-frequency reception, should be such that its fundamental frequency will be slightly higher than the maximum frequency for which it is to be used.

3-4. Variable Inductance Tuning.   *Tuning.*   The antenna circuit of Example 3-1 was found to have a fundamental frequency of 1590 kc.   If it were used in a circuit similar to Fig. 3-8, it would be possible to receive the signal from a station transmitting at 1590 kc.   In order to receive the signals of any other stations, it is necessary to change the resonant frequency of the receiving circuit. This may be done by varying either the capacitance or the inductance of the antenna circuit. The process of selecting the signals from any one particular station is called *tuning*.

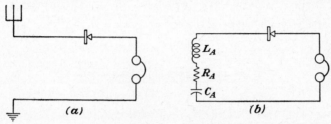

FIG. 3-8.—A simple crystal receiver circuit. (*a*) Circuit diagram showing the antenna, crystal detector, earphones, and ground, (*b*) the equivalent circuit.

Tuning can therefore be accomplished by adjusting the antenna circuit so that its frequency of resonance is the same as that of the station that is to be heard.

Example 3-2. What frequency of resonance would the receiving circuit in Example 3-1 have, if a 450-μh inductance is connected in series with the antenna circuit as shown in Fig. 3-9?

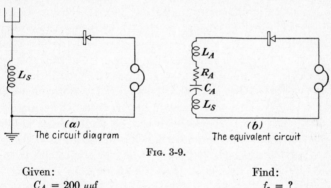

(*a*)
The circuit diagram

(*b*)
The equivalent circuit

FIG. 3-9.

Given: Find:
$\quad C_A = 200 \ \mu\mu f$ $\quad f_r = ?$
$\quad L_A = 50 \ \mu h$
$\quad L_S = 450 \ \mu h$

Solution:

$$L_T = L_A + L_S = 50 + 450 = 500 \ \mu h$$
$$f_r = \frac{159}{\sqrt{L_T C_A}} = \frac{159}{\sqrt{500 \times 200 \times 10^{-6}}} = 503 \ \text{kc}$$

If the 450-μh coil is made adjustable (Fig. 3-2) so that any amount of inductance from zero to 450 μh can be connected in series with the antenna circuit, the receiver can then be tuned for any frequency between 503 and 1590 kc.

Slide-wire Tuning Coil. A simple variable inductance coil consists of a number of turns of wire wound about a cylindrical form. A narrow band of insulation, approximately $\frac{1}{4}$ inch wide, is removed along the full length of the coil. A brass bar is mounted along the entire length of the coil and a sliding contact with spring action is placed on this bar so that contact can be made between the bar and any turn of wire. This type of

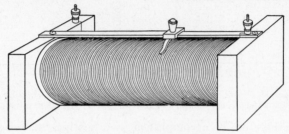

Fig. 3-10.—A slide-wire tuning coil.

variable inductance was used in the early stages of radio development, and Fig. 3-10 is an illustration of a slide-wire tuning coil.

Variometer. The slide-wire tuning coil is not very efficient because the contact between the slider and the coil turns in time becomes poor owing to oxidation and because the spring loses its tension with use. A more efficient method has been developed by using the principles of mutual inductance. Two coils, one stationary and the other movable,

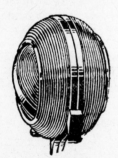

are connected in series. The movable coil is so mounted that it is free to rotate inside of the stationary coil. This type of unit is called a *variometer* and is shown in Fig. 3-11. The inductance of the variometer can be varied from minimum to maximum by varying the position of the movable coil. By connecting the two coils in series so that they are either aiding or opposing, a wide range of inductances may be obtained (see Art. 2-5). Another method of increasing the range of inductance of the variometer is to provide a series

Fig. 3-11.—A variometer.

of taps taken off the stationary coil at various numbers of turns and connect them to the contacts of a rotary switch.

The circuit diagram of a simple crystal receiving circuit using a variometer is quite similar to that for one using a slide-wire tuning coil. Figure 3-12 shows the connections necessary for a circuit using a variometer having a tapped secondary.

3-5. Variable Capacitance Tuning. Instead of varying the inductance and keeping the capacitance of the antenna circuit constant, the capacitance may be varied and the inductance kept constant. A simple crystal receiver circuit using a variable capacitor for tuning is shown in Fig. 3-13a. When the capacitor is adjusted so that its rotor plates are completely out of mesh, the capacitance is theoretically zero. With the capacitor in this position, no capacitance is added to the circuit, and therefore it will tune to the same frequency as it would without the capacitor.

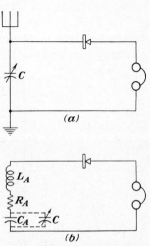

(a)

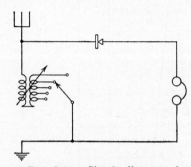

Fig. 3-12.—Circuit diagram of a simple crystal receiver using a variometer having a tapped secondary coil.

(b)

Fig. 3-13.—A simple crystal receiver circuit using a variable capacitor for tuning. (a) The circuit diagram, (b) the equivalent circuit.

If the capacitance of the circuit is increased by adding a capacitor in parallel, the frequency of resonance is decreased in the same manner as by adding an inductance in series with the circuit.

Example 3-3. What capacitance must the variable capacitor in Fig. 3-13a have if it is to be used with the antenna circuit of Example 3-1 and provide the same frequency range?

Given:

$$L_A = 50 \ \mu h$$
$$C_A = 200 \ \mu\mu f$$
Frequency range = 503 to 1590 kc

Find:

$$C = ?$$

Solution:

Using Eq. (2-50):

$$C_T = \frac{25{,}300}{f_r^2 L_A} = \frac{25{,}300}{503 \times 503 \times 50} = 0.002 \ \mu f$$
$$C = C_T - C_A = 0.002 - 0.0002 = 0.0018 \ \mu f$$

3-6. Two-circuit Tuner. *Method of Isolating the Resistance in the Antenna Circuit.* In the receiving circuits just discussed, the antenna circuit was a part of the tuning circuit. The effect of the inductance and the capacitance upon the tuning circuit has been described but the effect of the resistance has not yet been mentioned.   In Art. 2-23 it was shown that resistance in a series tuned circuit decreases the current flow and broadens its tuning.   This is also illustrated by the curves *A*, *B*, and *C* of Fig. 3-14.   These curves represent a series tuned circuit with three different values of circuit resistance, but with each circuit tuned to a resonant frequency of 1500 kc.   The circuit with the least resistance,

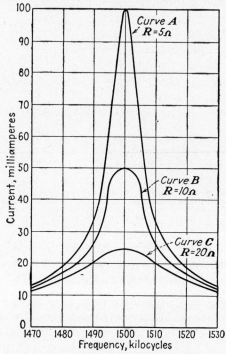

Fig. 3-14.—Curves showing the effect of resistance upon the tuning circuit.

represented by curve *A*, provides a higher signal current and sharper tuning than the circuits represented by curves *B* and *C*.

By using the transformer principle, the resistance of the antenna circuit can be isolated from the tuning circuit.   This is done by connecting the primary winding of the transformer between the antenna and the ground and the secondary winding to the detector and earphones.   It should be noted that a variable capacitor is connected across the secondary winding in order to tune the circuit and that the detector and earphones are then connected to the circuit in the same manner as in the circuits previously discussed.   This type of tuning circuit is called a two-circuit tuner, and Fig. 3-15 shows a wiring diagram of such a circuit.

The two-circuit tuner provides better selectivity and a higher signal current output than the methods previously described.

The magnetic field about the primary winding will vary in accordance with the high-frequency voltage varia-
tions induced in the antenna circuit. This magnetic field links the secondary winding and sets up an induced voltage that corresponds to the variations of voltage in the antenna circuit. The variable capacitor and the secondary winding of the transformer form a series resonant circuit, whose frequency of resonance is determined by the capacitance of the variable capacitor and the inductance of the secondary winding of the transformer.

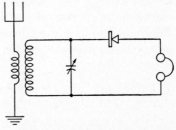

FIG. 3-15.—Circuit diagram of a simple crystal receiver using a two-circuit tuner and a variable capacitor.

Example 3-4. A variable capacitor having a capacitance of 250 $\mu\mu$f is used in a radio receiver to tune the secondary of the r-f transformer to 500 kc. What value of inductance must the secondary winding have?

Given:
$$C = 250 \ \mu\mu\text{f}$$
$$f_r = 500 \text{ kc}$$

Find:
$$L_S = ?$$

Solution:

Using Eq. (2-49)

$$L_S = \frac{25{,}300}{f_r{}^2 C} = \frac{25{,}300}{500 \times 500 \times 250 \times 10^{-6}} = 404.6 \ \mu\text{h}$$

Ratio of Primary and Secondary Voltages. The ratio of the voltages across the primary and secondary windings of an r-f transformer used in a tuning circuit will not be equal to the ratio of the number of turns alone. The voltage ratio is dependent upon the ratio of the number of turns, the coefficient of coupling, and the Q of the tuned circuit. In Art. 2-20 it was shown that at resonance the voltage across the inductor of a series tuned circuit is Q times greater than the applied voltage. Since the secondary is part of a series tuned circuit (see Art. 2-19) and since its circuit Q is generally high, it can be seen that the secondary voltage will be much higher than that resulting from transformer action alone. This gain in voltage is another advantage of the two-circuit tuner.

3-7. LC Tables. Observation of the equation for finding the resonant frequency of a tuned circuit [Eq. (2-48)] shows that the frequency of resonance is dependent upon the product of two variable quantities, namely, the inductance L and the capacitance C. It can be further observed that for each value of the product of L times C there can be only one frequency at which resonance occurs, and conversely there can be only one LC product for each resonant frequency.

The values of the LC product for frequencies between 300 kc and 600 mc are arranged in tabular form in Appendix XIV. In this table L is expressed in microhenries, C in microfarads, and f in kilocycles. Use of this table simplifies the calculations necessary to determine the frequency of resonance when either the inductance or the capacitance of a tuned circuit is known.

Example 3-5. If the inductance of a tuned circuit is 100 μh what value of capacitance is required to produce resonance at 3000 kc?

Given:
$$L = 100 \ \mu h$$
$$f_r = 3000 \text{ kc}$$

Find:
$$C = ?$$

Solution:

$$LC = 0.002811 \text{ (from Appendix XIV)}$$
$$C = \frac{LC}{L} = \frac{0.002811}{100} = 0.00002811 \ \mu f = 28.11 \ \mu\mu f$$

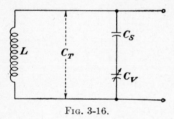

Fig. 3-16.

Example 3-6. A tuned circuit having an inductance of 290 μh is resonant at 500 kc when its variable capacitor is set at its maximum value of 350 $\mu\mu$f. What value of capacitance must be connected in series with the variable capacitor in order that the circuit will be resonant at 1500 kc when the variable capacitor is set at its maximum value?

Given:
$$L = 290 \ \mu h$$
$$f_r = 1500 \text{ kc}$$
$$C = 350 \ \mu\mu f$$

Find:
$$C_S = ?$$

Solution:

$$LC = 0.01124 \text{ (from Appendix XIV)}$$
$$C_T = \frac{LC}{L} = \frac{0.01124}{290} = 0.0000388 \ \mu f = 38.8 \ \mu\mu f$$

Using Eq. (2-24b)

$$C_S = \frac{C_T C}{C - C_T} = \frac{38.8 \times 350}{350 - 38.8} = 43.3 \ \mu\mu f$$

3-8. Crystal Detectors. *Detector Action.* In the discussion on the functions of a receiver, it was stated that the purpose of a detector is to separate the audio-frequency signal wave from the modulated carrier wave. The manner in which this is accomplished may be seen from Fig. 3-17. Curve *a* represents the modulated wave as it is transmitted by the broadcasting station and also as it is received by the radio receiver. This is also a typical representation of the output of the tuning circuit. The form of the sound wave is represented by the envelope formed by

joining the peaks of each individual cycle of the modulated wave. This
envelope is the same for both halves of the cycle but is opposite in direction. Therefore, in order to obtain the sound wave either half of the
alternating current cycle may be used.

A crystal offers very little resistance to current flowing into it and a
very high resistance to current flowing out of it. Crystals can therefore
be used as rectifiers of alternating currents and, since detection is a process
of rectification, they can be used as detectors. Curves *b* and *c* of Fig.
3-17 represent the wave after it has been rectified.

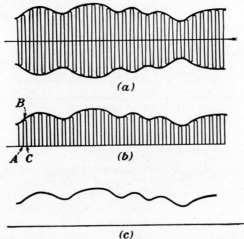

(a)

(b)

(c)

FIG. 3-17.—Waveform of a radio signal at various stages in a receiver. (*a*) As received
by the antenna, (*b*) rectified current waveform at the detector, (*c*) average current output
from the detector.

Construction and Operation of a Crystal Detector. The crystal detector
generally consists of a crystal and a very fine wire called a *catwhisker*.
In order to hold the crystal rigid, it is mounted in a metal alloy having a
very low melting point. The catwhisker is fastened to an adjustable arm
pivoted so that it can make contact with any part of the crystal. Various
mineral substances such as galena, carborundum, silicon, iron pyrites,
etc., may be used as the crystal, the most popular being galena and
carborundum.

When a high-frequency modulated voltage is applied to the crystal
detector, the catwhisker and crystal are alternately made positive and
negative for each half-cycle. When the crystal is made positive, the free
electrons are attracted to it, and since its resistance is very low, current
will flow into the crystal during this half-cycle. When the catwhisker
is made positive, it attempts to draw the free electrons to it, and, since
the resistance of the crystal is very high when current attempts to flow

out of it, very little or no current will flow during this half-cycle. This action is repeated for each cycle of the high-frequency alternating current applied to the detector. The resultant wave is shown in Fig. 3-17b. The high-frequency varying current will therefore flow in only one direction. A small amount of current may flow in the opposite direction, the amount varying with the quality of the crystal, but it is generally ignored since its ratio to the rectified current is small. A good crystal detector will almost entirely eliminate the flow of current in one direction.

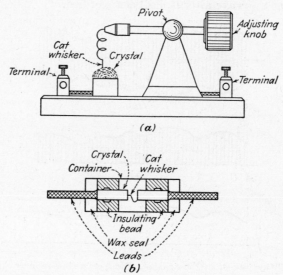

Fig. 3-18.—Crystal detectors. (a) Adjustable type, (b) sealed fixed-position type.

3-9. Audible Device. Since the human ear does not respond to variations in electric currents or voltages, these variations must be converted to sound waves. The ordinary telephone receiver could be used for this purpose but was found to be too heavy and inconvenient. A modified construction that is much lighter in weight and that has two earpieces is used. It is known by such names as headset, earphones, watchcase receiver, phones, etc.

Construction of Earphones. Earphones operate on the electromagnetic principle, and the construction of both earpieces is the same. Figure 3-19b is a cross-section diagram showing the construction of a typical earphone. Two permanent magnets, N and S, are used as cores for the coils C_1 and C_2. A curved permanent magnet D connects these two pole pieces and forms a U-shaped magnet, which provides more uniform action than two single magnets. Each coil is wound with several thousand turns of very small insulated copper wire, generally No. 40 or smaller.   The two coils are connected in series so that the signal current will pass through both windings.   The magnetic field produced by this current will either aid or oppose the constant field of the permanent magnet, depending on the direction in which the current flows through the coils.   A thin, flexible, soft-iron diaphragm E, approximately 0.005 inch thick, is mounted above the pole pieces and very close to them. The edge of the diaphragm rests on the case A and is held fixed by the cap B.

Operation of Earphones with Alternating Current.   When no current flows through the coils, the magnetism of the pole pieces attracts the diaphragm and bends it slightly.   This initial deflection is shown as position 1 in Fig. 3-19b.   If an alternating current is caused to flow through the coils, this force of attraction will be increased for one half

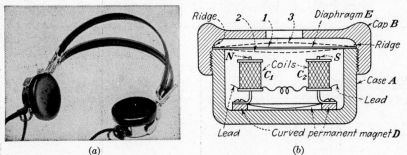

(a)   (b)

FIG. 3-19.—Earphones.   (a) A set of earphones, (b) cross-section view showing the construction of an earphone.

of the cycle and decreased during the other half.   During the half-cycle when the current flowing aids the magnetic field of the permanent magnet, the diaphragm will be attracted to position 2.   When the current is reversed its field opposes the permanent magnet's original field and the force of attraction is decreased to a value less than that required to produce the initial deflection.   The diaphragm will therefore spring to position 3.   At the end of the cycle no current is flowing so the diaphragm returns to position 1.

The diaphragm therefore makes a complete vibration for each cycle of an alternating current.   Its motion will depend on the variation of current flowing through the coils.   The rapid vibration of the diaphragm sets the surrounding air into motion, and sound waves will be produced. If the frequency of the current flowing through the coils is within the audible range, the sound waves produced by the vibrations of the diaphragm (which are of the same frequency) may be heard by the human ear.

Operation of Earphones with Varying Unidirectional Current. It is not necessary to have alternating current flowing through the coils to produce vibrations of the diaphragm. A varying unidirectional current will cause the diaphragm to vibrate in the same manner that the unidirectional current varies. By referring to Fig. 3-17*b* it can be seen that at the instant *A* no current is flowing from the detector and the diaphragm will remain at its initial deflection. At the instant *B* the maximum

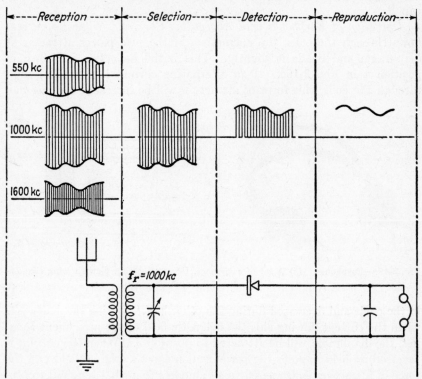

Fig. 3-20.—Diagram of a crystal detector receiving circuit and the type of current flowing through each of its parts.

amount of current is flowing and the strength of the pole pieces will be increased; the diaphragm is then deflected to position 2. At the instant *C* the current flow is again zero and the diaphragm should return to its initial deflection. The inertia of the diaphragm is too great to follow these rapid variations in current changes, hence before the diaphragm has a chance to return to its initial deflection, the current is again forcing it in the opposite direction. The diaphragm of the audible device, therefore, is not actuated by the instantaneous variations in current indicated by the envelope formed by joining the peak values of each cycle, but by the average of these instantaneous currents. The curve shown at *c* in Fig. 3-17 is identical in every respect to the ones in *a* and *b* except for intensity. A small capacitor is generally connected across the earphones to provide a low impedance path for the r-f currents. Figure 3-20 shows the complete circuit diagram for a crystal detector circuit and the type of signal current flowing through each of its parts.

Action of the Radio-frequency By-pass Capacitor. The small capacitor connected across the earphones provides an easy path for the r-f currents and thus allows only the varying direct current to flow through the earphones. It also increases the strength of the signal current flowing through the audible device, which is accomplished in the following manner. The capacitor is charged during the half-cycle that current flows from the detector and discharges during the half-cycle when no current flows. Since it cannot discharge the current through the crystal it must discharge it through the earphones. This action causes current to flow through the earphones during the interval when no current is flowing from the crystal. It thereby maintains a varying unidirectional current flow through the phones, the value of which is almost equivalent to the peak value of the radio-frequency variations in current. This capacitor therefore eliminates the radio-frequency pulsations and increases the audio-frequency voltage across the phones. This capacitor should not be too large, otherwise it will by-pass the audio-frequency currents as well as the radio-frequency currents.

The use of earphones is inconvenient for radio sets in the home since under this condition only one person at a time can listen to the radio program. In order that more than one person may listen to the radio and at the same time enjoy the comforts of the home, it becomes necessary to amplify the signals so that they can operate a loudspeaker. As the vacuum tube provides an excellent means of amplifying the currents, circuits have been developed to provide amplification by use of these tubes. It is thus essential to understand the theory and operation of vacuum tubes, which is presented in the following chapters.

BIBLIOGRAPHY

DEXTER, GUY, Emergency Radio Receivers, *Radio News*, January, 1943.
GHIRARDI, A. A., *Radio Physics Course*, Murray Hill Books, Inc., New York.
MANLY, H. P., *Drake's Cyclopedia of Radio and Electronics*, Frederick J. Drake & Company, Chicago.
WATSON, H. M., WELCH, H. E., and EBY, G. S., *Understanding Radio*, McGraw-Hill Book Company, Inc., New York.

QUESTIONS

1. How do the basic operations of a simple crystal receiver compare with those of a complex multitube modern receiver?

2. Name the four essential functions of a receiver.

3. Explain briefly each of the four essential functions of a receiver.

4. Define antenna. Name and describe the construction of three common types of antenna.

5. What factors determine the power induced in an antenna?

6. How do the power and voltage at a receiving antenna compare with the power and voltage at the transmitting antenna?

7. Describe three factors that must be taken into consideration when constructing a receiving antenna.

8. What is the advantage of the loop antenna?

9. What is meant by the fundamental frequency of an antenna?

10. What factor determines the desired electrical characteristics of the antenna circuit?

11. Explain the principle of variable inductance tuning.

12. Explain the advantages and disadvantages of varying the inductance by use of (*a*) a slide-wire tuner, (*b*) a variometer.

13. Explain the principle of variable capacitance tuning.

14. Describe the two-circuit tuner.

15. Describe two advantages of the two-circuit tuner. Explain how each of the advantages is obtained.

16. What is meant by the *LC* product? What is the purpose of the *LC* tables?

17. What is the purpose of the detector? Explain its action.

18. What property does a crystal possess that makes it possible to use the crystal as a detector?

19. Explain the operation of a crystal detector when a high-frequency modulated voltage is applied to it.

20. Explain the basic principle of operation of the earphones.

21. Explain the operation of an earphone when the following types of current are flowing in its coils: (*a*) alternating current, (*b*) varying unidirectional current.

22. What is the purpose of connecting a capacitor in parallel with the earphones?

23. Explain the action of the r-f by-pass capacitor.

24. Should the capacitance of the r-f by-pass capacitor be large or small? Why?

PROBLEMS

1. The inductance of an antenna circuit is equal to 60 μh and its capacitance is equal to 188 $\mu\mu$f. What is the resonant frequency of this antenna circuit?

2. The antenna of Prob. 1 is reconstructed so that its inductance is reduced to 40 μh and its capacitance is increased to 282 $\mu\mu$f. What is the resonant frequency of this antenna circuit?

3. It is desired that the fundamental frequency of an antenna circuit be equal to 15,000 kc. If the capacitance of the antenna circuit is equal to 22.5 $\mu\mu$f, what value of inductance is required?

4. It is desired that the fundamental frequency of an antenna circuit be equal to 6000 kc. If the inductance of the antenna circuit is equal to 8 μh, what value of capacitance is required?

5. The resonant frequency of an antenna circuit having an inductance of 40 μh is equal to 1600 kc. What is the capacitance of this circuit?

6. The resonant frequency of an antenna circuit having a capacitance of 140 $\mu\mu$f is equal to 1.6 mc. What is the inductance of this circuit?

7. The capacitance of an antenna circuit is equal to 50 $\mu\mu$f and its inductance is 5.12 μh. What is its resonant frequency?

8. What resonant frequency will the antenna circuit of Prob. 1 have if a 390-μh inductance coil is connected in series with the antenna circuit?

9. What value of inductance must be connected in series with the antenna circuit of Prob. 2 in order that it will be resonant at 550 kc?

10. What is the resonant frequency of an antenna circuit having a capacitance of 200 $\mu\mu$f and an inductance of 10 μh when a 40-μh inductance coil is connected in series with the antenna circuit?

11. What value of inductance must be connected in series with an antenna circuit having an inductance of 5 μh and a capacitance of 100 $\mu\mu$f in order to make it resonant at 4.1 mc?

12. A variable capacitor is connected in the antenna circuit as shown in Fig. 3-13. The inductance of the antenna circuit is 124 μh and its capacitance is 188 $\mu\mu$f. (*a*) What must the maximum value of the variable capacitor be in order to obtain resonance at 550 kc? (*b*) What is the frequency range of this circuit?

13. Repeat Prob. 12 for an antenna circuit whose inductance is 136 μh and whose capacitance is 281 $\mu\mu$f.

14. A variable capacitor having a maximum capacitance of 320 $\mu\mu$f is connected across the secondary of an r-f transformer to tune the circuit to 500 kc. What value of inductance is required in the secondary winding?

15. It is desired to obtain various frequency bands by using plug-in coils and a variable capacitor whose maximum capacitance is 260 $\mu\mu$f. What value of inductance is required for the secondary of each coil in order to obtain a minimum frequency of (*a*) 500 kc for range *A*, (*b*) 1500 kc for range *B*, (*c*) 4 mc for range *C*?

16. A variable capacitor having a maximum capacitance of 320 $\mu\mu$f is used with a set of three plug-in coils in order to obtain three frequency bands. What value of inductance is required for the secondary of each coil in order to obtain a minimum frequency of (*a*) 550 kc for range *A*, (*b*) 1600 kc for range *B*, (*c*) 4.2 mc for range *C*?

17. The inductance of a resonant circuit is 5.2 μh. (*a*) What value of capacitance is required in this circuit to produce resonance at 5 mc? (*b*) Check the answer by using the *LC* tables.

18. The capacitance of a resonant circuit is 20 $\mu\mu$f. (*a*) What value of inductance is required in this circuit to produce resonance at 30 mc? (*b*) Check the answer by using the *LC* tables.

19. A tuned circuit having an inductance of 328 μh is resonant at 550 kc when its variable capacitor is at its maximum value of 260 $\mu\mu$f. What value of capacitance must be connected in series with the variable capacitor in order that the circuit will be resonant at 1500 kc when its maximum capacitance is being used?

20. A variable capacitor having a maximum capacitance of 350 $\mu\mu$f is connected across the secondary of a radio-frequency transformer in order to tune the circuit to a minimum frequency of 550 kc. (*a*) What value of inductance is required in the secondary circuit? (*b*) What is the maximum frequency of the tuning circuit if its minimum capacitance is 25 $\mu\mu$f?

CHAPTER IV

VACUUM TUBES

The vacuum tube is often referred to as the heart of radio because of the vital part it plays in the operation of radio receivers and transmitters. As the energy of a transmitted wave varies approximately as the inverse of the square of the distance between the transmitter and receiver, the signals from early transmitters did not have sufficient energy to actuate the earphones of receivers many miles away. Engineers knew that, in order to increase the range of radio communication, it would be necessary to develop some method that would make it possible to strengthen the signal picked up at the receiver. The vacuum tube furnished this needed means of amplification and is used in all modern installations. The tube receives the small amount of signal energy available and by its action, and with the aid of the receiver's power supply, delivers a much greater amount of energy. The energy delivered by the tube will be a magnified replica of the signal received.

In addition to its use as an amplifier, the vacuum tube has many other uses such as generating, controlling, or rectifying voltages over a wide range of frequencies. The importance of the vacuum tube lies in its ability to operate efficiently over a wide range of frequencies and to control almost instantaneously the flow of millions of electrons. Vacuum tubes have a large variety of uses in industrial equipment; in fact the field of electronic devices is practically unlimited.

4-1. Edison Effect. While experimenting with the incandescent lamp, Thomas A. Edison found that the carbon filaments burned out quite rapidly. In order to remedy this fault, he constructed a special lamp in which he placed an additional electrode (see Fig. 4-1). The filament was heated by the current flowing from the generator. The additional electrode, with a galvanometer connected in series, was connected first to the positive terminal of the generator and then to the negative. When the electrode was connected to the positive terminal (Fig. 4-1a), the galvanometer indicated a current flow from the plate to the filament, but when the electrode was connected to the negative terminal (Fig. 4-1b), no current flow was indicated on the galvanometer. This phenomenon is known as the *Edison effect*. Edison was interested mainly in the incandescent lamp, and therefore the now important Edison effect appeared merely as a memorandum in his laboratory notes.

150

Professor J. A. Fleming of England later conducted experiments with the incandescent lamp and in one of his earlier experiments showed that, if the cold electrode is heated to incandescence, an electric current may be made to flow through the vacuum by use of an external battery. Fleming succeeded in producing a curve showing the relation between the voltage across the lamp and the current flowing through the vacuum. In his search for a means of rectifying high-frequency alternating currents, Fleming utilized the principles of the Edison effect and developed what he referred to as an *oscillation valve*.   He also proved that a unidirectional current would flow in the cold electrode circuit even if an alternating current were used to heat the filament.   By this rectifying action, he was able to use the tube as a detector of radio waves.

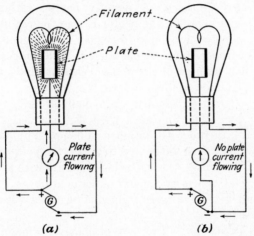

Fig. 4-1.—Edison effect. (*a*) Plate connected to the positive terminal of the generator (*b*) plate connected to the negative terminal of the generator.

In 1905 Fleming patented the vacuum tube, then called the *Fleming valve*.   This tube, which consisted of a filament and a plate, is the simplest type of vacuum tube is still used although it is now commonly referred to as *a diode*.   Many present-day receivers use a diode as a detector, and the rectifier tubes in a-c operated receivers are also diodes.

4-2. The Cathode. *Purpose of the Cathode.*   All matter is made up of molecules, each molecule containing one or more atoms and each atom containing a number of electrons and protons.   When any substance is heated, the speed of the electrons revolving about their nucleus is increased and some electrons acquire sufficient speed to break away from the surface of the material and go off into space.   This action, which is accelerated when the substance is heated in a vacuum, is utilized in radio tubes to produce the necessary electron supply.   When used for this purpose, the substance is called the *cathode*. All vacuum tubes contain a cathode and one or more electrodes mounted in an evacuated envelope, which may be a glass bulb or a compact metal shell.

Purpose of the Heater. The cathode is an essential part of a vacuum tube because it supplies the electrons necessary for its operation. The electrons are generally released from the cathode by the heating of the cathode. The operation of the heater in a vacuum tube is based on the principle that a conductor will radiate heat when an electric current flows through it. The amount of heat that is radiated is dependent on the material of which the conductor is made and the amount of current flowing in the conductor. The source of power used to supply current for heating the cathode is generally referred to as the *A power supply*.

Directly Heated Cathodes. A directly heated cathode, called the *filament type*, is one in which the heater is also the cathode. Materials that are good conductors are found to be poor electron emitters; therefore directly heated cathodes must be operated at high temperatures in order to emit a sufficient number of electrons. Various kinds of materials are used in the construction of directly heated cathodes.

TUNGSTEN. Tungsten filaments are made from pure tungsten; in comparison to the other materials used as cathodes, tungsten is the poorest emitter. In order to obtain a sufficient number of electrons, this type of cathode must be heated to a high temperature, about 4300° Fahrenheit. This causes the cathode to operate with a white glow and also requires a relatively large amount of filament power. It is, however, very rugged and is used in large transmitting tubes where a high plate voltage is necessary.

THORIATED TUNGSTEN. This type of filament is made from tungsten bars that have been impregnated with thorium. Because of the presence of thorium, the electron emission for a given filament temperature is many times greater than for pure tungsten. Less power is required to heat the filament and the thoriated tungsten is therefore more economical than pure tungsten. It is generally operated at temperatures of approximately 3600° Fahrenheit and produces a yellow glow at the cathode. Its main disadvantage is that the thorium wears off the surface of the cathode and it then must be reactivated in order to bring more thorium from the inside of the cathode to its surface. Thoriated tungsten filaments are generally used for heating power tubes.

OXIDE COATING. The oxide-coated filament is made by applying successive coatings of calcium, barium, or strontium oxides, used separately or mixed, on a nickel-alloy wire. The oxide is baked on the filament after each application and a number of coats are applied in order to form a relatively thick layer on the cathode. It has long life, is very efficient, and requires relatively little filament power to emit a sufficient number of electrons. Oxide-coated filaments are generally operated at about 2200° Fahrenheit and produce a dull red or orange glow at the cathode. They cannot be used for gas-filled tubes as the gas ions present in such a tube are very heavy. These gas ions are in violent motion and such ions as strike the cathode will knock off some of the oxide coating. Coated filaments are used only for receiving tubes and must be operated at or near rated voltage.

Directly heated cathodes require a comparatively small amount of heating power and are used in almost all the tubes designed for battery

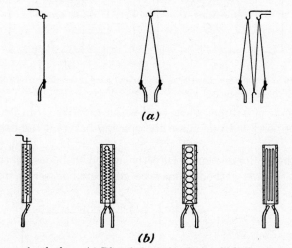

(a)

(b)

Fig. 4-2.—Types of cathodes.   (a) Directly heated cathodes, (b) indirectly heated cathodes.

operation. Alternating-current-operated tubes seldom use the filament-type cathode.

Indirectly Heated Cathodes. Certain materials are better emitters than others, that is, they emit more electrons yet require less heat. Most of these materials are poor conductors and therefore cannot be used for directly heated cathodes. An *indirectly heated cathode* is one in which the emitting material is coated on a thin metal sleeve. This cathode is heated by radiation from a heater placed inside the sleeve and insulated from it. The advantages of this type of cathode are:

1. A material that will radiate heat with the least amount of current can be used for the heater; therefore a material that is a good electron emitter can be used for the cathode.

2. The insulation between the heater and cathode and the shielding effect of the sleeve can be used to minimize the a-c hum and other elec-

trical interference.   These disturbances enter the tube's heating circuit when the heater is operated from an a-c power supply (see Fig. 4-3b).

3. The regulation of a rectifier tube can be improved because it is possible to decrease the spacing between the cathode and the plate.

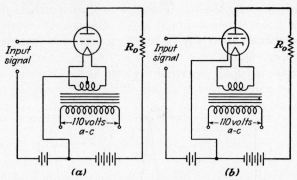

FIG. 4-3.—Method of isolating the alternating current used to supply current for the heater from entering other circuits.   (a) Directly heated cathode, (b) indirectly heated cathode.

4. The gain of a tube, when used as an amplifier, can be increased because it is possible to decrease the spacing between the cathode and the grid.

4-3. Cathode Connection.   Directly heated cathodes, or the heaters of indirectly heated cathodes, may be connected in series, parallel, or

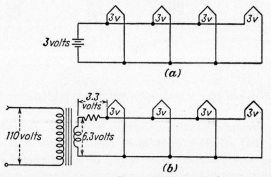

FIG. 4-4.—Circuits with heaters (or directly heated cathodes) connected in parallel. (a) Voltage of the heaters equal to the voltage of the power supply, (b) using a dropping resistor to compensate for the difference in power supply and heater voltages.

series-parallel.   The choice of connection used is determined by the number of tubes, the voltage of the power supply, the voltage of the heaters, the current rating of the heaters, and the circuit design.

Dropping-resistor Connections.   When the rated voltage of each heater is equal to or slightly less than the supply voltage, they are connected in parallel (Fig. 4-4a).   If the voltage of the power supply is

fixed, it may be brought down to the rated value of the tubes by connecting a fixed resistor in series with the power supply (Fig. 4-4*b*). If one
or more tubes are rated at a lower voltage than the others, a dropping
resistor is connected in series with its heater or filament to adjust it to the
rated voltage (see Fig. 4-5).

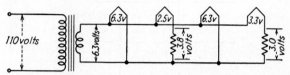

FIG. 4-5.—A separate dropping resistor may be used to compensate for the difference
between the voltage of the power supply and the voltage required by each heater.

In radio receivers that do not use transformers for their power supply,
the heaters are generally connected in series. In many modern receivers
the types of tubes used are selected so that the sum of the rated heater
voltages is equal to the applied voltage. In some receivers the sum of

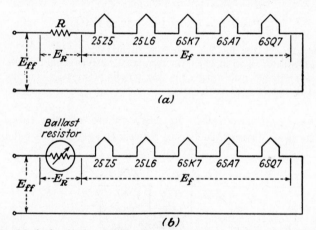

FIG. 4-6.—Methods of using a series dropping resistor in order to operate the heaters
directly from a 110-volt line. (*a*) With a fixed resistor, (*b*) with an automatic ballast-
regulating resistor.

the rated heater voltages is less than the line voltage. In the latter case,
a resistor is connected in series with the heater circuit to cause a drop in
voltage equal to the difference between the line voltage and the sum of
the rated heater voltages; this is illustrated in Fig. 4-6*a*.

Example 4-1. A radio receiver contains the following tubes: 6SA7, 6SK7, 6SQ7,
25L6, and a 25Z5. If the heaters of these tubes are connected in series, what value
resistor must be connected in series with the heater circuit in order to operate the
receiver from a 110-volt line?

Given: Find:
  6SA7, 6SK7, 6SQ7, $R = ?$
  25L6, 25Z5
Solution:

From Appendix XV

Tube	Heater voltage	Heater current
6SA7	6.3	0.3
6SK7	6.3	0.3
6SQ7	6.3	0.3
25L6	25	0.3
25Z5	25	0.3
Total	68.9 volts	

$$E_R = E_{ff} - E_f = 110 - 68.9 = 41.1 \text{ volts}$$
$$R = \frac{E_R}{I_f} = \frac{41.1}{0.3} = 137 \text{ ohms}$$
$$P = I^2R = 0.3^2 \times 137 = 12.33 \text{ watts}$$

As resistors are rated for their capacity in mid-air, that is, with unrestricted ventilation, a resistor rated at twice the computed wattage should be used when the ventilation is restricted, as is usually the case in radio receivers. Thus the resistor in Example 4-1 should be rated at 25 watts.

Shunt-resistor Connections. In cases where all the tubes are not rated at the same current, the series resistance necessary is calculated by

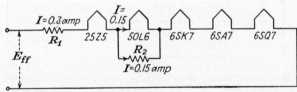

FIG. 4-7.—Use of a shunt resistor to supply the heater of one tube with a current less in amount than the line current.

using the highest current rating. Additional resistors must be connected across the heaters of those tubes of lower current rating in order that all the heaters will draw their rated current (see Fig. 4-7).

Example 4-2. If in Example 4-1 a 50L6 tube is substituted for the 25L6, what value resistor must be used in the line and what value resistor should be connected across the heater of the 50L6 in order that its rated current of 0.15 ampere will flow through the heater?

Given: Find:
    6SA7, 6SK7, 6SQ7, $R_1 = ?$
    50L6, 25Z5. $R_2 = ?$
    Circuit—Fig. 4-7

Solution:

From Appendix XV

Tube	Heater voltage	Heater current
6SA7	6.3	0.3
6SK7	6.3	0.3
6SQ7	6.3	0.3
50L6	50	0.15
25Z5	25	0.3
Total	93.9 volts	

$$R_1 = \frac{E_{R1}}{I_{R1}} = \frac{110 - 93.9}{0.3} = 53.7 \text{ ohms}$$

$$P_{R1} = I_{R1}{}^2 R_1 = 0.3^2 \times 53.7 = 4.833 \text{ watts}$$
$$\text{(Use a 10-watt resistor)}$$

$$R_2 = \frac{E_{R2}}{I_{R2}} = \frac{50}{0.15} = 333 \text{ ohms}$$

$$P_{R2} = I_{R2}{}^2 R_2 = 0.15^2 \times 333 = 7.5 \text{ watts}$$
$$\text{(Use a 15-watt resistor)}$$

Parallel-series Connections. The filaments or heaters of tubes may also be arranged in any parallel-series combination to suit the particular requirements of the tubes and the source of power supply used. For example, if a number of tubes with 6-volt heaters are to be operated from a 12-volt battery, two tubes of similarcurrent rating may be connected in series and any number of series-connected pairs may be connected in parallel (see Fig. 4-8).

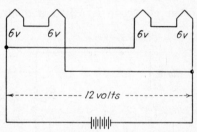

Fig. 4-8.—Parallel-series operation of filaments or heaters.

Automatic Ballast Regulation. In a series filament or heater circuit the amount of current flowing in the circuit varies directly with the voltage. If the line voltage increases, the current in the circuit will increase. If the increase in voltage is such that it causes the current to rise above the rated current of the heater, it may cause unsatisfactory operation and may even burn out the tube. If the line voltage decreases, the current in the circuit will also decrease, thus causing the heaters of all the tubes in the circuit to operate at a lower temperature. A decrease in temperature will decrease the electron emission of the cathode and thereby decrease the output of the tube.

The voltage of the power circuits in most homes is generally 115 volts but may vary from 105 to 125 volts. Dry-cell batteries will supply 1.5 volts when new, but this voltage decreases with age. In order to counteract such variations in supply voltages, some receivers use an automatic ballast-regulating tube in place of the series line dropping resistor (see Fig. 4-6b). Thus, the dropping resistor in Example 4-1 can be replaced by a ballast tube having the same resistance and current rating as the resistor.

The automatic ballast-regulating tube (see Fig. 2-2) consists of an iron wire hermetically sealed in a bulb containing hydrogen or helium. If the line voltage increases, it causes the current to increase. When the current flowing through the automatic ballast-regulating tube increases, it causes an increase in the temperature of the wire. The increase in temperature causes an increase in resistance, which regulates the current and prevents it from rising excessively. An automatic ballast-regulating tube in a battery-operated receiver can reduce the effect of a 36 per cent variation in voltage to an 8 per cent variation in current. In a similar manner, this type of tube when used in a receiver operated from a lighting circuit can reduce the effect of a 20 per cent voltage variation to a 7 per cent variation in current.

4-4. Diodes. *The Plate.* A vacuum tube having a cathode and one other electrode is called a *diode*. The second electrode is called the plate or *anode*. If a voltage is applied to the plate and its polarity is made positive, the electrons emitted from the cathode, being negative, will be attracted to the plate as opposite charges attract one another. These electrons will flow through the external plate battery circuit as indicated by the arrow in Fig. 4-9. This flow of electrons is called the *plate current*. If the polarity of the plate is made negative, the electrons will be forced back to the cathode because like charges repel one another and thus no current will flow in the plate circuit.

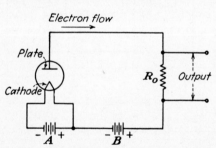

Fig. 4-9.—Circuit diagram of a diode showing the electron flow and the proper connections for the A and B power supplies.

When an alternating current is applied to the plate, its polarity will be positive during every other half-cycle. As electrons will flow to the plate only when it is positive, the current in the plate circuit will therefore flow in only one direction and the current is said to be a *rectified current* (see Fig. 4-10).

Diode rectifiers are used in radio receivers as detectors, and in a-c-operated receivers and transmitters to convert alternating current to direct current. Rectifier tubes having one plate and one cathode are called *half-wave rectifiers* because the rectified current only flows during one-half of the cycle. Typical half-wave rectifier tubes include the type 81, 1V, 12Z3, and 35Z5.

Duo-diodes. Rectifier tubes having two plates and one or two cathodes have their plates connected into the external circuit so that each plate will be positive for opposite halves of the cycle. As one of the plates will always be positive, current will flow continually in the external plate circuit. Tubes of this type are called *full-wave rectifiers* because current will flow in the plate cir-

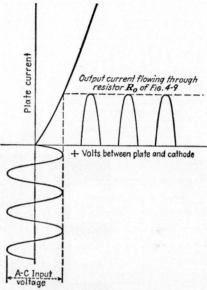

FIG. 4-10.—The diode as a rectifier.

cuit during the entire cycle. One of the first full-wave rectifier tubes used was the type 80; it is very efficient and rugged and is still used. Other typical full-wave rectifier tubes include types 83, 6X5GT, 5Z3, and 5T4.

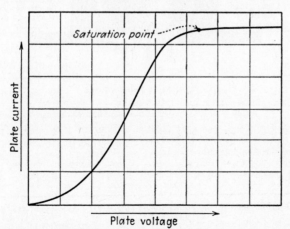

FIG. 4-11.—Variation of plate current with changes in plate voltage.

Space Charge. The number of electrons drawn to the plate depends on the number given off by the cathode and the value of the plate voltage.

If the plate voltage is not high enough to draw off all the electrons emitted by the cathode, those not drawn off will remain in space. These

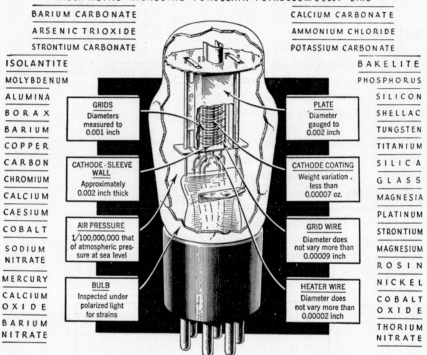

LAVA · MICA · TIN · SODIUM CARBONATE · M O N E L · SILVER OXIDE

SODIUM ALUMINUM FLUORIDE · RESIN (SYNTHETIC) · ETHYL ALCOHOL

LEAD ACETATE · MALACHITE GREEN · GLYCERINE · ZINC CHLORIDE · IRON

MARBLE DUST · WOOD FIBER · STRONTIUM NITRATE · LEAD OXIDE · ZINC OXIDE

MISCH METAL · NIGROSINE · PORCELAIN · PETROLEUM JELLY · ZINC

BARIUM CARBONATE	CALCIUM CARBONATE
ARSENIC TRIOXIDE	AMMONIUM CHLORIDE
STRONTIUM CARBONATE	POTASSIUM CARBONATE

ISOLANTITE	BAKELITE
MOLYBDENUM	PHOSPHORUS
ALUMINA	SILICON
BORAX	SHELLAC
BARIUM	TUNGSTEN
COPPER	TITANIUM
CARBON	SILICA
CHROMIUM	GLASS
CALCIUM	MAGNESIA
CAESIUM	PLATINUM
COBALT	STRONTIUM
SODIUM NITRATE	MAGNESIUM
	ROSIN
MERCURY	NICKEL
CALCIUM OXIDE	COBALT OXIDE
BARIUM NITRATE	THORIUM NITRATE

GRIDS
Diameters measured to 0.001 inch

PLATE
Diameter gauged to 0.002 inch

CATHODE - SLEEVE WALL
Approximately 0.002 inch thick

CATHODE COATING
Weight variation less than 0.00007 oz.

AIR PRESSURE
1/100,000,000 that of atmospheric pressure at sea level

GRID WIRE
Diameter does not vary more than 0.00009 inch

BULB
Inspected under polarized light for strains

HEATER WIRE
Diameter does not vary more than 0.00002 inch

Gases Used in Manufacture

NEON — HYDROGEN — CARBON DIOXIDE — ILLUMINATING GAS
HELIUM — ARGON — NATURAL GAS — NITROGEN — OXYGEN

Elements Entering into the Manufacture

ARGON — ALUMINUM — BORON — BARIUM — CAESIUM — CALCIUM — COPPER — CARBON — CHROMIUM — CHLORINE
COBALT — HYDROGEN — HELIUM — IRIDIUM — IRON — LEAD — MAGNESIUM — MERCURY — MOLYBDENUM
NICKEL — NEON — NITROGEN — OXYGEN — POTASSIUM — PHOSPHORUS — PLATINUM — SODIUM — SILVER
SILICON — STRONTIUM — TUNGSTEN — THORIUM — TANTALUM — TITANIUM — TIN — ZINC — RARE EARTHS

Fig. 4-12.—Materials used in the construction of radio tubes. (*Courtesy of RCA Manufacturing Co., Inc.*)

electrons form a repelling force to the other electrons being given off by the cathode, thus impeding their flow to the plate. This repelling action is called the *space charge*.   Space charge can be reduced in high-vacuum tubes by decreasing the spacing between the plate and cathode.   In gas-filled tubes, space charge is reduced by ionization.

Emission Current.   Increasing the plate voltage will increase the plate current until all the electrons given off by the cathode are drawn to the plate.   Further increase in plate voltage will not increase the plate current, as there are no more electrons that can be drawn to it (see Fig. 4-11).   The point on the curve at which the current has reached its highest value is called the *saturation point,* and the plate current for this condition is called the *saturation current* or *emission current.*

4-5. The Triode.   *Action of the Control Grid.*   When a third electrode is used, the tube is called a *triode.*   This third element is known as the *control grid* and usually consists of a spiral winding or a very fine-mesh

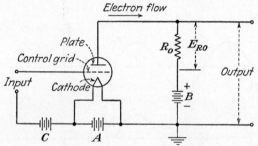

Fɪɢ. 4-13.—Circuit diagram for a triode showing the electron flow and the proper connections for the *A, B,* and *C* power supplies.

screen extending the length of the cathode and placed between the cathode and plate.   The circuit connections and the direction of electron flow for a triode is shown in Fig. 4-13.   If the grid is made more negative than the cathode, it will cause some of the electrons going toward the plate to be repelled by the grid, thus reducing the plate current.   By making the grid still more negative, it is possible to reduce the plate current to zero.   This condition is referred to as *cutoff.*

Grid Bias.   The third electrode is called the *control grid* because it controls the number of electrons allowed to flow from the cathode to the plate.   The source of power used to keep the grid negative is called the *C power supply* and the amount of *negative voltage* used is referred to as the *grid bias.*

Relation between the Grid Bias and the Plate Current.   If a varying signal voltage is applied to the grid, the number of electrons flowing in the plate circuit will vary in the same manner as the signal voltage. This is illustrated by the following example.   The tube used in Fig. 4-13 has a grid bias of 3 volts (Fig. 4-14*b*).   This bias allows a steady plate current I_b to flow (Fig. 4-14d). (See Appendix II for listing of vacuum-tube symbols.) If an alternating signal voltage of 1 volt (Fig.

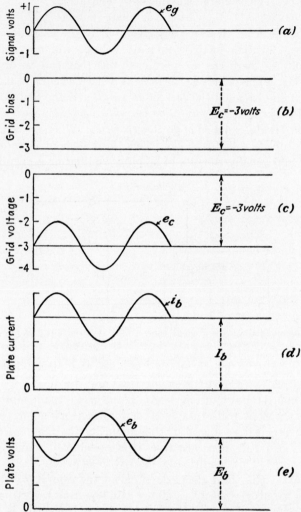

Fig. 4-14.—Illustration of the effect of the signal voltage upon grid voltage and plate current. (*a*) Signal voltage (instantaneous values of the varying component of the grid voltage), (*b*) grid bias (average or quiescent value of the grid voltage), (*c*) grid voltage (instantaneous total grid voltage), (*d*) plate current I_b (average or quiescent value of plate current) and plate current i_b (instantaneous total plate current), (*e*) plate voltage E_b (average or quiescent value of plate voltage) and plate voltage e_b, also output voltage (instantaneous total plate voltage).

4-14a) is impressed across the input terminals of the grid circuit (Fig. 4-13), the voltage on the grid of the tube will vary from -2 to -4 volts, as shown in Fig. 4-14c. As the number of electrons flowing to the plate is controlled by the negative potential on the grid, the plate current will vary in the same manner as the signal voltage. This is illustrated by the varying plate current shown in Fig. 4-14d, maximum plate current flowing when the grid is least negative and minimum plate current flowing when it is most negative.

Phase Relation between the Varying Grid Voltage, Varying Plate Current, and Varying Plate Voltage. It has just been shown that the plate current of a tube will vary in the same manner as the signal voltage that is applied to its grid. It may therefore be stated that the plate current variations are in phase with the grid voltage variations.

The output of the tube circuit shown in Fig. 4-13 is generally taken off at the plate, or top of resistor R_o, and the ground. The voltage available between these two points is equal to the B supply voltage minus the voltage drop at the resistor R_o. If the tube has a grid bias of 3 volts (Fig. 4-14b), a steady plate current I_b will flow (Fig. 4-14d) and the output voltage will have a value indicated as the steady voltage E_b (Fig. 4-14e). When a signal is applied to the grid, the positive portions of the signal voltage will cause an increase in the plate current, which will increase the voltage drop across the output resistor R_o and thus will decrease the output voltage e_b (Fig. 4-14e). The negative portions of the signal voltage will decrease the plate current, reduce the voltage drop across R_o, and increase the output voltage e_b. From this action, it can be seen that an increase in signal voltage will produce a decrease in the output voltage or that a decrease in signal voltage will produce an increase in the output voltage. It may therefore be stated that the output voltage variations are 180 degrees out of phase with the signal voltage variations.

Action of the Grid with a Positive Voltage. If the value of the signal voltage is such that it will make the grid positive, the grid will act in the same manner as a plate and will draw electrons to it, thus causing a current to flow in the grid circuit. This condition can be avoided by using a grid bias whose value is larger than the maximum amount of input signal voltage that is applied.

4-6. Characteristic Curves of a Triode. *Curve and Tabular Representation of Operating Characteristics.* The major operating characteristics of a vacuum tube are used to identify the electrical features and operating values of the tube. These values may be listed in tabular form or plotted on graph paper to form a curve. When given in curve form they are called *characteristic curves.* These curves may be used for determining the performance of a tube under any operating condition. The tube's constants can also be calculated from these curves. Tabular

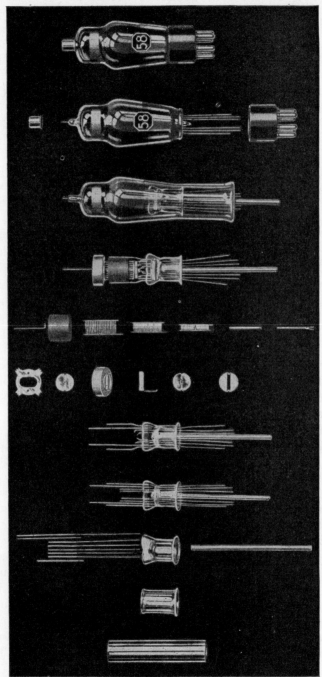

Fig. 4-15.—Structural parts of a typical glass tube.   (Courtesy of RCA Manufacturing Co., Inc.)

form listings as found in most tube manuals (also Appendix XV) are limited, as they list only the values of the characteristics for one or two of the operating conditions commonly used for that particular tube.

Methods Used to Obtain Operating Characteristics. Tube characteristics are obtained from electrical measurements of the tube with definite values of voltage applied to the various electrodes. Characteristic curves may be further classified as to the condition of the circuit when these values are obtained. *Static characteristics* are obtained by varying the d-c voltages applied to the electrodes, and with no load applied to the plate. *Dynamic characteristics* approximate the performance of a tube under actual working conditions. They are obtained by applying an alternating (or signal) voltage to the grid circuit and inserting a load

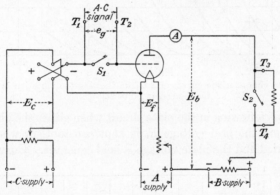

Fig. 4-16.—Diagram of a test circuit for obtaining static or dynamic characteristics for triodes.

resistance in the plate circuit, the d-c voltages on all electrodes being adjusted to the desired values. By varying the load resistance and the d-c voltages on the electrodes, the characteristics for any operating condition of the tube can be obtained. By using the circuit shown in Fig. 4-16, either the static or dynamic characteristics of a triode can be obtained. If static characteristics are desired, switches S_1 and S_2 are closed. For dynamic characteristics, switches S_1 and S_2 are opened, a signal voltage is applied at the input terminals T_1 and T_2, and a load resistance is placed across the output terminals T_3 and T_4. Rated filament voltage can be obtained by adjusting the rheostat in the A power supply. The voltage applied to the plate of the tube may be varied by means of the potentiometer in the B power supply. The voltage on the grid of the tube may be made positive or negative by means of the dpdt reversing switch and its value may be adjusted by varying the potentiometer in the C power supply.

Plate Voltage–Plate Current, and Grid Voltage–Plate Current Character-istic Curves. Values for plotting characteristic curves may be obtained by adjusting the heater or filament voltage to its rated value and record-

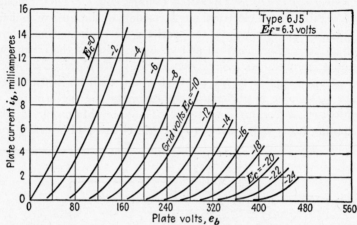

Fig. 4-17.—Plate characteristic curves of a triode showing the variation in plate current for changes in plate voltage.

ing the current i_b flowing in the plate circuit when either the plate voltage e_b is varied and the grid voltage E_c is kept constant, or when the grid voltage is varied and the plate voltage is held constant. Curves showing

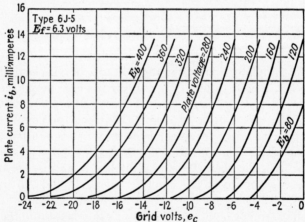

Fig. 4-18.—Transfer characteristic curves showing the variation in plate current for changes in grid voltage. These curves have been cross-plotted from Fig. 4-17.

the variation in plate current for changes in plate voltage with constant steps of grid voltage are called *plate characteristic curves*. A typical set, or family, of these curves, also called $e_b i_b$ or $E_p I_p$ curves, is shown in Fig.

4-17. Curves showing the variation in plate current for changes in grid voltage with constant steps of plate voltage are called *grid-plate transfer characteristic curves*. A typical set or family of these curves, also called $e_c i_b$ or $E_g I_p$ curves, is shown in Fig. 4-18.

Tube Constants. Vacuum-tube characteristics are often referred to as the constants of the tube. The constants most commonly used are the *amplification factor μ, (mu);* the *plate resistance, r_p;* and the *control-grid–plate transconductance, g_m.* Control-grid–plate transconductance is usually referred to as just *transconductance.* Transconductance is also known as *mutual conductance.*

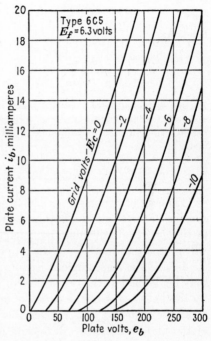

FIG. 4-19.—Plate characteristic curves.

4-7. Amplification Factor. *Definition.* The amplification factor of a tube may be defined as a measure of the relative ability of the grid and the plate to produce an equal change in the plate current. The amplification factor of any tube may be more precisely defined as the ratio of the change in plate voltage to a change in control-grid voltage for a constant value of plate current, with the voltages applied to all other electrodes maintained constant. It is expressed mathematically as

$$\mu = \frac{de_b}{de_c} \; (i_b - \text{constant}) \tag{4-1}$$

where μ = amplification factor
   d = a change or variation in value
   de_b = a change in the instantaneous total plate voltage, volts
   de_c = a change in the instantaneous total control-grid voltage necessary to produce the same effect upon the plate current as would be produced by de_b, volts
   i_b = instantaneous total plate current, amperes

Method of Obtaining the Amplification Factor. The amplification factor may be calculated from values obtained from the plate characteristic curves such as those shown in Fig. 4-19.

Example 4-3. What is the amplification factor of a type 6C5 tube when operated at its normal heater voltage and with a plate voltage of 150 volts and a grid bias of 4 volts?

Given: Find:
    Tube = 6C5 $\mu = ?$
      $e_b = 150$ volts
      $E_c = -4$ volts

Solution:

From Fig. 4-19

$$i_b = 6 \text{ ma} \quad \text{when} \quad e_b = 150 \text{ volts} \quad \text{and} \quad E_c = -4 \text{ volts}$$

Further examination of Fig. 4-19 shows that if the plate voltage is increased from 150 volts to 200 volts, the grid-bias voltage would have to be increased from -4 volts to -6.5 volts in order to maintain the plate current at 6 ma. Thus the amplification factor is

$$\mu = \frac{de_b}{de_c} = \frac{200 - 150}{6.5 - 4} = \frac{50}{2.5} = 20$$

The amplification factor of a tube depends upon the construction and spacing of the electrodes within the tube, especially of the grid. Changes in the grid that will more completely shield the plate from the cathode will produce an increase in the amplification factor.

4-8. Plate Resistance. *Definition.* The plate resistance of a tube may be defined as the resistance to the flow of alternating current offered by the path between the cathode and plate. This is sometimes referred to as the *dynamic plate resistance* or the *a-c plate resistance*. The value of the plate resistance will depend upon the value of the grid and plate voltages being applied to the tube. Mathematically it is defined as the ratio of a change in plate voltage to the corresponding change produced in the plate current with the grid voltage maintained constant, or

$$r_p = \frac{de_b}{di_b} \; (e_c - \text{constant}) \tag{4-2}$$

where r_p = dynamic plate resistance, ohms
    di_b = change in the instantaneous total plate current, amperes
    e_c = instantaneous total grid voltage, volts

Method of Obtaining the Plate Resistance. The plate resistance is obtained by determining the variation in plate current for a specific change in plate voltage with the control-grid voltage maintained at a constant value. The values for calculating the plate resistance can readily be obtained from the plate characteristic curves by constructing a triangle whose base extends equal amounts above and below the operating value of plate voltage as shown in Fig. 4-20.

Example 4-4.   What is the plate resistance of the tube whose characteristic curves are shown in Fig. 4-19, when operated with 150 volts applied to the plate and with a grid bias of 4 volts?

Given: Find:
$$e_b = 150 \text{ volts}$$ $$r_p = ?$$
$$E_c = -4 \text{ volts}$$

Solution:

Using the curve for -4 volts grid, construct a triangle whose base extends 20 volts above and below the operating plate voltage, or from 130 to 170 volts (see Fig. 4-20).

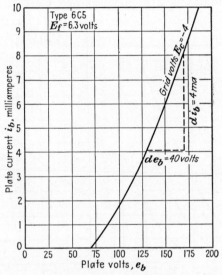

Fig. 4-20.—Method of determining the plate resistance of a tube.   This curve is an enlarged segment of Fig. 4-19.

The altitude of the triangle represents the variation in plate current produced by the change in plate voltage, or 4 ma as indicated on Fig. 4-20.   The plate resistance therefore is

$$r_p = \frac{de_b}{di_b} = \frac{40}{0.004} = 10,000 \text{ ohms}$$

The solution of Example 4-4 gives the dynamic or a-c plate resistance of the tube.   It should be noted that this is not the same value as would be obtained by dividing the operating plate voltage by its corresponding plate current.   Such a value is known as the *static resistance* or the *d-c resistance* of the tube, but it is seldom used in the study of tubes and their circuits.

The dimensions and relative positions of the electrodes of a tube will largely determine the value of its plate resistance.   The plate resistance is sometimes referred to as the *impedance* of the tube, the *internal resistance* of the tube, the *dynamic plate resistance*, or the tube's *a-c resistance*.

4-9. Transconductance. *Definition.* The transconductance of a tube may be defined as the ratio of the change in plate current to a change in the control-grid voltage when all other tube-element voltages are kept constant. This is expressed mathematically as

$$g_m = \frac{di_b}{de_c} \, (e_b - \text{constant}) \tag{4-3}$$

where g_m = transconductance, mhos

e_b = instantaneous total plate voltage, volts

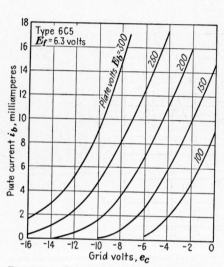

Fig. 4-21.—Grid–plate transfer characteristic curves.

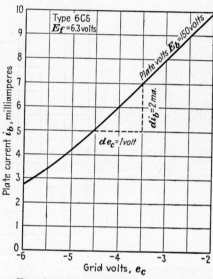

Fig. 4-22.—Method of determining the transconductance of a tube. This curve is an enlarged segment of Fig. 4-21.

Method of Obtaining the Transconductance. The transconductance is obtained by determining the variation in plate current for a specific change in grid voltage with the plate voltage maintained at a constant value. The values for calculating the transconductance can readily be obtained from the grid–plate transfer characteristic curves by constructing a triangle whose base extends equal amounts above and below the operating value of the grid voltage, as shown on Fig. 4-22.

Example 4-5. What is the transconductance of the tube whose characteristics are shown in Fig. 4-21, when operated with 150 volts applied to the plate and with a grid bias of 4 volts?

Given: Find:

     $e_b = 150$ volts $g_m = ?$

     $E_c = -4$ volts

Solution:

Using the curve for 150 volts, construct a triangle whose base extends 0.5 volt above and below the operating grid voltage or from -3.5 to -4.5 volts (see Fig. 4-22). The altitude of the triangle represents the variation in plate current produced by the change in grid voltage, or 2 ma as indicated on Fig. 4-22. The transconductance, therefore, is

$$g_m = \frac{di_b}{de_c} = \frac{0.002}{1} = 0.002 \text{ mho}$$

The unit of conductance is the mho and its name is obtained by spelling ohm backwards. For convenience of numbers, the transconductance is often expressed in micromhos. For instance, the answer to Example 4-5 might be expressed as 2000 micromhos.

(a)   (b)   (c)   (d)

Fig. 4-23.—Development of triodes.   (a) Early DeForest three-element tube, (b) early triode of the type UV-200, (c) early triode using an indirectly heated cathode, (d) modern triode with an indirectly heated cathode and metal tube construction.   (*Courtesy of RCA Manufacturing Co., Inc.*)

The dimensions and relative positions of the electrodes of a tube will largely determine the value of its transconductance. Examination of Eq. (4-3) will show that a tube that produces a relatively large change in plate current for a small change in grid voltage will have a relatively high value of transconductance, and, since such conditions are generally desired, tubes having a high value of transconductance are preferred.

4-10. Relation between Amplification Factor, Plate Resistance, and Transconductance. In each of the three previous articles describing the amplification factor, plate resistance, and transconductance, respectively, it was stated that the particular tube constant being discussed was affected by the construction and spacing of the tube's electrodes. It may further be stated that a definite relation exists between the three constants. This relation is developed mathematically in the following steps:

Step (1)

$$\mu = \frac{de_b}{de_c} \tag{4-1}$$

Step (2)

$$\mu = \frac{de_b}{de_c} \times \frac{di_b}{di_b} \tag{4-4}$$

$$\mu = \frac{di_b}{de_c} \times \frac{de_b}{di_b} \tag{4-4a}$$

Step (3) Substituting Eqs. (4-3) and (4-2) in (4-4a)

$$\mu = g_m r_p \tag{4-5}$$

$$g_m = \frac{\mu}{r_p} \tag{4-5a}$$

$$r_p = \frac{\mu}{g_m} \tag{4-5b}$$

Example 4-6.   What is the transconductance of a type 6SQ7 tube when operated at such values of voltage that its amplification factor is 100 and its dynamic plate resistance is 91,000 ohms?

Given: Find:
    Tube = 6SQ7 $g_m = ?$
     $\mu = 100$
     $r_p = 91{,}000$ ohms
Solution:

$$g_m = \frac{\mu}{r_p} = \frac{100}{91{,}000} = 0.0011 \text{ mho, or } 1100 \text{ micromhos}$$

Example 4-7.   What is the plate resistance of a type 6C5 tube when operated at such values of voltage that its amplification factor is 20 and its transconductance is 2000 micromhos?

Given: Find:
    Tube = 6C5 $r_p = ?$
     $\mu = 20$
     $g_m = 2000$ micromhos
Solution:

$$r_p = \frac{\mu}{g_m} = \frac{20}{2000 \times 10^{-6}} = 10{,}000 \text{ ohms}$$

4-11. Voltage Amplification per Stage.   The maximum theoretical value of voltage amplification per amplifier stage is indicated by the amplification factor of the tube.   However, this theoretical maximum value cannot be obtained in practical amplifier circuits, as the voltage amplification is limited by the plate resistance of the tube and the impedance of the load.

The signal output of the tube may be taken as the voltage drop across the output or load resistor R_o (see Fig. 4-24). According to Ohm's law, the output voltage e_p will be proportional to the value of the resistance R_o and the plate current i_p. The voltage amplification of the circuit will be

$$VA = \frac{e_p}{e_g} \qquad (4\text{-}6)$$

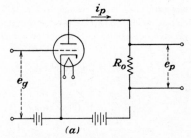

From Fig. 4-24b it can be seen that

$$e_p = i_p R_o \qquad (4\text{-}7)$$

also $$i_p = \frac{\mu e_g}{R_o + r_p} \qquad (4\text{-}8)$$

Substituting Eq. (4-8) for i_p in Eq. (4-7)

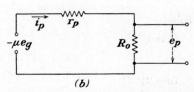

$$e_p = \frac{\mu e_g R_o}{R_o + r_p} \qquad (4\text{-}9)$$

Fig. 4-24.—Simple triode amplifier. (*a*) The circuit diagram, (*b*) the equivalent plate circuit diagram.

Substituting Eq. (4-9) for e_p in Eq. (4-6)

$$VA = \frac{\mu R_o}{R_o + r_p} \qquad (4\text{-}10)$$

where VA = voltage amplification of the stage

e_p = instantaneous value of varying component of plate voltage, volts

e_g = instantaneous value of varying component of grid voltage, volts

R_o = resistance of the output or load resistor, ohms

Equation (4-10) represents the voltage amplification per stage for a circuit using a tube and an output load resistor R_o (Fig. 4-24). In this circuit the load is considered as a pure resistance. The load may not always be a resistance load but may sometimes be an inductance or capacitance load. The conditions for impedances other than pure resistance are presented in Chaps. VII, VIII, and IX.

Relation between r_p, R_o, and the Voltage Amplification. In order to obtain the maximum voltage amplification per stage with tubes having approximately the same amplification factor, a tube whose plate resistance is as low as is practicable should be used. This may be seen by examination of Eq. (4-10), which indicates that for a definite plate load the voltage amplification will increase as the plate resistance is decreased.

This should not be confused with the maximum power output, which occurs when R_o is equal to r_p, as is explained in Chap. IX.

Example 4-8. Two tubes, each with an amplification factor of 9 but with plate resistances of 10,000 ohms and 20,000 ohms respectively, are alternately placed in a circuit whose load resistor has a value of 20,000 ohms. Which tube produces the greater voltage amplification for the circuit?

Given:
$R_o = 20,000$ ohms
Tube 1
$\mu = 9$
$r_p = 10,000$ ohms
Tube 2
$\mu = 9$
$r_p = 20,000$ ohms

Find:
VA for tube 1 = ?
VA for tube 2 = ?

Solution:

Tube 1

$$VA = \frac{\mu R_o}{R_o + r_p} = \frac{9 \times 20,000}{20,000 + 10,000} = 6$$

Tube 2

$$VA = \frac{\mu R_o}{R_o + r_p} = \frac{9 \times 20,000}{20,000 + 20,000} = 4.5$$

Thus the tube with the lower value of r_p produces the greater voltage amplification for the circuit.

Further examination of Eq. (4-10) shows that for a given value of plate resistance and amplification factor of a tube, the voltage amplification of a circuit will increase if the value of the load resistor is increased.

Example 4-9. A tube whose amplification factor is 9 and whose plate resistance is 10,000 ohms is alternately used with circuits containing load resistors of 10,000 ohms and 20,000 ohms respectively. With which circuit does the tube produce the greater voltage amplification?

Given:
$\mu = 9$
$r_p = 10,000$ ohms
Circuit 1
$R_o = 10,000$ ohms
Circuit 2
$R_o = 20,000$ ohms

Find:
VA for circuit 1 = ?
VA for circuit 2 = ?

Solution:

Circuit 1

$$VA = \frac{\mu R_o}{R_o + r_p} = \frac{9 \times 10,000}{10,000 + 10,000} = 4.5$$

Circuit 2

$$VA = \frac{\mu R_o}{R_o + r_p} = \frac{9 \times 20,000}{20,000 + 10,000} = 6$$

Thus the circuit with the higher value of R_o produces the greater voltage amplification.

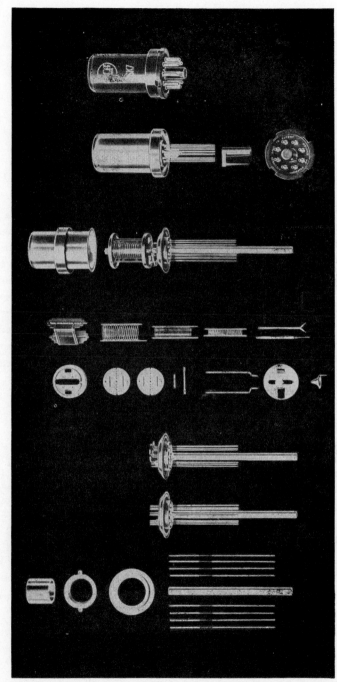

FIG. 4-25.—Structural parts of a typical metal tube. *(Courtesy of RCA Manufacturing Co., Inc.)*

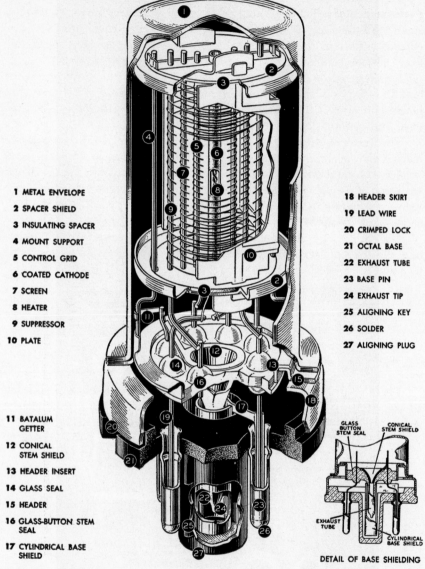

1 METAL ENVELOPE
2 SPACER SHIELD
3 INSULATING SPACER
4 MOUNT SUPPORT
5 CONTROL GRID
6 COATED CATHODE
7 SCREEN
8 HEATER
9 SUPPRESSOR
10 PLATE

11 BATALUM GETTER
12 CONICAL STEM SHIELD
13 HEADER INSERT
14 GLASS SEAL
15 HEADER
16 GLASS-BUTTON STEM SEAL
17 CYLINDRICAL BASE SHIELD

18 HEADER SKIRT
19 LEAD WIRE
20 CRIMPED LOCK
21 OCTAL BASE
22 EXHAUST TUBE
23 BASE PIN
24 EXHAUST TIP
25 ALIGNING KEY
26 SOLDER
27 ALIGNING PLUG

GLASS BUTTON STEM SEAL
CONICAL STEM SHIELD
EXHAUST TUBE
CYLINDRICAL BASE SHIELD

DETAIL OF BASE SHIELDING

Fig. 4-26.—Structure of a single-ended metal tube.   (*Courtesy of RCA Manufacturing Co.,
Inc.*)

4-12. Relation between the Transconductance and the Operating Performance of a Tube. Vacuum tubes are ordinarily operated so that small variations in voltage of the grid or input circuit will produce large current variations in the plate or output circuit. It is therefore important that the transconductance of a tube be as high as possible.

Furthermore, since it is usually desired to keep the plate resistance low, the transconductance must be high if a high value of amplification factor is desired. This may readily be seen from examination of Eqs. (4-3) and (4-5).

The transconductance is very useful when comparing the relative merits and performance capabilities of tubes designed for the same service. A comparison of the transconductance of a power output tube with that of a tube used as a converter would, however, have no practical value. Generally, the value of transconductance is accepted as the best single figure of merit for vacuum-tube performance.

For easy comparison, Table IV-I shows the d-c operating voltages and the tube characteristics, obtained from Appendix XV, for a type 6C5 and a type 6P5 tube.

TABLE IV-I.—COMPARISON OF TUBE CHARACTERISTICS

Tube type	E_f	E_b	E_c	g_m	μ
6C5	6.3	250	−8	2000	20
6P5	6.3	250	−13.5	1450	13.8

These values indicate that the type 6C5 would be used in preference to the 6P5. It is also observed that the higher transconductance is accompanied by an increase of amplification factor from 13.8 to 20.

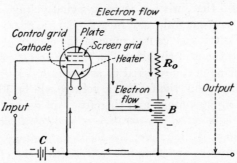

Fig. 4-27.—Circuit diagram for a tetrode showing the electron flow and the proper connection for the screen grid.

4-13. The Tetrode. *The Screen Grid.* When a fourth electrode is used, the tube is called a *tetrode;* it is also occasionally referred to as a *screen-grid tube* or a *four-electrode tube.* The fourth electrode is known as the *screen grid* and usually consists of a spiral-wound wire or a screen, slightly coarser than that used for the control grid, placed between the plate and the control grid of the tube (see Fig. 4-27). The circuit connections and the direction of electron flow for a tetrode are shown in Fig. 4-27.

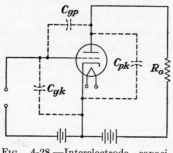

Fig. 4-28.—Interelectrode capacitances of a triode.

Interelectrode Capacitance. Capacitance is present whenever two conductors are separated by an insulator. In any tube, the electrodes act as conductors and the space between the electrodes acts as an insulator; therefore a capacitance will exist between each pair of electrodes. These capacitances, known as *interelectrode capacitances*, may form undesired paths through which current can flow.

The interelectrode capacitances of a triode are shown in Fig. 4-28. These capacitances are usually of very low values, as is indicated in Table IV-II, which shows the interelectrode capacitances for a type 6C5 tube.

TABLE IV-II.—INTERELECTRODE CAPACITANCES, TYPE 6C5 TUBE

Grid–plate capacitance (approximate)...................... 2.0 $\mu\mu f$
Grid–cathode capacitance (approximate)................... 3.0 $\mu\mu f$
Plate–cathode capacitance (approximate).................. 11 $\mu\mu f$

Effect of the Interelectrode Capacitance. The capacitance between the grid and plate is generally the most troublesome. It has been shown in Art. 4-5 that, when a varying signal voltage is applied to the grid, the plate voltage will vary in a similar manner. The grid–plate interelectrode capacitance causes some of the energy of the plate circuit to be applied to the grid circuit. The energy transferred from the output to the input circuit is referred to as *feedback*. If the output circuit contains resistance load, the feedback voltage will be 180 degrees out of phase with the input voltage and therefore will reduce the effect of the input signal; this is called *degeneration* or *negative feedback*. When the output circuit load is inductive, the feedback voltage will be in phase with the input voltage and therefore will increase the effect of the input signal; this is called *regeneration* or *positive feedback*.

The amount of feedback caused by the interelectrode capacitance is usually very small at audio frequencies because the capacitive reactance [Eq. (2-20)] at these frequencies is very high. At radio frequencies, however, the capacitive reactance becomes much lower and the feedback may reach an amount sufficient to cause trouble in the operation of the circuit.

Positive feedback has the advantage of increasing the gain of a circuit but has the disadvantage of causing distortion. Negative feedback has the advantage of reducing distortion but has the disadvantage of causing a reduction in the voltage gain of the circuit. If either regeneration or degeneration gets out of control, the tube no longer operates successfully as an amplifier. Under this condition the tube will act as an oscillator.

Neutralizing Circuits. In order to overcome the undesirable effect of feedback, some types of receivers were equipped with neutralizing circuits. The purpose of these circuits was to produce a voltage in each grid circuit equal in amount and opposite in phase to the voltage produced by the grid–plate capacitance of the tube used in that circuit. The resultant of these two voltages theoretically equaled zero, and oscillation or feedback was thereby prevented.

Elimination of Feedback by Use of a Screen Grid. The capacitance between the control grid and the plate of a triode can be reduced to a negligible value by adding a fourth electrode or *screen grid.* The screen grid is mounted between the control grid and the plate and acts as an electrostatic shield between the two, thus reducing the control-grid–plate capacitance. Connecting a by-pass capacitor between the screen grid and the cathode will increase the effectiveness of this shielding action. The control-grid–plate capacitance of screen-grid tubes is generally 0.01 $\mu\mu f$ or less.

Another advantage of the tetrode is that it can be operated over quite a wide range of plate voltage, but only for values of voltage greater than the screen-grid voltage, with comparatively little change in the plate current. This is made possible by constructing the screen grid with comparatively large spacing between its wires, thereby permitting most of the electrons drawn toward the screen grid to pass through it and on to the plate. As the screen grid is operated at a comparatively high potential and because of the spacing of its wires, it produces an electrostatic force pulling electrons from the cathode to the plate. At the same time, the screen grid shields the electrons between the cathode and the screen grid from the plate and therefore the plate exerts very little electrostatic force on electrons near the cathode. Hence, as long as the plate voltage is higher than the screen-grid voltage, the plate current depends largely on the screen-grid voltage and very little on the plate voltage. The fact that the plate current of the tetrode is largely independent of the plate voltage makes it possible to obtain much higher amplification with the tetrode than with a triode. In other words, the ratio of plate voltage change to grid voltage change (for a constant plate current) will be much higher for tetrodes than for triodes. The low control-grid–plate capacitance makes it possible to obtain this high amplification without plate-to-control-grid feedback and the resultant instability.

The screen grid also serves to reduce the space charge. Being situated between the control grid and the plate, and having a positive potential, the electrons coming from the cathode receive added acceleration on their way to the plate, and the tendency to form a space charge is reduced.

Characteristic Curves for a Tetrode. A family of plate characteristic curves for a tetrode is shown in Fig. 4-29. It should be noted that the

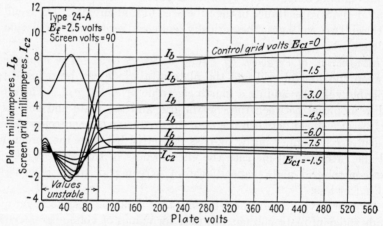

Fig. 4-29.—Family of plate characteristic curves for a tetrode.

curves have a peculiar shape as compared to the curves of the triode. Each curve represents the variations in plate current with changes in plate voltage for a different value of grid bias. It should be kept in mind that the screen-grid voltage of the tube under test was maintained at 90 volts for all conditions. The dip that occurs in the curve when the plate voltage is less than the screen-grid voltage is caused by the secondary emission of electrons at the plate. Secondary emission occurs when electrons from the cathode, called the *primary emission,* strike other electrodes with sufficient force to dislodge other electrons. The electrons liberated in this manner are secondary to the original cathode or primary emission, and this effect is therefore called *secondary emission.* If the screen-grid voltage is higher than the plate voltage, the secondary electrons will be attracted by the screen grid and will flow in that circuit.

The dip in the curve occurs because the plate current is decreased by the amount of the secondary emission that finds its way into the screen-grid circuit.

When the plate voltage reaches the value of the screen-grid voltage, the secondary electrons find it more difficult to reach the screen grid, since the plate itself now attracts some of the secondary electrons.   When the plate voltage exceeds the screen-grid voltage, practically all the secondary electrons return to the plate, and therefore the curve approaches a horizontal line.

The curves of Fig. 4-29 indicate that the tube would have very unstable operation for values of plate voltage under 100 volts.   This means that, if the plate voltage variations, owing to the signal input, cause the plate voltage to drop below 100 volts, large changes in plate current will result.   In order to prevent unstable operation, the variations in plate voltage, commonly referred to as the *plate voltage swing*, should at no time cause the plate voltage to drop below 100 volts for this tube.

Constants of the Tetrode.   The constants for the tetrode are found by constructing a triangle on the characteristic curve about the operating point desired in the same manner as for triodes.   It can be observed that a small change in grid voltage produces a very large change in plate current compared to the change in plate voltage required to produce an equal change in the plate current.   The amplification factor of the tube as determined by Eq. (4-1) is therefore very high.   It can also be noted that a large change in plate voltage produces very little change in plate current, hence the plate resistance [Eq. (4-2)] will be very high.   The transconductance, however, is equal to or slightly lower than for a triode of similar construction.

The amplification factor for triodes ranges from approximately 3 to 100.   The plate resistance of triodes ranges from approximately 800 to 50,000 ohms.   Tetrodes can be obtained with amplification factors as high as 800.   The plate resistance increases with the amplification factor and some tetrodes have a plate resistance of over a million ohms.

The high plate resistance and the correspondingly high value of load resistance required to make the voltage amplification of a tetrode amplifier circuit approach the amplification factor of the tube make this condition impracticable because of the high voltage required of the plate power supply.   However, with practical values of load resistance and plate supply voltage, the voltage amplification obtained is much greater than can be obtained with triodes.

Tetrodes were formerly used as voltage amplifiers in the r-f amplifier stages of receivers.   However, pentodes have all the advantages of tetrodes and in addition they minimize the disadvantages. For this reason tetrodes are very seldom used in modern receivers.

4-14. The Pentode. *The Suppressor Grid.* A tube with five electrodes—namely, a cathode, three grids, and a plate—is called a *pentode* or a *five-electrode tube.* The fifth electrode is an extra grid called the *suppressor grid.* The electrodes of the pentode are arranged with the cathode at the center and surrounded by the control grid, the screen grid, the suppressor grid, and the plate in the order named (see Fig. 4-30). The circuit connections and the direction of electron flow for the pentode are shown in Fig. 4-30.

The suppressor grid usually consists of a spiral-wound wire or a coarse-mesh screen placed between the screen grid and the plate. When the various grids of the tube are in the form of a screen, the control grid

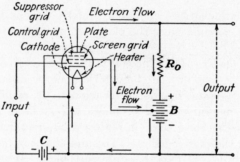

FIG. 4-30.—Circuit diagram for a pentode showing the electron flow and the proper connection for the screen grid and the suppressor grid.

is of a very fine mesh so that small changes in control-grid voltage will produce relatively large changes in plate current and consequently will produce a high value of transconductance for the tube. The screen grid is of a somewhat coarser mesh so that it will not appreciably affect the flow of electrons to the plate, its purpose being largely to reduce the control-grid–plate capacitance. The suppressor grid is of a comparatively coarse mesh in order that it will not retard the flow of electrons to the plate while serving its function of preventing the secondary emission from reaching the screen grid. In most pentodes the suppressor grid is internally connected to the cathode. There are, however, some types of pentodes that have the suppressor grid brought out as a separate terminal thereby making possible additional circuit uses.

Action of the Suppressor Grid. Secondary emission is present whenever electrons strike a plate with sufficient velocity to dislodge other electrons. It does not cause trouble in the usual operation of diodes and triodes because the only positive electrode in the tube is the plate and

the secondary electrons will be drawn to it.   In tetrodes, however, the
screen grid offers a strong attraction to the secondary electrons, particularly if the plate voltage is lower than the screen-grid voltage.   This

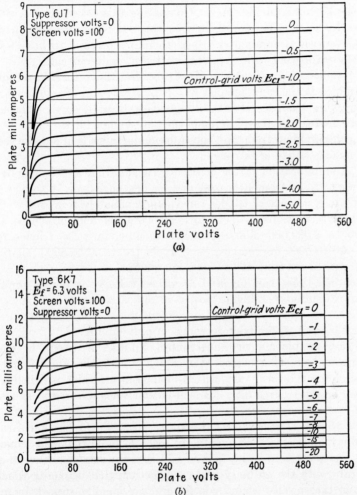

Fig. 4-31.—Family of plate characteristic curves for a pentode.   (a) Type 6J7 tube with
uniformly spaced grid, (b) type 6K7 tube with supercontrol grid.

effect lowers the plate current and limits the permissible plate-voltage
swing for tetrodes.

In pentodes, the suppressor grid is added to prevent the secondary
electrons from traveling to the screen grid.   In order to accomplish this
the suppressor grid is connected directly to the cathode.   Being at

cathode potential, the suppressor grid is negative with respect to the plate, and because it is close to the plate it will repel the secondary electrons and drive them back into the plate.

Characteristic Curves for a Pentode. A family of curves for a typical pentode is shown in Fig. 4-31. Comparing this set of curves with the curves for a tetrode, it will be seen that the unstable portion of the tetrode curves is eliminated. It is therefore possible to have a larger plate-voltage swing with a small variation in plate current.

Constants of the Pentode. The tube constants for a pentode are determined in the same manner as for the triode and tetrode, that is, by constructing triangles about the operating point desired. The amplification factor and the plate resistance are higher for the pentode than for a comparable tetrode and the transconductance is about the same as for a similar triode or tetrode.

The amplification factor of triodes ranges from approximately 3 to 100, for tetrodes from 40 to 800, and for pentodes from 70 to over 5000. The plate resistance of triodes ranges approximately from 800 to 50,000 ohms, for tetrodes from 10,000 to 1,000,000 ohms, and for pentodes from 35,000 to 2,000,000 ohms. The transconductance for triodes ranges from 200 to 6000 micromhos, for tetrodes from 500 to 8000 micromhos, and for pentodes from 500 to 8000 micromhos.

Pentode tubes can be used as either voltage or power amplifiers. In power pentodes, a higher power output is obtained with lower grid voltages. Pentodes used as r-f amplifiers give a high voltage amplification when used with moderate values of plate voltage.

4-15. Variable-mu or Supercontrol Tubes. A triode or pentode with its control grid constructed in such a manner that the amplification factor of the tube will vary with a change in grid bias is called a *variable-mu* or *supercontrol tube*. It is also sometimes referred to as a *remote cutoff tube*.

Cutoff with Ordinary Grid Structure. If the grid bias on a tube is steadily increased, it will eventually reach a value that will reduce the plate current to zero and it is then said that the tube has reached *cutoff*. In a tube with the ordinary grid construction, that is, one in which the turns of the spirally wound control grid are equally spaced, increasing the grid bias causes the plate current to decrease very rapidly to cutoff (see Fig. 4-32). A further effect of this type of grid construction is to produce a tube with a practically constant amplification factor for all values of grid bias. Such a tube is generally referred to as being a *sharp cutoff* or *constant-mu tube*.

Effects of Sharp Cutoff. A tube with a sharp cutoff is limited to use in circuits with relatively small changes in grid voltage. In circuits that have a large signal voltage, sharp cutoff would produce distortion in the form of cross modulation and modulation distortion.

Cross modulation or *cross talk* is the effect produced when the undesired signal from a second station is heard in addition to the signal of the desired station. When cross modulation is present, it is generally caused in the first stage of the r-f amplification.

Modulation distortion is the effect produced when the signal voltage drives the tube beyond cutoff and thereby distorts the

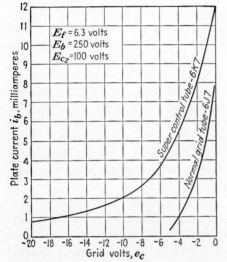

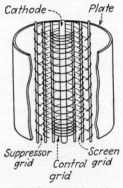

Fig. 4-32.—Comparative characteristic curves of a tube with a supercontrol grid and a tube with a uniformly spaced grid.

Fig. 4-33.—Cross-section view showing the construction of the electrodes of a supercontrol amplifier tube.

desired audio signal. When modulation distortion is present, it is generally caused by the last stage of i-f amplification.

Action of the Supercontrol Tube. The characteristics of the supercontrol tube are such that they enable the tube to handle both large and small input signals with a minimum amount of distortion over a wide range of signal voltage. The supercontrol action is accomplished by the special construction of the control grid, which provides a variation in the amplification factor for changes in grid bias. The grid is spiral wound with its turns close together at the ends but with considerable space between turns at the middle (see Fig. 4-33). For weak signals and a low grid bias, the tube operates practically the same as one with a uniformly spaced grid. With larger input signals, more grid bias is required. The increased grid bias will produce a cutoff effect at the section of the cathode enclosed by the ends of the grid because of the close spacing of the grid wires. The plate current and other tube characteristics are now dependent on the electron flow through the center section of the grid, where the turns are spaced farther apart. The wide spacing changes the gain of the tube and enables it to handle large signals with a minimum amount of distortion.

The curves of Fig. 4-32 show the characteristics for a sharp cutoff and a supercontrol tube. It will be noted that the rate of plate-current change is approximately the same in both tubes for small values of grid-bias voltage, while for large values of grid bias the plate current decreases at a much lower rate for the supercontrol tube. This low rate of change makes it possible for the tube to handle large signals satisfactorily. The variable-mu permits the tube to be used in automatic-volume-control circuits.

4-16. The Beam Power Tube. A further improvement in the operating characteristics of the vacuum tube is obtained with the beam power tube. This type of tube is constructed so that the electrons flowing to the plate are made to travel in concentrated beams. As it is capable of handling larger amounts of power it is called a *beam power tube.* This tube, which is actually either a modified tetrode or pentode, contains a cathode, a control grid, and a screen grid, and in the case of the pentode type it also contains a suppressor grid.

Action of the Beam Power Tube. When the beam power tube is of the tetrode type, that is, without a separate suppressor grid, the control grid and the screen grid are of the spiral-wound wire construction and their respective turns are placed so that each turn of the screen grid is shaded from the cathode by a turn of the control grid. This arrangement of the grid wires causes the electrons to flow in directed paths between the turns of the screen grid. Beam-forming plates (see Fig. 4-34) are added to aid in producing the desired beam effect and to prevent stray electrons from the plate from flowing into the screen-grid circuit. This results in the tube having a relatively low value of screen-grid current. The beam-forming plates are operated at cathode potential by connecting them directly to the cathode. By increasing the spacing between the screen grid and the plate, a space charge is set up in this area. This space charge repels the secondary electrons emitted from the plate and forces them back into the plate.

Characteristics of a Beam Power Tube. The characteristics of the beam power tube are similar to those of the pentode. A family of curves for a typical beam power tube is shown in Fig. 4-35. The beam power tubes provide a straighter curve at the lower plate voltages than the pentodes and hence will have less chance of producing distortion. The amplification factor is high when compared with triodes and low when compared with tetrodes and pentodes. The plate resistance is high but not so high as that of pentodes. The transconductance is generally higher than for any other type of tube.

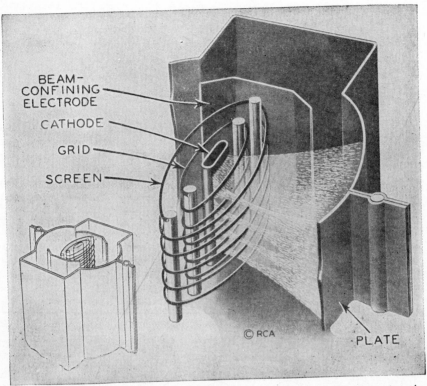

FIG. 4-34.—Internal structure of a beam power tube.   *(Courtesy of RCA Manufacturing Co., Inc.)*

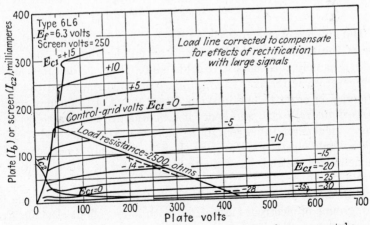

FIG. 4-35.—Family of plate characteristic curves for a beam power tube.

The combined effects of the directed concentrated beam of electrons, the suppressor action of the space charge, and the low value of the screen-grid current result in a tube of high power output, high efficiency, and high power sensitivity.

Beam power tubes are used for a-f amplifiers in receivers. The same principle is used for the larger size tubes employed in transmitters.

4-17. Multielectrode and Multiunit Tubes. *Multielectrode Tubes.* It has been shown in the previous articles that additional electrodes were added to the simple diode and triode to improve the operating characteristics of the vacuum tube. As a result, there were developed such tubes as the full-wave rectifier, tetrode, pentode, and beam power tube.

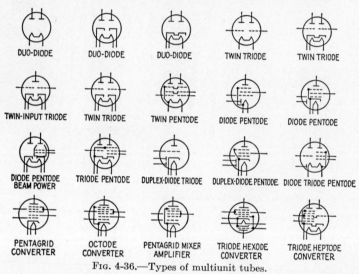

Fig. 4-36.—Types of multiunit tubes.

The number of electrodes in a tube may be further increased, as in the case of the type 6L7, which contains seven electrodes (exclusive of the heater), namely, a cathode, five grids, and a plate. The tube is used in a superheterodyne receiver to mix the carrier frequency and the oscillator frequency in order to obtain a new lower value of frequency (called the *intermediate frequency*) and hence it is commonly called a *mixer* or a *converter*. In general, tubes containing more than three electrodes associated with a single electron stream are classed as *multielectrode tubes*. Under this definition, tetrodes and pentodes may also be called multielectrode tubes.

Multiunit Tube. When a tube contains within one envelope two or more groups of electrodes associated with independent electron streams, it is called a *multiunit tube*.

The type 80 full-wave rectifier was one of the first multiunit tubes to be used. It consists essentially of two half-wave rectifier units in a single envelope. Advancement in circuit design and the corresponding advancement in tube design have resulted in numerous combinations in the multiunit tubes. In general, the combinations are easily identified by the names given to the tubes, such as duplex-diode, twin-triode, duplex-diode-triode, diode-triode-pentode, and rectifier-beam power amplifier. In most cases a single cathode is used for all the units in a tube, although in some types separate cathodes are provided for each unit. A more complete listing of the combinations is available from Fig. 4-36 and from the chart in Appendix XV.

An example of the multiunit tube is the 1D8-GT, which is listed as a diode-triode-pentode. Its name indicates that the tube contains a diode, a triode, and a pentode. The tube performs three functions, namely, the diode is used as a detector and automatic volume control; the triode is used as an a-f amplifier; and the pentode is used as a power output tube.

4-18. New Types of Tubes. *Advantages of the Newer Types of Tubes.* The large number of tube types that have been produced are the results of improvements in tube design, demand for tubes requiring less space, and changes in style made for sales appeal. The number of tube types introduced for receiver circuits already exceeds 500.

The following developments represent the major advances in tube engineering.

1. *The* 1.4-*volt tubes* for battery-operated receivers. These tubes may be operated directly from a 1.5-volt dry cell. This is an improvement over the 2-volt tubes, which required the use of two dry cells and also a dropping resistor.

2. *The single-ended metal tube.* This eliminates the grid cap and results in simplified wiring of receivers.

3. *The low heater-current tubes* requiring only 150 milliamperes for the heater circuit. These are available for many of the 12.6-, 25-, 35-, and 50-volt tubes. The use of these tubes in place of the 300-milliampere heater types cuts the power consumption in half and provides greater efficiency in the series-connected filament circuits of the a-c/d-c sets.

4. *The GT (bantam) type tubes.* These tubes provide considerable saving in space.

5. *The loktal base tubes.* This is an octal base tube that is provided with a locking feature and is also known as *loctal, octalox,* or *lock-in.*

6. *The* 117-*volt tubes* for operating directly from the power line.

Duplicate Type Tubes Having Different Bases. Because of the developments in tube design, there are a number of instances in which tubes of similar electrical characteristics are duplicated in several forms of base design and in different dimensions. For example, the 6Q7, 6Q7-G, and 6Q7-GT are all of the same electrical characteristics and differ only in their dimensions and base arrangement. The 6Q7 is of metal construc-

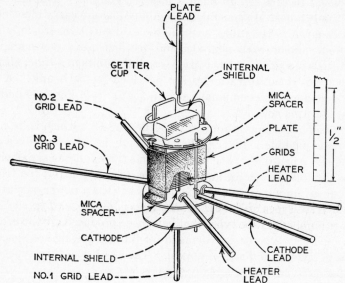

Fig. 4-37.—Internal structure of an acorn pentode. (*Courtesy of RCA Manufacturing Co., Inc.*)

Fig. 4-38.—Acorn pentode and triode compared with a golf ball. (*Courtesy of RCA Manufacturing Co., Inc.*)

tion, the 6Q7-G is of glass construction and quite large in size, and the 6Q7-GT is of glass construction but of small size. The base of each tube fits the standard octal socket, and each tube has its grid terminal in the form of a cap at the top of the tube.

The 6SQ7 (metal) and the 6SQ7-GT (bantam glass) have electrical characteristics similar to each other and are also approximately equal to the 6Q7, 6Q7-G, and the 6Q7-GT. These two tubes have their grid leads brought out through a pin in the base, thereby eliminating the grid cap. While the characteristics of the 6Q7 tubes and the 6SQ7 tubes are enough alike to have them operate equally well in most instances, they could not be interchanged without first rewiring the socket connections because their leads are not brought out in the same order. The arrangement of the socket connections can be determined from Appendix XV or any tube manual.

The type 75 tube has electrical characteristics that are also approximately the same as the 6Q7 and 6SQ7 tubes. This tube has its grid lead brought out to a grid cap, and its base fits the standard 6-pin socket. In order to interchange these tubes it would be necessary first to change the sockets.

The ever-increasing demand for smaller receivers has resulted in the development of smaller tubes. These tubes have a glass envelope and are made as a small tubular bulb. They are known under various names such as dwarf, bantam, miniature, doorknob, and acorn tubes. The tubes may be as small as $1\frac{5}{8}$ inches in height (including the base) and $\frac{3}{4}$ inch in diameter.

Fig. 4-39.—Miniature type tube with a button base. (*Courtesy of RCA Manufacturing Co., Inc.*)

4-19. Tube Bases and Socket Connections. *Need for a Means of Identification.* Because of the large number of tube types that are manufactured and because of the variation in the number of electrodes and types of tube bases used, it has become necessary to establish a system of identifying the socket connections and the tube electrodes with which they are to make contact.

In diagrams of circuits that include tubes, it is common practice to show the socket connections, which in turn correspond to the connecting pins in the base of the tube to be used. Also, to be consistent with general practice, all references to socket connections and tube-pin numbering are made for bottom views of sockets and tubes. The arrangement of tube-base and socket designations has been standardized by the RMA and the two systems described below represent two methods used for numbering the tube pins and socket connections.

Methods of Identifying Socket Connections. The method of numbering the socket or tube-base connections for the early tube types is shown in Fig. 4-40. In this system, the filament or heater pins of the tube and the corresponding holes in the socket are of a larger diameter than the others and are generally shown at the bottom of the diagram. The lower left-hand pin is designated as number 1 and the remaining pins are numbered consecutively in a clockwise direction. This designation sets up a system of numbering but makes no provision for identifying the various tube elements with these numbers. The order in which the tube elements are arranged varies with tube types and may best be obtained from Appendix XV or any suitable tube manual.

Metal tubes and other octal base tubes all use the same type of socket, that is, one which provides for eight pins. The octal socket, as it is commonly called, has eight equally spaced holes arranged in a circle. All of the holes in the socket are of the same size and, in order to ensure

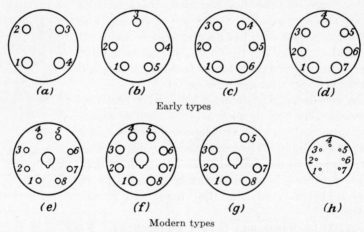

(a)   *(b)*   *(c)*   *(d)*

Early types

(e)   *(f)*   *(g)*   *(h)*

Modern types

Fig. 4-40.—Tube base and socket connections. (*a*) Standard four-pin base, (*b*) standard five-pin base, (*c*) standard six-pin base, (*d*) standard seven-pin base, (*e*) eight-pin loktal base, (*f*) eight-pin octal base, (*g*) six-pin octal base, (*h*) miniature or button base.

correct placement of the tube in the socket, a large center hole with an extra notch is provided. The socket connection to the left of the centering notch is designated as number 1 and the remaining connections are numbered consecutively up to 8. The pins in the base of the tube are all of equal size and are arranged in a circle. A large insulated pin, provided with a centering key to fit the notch in the socket, is located in the center of the tube base. Some tubes using octal sockets have only six or seven pins, while others have eight. The six or seven pin bases merely omit one or two of the eight pins according to the number used. This, however, does not alter the numbering of the socket connections, as may be seen from Fig. 4-40. As in the previous method, this only provides a system of numbering the socket connections. The order in which the tube elements are arranged may best be obtained from Appendix XV or a suitable tube manual.

The development of the new acorn and miniature types of tubes also resulted in the introduction of a new means of connection for the acorn type and a new socket for the miniature type. The acorn tube has its leads brought out of the side of the tube, as shown in Figs. 4-37 and 4-38. The miniature tube, shown in Fig. 4-39, has a thin glass base, referred to as a *button base*, and its socket is called a *button socket*.

4-20. Tube Type Numbers. The type number of a tube is intended to give information concerning its construction and application. The early tubes were numbered consecutively and their numbers had no particular significance. A few of these early tubes, such as the 42, 56, 75, 78, and 80, are still used.

The numbers assigned to the newer tubes now provide a means of identifying some of the tube characteristics. The tube number consists of at least three units. The first unit is a number, the second consists of one or more letters, and the third is a number. In some cases a letter or group of letters is added as a fourth unit.

The first unit is used to represent the filament or heater voltage. It is always expressed as a whole number, and when the rated voltage contains a decimal value its decimal numbers are dropped. An exception to this is 2-volt battery tubes, which are represented by the number 1 in order to avoid conflict with the 2.5-volt tubes, which bear the number 2. Another exception is the series of tubes whose first unit designation is 7. Although these tubes are nominally rated at 7 volts, they are generally operated at 6.3 volts.

The second unit is a letter separating the first and third units, which are numbers. One version of the significance of this unit is that the letters at the beginning of the alphabet represent amplifiers and detectors while letters at the end of the alphabet represent rectifiers. The number of tube types has increased so rapidly that double letters have to be used, and it has become rather difficult to attach much significance to this unit. When the letter S is added, as in the case of the 6SQ7, it indicates that the tube is single-ended, that is, one with all of its leads brought out through the base. The 6Q7 differs from the 6SQ7 mainly in that its grid lead is brought out to a cap at the top of the tube instead of to a pin in the base.

The third unit of the numbering system appears to have at least two versions of its significance. One is that it represents the number of elements in the tube, and the second is that it represents the number of useful leads.

A fourth unit has been added since the introduction of metal tubes and the small glass tubes. This fourth unit is a letter or group of letters and is used to indicate the constructional features of the tube. A three-unit type number indicates a metal tube. The addition of the letter G indicates a standard-size glass tube of the same characteristics as the metal tube. The letters GT indicate a small tubular glass type of construction. In some tube types, the standard glass series G has been discontinued and the small tubular construction has been marked GT/G to indicate that it is to serve for both types.

The following examples will aid in understanding the tube numbering system. In the designation of the 6SA7-GT tube, the first unit is represented by the number 6, which indicates that the heater voltage is approximately 6 volts; actually it is rated at 6.3 volts. The second unit is represented by the letters SA, in which the letter S indicates a single-ended tube. The tube is used as a pentagrid-converter and in this case the code letter A does not bear any significance to its application. The third unit is represented by the number 7, which indicates that the tube has either seven elements or seven useful leads or possibly both. From Appendix XV, or a tube manual, it can be seen that the tube has seven elements, namely, a cathode, five grids, and a plate. It can also be seen that the tube has seven leads, namely, two heaters, one cathode, three grids, and one plate. Thus both versions of the significance of the third unit may be applied to this tube. The fourth unit is represented by the letters GT, which indicate that the tube is of the small tubular glass type.

In the designation of the 12SK7 tube, the first unit, 12, indicates that the heater voltage is approximately 12 volts; actually it is rated at 12.6 volts. In the second unit, SK, the letter S indicates a single-ended tube. The tube is classified as a triple-grid supercontrol amplifier and hence no significance is attached to the code letter K. The third unit, 7, indicates that the tube has seven useful leads, namely, two heaters, one cathode, three grids, and one plate. As the tube has only five elements, the third unit is not used to indicate the number of elements. As no fourth unit appears in this designation, the tube is of the metal type.

BIBLIOGRAPHY

ALBERT, A. L., *Fundamental Electronics and Vacuum Tubes*, The Macmillan Company, New York.

EASTMAN, A. V., *Fundamentals of Vacuum Tubes*, McGraw-Hill Book Company, Inc., New York.

REICH, H. J., *Theory and Applications of Electron Tubes*, McGraw-Hill Book Company, Inc., New York.

SMITH, F. L., *The Radiotron Designer's Handbook*, The Wireless Press, Sydney, Australia; distributed in U.S.A. by RCA Manufacturing Company, Inc., Harrison, N. J.

TERMAN, F. E., *Fundamentals of Radio*, McGraw-Hill Book Company, Inc., New York.

Receiving Tube Manual, various tube manufacturers.

QUESTIONS

1. What are the characteristics of a vacuum tube that make it one of the most important contributions to the fields of communication and industrial electronics?

2. What is meant by the Edison effect?

3. What was Dr. Fleming's contribution to the advancement of vacuum-tube design?

4. Define the following terms: (*a*) cathode, (*b*) filament, (*c*) heater, (*d*) directly heated cathode, (*e*) indirectly heated cathode.

5. Explain the purpose and theory of operation of (*a*) the cathode, (*b*) the heater.

6. Compare the operating characteristics of tungsten, thoriated tungsten, and oxide-coated filaments when used as directly heated cathodes.

7. What are the advantages of directly heated cathodes and where are they generally used?

8. Explain four advantages of indirectly heated cathodes.

9. (*a*) What is meant by a dropping resistor?   (*b*) What is its purpose?   (*c*) How is it connected in the circuit?

10. What conditions in the heater circuit of a radio receiver make it necessary to connect (*a*) a resistor in series with the heater or filament of a tube?   (*b*) A resistor in parallel with the heater or filament of a tube?

11. How should the power rating of a resistor used in the heating circuit of a receiver compare with its actual power loss?

12. Explain the purpose and the operation of automatic ballast regulation.

13. Explain the following terms: (*a*) plate, (*b*) diode, (*c*) duo-diode, (*d*) space charge, (*e*) emission current, (*f*) saturation current.

14. Explain the rectifier action of a diode.

15. Compare the half-wave and full-wave rectifier characteristics.

16. Explain the following terms: (*a*) control grid, (*b*) triode, (*c*) grid bias.

17. Draw the circuit diagram for a triode showing the connections for the A, B, and C power supplies.   Indicate the direction of the electron flow on the diagram.

18. Explain the action of the triode.

19. Explain the action of a triode for the following conditions: (*a*) grid bias but no signal input, (*b*) grid bias and a varying signal input, (*c*) positive grid voltage.

20. In the circuit of Fig. 4-13, what is the phase relation between the following quantities: (*a*) e_g and i_p?   (*b*) e_g and e_p?   (*c*) e_p and i_p?

21. Why should the fixed grid bias of a tube always be greater than the maximum value of the input signal voltage?

22. What are the advantages of a family of characteristic curves over the tabular listing of tube characteristics?

23. Explain the difference between the static and dynamic characteristics of a vacuum tube.

24. How are the static characteristics of a tube obtained?

25. How are the dynamic characteristics of a tube obtained?

26. (*a*) What is meant by a family of plate characteristic curves?   (*b*) What is meant by a family of grid-plate transfer characteristic curves?

27. What is meant by the tube constants?

28. (*a*) What does the amplification factor of a tube represent?   (*b*) How is it obtained?

29. What factors affect the amplification factor of a tube?

30. (*a*) What does the plate resistance of a tube represent?   (*b*) How is it obtained?

31. What factors affect the plate resistance of a tube?

32. (*a*) What does the transconductance of a tube represent? (*b*) How is it obtained?

33. What factors affect the transconductance of a tube?

34. What is the relation between the amplification factor, transconductance, and the plate resistance of a tube?

35. What is meant by the voltage amplification per stage?

36. What is the relation between the amplification factor of a tube and the voltage amplification of the stage in which it is used?

37. What is the relation between the resistance of the plate, the resistance of the load, and the voltage amplification per stage?

38. What is the relation between the transconductance of a tube and its operating characteristics?

39. (*a*) What is a tetrode? (*b*) By what other names is it also known?

40. Describe the construction and location of the screen grid.

41. (*a*) What is meant by interelectrode capacitance? (*b*) Why is it necessary to keep these capacitances at a minimum?

42. What is meant by (*a*) regeneration? (*b*) Degeneration?

43. (*a*) What is the purpose of neutralizing circuits? (*b*) How do these circuits accomplish this purpose?

44. How does the addition of a screen grid eliminate feedback?

45. Explain four advantages of screen-grid tubes.

46. What is meant by secondary emission?

47. What effect does secondary emission have upon the operating characteristics of a tetrode?

48. How do the amplification factor and plate resistance for tetrodes compare with those for triodes?

49. Where are screen-grid tubes used?

50. What is a pentode?

51. Describe the construction and location of the suppressor grid.

52. How does the addition of a suppressor grid reduce the effect of secondary emission?

53. How do the characteristic curves for a pentode compare with those for a tetrode?

54. How do the amplification factor and plate resistance for pentodes compare with those for a triode and tetrode?

55. Where are pentodes generally used?

56. What is a supercontrol tube? What are its constructional features?

57. Explain the meaning of the following terms: (*a*) sharp cutoff, (*b*) remote cutoff, (*c*) cross modulation, (*d*) modulation distortion.

58. Explain the action of the supercontrol tube.

59. What are the advantages of variable-mu tubes and where are they generally used?

60. Describe the beam power tube.

61. In a beam power tube, what factors are responsible for its high power output and high efficiency?

62. What is meant by multielectrode tubes and what are their advantages?

63. What is meant by multiunit tubes and what are their advantages?

64. What important developments have been made in the design of the newer type tubes?

65. What is meant by duplicate tube types and what is their purpose?

66. Describe two systems of tube-pin and socket-connection numbering.

67. Describe the system used to designate the various types of tubes.

PROBLEMS

1. The tube complement of a certain radio receiver includes a 6SA7, 6D6, 6SQ7-G, 25L6-G, and 25Z5. (*a*) If the heaters of the tubes are connected in series, what value of resistance must be connected in series with the heaters in order to operate the receiver on a 115-volt line? (*b*) What minimum wattage rating should the resistor have, assuming that its ventilation is restricted?

2. A receiver with a tube complement of a 6A8, 6SK7, 6SQ7, 6V6, and 25Z6 has its heaters connected in series and uses an additional series-connected resistor in order that the receiver may be operated on a 115-volt line. As the current rating of the tube heaters are not all of the same value, it is necessary to include a shunt (parallel-connected) resistor. (*a*) Draw a circuit diagram showing the series-connected resistor, the heaters connected in a sequence that will permit the use of a single parallel-connected resistor, and the parallel-connected resistor. (*b*) What value of series resistor is required? (*c*) What value of shunt resistor is required? (*d*) What minimum wattage rating is recommended for the resistors in parts (*b*) and (*c*)?

3. The tube heaters of a certain receiver are to be connected in parallel with one another and operated from a 3-volt power supply provided by batteries. The tubes used include three 1A4-P's, one 1C6, one 1B5, one 30, and one 1J6-G. (*a*) Draw a circuit diagram showing the connections necessary for the series resistor. (*b*) What value resistor is required? What minimum wattage rating should the resistor have?

4. It is desired to operate the heaters of a four-tube receiver from a power supply consisting of three 1.5-volt cells connected in series. The heaters are connected to form a parallel-series circuit consisting of a 1A7-G and a 1N5-G connected in series to form one of the parallel members and a 1J5-G and a 1H5-G connected in series to form the second parallel member. (*a*) Draw a circuit diagram showing the resistors and connections required for this circuit. (*b*) What is the resistance value and the recommended wattage rating of each resistor?

5. A certain radio receiver has its heaters connected in parallel to a 12.6-volt power supply. It is desired to substitute a 6SA7 for a 12SA7 in this circuit. (*a*) Draw a circuit diagram showing the resistor that must be added in order to make this change. (*b*) What value resistor is required? (*c*) What is the minimum wattage rating recommended for this resistor?

6. A certain radio receiver has its heaters connected in series with one another. It is desired to substitute a type 1A6 tube for the 1C6 tube used in the receiver. (*a*) Draw a circuit diagram showing the resistor that must be added in order to make this change. (*b*) What value resistor is required? (*c*) What is the minimum wattage rating recommended for this resistor?

7. A certain radio receiver has all its heaters connected in series and is supplied by a 115-volt line. It is desired to substitute a type 6SA7 tube for a type 12SA7. (*a*) Draw a circuit diagram showing the two resistors required in order to make this change. (Assume that the tube being changed is the first one in the series circuit.) (*b*) What is the value of each of the resistors? (*c*) What is the minimum wattage rating recommended for each of the resistors?

8. A certain radio receiver has all of its heaters connected in series and is to be operated from a 115-volt a-c line. It is desired to substitute a type 35L6-GT tube for a type 50L6-GT. (*a*) Draw a circuit diagram showing the resistor that must be added to the heater circuit in order to make this change. (*b*) What value resistor is required? (*c*) What is the minimum wattage rating recommended for the resistor?

9. The following data was obtained from a test of a type 6SF5 tube operated at its rated heater voltage. Plot the plate characteristic curves from the test data.

TEST DATA—TYPE 6SF5

e_b, volts	i_b, milliamperes		
	$E_c = -1$	$E_c = -1.5$	$E_c = -2$
20	0.00	0.00	0.00
40	0.00	0.00	0.00
60	0.08	0.00	0.00
80	0.17	0.00	0.00
100	0.30	0.03	0.00
120	0.50	0.11	0.00
140	0.77	0.25	0.02
160	1.10	0.40	0.09
180	1.40	0.60	0.18
200	1.75	0.90	0.30
220	....	1.25	0.50
240	....	1.60	0.75
260	....	....	1.08
280	....	....	1.40

10. What is the amplification factor of a type 6C5 tube operating at its rated heater voltage, with 200 volts on its plate, and with a grid bias of 6 volts? (NOTE: Use the curves of Fig. 4-19 for the solution of this and the following problems.)

11. What is the amplification factor of the tube used in Prob. 10 when its plate voltage is increased to 250 volts, the grid bias remaining at 6 volts?

12. What is the amplification factor of the tube used in Prob. 10 when its plate voltage is decreased to 150 volts, the grid bias remaining at 6 volts?

13. What is the amplification factor of the tube used in Prob. 10 when the grid bias is increased to 8 volts and the plate voltage is kept at 200 volts?

14. What is the amplification factor of the tube used in Prob. 10 when the grid bias is decreased to 4 volts and the plate voltage is kept at 200 volts?

15. What is the plate resistance of a type 6C5 tube operating at rated heater voltage, with 200 volts on its plate and with a grid bias of 6 volts? (NOTE: This is for the same operating condition as in Prob. 10. Use the curves of Fig. 4-19 for the solution of this and the following problems.)

16. What is the plate resistance of the 6C5 tube of Prob. 15 when its plate voltage is increased to 250 volts, the grid bias remaining at 6 volts?

17. What is the plate resistance of the 6C5 tube of Prob. 15 when its plate voltage is decreased to 150 volts, the grid bias remaining at 6 volts?

18. What is the plate resistance of the 6C5 tube of Prob. 15 when the grid bias is increased to 8 volts and the plate voltage is kept at 200 volts?

19. What is the plate resistance of the 6C5 tube of Prob. 15 when the grid bias is decreased to 4 volts and the plate voltage is kept at 200 volts?

20. What is the transconductance of a type 6C5 tube operating at its rated heater voltage, with 200 volts on its plate, and with a grid bias of 6 volts? (*a*) Find the value by constructing a triangle about the operating point on the grid-plate transfer characteristic curves of Fig. 4-21. (*b*) Check the answer to part (*a*) by use of Eq. (4-5*a*) and the answers of Probs. 10 and 15.

21. What is the transconductance of the 6C5 tube of Prob. 20 when its plate voltage is increased to 250 volts, the grid bias remaining at 6 volts? (*a*) Find the value from the curves of Fig. 4-21. (*b*) Find the value by use of Eq. (4-5*a*) and the answers of Probs. 11 and 16.

22. What is the transconductance of the 6C5 tube of Prob. 20 when its plate voltage is decreased to 150 volts, the grid bias remaining at 6 volts? (*a*) Find the value from the curves of Fig. 4-21. (*b*) Find the value by use of Eq. (4-5*a*) and the answers of Probs. 12 and 17.

23. What is the transconductance of the 6C5 tube of Prob. 20 when the grid bias is increased to 8 volts and the plate voltage is kept at 200 volts? (*a*) Find the value from the curves of Fig. 4-21. (*b*) Find the value by use of Eq. (4-5*a*) and the answers to Probs. 13 and 18.

24. What is the transconductance of the 6C5 tube of Prob. 20 when the grid bias is decreased to 4 volts and the plate voltage is kept at 200 volts? (*a*) Find the value from the curves of Fig. 4- 1. (*b*) Find the value by use of Eq. (4-5*a*) and the answers to Probs. 14 and 19.

25. A type 6SF5 high-mu triode is operated at rated heater voltage, with 250 volts on its plate, and a grid bias of 2 volts. Under these operating conditions the tube has a plate resistance of 66,000 ohms and a transconductance of 1500 micromhos. What is the amplification factor of the tube?

26. A type 6SF5 high-mu triode is operated at rated heater voltage, with 100 volts on its plate, and a grid bias of 1 volt. Under these operating conditions the tube has a plate resistance of 85,000 ohms and an amplification factor of 100. What is the transconductance of the tube?

27. The triode of a type 6R7 tube is operated at rated heater voltage, with 250 volts on its plate, and a grid bias of 9 volts. Under these operating conditions the transconductance is 1900 micromhos and the amplification factor is 16. What is the plate resistance of the tube?

28. A type 6C5 tube when operating at rated heater voltage, with 200 volts on its plate, and with a grid bias of 6 volts, has a plate resistance of 10,000 ohms and an amplification factor of 20. If the tube is used in an amplifier stage, what is the voltage amplification of the stage when the value of the load resistor is (*a*) 1500 ohms? (*b*) 30,000 ohms? (*c*) If a 1.5-volt input signal is applied to the grid of the tube, what is the voltage across the load resistor for part (*a*)? For part (*b*)?

29. The type 6C5 tube (same tube as Prob. 28) when operating at rated heater voltage, with 250 volts on its plate, and with a grid bias of 6 volts, has a plate resistance of 8000 ohms and an amplification factor of 20. If the tube is used in an amplifier stage, what is the voltage amplification of the stage when the value of the load resistor is (*a*) 1500 ohms? (*b*) 30,000 ohms? (*c*) If a 1.5-volt input signal is applied to the grid of the tube, what is the voltage across the load resistor for part (*a*)? For part (*b*)?

30. The type 6C5 tube (same tube as Prob. 28) when operating at rated heater voltage, with 150 volts on its plate, and with a grid bias of 6 volts, has a plate resistance of 16,000 ohms and an amplification factor of 20. If the tube is used in an amplifier stage, what is the voltage amplification of the stage when the value of the load resistor is (*a*) 1500 ohms? (*b*) 30,000 ohms? (*c*) If a 1.5-volt input signal is applied to the grid of the tube, what is the voltage across the load resistor for part (*a*)? For part (*b*)?

31. The type 6C5 tube (same tube as Prob. 28) when operating at rated heater voltage, with 200 volts on its plate, and with a grid bias of 8 volts, has a plate resistance of 14,000 ohms and an amplification factor of 20. If the tube is used in an amplifier stage, what is the voltage amplification of the stage when the value of the load resistor is (*a*) 1500 ohms? (*b*) 30,000 ohms? (*c*) If a 1.5-volt input signal is applied to the grid of the tube, what is the voltage across the load resistor for part (*a*)? For part (*b*)?

32. The type 6C5 tube (same tube as Prob. 28) when operating at rated heater voltage, with 200 volts on its plate, and with a grid bias of 4 volts, has a plate resistance of 8000 ohms and an amplification factor of 18.5.   If the tube is used in an amplifier stage, what is the voltage amplification of the stage when the value of the load resistor is (*a*) 1500 ohms? (*b*) 30,000 ohms? (*c*) If a 1.5-volt input signal is applied to the grid of the tube, what is the voltage across the load resistor for part (*a*)? For part (*b*)?

33. A type 6K5-G tube being operated at its rated heater voltage, with 100 volts on its plate, and with a grid bias of 1.5 volts, is used in a stage of amplification.   What value of load resistance is required to produce a voltage amplification of (*a*) 35? (*b*) 45? (NOTE: Obtain the values required for the solution of this problem from Appendix XV.)

34. The type 6K5-G tube (same tube as Prob. 33) being operated at its rated heater voltage, with 250 volts on its plate, and with a grid bias of 3 volts, is used in a stage of amplification.   What value of load resistance is required to produce a voltage amplification of (*a*) 35? (*b*) 45?

35. A 2-mv signal is applied to the circuit of a type 6D6 amplifier tube that is being operated at its rated heater voltage, with 100 volts on the plate, with 100 volts on the screen grid, and with a grid bias of 3 volts.   What value of load impedance is required to produce a 375-mv output signal?

36. The voltage on the plate of the type 6D6 tube used in Prob. 35 is increased to 250 volts with all other operating voltages, including the input signal voltage, remaining the same.   What value of load impedance is required to produce a 640-mv output signal?

CHAPTER V

DETECTOR CIRCUITS

One of the functions of a radio receiver is the demodulation of a modulated radio wave picked up by the receiving antenna. This function is called *detection*. In Chap. III, it was shown that detection involves two operations: (1) rectification of the modulated wave; (2) elimination of the radio frequency component of the modulated wave.

5-1. Detection. *Detector Action.* The average value of a modulated radio wave for one cycle of the audio-frequency wave is zero, and therefore the average change of current during the same period is zero (see Fig. 5-1a). The radio-frequency waves produced during one audio-frequency cycle are referred to as a *wave train*. A modulated r-f wave consists of a number of consecutive wave trains, and therefore the average change of current of a modulated r-f wave will always be zero. If the modulated r-f wave is rectified, one-half of the wave is eliminated and the average change in current for each cycle of each wave train will no longer be zero (see Fig. 5-1b). The changes in current will be similar to the a-f signal that modulates the r-f carrier wave at the transmitter.

Because the electromechanical devices used to produce audible sound waves cannot respond to the rapid variations in current of an r-f wave, it is necessary to remove the r-f component of the demodulated a-f wave. The modulation envelope, formed by joining the peaks of each of the r-f cycles, varies in the same manner as the signal impressed upon the r-f carrier wave. The a-f component of the modulated wave is therefore represented by the a-f variations of the modulation envelope. The current flowing through the detector circuit will be equal to the average value of the current, as is illustrated in Fig. 5-1b. Its variations are identical in all respects, except intensity, to the variations in current represented by the modulation envelope.

The Vacuum Tube as a Detector. Because current can flow in the plate circuit of a vacuum tube only when the plate is positive with respect to the cathode, vacuum tubes can be used as rectifiers of alternating currents. Furthermore, as detection involves the function of rectification, vacuum tubes may be used as detectors. Because of their sensitivity and current handling ability, vacuum tubes are used as detectors in modern receivers.

Factors That Determine the Type of Detector Circuit to Be Used.   There
are numerous tubes and a variety of circuits that can be used with such
tubes to perform the function of detection.   Each circuit has particular
advantages which may be compared with one another in regard to their
performance.   The following important factors should be taken into
consideration when determining which tube and circuit to use: (1)
sensitivity, (2) signal-handling ability, (3) fidelity of reproduction.   No
one detector circuit possesses a high value of all three factors, and

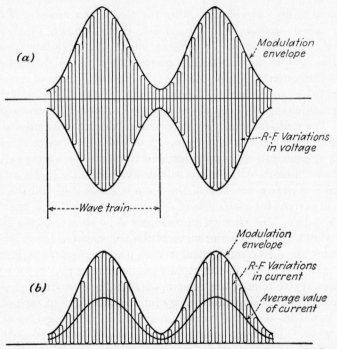

Fig. 5-1.—Detector action.   (*a*) Input signal voltage, (*b*) current through the detector.

receivers generally incorporate the type of tube and detector circuit that
will provide the characteristics most nearly suited to the needs of the
particular receiver.

The average radio receiver is used for reproducing speech and music
as transmitted by broadcasting stations.   Fidelity is a very important
factor in this type of receiver, and the detector circuit used should be
capable of reproducing the sound waves with a minimum amount of
distortion.   Radio receivers designed for broadcast reception employ
high-gain amplifier circuits, and hence sensitivity is not an important
consideration.   In these receivers the r-f signal is amplified before it

reaches the detector.   The detector circuit used should therefore be
capable of handling a large signal input.

In the design of portable receivers the overall physical size is an
important factor.   In order to obtain small units, r-f amplifier circuits
are sometimes omitted.   Detector circuits used in this type of receiver
should have a high degree of sensitivity.

If a receiver is to be used for code reception only, the fidelity of the
detector circuit can generally be ignored.   For portable receivers of code
signals the important factor is sensitivity.   For a fixed unit, where
sufficient amplifier circuits can be used, the main consideration is the
power-handling ability of the detector circuit.

5-2. Diode Detection.   *Action of a Simple Diode Detector.*   The
simplest vacuum-tube detector circuit is obtained by using a two-element
tube as a half-wave rectifier; its circuit diagram is shown in Fig. 5-2

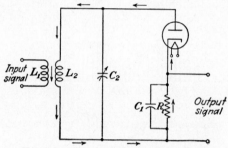

FIG. 5-2.—Simple diode detector circuit.

When the tuning circuit consisting of the inductor L_2 and the tuning
capacitor C_2 is in resonance with a desired input signal, an r-f voltage is
developed across the tuned circuit.   This voltage is applied as an input
voltage to the plate-cathode circuit of the tube through the diode by-pass
capacitor C_1 and the diode load resistor R_1.

When the plate of the diode is positive, it attracts the electrons
emitted from the cathode, and these electrons will return to the cathode
through the external circuit consisting of the secondary winding L_2 and
the output resistor R_1.   The path taken by the electrons is indicated by
the arrows on Fig. 5-2.

When the potential on the plate is negative, no electrons are attracted
to it, and therefore no current flows through the external plate circuit
during the time that the signal voltage makes the plate negative with
respect to the cathode.   It can thus be seen that the current in the output
resistor R_1 will flow in only one direction.

The capacitor C_1 and the resistor R_1 serve to eliminate the r-f pulsations and to increase the a-f voltage developed across the output load

resistor R_1. This is accomplished in the following manner. During the initial half of the first positive half-cycle of the applied r-f voltage, shown at 0-1 on Fig. 5-3, the capacitor C_1 charges to the peak value indicated by point 1. The applied r-f voltage, continuing its cycle, then rapidly diminishes to zero. As the r-f voltage starts decreasing from its first positive peak value, the capacitor C_1 starts to discharge through the load resistor R_1 but at a very slow rate as indicated by points 1 to 3 on Fig. 5-3. The time constant of this *RC* circuit is very long compared to the

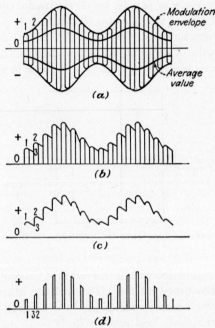

Fig. 5-3.—Waveforms illustrating the operation of a diode detector circuit. (*a*) Modulated input voltage, (*b*) charging and discharging of the diode capacitor, (*c*) voltage across the diode capacitor, (*d*) diode plate current.

short interval required for the r-f voltage to change from the positive peak value at 1 to the next positive peak at 2. The voltage on the capacitor, therefore, will decrease only slightly during this interval. Because of this capacitor action, the voltage on the cathode will be kept more positive than the voltage applied to the plate. When the signal voltage is lower than the voltage charge on the capacitor C_1, electrons will cease to flow in the plate circuit; hence no current will flow in the plate circuit during the interval 1 to 3. During the positive half of the second r-f cycle, current will again flow in the plate circuit when the signal voltage exceeds the voltage at which the charge on the capacitor holds the cathode.   The capacitor will then be charged to the peak value of the second positive half-cycle.   This action will be repeated for each succeeding r-f cycle, thus causing the voltage across the capacitor to follow the peak values of the applied r-f voltage.   The audio-frequency modulation is therefore reproduced at the capacitor as indicated in Fig. 5-3c.

The voltage across the load resistor R_1 will be the same as the voltage across the capacitor C_1.   This voltage will be a pulsating voltage representing the positive half of the modulated r-f voltage, whose average value has been increased by the capacitor C_1.   The combination of the diode, capacitor C_1, and resistor R_1 have therefore changed the r-f signal input voltage to a pulsating voltage.

The capacitor C_1 is generally referred to as the r-f by-pass or r-f filter capacitor because its action tends to smooth out the r-f pulsations at the diode load resistor.   The value of the capacitor is dependent on the frequency—the higher the frequency the smaller the amount of capacitance required.   For ordinary broadcast reception, values of 250 $\mu\mu f$ or smaller are generally used.

Example 5-1.   A certain diode-detector circuit, similar to Fig. 5-2, uses a $\frac{1}{4}$-megohm resistor for the diode load resistance R_1 and a 250-$\mu\mu f$ capacitor for the diode by-pass capacitor C_1.   (a) What is the time constant of this RC circuit?   (b) If the resonant frequency of the tuned circuit L_2C_2 is 710 kc, what time is required for the r-f wave to complete one cycle?   (c) How many times greater is the time constant of the RC circuit than the time of one cycle of the r-f wave?

Given:

$R = \frac{1}{4}$ megohm

$C = 250 \ \mu\mu f$

$f = 710$ kc

Find:

(a) $t = ?$

(b) $t_1 = ?$

(c) $\dfrac{t}{t_1} = ?$

Solution:

(a) $t = RC = 0.25 \times 10^6 \times 250 \times 10^{-12} = 62.5 \times 10^{-6}$ second

(b) $t_1 = \dfrac{1}{f} = \dfrac{1}{0.710 \times 10^6} = \dfrac{10^{-6}}{0.710} = 1.408 \times 10^{-6}$ second

(c) $\dfrac{t}{t_1} = \dfrac{62.5 \times 10^{-6}}{1.408 \times 10^{-6}} = 44.3$ times greater

Example 5-2.   The circuit of Example 5-1 also acts as a filter circuit.   (a) What is the reactance of the capacitor to a 710-kc r-f current?   (b) How does the reactance to the 710-kc r-f current compare with the value of the diode load resistance?   (c) Which path will the r-f currents take?   (d) What is the reactance of the capacitor to a 400-cycle a-f current?   (e) How does the reactance to the 400-cycle a-f current compare with the value of the diode load resistance?   (f) Which path will the a-f currents take?

Given:

$R = \frac{1}{4}$ megohm

$C = 250 \ \mu\mu f$

r-f = 710 kc

a-f = 400 cycles

Find:

(a)　$X_C = ?$

(b)　$\dfrac{R}{X_C} = ?$

(c)　path = ?

(d)　$X_C = ?$

(e)　$\dfrac{X_C}{R} = ?$

(f)　path = ?

Solution:

(a)　$X_C = \dfrac{159,000}{fC} = \dfrac{159,000}{710 \times 10^3 \times 250 \times 10^{-6}} = 895$ ohms

(b)　$\dfrac{R}{X_C} = \dfrac{250,000}{895} = 279$ (R is 279 times greater than X_C)

(c)　The r-f currents will take the capacitor path.

(d)　$X_C = \dfrac{159,000}{fC} = \dfrac{159,000}{400 \times 250 \times 10^{-6}} = 1,590,000$ ohms

(e)　$\dfrac{X_C}{R} = \dfrac{1,590,000}{250,000} = 6.36$ (X_C is 6.36 times greater than R)

(f)　The a-f currents will take the resistor path.

Full-wave Diode Detectors. Crystal and diode detectors are essentially half-wave rectifiers and do not contribute to the amplification of the

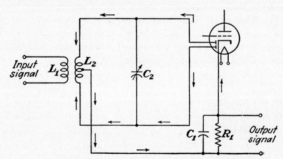

Fig. 5-4.—Duplex-diode full-wave detector circuit.

signal as do other methods of detection. Two diodes, or a duplex diode, can be connected in a detector circuit so that current will flow in either plate during opposite halves of each r-f signal input cycle (Fig. 5-4). Current will flow continually in one direction through the output resistor and full-wave detection is obtained. This type of circuit is seldom used, since its advantage generally does not justify the extra circuit complications. The only advantage gained with full-wave detection is that the circuit may be balanced so that no carrier frequency flows to the grid of the tube in the following amplifier stage. Then, theoretically, no carrier frequency filtering is required. Figure 5-4 shows the schematic circuit diagram of a duplex-diode full-wave detector circuit and the paths taken by the electrons flowing from the cathode to each plate during alternate half-cycles.

Advantages and Disadvantages of Diode Detectors. The advantages of the diode detector are (1) its ability to handle large signal voltages; (2) its low distortion factor. These qualities are due to the linear characteristics of certain types of tube, as illustrated by the curves in Fig. 5-5. These curves show the linearity of the type 6H6, which is used in some detector circuits.

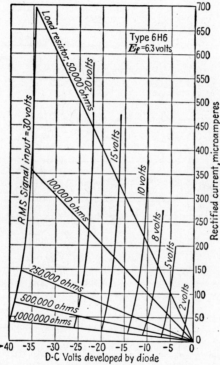

Fig. 5-5.—Average characteristics of a type 6H6 tube. Half-wave rectification, using a single diode.

One disadvantage of the diode detector is that during part of the positive half of each r-f cycle current flows through the coil in the tuned circuit. This causes a loading effect on the tuned circuit and produces the same results as a resistance connected in series with the tuned circuit. Adding resistance to a tuned circuit decreases the gain and selectivity of the circuit; thus the diode detector is characterized by its low sensitivity.

Modern receivers generally employ one or more stages of r-f amplification, and the desired selectivity and gain are obtained before the signal reaches the detector circuit. The low sensitivity characteristic of the diode detector is therefore not of very great importance in these receivers. Because the diode method of detection produces less distortion and because it permits the use of simple automatic-volume-control circuits without the necessity of an additional voltage supply, the diode method of detection is used widely in broadcast receivers. Several typical diode-detector circuits are shown in Fig. 5-6.

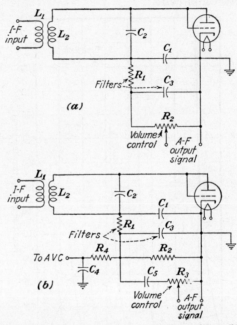

Fig. 5-6.—Diode-detector circuits. (a) Diode circuit with filter, (b) diode circuit with provision for obtaining voltage for automatic-volume-control.

Practical Diode-detector Circuits. Simple diode tubes are seldom used for practical detector circuits. In some circuits a triode is used, in which case the grid and plate are connected together externally to form a diode. Two such circuits are shown in Fig. 5-6. In superheterodyne receivers, an adjustable capacitor C_2 is generally used in the tuned circuit, as the intermediate frequency input is kept steady at some value, such as 456 kc.

Practical detector circuits require a filter to prevent the r-f voltages from reaching the output. Such a filter circuit is shown in Fig. 5-6 and consists of the resistor R_1 and the capacitor C_3. In Fig. 5-6a, the diode load resistance consists of the sum of R_1 and R_2; the output, however, is taken off R_2 only. While capacitor C_1 will by-pass most of the r-f current, the output filter capacitor C_3 is added to by-pass any r-f current from R_2

that may have entered into the R_1 path. In Fig. 5-6b, the diode load resistance consists of R_1 and R_3. The capacitors C_1 and C_3 serve the same purpose as in the circuit of Fig. 5-6a. The capacitor C_5 is used as a coupling capacitor and also serves to block the d-c component from the output circuit. In these circuits, the capacitance of C_1 and C_3 are generally equal. In the circuit of Fig. 5-6a, the value of R_2 is generally several times the value of R_1. In the circuit of Fig. 5-6b, the value of R_3 is generally several times the value of R_1. The r-f filter, however, has a disadvantage in that it reduces the useful rectified output by the amount of the voltage drop at R_1.

Example 5-3. The circuit elements shown in Fig. 5-6a have the following values: $R_1 = 50,000$ ohms, $R_2 = 250,000$ ohms, $C_1 = 100$ μμf, $C_3 = 100$ μμf. (a) What impedance does the capacitor C_1 offer to a 456-kc i-f current? (b) Which path will the i-f current take? (c) Will any of the i-f current flow into the R_1 path? (d) What impedance does the capacitor C_3 offer to any 456-kc i-f current? (e) What purpose does C_3 serve? (f) Neglecting the effect of the capacitors C_1 and C_3, what per cent of the a-f voltage developed across R_1 and R_2 is available at the output terminals?

Given:	Find:	
$R_1 = 50,000$ ohms	(a)	$X_{C1} = ?$
$R_2 = 250,000$ ohms	(b)	path $= ?$
$C_1 = 100$ μμf	(d)	$X_{C3} = ?$
$C_3 = 100$ μμf	(f) Per cent $= ?$	
i-f $= 456$ kc		

Solution:

(a) $X_{C1} = \dfrac{159,000}{fC} = \dfrac{159,000}{456 \times 10^3 \times 100 \times 10^{-6}} = 3486$ ohms

(b) The i-f current will take the capacitor path.

(c) Yes. A small amount.

(d) Same as (a). $X_{C3} = 3486$ ohms

(e) Provides a low impedance path for any i-f current that was not by-passed by the capacitor C_1.

(f) % a-f voltage at $R_2 = \dfrac{i_{af}R_2}{i_{af}(R_1 + R_2)} \times 100$

Because the current is the same in both the numerator and the denominator, then

Per cent $E = \dfrac{R_2}{R_1 + R_2} \times 100 = \dfrac{250,000}{50,000 + 250,000} \times 100 = 83.3$ per cent

Use of Multiunit Tubes as Diode Detectors. In modern receivers, it is general practice to use a multiunit tube such as a duplex-diode–triode as a detector and amplifier. The two diodes are usually connected together to form a simple diode that is used as a half-wave detector. The triode is used to amplify the signal after it has been rectified. Two typical circuits using a duplex-diode–triode are shown in Fig. 5-7. In these circuits, R_1 is the diode load resistor. The bias voltage for the triode section is obtained by the cathode bias resistor R_3. The by-pass capacitor C_3 is used to keep the a-f current out of the bias resistor R_3. The manner in which this is accomplished will be discussed in a later part of this chapter. The function of the capacitor C_4 is to block the d-c bias of the cathode from the grid. The function of the capacitor C_5 is to by-pass any r-f current from the grid circuit to the cathode and thus prevent any r-f voltage from reaching the grid of the tube.

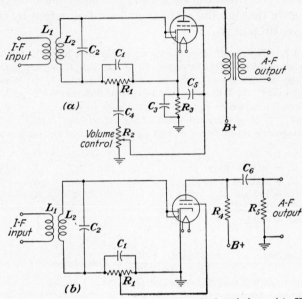

FIG. 5-7.—Diode-detector circuits using duplex-diode–triodes. (*a*) Using cathode bias (resistor R_3) for triode section, (*b*) using diode bias (portion of the diode load resistor R_1) for the triode section of the tube.

5-3. Plate Detection. *Theory of Plate Detection.* Plate detection makes use of the cutoff characteristics of a tube to accomplish the necessary rectification. The rectification takes place in the plate circuit of the tube, and therefore this type of circuit is known as *plate detection*. The grid is biased almost to cutoff, that is, it is operated so that practically no current flows in the plate circuit when the signal applied to the grid is zero. A C-battery was formerly used to obtain the necessary grid bias and because of this the plate detector is also known as a *C-bias detector*, or simply a *bias detector*. It is also referred to as a *grid-bias detector*.

Theoretical Operating Points of a Bias Detector. In the study of the characteristics of vacuum tubes, it will be found that two bends occur in the grid-plate transfer characteristic curves of some types of tubes.

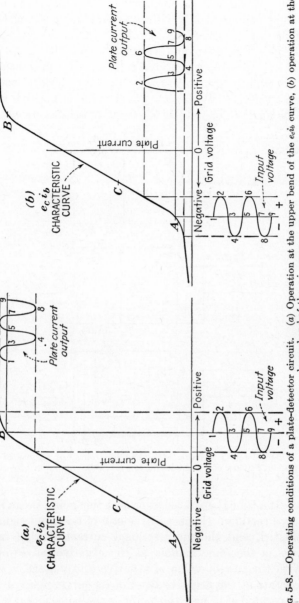

FIG. 5-8.—Operating conditions of a plate-detector circuit. (a) Operation at the upper bend of the $e_c i_b$ curve, (b) operation at the lower bend of the $e_c i_b$ curve.

While an upper bend will theoretically occur in all types of tubes, in practice it can be obtained only with tubes employing a tungsten cathode. Because of the copious emission of electrons from oxide-coated cathodes, the upper bend is difficult to obtain with tubes using this type of cathode.

With tubes employing a tungsten cathode, the upper bend occurs at some value of positive grid voltage and the lower bend at some value of negative grid voltage. With the correct value of positive grid voltage a tube can be made to operate at the positive bend of its curve, point B

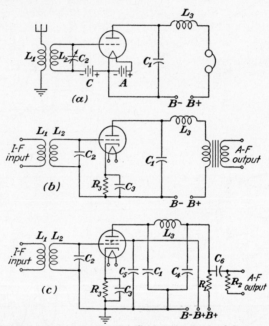

Fig. 5-9.—Plate-detector circuits. (*a*) Grid bias obtained by use of a C battery, (*b*) grid bias obtained by use of a cathode resistor, (*c*) grid bias obtained by use of a cathode resistor.

in Fig. 5-8. If a tube is operated at or near this point, it can be seen that it will act as a rectifier. Each positive half of the input signal is practically eliminated, and the unidirectional current flowing in the plate circuit varies in the same manner as the negative halves of the input signal. With the correct value of negative grid voltage, a tube can be made to operate at the negative bend of its curve, point A in Fig. 5-8. If a tube is operated at or near this point, it can be seen that it too will act as a rectifier. Each negative half of the input signal is practically eliminated, and the unidirectional current flowing in the plate circuit varies in the same manner as the positive halves of the input signal.

Positive and Negative Values of Grid Voltage.   If a tube is to be used as a grid-bias detector, theoretically it can be operated at either the negative or positive bend of its grid-plate transfer characteristic curve.   If a tube is operated with a positive grid voltage, the grid will act the same as a plate, thus causing a current to flow in the grid (input) circuit.   This current changes the variations of the grid voltage and distorts the input signal.   The plate current, being dependent on the changes in grid voltage, therefore, will also be distorted.   For this reason, tubes are operated with a negative grid voltage.   The sharper the negative bend of the curve and the nearer the grid bias is adjusted to the value corresponding to this bend, the more perfect will be the elimination of the negative half-cycle of the input signal voltage.   Three plate-detector circuits are shown in Fig. 5-9.

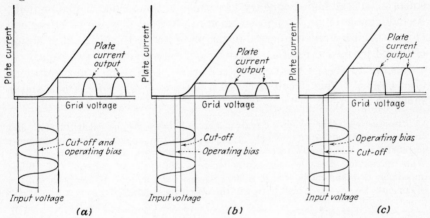

Fig. 5-10.—Operating points of a grid-bias detector.   (*a*) At cutoff, (*b*) beyond cutoff, (*c*) before cutoff.

Practical Operating Point of a Grid-bias Detector.   Theoretically, a tube used as a grid-bias detector should be operated at cutoff.   Under this condition the current flow in the plate circuit with no signal voltage applied will be zero (Fig. 5-10*a*).   In actual practice, however, the voltage on the grid is set at slightly less than cutoff value, so that a small amount of current will flow in the plate circuit when the signal applied to the grid of the tube is zero.   This no-load value of the plate current will vary from approximately 100 to 600 μa and will depend upon the tube used and the plate voltage at which it is operated.

If the value of the negative grid voltage is too large, the tube will be operated beyond cutoff.   If the tube is operated under this condition, part of the positive half-cycle of each alternating current wave impressed on the input circuit will be eliminated in addition to the entire negative half-cycle (Fig. 5-10*b*).   As the rectified signal is not a true representation of the modulated input signal voltage the resulting output is said to be distorted.

If the value of the negative grid voltage is too small, the tube will be operated before cutoff. If the tube is operated under this condition, a portion of each negative half-cycle will appear in the output (Fig. 5-10c). The rectification is therefore not complete and the resulting output will be distorted.

R-F Filter Circuits. The output of the detector tube is a unidirectional current whose strength is varying in accordance with the modulated radio frequency (Fig. 5-1b). A filter circuit is necessary to separate the audio-frequency and radio-frequency components of the rectified wave. In order to accomplish this, an r-f by-pass capacitor (Fig. 2-21) is connected between the plate and cathode. This capacitor acts as a filter and smooths out the high-frequency variations in the output or plate circuit. As inductance tends to oppose changes in current flow, an r-f choke coil (Fig. 2-13) is usually connected in the plate circuit to aid the filter action of the r-f by-pass capacitor. Many modern receivers use two capacitors connected to the r-f plate choke coil in order to form a more efficient filter circuit. This circuit is called a *low-pass π-type filter circuit* and is shown in Fig. 5-9c.

Example 5-4. The r-f filter circuit of Fig. 5-9b has a 500-$\mu\mu f$ capacitor at C_1 and an 80-mh choke at L_3. (a) What impedance does the capacitor offer to a 456-kc i-f current? (b) What impedance does the choke offer to a 456-kc i-f current? (c) What impedance does the capacitor offer to a 500-cycle a-f current? (d) What impedance does the choke offer to a 500-cycle a-f current? (e) Which path will the i-f currents take? (f) Which path will the a-f currents take?

Given:
$$C = 500 \ \mu\mu f$$
$$L = 80 \ \text{mh}$$
$$f = 456 \ \text{kc}$$

Find:
(a) $Z = ?$
(b) $Z = ?$
(c) $Z = ?$
(d) $Z = ?$
(e) path of i-f?
(f) path of a-f?

Solution:

(a) $Z = \dfrac{159,000}{fC} = \dfrac{159,000}{456 \times 10^3 \times 500 \times 10^{-6}} = 697$ ohms

(b) $Z = 2\pi fL = 2 \times 3.14 \times 456 \times 10^3 \times 80 \times 10^{-3} = 239,094$ ohms

(c) $Z = \dfrac{159,000}{fC} = \dfrac{159,000}{500 \times 500 \times 10^{-6}} = 636,000$ ohms

(d) $Z = 2\pi fL = 2 \times 3.14 \times 500 \times 80 \times 10^{-3} = 251.2$ ohms

(e) The i-f currents will take the capacitor path

(f) The a-f currents will take the inductor path

Plate Load. The plate circuit contains a loading device through which the plate current will flow. The modulated voltage developed across this device will be equal to the product of the plate current and the impedance of the output load.　The plate load may be a resistor, primary of a transformer, audio choke coil, earphones, loudspeaker, or some other device.

Amount of Grid Bias Required.　Plate detectors are comparatively insensitive to weak signals, have a high distortion factor, and are capable of handling large signal voltages.　As it is desirable to avoid driving the grid positive, the largest signal voltage that can be applied to the grid of a tube should not be greater than the value of the grid bias that is used.

When a signal is applied to the grid, the amount of voltage at the grid will depend upon the value of the grid bias and the input signal voltage. In other words, the value of the grid bias will be increased during the negative halves of the input signal and decreased during the positive halves.　The upper and lower values of the grid bias indicate the range of the grid voltage, which is generally referred to as the *grid-voltage swing.* These values may be expressed mathematically as

$$e_{c \cdot \text{max}} = E_c - E_{g \cdot \text{max}} \tag{5-1}$$

$$e_{c \cdot \text{min}} = E_c + E_{g \cdot \text{max}} \tag{5-2}$$

where e_c = instantaneous total grid voltage, volts

$\quad\ E_c$ = average or quiescent value of grid voltage, volts

$\quad E_{g \cdot \text{max}}$ = maximum value of varying component of grid voltage, volts

Example 5-5.　A tube is operated with a grid bias of nine volts.　What is the grid-voltage swing when an a-c signal is applied to the input circuit if the maximum value of the signal voltage is (*a*) 6 volts? (*b*) 9 volts? (*c*) 10 volts?

Given:

$$E_c = -9 \text{ volts}$$
(*a*) $E_{g \cdot \text{max}} = \quad 6 \text{ volts}$
(*b*) $E_{g \cdot \text{max}} = \quad 9 \text{ volts}$
(*c*) $E_{g \cdot \text{max}} = \quad 10 \text{ volts}$

Find:

(*a*)
(*b*) $\left. \begin{array}{l} e_{c \cdot \text{max}} \\ e_{c \cdot \text{min}} \end{array} \right.$
(*c*)

Solution:

(*a*)　$e_{c \cdot \text{max}} = E_c - E_{g \cdot \text{max}} = -9 - 6 = -15$ volts

$\quad\ \ e_{c \cdot \text{min}} = E_c + E_{g \cdot \text{max}} = -9 + 6 = -3$ volts

(*b*)　$e_{c \cdot \text{max}} = E_c - E_{g \cdot \text{max}} = -9 - 9 = -18$ volts

$\quad\ \ e_{c \cdot \text{min}} = E_c + E_{g \cdot \text{max}} = -9 + 9 = 0$ volts

(*c*)　$e_{c \cdot \text{max}} = E_c - E_{g \cdot \text{max}} = -9 - 10 = -19$ volts

$\quad\ \ e_{c \cdot \text{min}} = E_c + E_{g \cdot \text{max}} = -9 + 10 = +1$ volt

The factors that determine the efficiency of rectification of a plate detector are the grid bias, plate voltage, and signal voltage.　The value of grid bias to be used will depend on the plate voltage and the tube used. Different types of tubes require different values of grid bias to produce cutoff for similar plate voltages.　These values can be obtained from

Appendix XV or from the grid-plate transfer characteristic curves in standard tube manuals. The value of the grid bias used will determine the amount of signal voltage that can be applied to the tube without causing distortion of the signal in the output circuit.

Example 5-6. A type 6C5 tube (triode) is used as a grid-bias detector and is operated with 250 volts on its plate. (*a*) What grid voltage is recommended for these operating conditions? (*b*) What is the greatest amount of signal voltage that can be applied to the input circuit without causing distortion?

Given: Find:
    Tube = 6C5   (*a*) E_c = ?
    E_b = 250 volts   (*b*) Maximum input volts?

Solution:

(*a*) From Appendix XV (or standard tube manual) $E_c = -17$ volts
(*b*) In order to avoid distortion, the grid should never be driven positive, therefore the maximum input signal should not exceed 17 volts.

5-4. Automatic Grid Bias. *Methods of Obtaining the Required Amount of Grid Bias.* It has previously been explained that the value of negative grid voltage at which a tube operates is called the *grid bias*. In the early stages of radio, this bias was obtained by means of a separate power supply such as a C battery (Fig. 5-9a) or from the voltage divider in the power supply. The grid bias for the various tubes in a receiver can also be obtained by causing the plate current to flow through a resistor. This resistor is placed in the cathode circuit and is called the *cathode bias resistor* (Fig. 2-1). It has been used in the detector circuits explained in the previous articles. The manner in which the cathode bias resistor produces the correct value of grid bias will now be presented in detail.

Obtaining Grid Bias by Use of a Cathode Bias Resistor. In the circuit shown in Fig. 5-11, the grid bias for the 6J5 tube is obtained by placing the resistance R_k between the cathode and the negative side of the B supply, or ground. In order to obtain this automatic grid bias, the d-c component of the plate current is made to return to the cathode through the resistor R_k. The voltage drop across this resistor, therefore, is determined by the value of its resistance and the amount of current flowing through it. The value of resistance required can be obtained by applying Ohm's law.

$$R_k = \frac{E_c}{I_b} \qquad (5\text{-}3)$$

where R_k = value of cathode bias resistance, ohms
    E_c = grid bias, volts
    I_b = average or quiescent value of plate current, amperes

From Fig. 5-11, it can be seen that point A will be negative with respect to the cathode. The grid, being connected to point A through the secondary of the input transformer, will therefore also be negative with respect to the cathode, and its potential will be equal to the voltage drop across the cathode bias resistor R_k.

The grid-bias voltage furnished by the cathode bias resistor is dependent on the amount of plate current, which in turn is dependent on the value of plate voltage used. If the plate voltage is increased, the plate current will increase and the amount of grid bias furnished by the cathode bias resistor will increase accordingly. In a similar manner, if the plate voltage is decreased, the plate current will decrease and the amount of grid bias furnished by the cathode bias resistor will decrease accordingly. Therefore, the correct value of grid-bias voltage is automatically main-

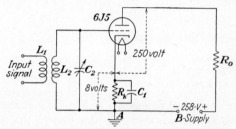

FIG. 5-11.—Method of obtaining grid bias by use of a cathode bias resistor.

tained regardless of changes in plate voltage. For this reason, this method of obtaining the grid-bias voltage is referred to as the *automatic* or *self-biasing method*.

A-f By-pass Capacitor. The cathode bias resistor must be shunted by a large capacitor in order to by-pass the a-c component of the plate current, which otherwise would cause the voltage across the grid circuit to vary continually. The value of this capacitor should be one microfarad or larger. In Fig. 5-9 this capacitor is indicated as C_3, while in Fig. 5-11 it appears as C_1.

Example 5-7. A type 6J7 tube, used as a self-biased detector, is to be operated with 250 volts applied to its plate and 100 volts on its screen grid. The plate current is to be adjusted to 0.43 milliampere when the input signal is zero. (*a*) What value of cathode bias resistor is necessary for these conditions? (*b*) How much power is consumed by this resistor? (*c*) What power rating should the resistor have?

Given: Find:
$E_b = 250$ volts   (*a*) $R_k = ?$
$E_{c2} = 100$ volts   (*b*) $P = ?$
$I_b = 0.43$ ma   (*c*) Rating?

Solution:

(a) For these operating conditions, $E_c = -4.3$ volts (from Appendix XV or a standard tube manual)

$$R_k = \frac{E_c}{I_b} = \frac{4.3}{0.00043} = 10{,}000 \text{ ohms}$$

(b) $P = I_b{}^2 R_k = (0.00043)^2 \times 10{,}000 = 0.1849$ watt

(c) A $\frac{1}{2}$-watt resistor should be used.

Example 5-8. The cathode bias resistor of the tube used in Example 5-7 was found to be 10,000 ohms. (a) What value of by-pass capacitor should be used with this resistor if it is desired that the resistor offer at least 100 times more impedance to a 500-cycle a-f current than the capacitor? (b) What standard rating and type of capacitor is recommended for this application?

Given:
$$R_k = 10{,}000 \text{ ohms}$$
$$f = 500 \text{ cycles}$$

Find:
(a) $C = ?$
(b) Rating, type?

Solution:

(a) $X_C = \dfrac{10{,}000}{100} = 100$ ohms (maximum)

$C = \dfrac{159{,}000}{f X_C} = \dfrac{159{,}000}{500 \times 100} = 3.18 \ \mu\text{f}$ (minimum)

(b) A 4-μf, 25-volt, electrolytic capacitor.

Plate, Grid, and B-supply Voltages. In Fig. 5-11, it should be observed that the voltage of the B supply must be equal to the sum of the plate voltage and the voltage drop at the cathode bias resistor. In this case it is equal to 250 volts plus 8 volts, or 258 volts. It is assumed that there is no drop in voltage at the load impedance, which may be the primary of a transformer, a loudspeaker, or other device having a negligible d-c resistance. Plate voltages are measured between cathode and plate terminals and grid voltages are measured between grid and cathode terminals. The d-c resistance of the input tuning coil L_2 is negligible and therefore its voltage drop can be disregarded.

5-5. Grid Detection. *Grid Resistor-capacitor Detector Circuits.* The most sensitive type of detector circuit is the *grid detector*, sometimes called the *grid-rectification detector* or the *grid-leak detector*. Because of its high sensitivity, this circuit was frequently used in the earlier stages of radio design. The development of the screen-grid tube made it possible to amplify the r-f signal without producing distortion. Sensitivity then no longer remained an important factor, for the signal could now be increased a sufficient amount before it reached the detector circuit. This type of detector circuit is therefore seldom used in modern receivers designed for broadcast reception.

Three grid-detection circuits are shown in Fig. 5-12. The output of these circuits is similar to the circuits for the diode and plate detectors

already studied.   In the circuit shown in Fig. 5-12a a triode is used, and
the grid capacitor C_g is connected in parallel with the grid resistor R_g.
This combination is connected between the grid of the tube and one side
of the secondary of the input transformer.   In the circuit shown in Fig.
5-12b a triode is again used; the grid capacitor is connected as before, but
the grid resistor is now connected from the grid side of the capacitor to
the cathode.   In the circuit shown in Fig. 5-12c a pentode is used.   The

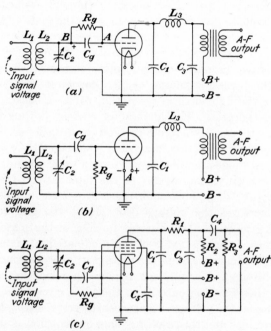

FIG. 5-12.—Grid-leak detector circuits.   (*a*) Grid resistor connected in the grid side
of the grid circuit, (*b*) grid resistor connected from the grid of the tube to the cathode,
(*c*) grid resistor connected in the cathode side of the grid circuit.

grid resistor and grid capacitor are connected in the cathode side of the
grid circuit instead of the grid side as in Fig. 5-12a.

Principle of Grid Detection.   The principle of detector operation is the
same for all three circuits.   The grid resistor R_g and the capacitor C_g
form an impedance that corresponds to the load impedance C_1 and R_1 of
the diode detector (Fig. 5-2).   The grid circuit, consisting of the source
of input signal voltage, the grid and cathode of the tube, and the resistor-
capacitor combination R_gC_g, operates as a half-wave rectifier in the same
manner as a diode detector.

Circuit Action.   In grid-circuit detection, a triode is used simultaneously as a diode detector and a triode amplifier.   The grid and cathode

of the triode operate as a diode detector and at the same time serve as the input circuit of the triode amplifier. Because of this simultaneous dual operation of the grid, the circuit action of grid detection becomes complex. To understand the operation of this type of detection it is therefore necessary to study the instantaneous action of the grid both as a plate for the diode detector and as a grid for the triode amplifier.

When the signal input is zero, the voltages on the grid and the cathode are the same, that is, zero. The voltage on the plate will cause a steady stream of electrons to flow from the cathode to the plate. As the grid is in the path of this electron flow, some of the electrons will strike it, thus making the grid negative with respect to the cathode. The grid capacitor C_g (Fig. 5-12a) becomes charged, plate A negatively and plate B positively. This charge remains on the capacitor and the resultant current flowing through the grid resistor R_g causes a constant bias to be maintained on the grid. The amount of current flowing through the grid resistor is very small, therefore the voltage drop across it is also very small, generally only a fraction of a volt. Consequently, when the tube is considered as a triode amplifier, it will have a small amount of grid bias.

During the positive half-cycles of the modulated r-f input signal, additional current will flow through the grid resistor. This increase in grid current increases the voltage drop across the grid resistor, thus increasing the grid bias. The current flowing in the plate circuit will therefore decrease. As the value of the modulated r-f signal voltage is varied with succeeding r-f cycles, the voltage drop across the grid resistor will vary accordingly. The plate current is dependent on the amount of grid bias and therefore the current in the plate circuit will decrease in the same manner as the voltage drop across the grid resistor, R_g, increases. The shift in grid bias and the resulting plate current flow is shown in Fig. 5-13.

The grid capacitor has a low value of capacitance and will pass the high-frequency signal input. The current is rectified by means of the diode-detector action of the grid and cathode. The rectified signal current will then flow through the grid resistor, thus causing a voltage to be developed across it. This voltage is applied to the input (grid-cathode) circuit of the tube which may then be considered as operating as an amplifier. The various stages of grid-circuit detection are shown in Fig. 5-13.

Summary of Grid-circuit Detection. The action of grid-circuit detection may be summarized as follows: (1) the small flow of electrons in the grid circuit develops a voltage across the grid resistor, thus causing the tube to operate with a negative grid voltage (grid bias) equal to this voltage drop; (2) the modulated r-f signal input current is rectified by the diode-detector action of the grid and cathode; (3) the rectified r-f current flows through the grid resistor, thus developing a voltage across it, and this voltage increases the negative bias on the grid and decreases the plate-current flow; (4) the tube amplifies the rectified r-f pulsations.

Filter Circuit. The plate current, being dependent on the grid bias, will vary in the same manner as the variations in grid voltage. In grid-

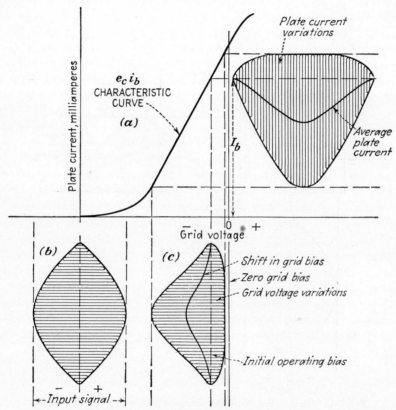

Fig. 5-13.—Plate circuit operating characteristics of a grid-leak detector.

detector circuits, the grid operates with a negative voltage that varies at radio frequencies, and consequently the plate current will vary in the same manner, see Fig. 5-13a. The filter circuit, consisting of the capacitors C_1, C_3, and the r-f choke L_3 (Fig. 5-12a), will smooth out the high-frequency variations, and the output of the filter will be a unidirectional current varying at an audio frequency similar to the average plate current indicated on Fig. 5-13a. Because rectification is accomplished in the grid circuit, this type of detection is also known as *grid-circuit rectification*.

Operating Voltage of Grid Detectors. In analyzing the operation of the grid-circuit detector its two functions can be considered separately. The detector or grid-cathode circuit may be analyzed from inspection of the grid characteristic curves in Fig. 5-14. This illustration indicates that the curved portion of the curve is used and hence rectification or detection is accomplished. The amplifying action involves the grid,

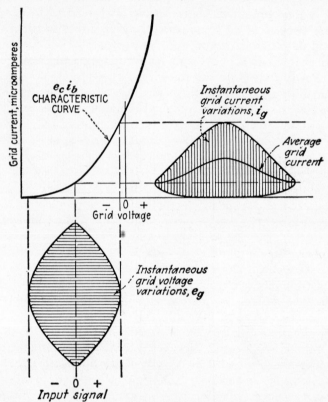

Fig. 5-14.—Grid circuit operating characteristics of a grid-leak detector.

plate, and cathode, and may be analyzed from examination of the grid-plate transfer characteristic curve. As grid-circuit detectors operate with practically zero grid bias, the operating point on the grid-plate transfer characteristic curve is determined by the plate voltage. In order to obtain the maximum amount of amplification with a minimum amount of distortion, the operating point as an amplifier should be as near as possible to the middle point of the straight portion of the curve, point C in Fig. 5-8. The relation between the operating point and the amplification will be discussed in detail in Chaps. VII and VIII.

Characteristics of Grid Detection.   The current in the grid circuit of a grid detector does not vary in the same proportion as the variations of the input signal voltage.   Figure 5-14 shows a typical grid characteristic curve.   Because of the small grid bias, the tube will operate on the curved portion of the curve.   Under this condition, the variation in grid current is practically proportional to the square of the grid-voltage variations. Because of this, grid-circuit detectors are often referred to as *square-law detectors.*   Because of the square-law variation, the strength of the input signal will be increased but it will also be distorted.   Grid detection is therefore characterized by its high distortion factor and high sensitivity.

5-6. Power Detection.   In the early stages of radio development the power-handling ability of the tubes used for detector circuits was limited and therefore the input signal could not be amplified extensively before it reached the detector without producing distortion of the output signal. Because of feedback in the tube and circuit, it was impossible to produce any great amount of amplification in a radio-frequency stage because the three-electrode tubes used at that time would oscillate when the input signal voltage became too large.   This made it necessary to use one or more stages of audio-frequency amplification in order to obtain the desired volume.   The a-f amplifiers, however, did not provide a perfect solution to the problem, since, in addition to amplifying the desired signal, they also amplified the undesired static noises.

Power Detectors.   The screen-grid tube made it possible to construct high-gain r-f amplifier circuits without producing oscillation.   Improvements in tube design also increased the power-handling ability of the detector tubes.   Modern receivers use multiple stages of high-gain amplifier circuits and a number of tuned circuits before the detector in order to obtain the desired gain and selectivity.   The detector circuit used in these receivers must be capable of handling large signal voltages without producing distortion.   This type of detector circuit is called a *power detector* and may be either a grid-circuit or plate-circuit detector.

It has previously been mentioned that the voltage of the input signal should never drive the grid voltage of plate detectors positive.   Therefore, the power-handling ability of a plate detector is determined by the amount of grid bias used.   In grid-circuit detection, the amount of signal voltage that can be applied to the input circuit of the tube without producing distortion in its amplifying action is determined by the amount of voltage required to operate the tube as an amplifier on the straight portion of its grid-plate transfer characteristic curve.   The input signal voltage of power detectors is generally greater than one volt.

Grid- and Plate-circuit Power Detectors.   The operating voltages and external circuits for power detectors are different from those used for detectors having a weak signal input. For grid-circuit detection, the plate voltage is generally very high and the value of grid capacitor and grid resistor is lower than that used in detectors having a weak signal input. In plate-circuit rectification, the tube is operated with a high grid bias. This negative grid voltage is approximately one-tenth of the voltage applied to the plate. A grid-circuit power detector is shown in Fig. 5-15a. With zero signal input, the plate current would be very high because the tube is operating with a zero grid bias. In order to keep the plate current at a safe value, the plate voltage is reduced by means of the

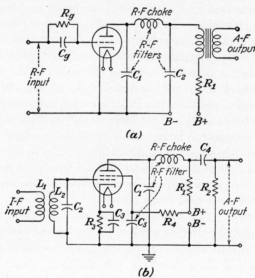

Fig. 5-15.—Power-detector circuits. (a) Grid-circuit power detector, (b) plate-circuit power detector.

resistor R_1. When an input signal is applied, the grid becomes negative, thus lowering the plate current. This decrease in plate current lowers the voltage drop across R_1 and restores the plate voltage to normal. A plate-circuit power detector is shown in Fig. 5-15b. The values of grid bias and screen-grid voltage to be used are determined by the plate voltage and the resistance of the plate circuit. In general, it is desirable to use as high a plate voltage as is practical in order to produce a high degree of amplification.

5-7. Heterodyne Detection. *Detection of Continuous-wave Code Signals.* Code signals are generally transmitted by interrupting the carrier wave at definite intervals, corresponding to the dits and dahs (dots and dashes) of the Morse code. During the periods of time when a dit or dah is being transmitted, an r-f signal of constant amplitude is being sent out. This method of transmission is commonly referred to as *continuous-wave* or *c-w transmission*.

If a c-w signal is applied to any of the detector circuits previously described, rectification of the r-f wave will take place, and a series of interrupted currents whose average values will be of constant amplitude will appear at the output side of the detector circuit. If this output current is applied to earphones or a loudspeaker, the only sound it can

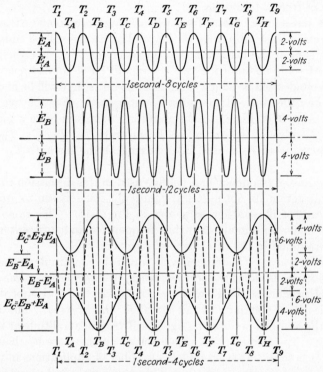

FIG. 5-16.—Illustration of the heterodyne action resulting when two waves of unequal amplitude and frequency are combined.

produce is a click, which may occur at the start and finish of each dit or dah. In order to reproduce signals similar to those sent out by the transmitter, a new method called *heterodyne detection* is introduced.

Principle of Heterodyne Action. Heterodyne action is the result of combining two alternating voltages of different frequencies in a common detector in order to obtain a signal voltage of a third value of frequency. The envelope of the resultant wave will vary in amplitude at a frequency that is equal to the difference between the frequencies of the two signal voltages that are being combined. The range of the amplitude swing of the new voltage is determined by the sum and difference of the two voltages being combined. Figure 5-16 shows two signal waves, A and B, and the resultant voltage wave C. The frequency of signal A is 8 cycles per second and that of signal B is 12 cycles per second; the envelope of the resultant wave has a frequency of 12 minus 8, or 4 cycles per second. The maximum voltage of signal A is 2 volts and that of B is 4 volts. The envelope of the resultant wave will therefore vary in voltage from E_B minus E_A to E_B plus E_A. In this case, it will vary from 4 minus 2 to 4 plus 2, or from 2 to 6 volts.

These results are obtained when two waves are combined in a non-linear circuit. The amplitude of the resultant wave will be equal to the algebraic sum of the instantaneous values of the two waves being combined. At some instants the two waves will be of similar polarity and the two voltages will be added. At other instants they will be of opposite polarity and the two voltages must be subtracted. For the two voltage waves A and B of Fig. 5-16 the resultant wave will have a maximum value of E_B plus E_A occurring at the instants T_B, T_D, T_F, T_H, and a minimum value of E_B minus E_A occurring at the instants T_A, T_C, T_E, T_G.

The values of frequency and voltage used in this discussion to explain heterodyne action are not practical values but were chosen to provide an easier means of illustration, as shown in Fig. 5-16. This same action, however, holds for signals of higher frequencies and different voltages such as are found in the r-f circuits of receivers.

Beat Frequency. The frequency at which the amplitude of the resultant wave varies is called *the beat frequency,* or *difference frequency.* The process of producing these beats by combining two waves of different frequencies in a nonlinear circuit is called *heterodyning.* The average value of the rectified heterodyne signal will vary in amplitude at the beat frequency. The frequency of an a-c wave can therefore be changed by heterodyne action. This action has a number of applications in the field of radio communications. An inaudible c-w signal can be made audible by combining it with another wave and producing a beat frequency that lies within the audible sound range. This is known as *heterodyne code reception.* In this type of reception, the incoming signal is usually combined with a frequency of such a value that the beat frequency produced will be approximately 1000 cycles.

Intermediate-frequency Amplifiers. Another use of heterodyne action is to convert the frequency of an input signal to a definite intermediate frequency. Amplification of the signal can thus be made more efficient as the amplifiers can then be designed for a definite frequency. In this method, the i-f signal is adjusted to the frequency for which the amplifier is designed instead of the amplifier being made to amplify signals over a wide range of frequencies.   Superheterodyne receivers use this principle in the intermediate-frequency amplifier stages.   The theory and construction of i-f amplifiers will be taken up in Chaps. VII and XIV.

Heterodyne-detector Circuits.   A simple heterodyne-detector circuit is shown in Fig. 5-17.   This circuit contains two fundamental parts, one a plate detector and the other a tuned-grid oscillator.   The oscillator circuit, the theory of which is described in Chap. X, is adjusted to a frequency slightly above or below the frequency of the input signal. The current in the plate circuit of the oscillator T_2 is made to flow through

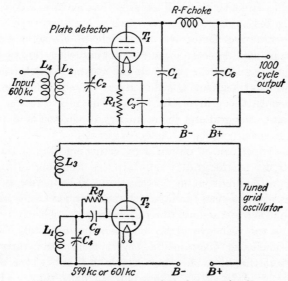

FIG. 5-17.—Simple heterodyne-detector circuit.

the coil L_3, which is inductively coupled to the coil L_2 in the grid circuit of the plate detector T_1.   In this manner, both the input signal from the coil L_4 and the oscillator output from the coil L_3 are applied to the grid of the plate detector.   As a result of the heterodyne action that takes place when two alternating voltages are combined, the output of the detector circuit will be an alternating voltage whose frequency is equal to the difference of the input voltages, or the beat frequency.

Example 5-9.   A c-w signal is transmitted at a frequency of 600 kc.   To what frequency must the oscillator circuit of a receiver be adjusted if the receiver is to produce a 1000-cycle audio signal from the received signal?

Given: Find:
$$f_{\text{c-w}} = 600 \text{ kc}$$ $$f_{\text{osc.}} = ?$$
$$f_{\text{a-s}} = 1 \text{ kc}$$
Solution:

$$f_{\text{osc.}} = f_{\text{c-w}} \pm f_{\text{a-s}} = 600 \pm 1 = 601 \text{ or } 599 \text{ kc}$$

Whether the oscillator frequency is higher or lower than the frequency of the c-w signal is not important, as it is the difference between the two frequencies that determines the frequency of modulation or beat frequency. A more efficient method, which uses a single tube for both the detector and oscillator, is generally used in small receivers. This type of detector circuit is called an *autodyne detector* and is taken up in a later part of this chapter. The energy of the oscillator can be transferred to the detector by coupling the oscillator to the plate circuit of the detector instead of to the grid circuit. Also, the method used to couple these two circuits can be capacitive as well as inductive, as was used in the circuit shown in Fig. 5-17.

5-8. Regenerative Detectors. *Principle of Regenerative Detection.* The output of any detector circuit will vary with the signal voltage impressed on the grid of the tube. If the resistance of the resonant grid circuit is lowered, the circuit Q will increase, thereby increasing the input signal applied to the grid of the tube. The ratio between the input signal applied to the grid and the input signal received is increased, thus increasing the sensitivity of the detector circuit.

The same effect can be obtained by returning part of the energy of the plate circuit to the grid circuit. If this feedback is of the proper phase relation, the input voltage on the grid will be increased. This will increase the ratio between the input voltage applied to the grid and the output voltage across the load, thus increasing the sensitivity of the circuit. This is the principle of the regenerative detector. Figure 5-18 shows the schematic diagrams of two typical regenerative detector circuits. From these two diagrams, it can be seen that the basic circuit of the regenerative detector is somewhat similar to the tuned-grid oscillator section of Fig. 5-17.

Action of a Regenerative-detector Circuit. When an input signal is applied to the coil L_3 of Fig. 5-18, a voltage is induced in the coil L_2. This voltage will be at its maximum value when the grid circuit is resonant for the frequency of the signal being received. When this voltage is impressed on the grid of the tube, it will cause the plate current flowing through the coil L_1 to vary. This change in current in L_1 causes the magnetic field about the coil L_1 to vary in the same manner. This variation of the magnetic field causes a voltage to be induced in the coil L_2. If the induced voltage is in phase with the voltage due to the input signal, the feedback voltage will be added to the signal voltage, thus causing a still greater change in the amount of plate current. This effect is repeated until some limiting action takes place. If the original feedback voltage is slightly less than the original signal voltage, the amount of increase in voltage and current will decrease with each energy

transfer from plate to grid, until the action becomes stabilized.   If the
coupling between the plate and grid coils is such that the original amount

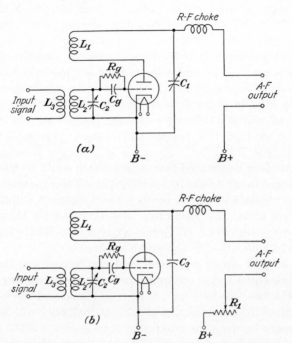

(a)

(b)

Fig. 5-18.—Regenerative detector.   (*a*) Capacitor controlled, (*b*) resistance controlled.

of feedback voltage is greater than the original input signal voltage, the
resistance of the circuit is made negative.   After a number of successive
transfers of energy from the plate to the grid circuit, the circuit will
break into oscillation.   The amplification of
the signal voltage at the grid will increase
with increases in the amount of feedback,
reaching a maximum at the point where the
detector starts to oscillate.

Methods of Controlling the Amount of Re-
generation.   The amount of regeneration may
be controlled in the following manners: (1) by
adjusting the amount of coupling between the
grid and plate coils of the three-circuit tuner
(see Fig. 5-19); (2) by varying the amount of

Fig.   5-19.—A   three-circuit
tuner.

capacitance C_1 between the plate coil and cathode (Fig. 5-18*a*); (3) by
varying the amount of voltage applied to the plate by means of the
resistor R_1 (Fig. 5-18*b*).   By varying the capacitor C_1 or the resistor R_1

to a point just below oscillation, the feedback to the grid circuit may be adjusted so that the amount of regeneration will remain constant.

Disadvantages of Regenerative Circuits. Regeneration is an economical means of obtaining radio-frequency amplification. Regenerative circuits, however, have a number of disadvantages and therefore this type of circuit is not generally used in commercial receivers. Among its disadvantages are: (1) critical adjustments are required to obtain the proper amount of regeneration; (2) squeals will result from accidentally allowing the tube to break into oscillation; (3) the detector acts as a transmitter when it is oscillating and these oscillations will be heard by other near-by receivers that happen to be tuned to the same frequency.

5-9. Autodyne Detection. *Principle of Autodyne Detection.* In the preceding article it was stated that regeneration could be increased to a point where the circuit breaks into oscillation. This characteristic makes it possible to obtain heterodyne reception of c-w signals with the use of a single vacuum tube. An oscillating detector used for this purpose is called an *autodyne detector.* Its circuit is the same as for the regenerative-detector circuits described in the previous article.

The tuned grid circuit produces local oscillations and the beat frequency will be equal to the difference between the frequency of the c-w signal and the local oscillations. If the c-w signal and the local oscillations are both of the same frequency, no beat frequency will be produced, as the difference between the two frequencies is zero. If the grid circuit is tuned progressively to a higher or lower frequency than the c-w signal, the beat frequency will increase in frequency and pitch with each change in grid circuit frequency until it is no longer audible. By tuning the grid circuit to a frequency whose value is 1000 cycles above or below the frequency of the incoming c-w signal, a 1000-cycle beat frequency is obtained. A beat frequency of 1000 cycles is commonly used because it produces an audible note at the earphones or loudspeaker that can be continually listened to easily and that will permit each dit, dah, or space to be quickly distinguished.

Advantages of Autodyne Detection. Autodyne or oscillating detectors are used quite frequently in receiver circuits designed for receiving code signals. The advantages of the autodyne detector are: (1) a single tuning control is used instead of two, as required for heterodyne detection; (2) the circuit is simple; (3) its sensitivity and selectivity are very high compared to other methods of detection; (4) a single-tube autodyne detector can produce as much power as can be obtained from two stages of r-f amplification followed by a heterodyne detector.

As in the case of a regenerative circuit, a signal is radiated when the circuit is in oscillation, thus causing interference with near-by receivers.

Frequency Limits of Autodyne Detectors. The autodyne detector can-not be used when the beat frequency is an appreciable percentage of the signal frequency, as is the case with superheterodyne receivers. When the difference in frequency becomes too large, the tuned circuit that con-trols the frequency of oscillation will be so far out of resonance with the incoming signal that the resultant response will be very weak.

5-10. Superregeneration. *Critical Operating Point of Regenerative Detectors.* In a regenerative detector, the amplification due to regenera-tion will build itself up to a point where the circuit breaks into oscillation. At this point, the output is the greatest because the effective resistance of the circuit is zero and the losses are therefore at a minimum. This operating point is very critical and therefore it is very difficult to maintain the circuit at the desired operating point. A slight change in any part of the circuit will cause the circuit to break into oscillation.

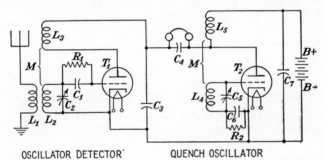

OSCILLATOR DETECTOR·   QUENCH OSCILLATOR

Fig. 5-20.—Separately quenched superregenerative detector circuit.

Principle of Superregeneration. Superregeneration is a means whereby the effective resistance of the circuit is kept at zero. This is accomplished by varying the regeneration from an oscillatory to a non-oscillatory condition at a low radio-frequency rate. During the oscilla-tory interval, the oscillations will build up, only to be suppressed by the low frequency that is applied to the plate. This causes the circuit to go in and out of oscillation at a periodic rate that is equal to the frequency being applied to the plate. This frequency is called the *quench frequency* and its value is generally slightly higher than that of the audio frequencies, being approximately 20 to 25 kc.

Separately-quenched Superregenerative Circuit. Superregeneration may be obtained by using a separate oscillator to supply the quench frequency or by providing a means whereby the grid is intermittently blocked at the desired frequency. The first method is called a *separately quenched circuit,* and a diagram of such a circuit is shown in Fig. 5-20. This circuit is basically the same as the regenerative circuit, except that the plate of the oscillating detector T_1 is supplied with a low r-f voltage of constant frequency in place of the steady direct voltage. During the interval that the plate of T_1 is positive, electrons will flow in its plate circuit. During the opposite half-cycle, the plate of T_1 is negative and no electrons will flow to it; therefore, the oscillations will die out during this interval. The average voltage of the oscillations existing across the tuned input circuit L_2C_2 will depend on the value of the signal voltage acting in this circuit. If this signal is rectified, the plate current in T_1 will vary in accordance with the envelope of its input grid signal. If a tetrode or a pentode is used, the quench frequency is applied to the screen grid instead of to the plate.

Self-quenched Superregenerative Circuits. The circuit of a self-quenching superregenerative detector is similar to the basic regenerative circuits shown in Fig. 5-18. The only changes made are in the values of the grid capacitor and grid resistor. Both of these values are increased considerably, thus increasing the time required for the grid capacitor to discharge. The grid resistor has a high resistance and blocks the electrons from the grid. This causes the value of the plate current to decrease and the input to the grid, being dependent on the plate output, will also decrease. The charge on the grid capacitor gradually leaks off through the grid resistor thus reducing the grid bias. The tube will now amplify and build up oscillations as before. The frequency of this self-quenching action is determined by the values of the grid resistor and grid capacitor.

Uses of Superregenerative Circuits. Superregenerative detector circuits are used in light, compact, portable code receivers. The ratio of quench frequency to signal frequency should be approximately 1 to 1000. Therefore, this type of circuit can only be used for frequencies over 25 megacycles. At the average operating point, the effective resistance of the circuit is practically zero; thus high amplification and sensitivity are obtained.

When the input signal is zero, the electron flow in the tube is irregular. This unsteady action causes a hissing noise to be heard in the output circuit. This noise becomes insignificant when strong input signals are applied. The selectivity of a receiver using superregenerative detection is very poor, but this factor is not important at the high frequencies for which this type of detection is used. As in the case of the regenerative detector, the superregenerative detector circuit also radiates a signal that interferes with the reception of near-by receivers. Superregenerative detectors are used primarily for the reception of signals whose frequencies are too high for other methods of detection to produce satisfactory results.

5-11. Automatic Volume Control. *Purpose of Automatic Volume Control.* In operating a receiver, it is sometimes found that the volume of the output varies without making any change in the setting of the volume control. This is generally referred to as *fading* and is most likely to be encountered only when receiving the signals of distant stations. Another disturbing change in volume occurs when tuning a receiver from a weak station to a strong station, or vice versa, without resetting the volume control. In order to compensate for these undesired changes in signal strength, many receivers use a special circuit to counteract this effect. These special circuits are called *automatic-volume-control* or *avc circuits* and are usually associated with the detector circuits. They are further classified as simple avc and delayed avc circuits.

A simple avc circuit is one in which the avc action is present at all times regardless of whether the incoming signal is weak or strong. This is in contrast to the delayed avc, in which the avc action becomes operative only when strong signals are being received.

Principle of AVC Circuits. The principle of avc is based on varying the bias applied to the control grids of one or more of the tubes preceding the detector. The tubes to which the avc bias is applied must be of the supercontrol or variable-mu type (Art. 4-15) so that when an increase in signal strength causes an increase in the grid bias, the voltage amplification of the circuit will be reduced.

The undesired changes in volume that make automatic volume control desirable will appear as fluctuations in the signal strength at both the input and output side of the detector circuit. Automatic volume control is achieved by applying a direct voltage to the control grids of the supercontrol tubes; this voltage is obtained by the rectified current of the detector circuit flowing through the diode load resistor. The voltage used for this purpose is negative with respect to ground and therefore acts as a bias on the grids of the tubes to which it is applied. Increases in signal strength will increase the value of this avc bias, which will result in a reduction in the strength of the signal applied to the detector. Conversely, decreases in signal strength will decrease the avc bias voltage, which will result in an increase in the strength of the signal applied to the detector. In this manner, the avc bias tends to maintain automatically the output of the detector circuit at a constant level. When automatic volume control is used, it is almost universally associated with diode detection, the principle of which has been explained earlier in this chapter.

Simple AVC Circuits. In the study of the diode detector (Art. 5-2) it was shown that the input signal causes a current to flow in the detector circuit during part of the positive half of each cycle. This current produces a voltage at the resistor R_1 and also charges the capacitor C_1 (Fig. 5-21). During the remainder of each cycle, the charged capacitor C_1 supplies current to the output circuit and the net result is that the output signal variations are a replica of the modulation envelope of the r-f input signal.

The charge on the capacitor C_1 will be such that point A will be negative with respect to ground. This is so because the rectifying action of the tube permits the electron movement caused by the input signal to flow only in the direction of A toward B; furthermore, as electrons always flow from negative toward positive, point A must be negative with respect to point B or ground. The voltage at A will be a pulsating voltage varying in strength according to the a-f component of the input signal (see Figs. 5-1b and 5-3c).

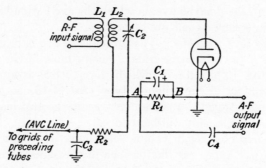

Fig. 5-21.—Diode detector with simple automatic voulme control.

As the voltage at point A is negative with respect to ground and as its value is proportional to the strength of the signal, it becomes an excellent source for the avc bias. This voltage, however, cannot be used directly as the avc bias because it varies in the same manner as the a-f component of the signal. If this voltage was applied to the grids of the preceding tubes, its effect would be to neutralize the variations in the strength of the modulation envelope, with the result that the output of the detector circuit would consist of variations of audio frequencies but all of a constant strength. In order to compensate for this undesirable effect, a filter circuit consisting of the resistor R_2 and the capacitor C_3 (Fig. 5-21) is added. The voltage from point A is now required to charge the capacitor C_3 through the resistor R_2. The voltage for the avc bias is thus dependent on the amount of charge on the capacitor C_3. By properly choosing the values of R_2 and C_3, it is possible to control the charging rate of the capacitor so that the variations due to the a-f component of the signal will not have any appreciable effect but that variations due to fading and other undesirable causes will be effective.

The problem of choosing the proper values of R_2 and C_3 is one of time constants (see Art. 2-31). The time constant of the circuit should be of sufficient length so that the lowest value of audio-frequency sound to be reproduced will not cause any appreciable amount of charge on the capacitor C_3. On the other hand, the time constant should not be too long, for then the avc would not compensate for sudden changes due to fading, etc. In general, it is common practice to use a time constant of approximately one-tenth to one-fifth second.

Example 5-10.   The avc filter circuit of a certain receiver consists of a 2-megohm resistor and a 0.1-μf capacitor.   (a) What is the time constant of this circuit?   (b) What per cent of the maximum voltage charge possible will be attained in the time that the current from 1 cycle of a 50-cycle a-f signal will flow in the detector circuit (assuming that a constant voltage was being applied)?   (c) How many cycles of the 50-cycle note would be completed in one time constant?   (d) If a sine-wave voltage, whose maximum value is equal to the constant voltage assumed in part (b), were applied to the detector circuit, would it require the same amount of time, more time, or less time for the capacitor to reach 63.2 per cent of its final charge?   Why?

<table>
<tr><td>Given:</td><td>Find:</td></tr>
<tr><td>R = 2 megohms</td><td>(a)</td><td>t = ?</td></tr>
<tr><td>C = 0.1μf</td><td>(b) per cent E = ?</td></tr>
<tr><td>f = 50 cycles</td><td>(c)</td><td>cycles = ?</td></tr>
<tr><td></td><td>(d)</td><td>t = ?</td></tr>
</table>

Solution:

(a)   from Eq. (2-89)
        $t = RC = 2 \times 10^6 \times 0.1 \times 10^{-6} = 0.2$ second or $\frac{1}{5}$ second

(b)   As current can flow only during the positive half of the signal, the maximum time of current flow in one cycle of the 50-cycle a-f signal is $\frac{1}{100}$ second. This corresponds to one-twentieth of a time constant and from Table II-IV or Fig. 2-67 (page 117) the charge produced will be approximately 5 per cent of the maximum voltage charge possible when $k = \frac{1}{20}$ or 0.05.

(c)   Time for 1 cycle of the 50-cycle a-f current,

$$t_1 = \frac{1}{f} = \frac{1}{50} = 0.02 \text{ second}$$

Cycles completed in one time constant,

$$\text{cycles} = \frac{t}{t_1} = \frac{0.2}{0.02} = 10 \text{ cycles}$$

(d)   A much greater amount of time will be required because the value of the sine-wave voltage is equal to the voltage of part (b) at its maximum point only and then only for a very small period of time.

The avc voltage that is applied to the grids of one or more of the tubes preceding the detector will therefore be a direct voltage of negative potential, which will follow the variations caused by changes in signal strength due to fading, etc., but will not follow the comparatively rapid variations produced by the a-f component of the input signal. This avc voltage will therefore compensate for changes in signal strength due to fading, etc., and will tend to maintain the volume of the receiver at a constant level. The avc bias may be applied to the grids of the tubes preceding the detector, such as the i-f amplifiers, r-f amplifiers, and mixers or converters. It has been found that for successful operation of the automatic volume control, the avc bias should be applied to two or more of the preceding tubes.

Delayed AVC Circuits. The simple avc circuit just described has a disadvantage in that it applies some amount of avc bias at all times. This may become undesirable when the receiver is tuned to a weak station, as it will reduce the amount of volume available at the loudspeaker. In order to overcome this undesired effect, the circuit may be arranged so that the avc bias must first overcome some fixed voltage before any

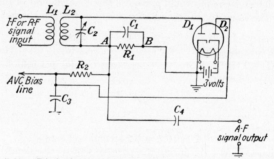

Fig. 5-22.—Diode detector with delayed automatic volume control.

avc bias can be applied to the grids of the preceding tubes. This type of circuit is called the *delayed avc circuit.* It should be observed that the delay referred to is not related to time but represents a value of voltage at which the avc first starts to become effective.

The circuit shown in Fig. 5-22 illustrates the fundamental principle of delayed avc operation. The tube used in this figure is a duplex diode (type 6H6) and the left half of the tube D_1, with its associated circuit, acts in the same manner as the diode-detector circuit of Fig. 5-21. The right half of the tube D_2 provides the action that produces the delayed avc feature of the circuit. Examination of Fig. 5-22 will show that the plate of the diode D_2 is positive with respect to its cathode and hence a current will flow in the circuit composed of D_2, R_2, R_1, and the 3-volt battery. Since the voltage drop at D_2 will be very small, the capacitor C_3 will charge to practically 3 volts and will produce an avc voltage of approximately -3 volts. It may also be observed that this current will produce a negative voltage at A, which will apply a negative voltage to the plate of D_1. Because of the relative values of R_1 and R_2 (R_2 is usually five or more times greater than R_1), this voltage is not great enough to prevent the flow of current in the diode D_1 during the positive halves of the input signal.

The rectified signal current flowing in the circuit of diode D_1 will still produce a voltage across the diode load resistor R_1 with terminal A negative with respect to ground. When weak signals are being received, this voltage may well be less than 3 volts. Under this condition the avc line will be supplied with a constant value of 3 volts provided by the battery in the circuit of the diode D_2.

When strong signals are being received, the voltage at R_1 may well exceed 3 volts. Under this condition the capacitor C_3 will become charged to the value of voltage across R_1 and the voltage of the avc line will correspond to the voltage of the capacitor C_3. It may further be observed that when the voltage at the capacitor C_3 exceeds 3 volts, the plate of the diode D_2 becomes negative with respect to the cathode and the electron flow in this circuit will cease.

From the above conditions it may be seen that for weak input signals the avc bias remains constant at 3 volts and the receiver can be operated with its maximum sensitivity and gain. When strong signals are being received the avc bias will exceed 3 volts and the volume will be maintained at a constant level by the automatic-volume-control circuit.

Practical Delayed AVC Circuit. The circuit shown in Fig. 5-22 shows a battery being used to provide a fixed amount of voltage to supply a constant minimum voltage for the avc line. In modern receivers it is considered desirable to eliminate batteries whenever possible, hence most circuits are arranged to provide some other means of obtaining this voltage. It is also common practice to use multipurpose tubes wherever practicable, hence the detector is often found in a common tube envelope with a triode or pentode amplifier. The circuit shown in Fig. 5-23 includes both of these modern practices.

The tube used in the circuit of Fig. 5-23 is a duplex-diode–triode such as the type 75, 6SQ7, 2A6, or 6B6-G. The top plate D_1 of the duplex-diode section of the tube acts as the plate for the diode detector. The bottom plate D_2, which is fed by the capacitor C_5, is used to supply the avc bias. The cathode biasing resistor R_4 provides the bias for the triode section of the tube. It also makes the avc diode plate D_2 negative with respect to the cathode and thereby provides the means of obtaining the delayed avc without the use of a battery. It should be observed that the diode-detector load resistor R_1 is connected directly to the cathode and hence the diode-detector plate D_1 is at cathode potential. Because of this, rectification will take place in the detector circuit during part of the positive half of each cycle of the input signal received, whether from a weak station or from a strong one. The rectified current flowing through the diode load resistor R_1 produces a unidirectional voltage at R_1, which varies in the same manner as the input signal. This output voltage is applied to the triode or amplifier portion of the tube through the coupling capacitor C_6 and the manual volume control R_5.

The avc diode plate D_2 is connected to ground through its load resistor R_3. When the input signal voltage is zero, the plate D_2 will be negative with respect to the cathode by the amount of cathode bias produced by

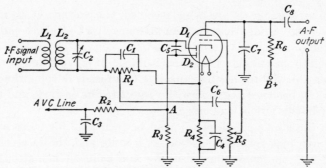

FIG. 5-23.—Diode detector using a multiunit tube. Delayed avc obtained from cathode bias.

R_4, usually 2 or 3 volts. Under this condition, no current will flow in the D_2 plate circuit and hence no avc voltage is developed. When a signal is being received, a voltage will be applied to the avc diode plate D_2 by means of the coupling capacitor C_5. When this voltage exceeds the value of the cathode bias, the avc plate D_2 will be positive with respect to the cathode and a rectified current will flow in the avc diode circuit consisting of the diode D_2, the resistor R_3, and the resistor R_4. A voltage will then be developed across the avc diode load resistor R_3, point A being negative with respect to ground. The avc filter network consisting of the resistor R_2 and the capacitor C_3 serves to eliminate the a-f voltage variations and to pass on to the avc line any variations due to fading and changes in signal strength when tuning in a new station. Thus, the delayed avc circuit results in having the maximum signal received from weak stations and automatic volume control applied only to the strong stations.

BIBLIOGRAPHY

ALBERT, A. L., *Fundamental Electronics and Vacuum Tubes*, The Macmillan Company, New York.

HICKS, H. J., *Principles and Practice of Radio Servicing*, McGraw-Hill Book Company, Inc., New York.

HOAG, J. B., *Basic Radio*, D. Van Nostrand Company, Inc., New York.

MANLY, H. P., *Drake's Cyclopedia of Radio and Electronics*, Frederick J. Drake & Company, Chicago.

NILSON, A. R., and HORNUNG, J. L., *Practical Radio Communication*, McGraw-Hill Book Company, Inc., New York.

REICH, H. J., *Theory and Applications of Electron Tubes*, McGraw-Hill Book Company, Inc., New York.

SMITH, F. L., *The Radiotron Designer's Handbook*, The Wireless Press, Sydney, Australia; distributed in U.S.A. by R.C.A. Manufacturing Company, Inc., Harrison, N. J.

TERMAN, F. E., *Fundamentals of Radio*, McGraw-Hill Book Company, Inc., New York.

Receiving Tube Manual, various tube manufacturers.

QUESTIONS

1. Explain the fundamental process of each of the two operations necessary in any detector circuit.

2. Define each of the following terms: (a) wave train, (b) r-f carrier, (c) audio component, (d) modulated wave, (e) modulation envelope.

3. What operating features of vacuum tubes made possible their universal use as detectors in modern radio equipment?

4. Explain what is meant by each of the following terms: (a) sensitivity, (b) signal handling ability, (c) fidelity of reproduction.

5. Which factors are most important in selecting a detector circuit for a receiver that is to be used for: (a) signals from a distant broadcasting station, (b) signals from a powerful local broadcasting station, (c) code?

6. Explain the basic principle of a diode detector.

7. Explain the purpose of the r-f by-pass capacitor. How is it connected in the circuit? What is its approximate value?

8. What is meant by a full-wave diode detector? What methods are used to obtain this type of detection? What are its advantages and disadvantages?

9. What are the advantages and disadvantages of diode detectors? Where are diode detectors generally used?

10. Where are each of the following parts used and what is their purpose: (a) r-f filter resistor, (b) a-f by-pass capacitor, (c) diode load resistor?

11. Why do r-f filter circuits reduce the useful rectified output of a detector circuit?

12. How are multiunit tubes used as diode detectors? What is the main advantage of using multiunit tubes?

13. Explain the basic principle of plate detection. What other names are also applied to this method of detection?

14. Explain the following terms: (a) cutoff, (b) grid bias, (c) positive bend, (d) negative bend, (e) bias detectors.

15. Explain the operation of a grid-bias detector when operated at its (a) negative bend, (b) positive bend.

16. How is the output of a plate detector affected when the grid bias is adjusted (a) too far beyond its cutoff point, (b) too far before its cutoff point?

17. What are the advantages and disadvantages of plate detectors? Where are plate detectors generally used?

18. Explain the purpose of the r-f choke coil. How is it connected in the circuit?

19. What is the relation between the grid voltage swing and the operating grid voltage?

20. Describe three methods used to obtain the correct amount of grid-bias voltage. Which of these methods is generally used?

21. Explain why the use of a cathode resistor to obtain the required grid bias is referred to as the *automatic* or *self-biasing method*.

22. How is the value of the cathode-bias resistor determined?

23. Explain the purpose of the a-f by-pass capacitor. How is it connected in the circuit? What is its approximate value?

24. Explain the principle of operation of grid detection.

25. How does the action and circuit of a grid detector compare with a half-wave diode detector?

26. Explain the circuit action of the grid capacitor.

27. Explain the circuit action of the grid resistor.

28. What are the advantages and disadvantages of grid detectors? Where are grid detectors generally used?

29. What is meant by power detection? What are its main advantages?

30. How do grid-circuit and plate-circuit power detectors differ from the regular grid-circuit and plate-circuit detectors?

31. Explain why c-w signals cannot be detected by using diode-, grid-, or plate-detector circuits.

32. Explain the principle of heterodyne action.

33. What is meant by (*a*) beat frequency, (*b*) heterodyning?

34. Explain three applications of heterodyne action.

35. What are the essential parts of a heterodyne circuit? How does this circuit operate?

36. Explain the action of a regenerative detector circuit.

37. Explain three methods of controlling the amount of regeneration.

38. What are the advantages and disadvantages of regenerative detectors?

39. Explain the principle of operation of an autodyne detector. How does it compare with regenerative and heterodyne detectors?

40. What are the advantages of autodyne detectors? Where are they generally used?

41. Explain what is meant by the frequency limits of autodyne detectors.

42. Explain the principle of superregeneration.

43. Explain the methods used to obtain superregeneration.

44. What is meant by the quench frequency?

45. How do the circuits for a regenerative detector and a self-quenching superregenerative detector compare?

46. What are the advantages and disadvantages of superregeneration?

47. Where are superregenerative circuits used?

48. What is the purpose of automatic volume control?

49. What is the principle of operation of avc circuits?

50. What is meant by simple avc? What is meant by delayed avc? Explain the meaning of the word *delayed* in the term *delayed avc*.

51. Can avc be applied to any type of tube? Explain.

52. Describe the action of the simple avc circuit.

53. What does the fundamental avc filter network consist of? Why is it necessary? What value of time constant is recommended for this circuit?

54. To how many tubes should the avc bias be applied? Where are these circuits located with respect to the detector? To which circuits may this avc bias be applied?

55. What is the disadvantage of simple avc? How does delayed avc overcome this disadvantage?

56. Explain the action of an avc circuit using a duplex-diode tube and a battery to provide the delayed voltage.

57. Why is the use of a battery undesirable in delayed avc circuits? What method is used to eliminate the need of a battery?

58. Describe the action of a delayed avc circuit using a duplex-diode–triode tube.

PROBLEMS

1. A certain diode-detector circuit, similar to Fig. 5-2, uses a ½-megohm resistor for the diode load resistance R_1 and a 100-$\mu\mu$f capacitor for the diode by-pass capacitor C_1. (a) What is the time constant of this RC circuit? (b) If the resonant frequency of the tuned circuit L_2C_2 is 1500 kc, what time is required for the r-f wave to complete 1 cycle? (c) How many times greater is the time constant of the RC circuit than the time of 1 cycle of the r-f wave?

2. The circuit of Prob. 1 also acts as a filter circuit. (a) What is the reactance of the capacitor to a 1500-kc r-f current? (b) How does the reactance to the 1500-kc r-f current compare with the value of the diode load resistance? (c) What path will the r-f currents take? (d) What is the reactance of the capacitor to a 500-cycle a-f current? (e) How does the reactance to the 500-cycle a-f current compare with the value of the diode load resistance? (f) Which path will the a-f currents take?

3. A certain diode-detector circuit, similar to Fig. 5-2, uses a 300,000-ohm resistor for the diode load resistance R_1 and a 250-$\mu\mu$f capacitor for the diode by-pass capacitor C_1. (a) What is the time constant of this RC circuit? (b) If the resonant frequency of the tuned circuit L_2C_2 is 500 kc, what time is required for the r-f wave to complete 1 cycle? (c) How many times greater is the time constant of the RC circuit than the time of 1 cycle of the r-f wave?

4. The circuit of Prob. 3 also acts as a filter circuit. (a) What is the reactance of the capacitor to a 500-kc r-f current? (b) How does the reactance to the 500-kc r-f current compare with the value of the diode load resistance? (c) What path will the r-f currents take? (d) What is the reactance of the capacitor to a 500-cycle a-f current? (e) How does the reactance to the 500-cycle a-f current compare with the value of the diode load resistance? (f) Which path will the a-f currents take?

5. The circuit elements shown in Fig. 5-6a have the following values: $R_1 = 100,000$ ohms, $R_2 = 400,000$ ohms, $C_1 = 100$ $\mu\mu$f, $C_3 = 100$ $\mu\mu$f. (a) What impedance does the capacitor C_1 offer to a 465-kc i-f current? (b) Which path will the i-f current take? (c) Will any of the i-f current flow into the R_1 path? (d) What impedance does the capacitor C_3 offer to any 465-kc i-f current? (e) What purpose does C_3 serve? (f) Neglecting the effect of the capacitors C_1 and C_3, what per cent of the a-f voltage developed across R_1 and R_2 is available at the output terminals?

6. The circuit elements shown in Fig. 5-6a have the following values: $R_1 = 50,000$ ohms, $R_2 = 200,000$ ohms, $C_1 = 250$ $\mu\mu$f, $C_3 = 250$ $\mu\mu$f. (a) What impedance does the capacitor C_1 offer to a 175-kc i-f current? (b) Which path will the i-f current take? (c) Will any of the i-f current flow into the R_1 path? (d) What impedance does the capacitor C_3 offer to any 175-kc i-f current? (e) What purpose does C_3 serve? (f) Neglecting the effect of the capacitors C_1 and C_3, what per cent of the a-f voltage developed across R_1 and R_2 is available at the output terminals?

7. The r-f filter circuit of Fig. 5-9a has a 100-$\mu\mu$f capacitor at C_1 and a 30-mh choke at L_3. (a) What impedance does the capacitor offer to a 1500-kc r-f current? (b) What impedance does the choke offer to a 1500-kc r-f current? (c) What impedance does the capacitor offer to a 500-cycle a-f current? (d) What impedance does the choke offer to a 500-cycle a-f current?   (e) Which path will the r-f currents take? (f) Which path will the a-f currents take?

8. The r-f filter circuit of Fig. 5-9b has a 500-$\mu\mu$f capacitor at C_1 and a 125-mh choke at L_3.   (a) What impedance does the capacitor offer to a 262-kc i-f current? (b) What impedance does the choke offer to a 262-kc i-f current?   (c) What impedance does the capacitor offer to a 500-cycle a-f current?   (d) What impedance does the choke offer to a 500-cycle a-f current?   (e) Which path will the i-f currents take? (f) Which path will the a-f currents take?

9. A tube is operated with a grid bias of 3 volts.   What is the grid-voltage swing when an a-c signal applied to the input circuit has a voltage of (a) 1 volt, (b) 3 volts, (c) 4 volts?

10. A tube is operated with a grid bias of 6 volts.   What is the grid-voltage swing when an a-c signal applied to the input circuit has a voltage of (a) 2 volts, (b) 4 volts, (c) 6 volts?

11. A type 6J7 tube is used as a pentode bias detector operating with 250 volts on its plate and 100 volts on the screen grid.   (a) What grid voltage is recommended for these operating conditions?   (See Appendix XV or a standard tube manual.)   (b) What is the greatest amount of signal voltage that can be applied to the input circuit without causing distortion?

12. A type 6P5-GT/G tube is used as a grid-bias detector and is operated with 250 volts on its plate.   (a) What grid voltage is recommended for these operating conditions?   (b) What is the greatest amount of signal voltage that can be applied to the input circuit without causing distortion?

13. A type 27 tube is used as a bias detector and is operated with 250 volts on its plate.   (a) What grid voltage is recommended for these operating conditions?   (b) What is the greatest amount of signal voltage that can be applied to the input circuit without causing distortion?

14. A type 77 tube is used as a bias detector and is operated with 250 volts on its plate and 50 volts on the screen grid.   (a) What grid voltage is recommended for these operating conditions?   (b) What is the greatest amount of signal voltage that can be applied to the input circuit without causing distortion?

15. A detector tube operates with a grid bias of 12 volts.   What value of cathode resistance is required if the no-load plate current is (a) 0.1 ma, (b) 0.25 ma, (c) 0.4 ma?

16. A type 6C5 tube, used as a self-biased detector, is to be operated with 250 volts applied to its plate.   The plate current is to be adjusted to 0.2 ma when the input signal is zero.   (a) What value of cathode-bias resistor is necessary for these conditions?   (b) How much power is consumed by this resistor?   (c) What power rating should the resistor have?

17. A 6P5-GT/G tube, used as a self-biased detector, is to be operated with 250 volts applied to its plate.   The plate current is to be adjusted to 0.2 ma when the input signal is zero.   (a) What value of cathode-bias resistor is necessary for these conditions?   (b) How much power is consumed by this resistor?   (c) What power rating should the resistor have?

18. A type 27 tube, used as a self-biased detector, is to be operated with 250 volts on its plate.   The plate current is to be adjusted to 0.2 ma when the input signal is· zero.   (a) What value of cathode-bias resistor is necessary for these conditions? (b) How much power is consumed by this resistor?   (c) What power rating should the resistor have?

19. A type 77 tube, used as a self-biased detector, is to be operated with 250 volts on its plate and 50 volts on the screen grid.   The cathode current is to be adjusted to 0.65 ma when the input signal is zero.   (a) What value of cathode-bias resistor is necessary for these conditions? (b) How much power is consumed by this resistor? (c) What power rating should the resistor have?

20. A type 6C5 tube, used as a self-biased detector similar to Prob. 16, uses a cathode-bias resistor of 85,000 ohms and has a no-load plate current of 0.2 ma. (a) What value of by-pass capacitor should be used with this resistor if it is desired that the resistor offer at least 100 times more impedance to a 500-cycle a-f current than the capacitor? (b) What standard rating and type of capacitor is recommended for this application?

21. A type 6P5-GT/G tube, used as a self-biased detector similar to Prob. 17, uses a cathode-bias resistor of 100,000 ohms and has a no-load plate current of 0.2 ma. (a) What value of by-pass capacitor should be used with this resistor if it is desired that the resistor offer at least 100 times more impedance to a 500-cycle a-f current than the capacitor? (b) What standard rating and type of capacitor is recommended for this application?

22. A type 27 tube, used as a self-biased detector similar to Prob. 18, uses a cathode-bias resistor of 150,000 ohms and has a no-load plate current of 0.2 ma. (a) What value of by-pass capacitor should be used with this resistor if it is desired that the resistor offer at least 100 times more impedance to a 500-cycle a-f current than the capacitor? (b) What standard rating and type of capacitor is recommended for this application?

23. A type 77 tube, used as a self-biased detector similar to Prob. 19, uses a cathode-bias resistor of 3000 ohms and has a no-load cathode current of 0.65 ma. (a) What value of by-pass capacitor should be used with this resistor if it is desired that the resistor offer at least 100 times more impedance to a 500-cycle a-f current than the capacitor? (b) What standard rating and type of capacitor is recommended for this application?

24. A type 6C5 tube, used as a self-biased detector, is to be operated with 250 volts applied to its plate. The cathode-bias resistor has a resistance of 85,000 ohms and the plate current is to be adjusted to 0.2 ma. What value of voltage must the B power supply provide in order to maintain 250 volts between the cathode and plate? (Assume that there is no drop in voltage at the load impedance.)

25. A type 6P5-GT/G tube, used as a self-biased detector, is to be operated with 250 volts applied to its plate. The cathode-bias resistor has a resistance of 100,000 ohms and the plate current is to be adjusted to 0.2 ma. What value of voltage must the B power supply provide in order to maintain 250 volts between the cathode and plate? (Assume that there is no drop in voltage at the load impedance.)

26. A type 27 tube, used as a self-biased detector, is to be operated with 250 volts applied to its plate. The cathode-bias resistor has a resistance of 150,000 ohms and the plate current is to be adjusted to 0.2 ma. What value of voltage must the B power supply provide in order to maintain 250 volts between the cathode and plate? (Assume that there is no drop in voltage at the load impedance.)

27. A type 77 tube, used as a self-biased detector, is to be operated with 250 volts applied to its plate and 50 volts to its screen grid. The cathode-bias resistor has a resistance of 3000 ohms and the cathode current is to be adjusted to 0.65 ma. What value of voltage must the B power supply provide in order to maintain 250 volts between the cathode and plate? (Assume that there is no voltage drop at the load impedance.)

28. Using the plate characteristic curves of the type 6C5 tube (Fig. 4-19), calculate the value of cathode-bias resistance necessary to operate the tube with the following plate and grid voltages: (a) $E_b = 250$, $E_c = -8$; (b) $E_b = 200$, $E_c = -6$; (c) $E_b = 150$, $E_c = -4$; (d) $E_b = 100$, $E_c = -2$.

29. (a) How much power is consumed by each cathode resistor in Prob. 28? (b) What power rating should the resistors have?

30. Using the grid-plate transfer characteristic curves of the type 6C5 tube (Fig. 4-21), calculate the value of cathode-bias resistance necessary to operate the tube with the following plate voltages and plate currents (milliamperes): (a) $E_b = 250$, $I_b = 4.8$; (b) $E_b = 300$, $I_b = 5.5$; (c) $E_b = 200$, $I_b = 9.0$; (d) $E_b = 100$, $I_b = 5.0$.

31. (a) How much power is consumed by each cathode resistor in Prob. 30? (b) What power rating should each resistor have?

32. Using the plate characteristic curves of the type 6J7 tube (Fig. 4-31), calculate the value of the cathode-bias resistance necessary to operate the tube with the following plate and grid voltages (the screen-grid voltage is kept at 100 volts): (a) $E_b = 120$, $E_c = -1$; (b) $E_b = 240$, $E_c = -2$; (c) $E_b = 320$, $E_c = -2.5$; (d) $E_b = 400$, $E_c = -3$. (NOTE: Screen-grid current is 0.5 ma.)

33. (a) How much power is consumed by each cathode resistor in Prob. 32? (b) What power rating should each resistor have?

34. (a) Plot the curves required to show the resultant wave when a 6-cycle sine-wave voltage whose maximum value is 4 volts is combined by heterodyne action with a 9-cycle sine-wave voltage whose maximum value is 8 volts. (b) What is the beat frequency of these two waves? (c) What is the voltage swing of the beat frequency?

35. A c-w signal transmitted on a frequency of 2000 kc is being received by an autodyne detector. At what frequency must the oscillator circuit of the receiver be set in order that the frequency in the output circuit will be (a) 500, (b) 1000, (c) 1500 cycles?

36. The avc filter circuit shown in Fig. 5-21 has the following constants: $R_2 = 1$ megohm, $C_3 = 0.1$ μf. (a) What is the time constant of this circuit? (b) What per cent of the maximum voltage charge possible will be attained in the time that the current from 1 cycle of a 100-cycle a-f signal will flow in the detector circuit (assuming that a constant voltage was being applied)? (c) How many cycles of the 100-cycle note would be completed in 1 time constant?

37. The avc filter circuit shown in Fig. 5-21 has the following constants: $R_2 = 2$ megohms, $C_3 = 0.05$ μf. (a) What is the time constant of this circuit? (b) What per cent of the maximum voltage charge possible will be attained in the time that the current from 1 cycle of a 50-cycle a-f signal will flow in the detector circuit (assuming that a constant voltage was being applied)? (c) How many cycles of the 50-cycle note would be completed in 1 time constant?

38. The delayed avc circuit shown in Fig. 5-23 has the following constants: $R_1 = 0.5$ megohm, $R_2 = 1$ megohm, $R_3 = 2$ megohms, $R_4 = 2500$ ohms, $C_1 = 250$ μμf, $C_3 = 0.1$ μf, $C_4 = 10$ μf. When the signal input is zero, the current in the cathode circuit is 1.2 ma. (a) What is the magnitude and the polarity of the voltage between D_2 and the cathode when the input signal is zero? (b) How much current flows in R_3 under the condition in part (a)? (c) What is the voltage of the avc line under the condition of part (a)? (d) To what voltage must the charge on the capacitor C_5 raise the plate D_2 in order to produce a current flow in R_3? (e) What are the magnitude and polarity of the voltage developed at point A when a current of 1μa flows through R_3? (f) What voltage will the avc line have under the condition in part (e)? (g) What is the time constant of the avc filter? (h) What is the time constant of the diode load resistor R_1 and the diode by-pass capacitor C_1? (i) What impedance does the capacitor C_4 offer to the lowest a-f current, assuming it to be 50 cycles? (j) What purpose does the capacitor C_4 serve?

CHAPTER VI

TUNING CIRCUITS

Tuning is the process of adjusting the capacitance or inductance of a tuned circuit in order to select the signals of a desired station. Tuning circuits, therefore, form an essential part of all radio receivers. Selecting a desired signal is only one of the three important functions performed by the tuning circuit. In addition to selecting the desired signal, it must reject all undesired signals. In most instances the tuning circuit also accomplishes an increase in the voltage of the desired signal before passing the signal on to the following circuit. This increase in voltage is due to the action of a tuned resonant circuit as explained in Art. 2-20.

6-1. Tuning. *Operating Characteristics.* The ability of a radio receiver to accomplish each of its three functions is referred to as its *sensitivity*, *selectivity*, and *fidelity*.

Sensitivity is a measure of the ability of a receiver to reproduce, with satisfactory volume, weak signals received by the antenna. It may further be defined as the minimum strength of signal input required to produce a specified a-f power output at the loudspeaker; it is generally expressed either in microvolts or in decibels below one volt. Theoretically, it would be desirable to have the sensitivity as high as possible in order to receive weak signals from distant stations. Practically, however, there is a limit beyond which the sensitivity should not be increased. This point is reached when the strength of the noise signals, caused by static and electrical appliances, exceeds the strength of the desired signal.

Selectivity is a measure of the ability of a receiver to reproduce the signal of one desired station and to exclude the signals from all others. The selectivity of a receiver (or a tuning circuit) is generally expressed in the form of a graph, also referred to as a *response curve*, showing the signal strength at its resonant frequency and the variation in signal current when the frequency is varied a specified amount above and below the frequency of resonance. When the sensitivity of a circuit is increased, its selectivity must also be increased in order that the circuit will reject the signals from unwanted stations.

Fidelity is a measure of the ability of a receiver to reproduce faithfully all the frequencies present in the original signal. The fidelity of a

245

receiver is generally expressed in the form of a graph showing the ratio of the actual output to the output at a standard audio frequency of 400 cycles. For good fidelity of reproduction, the band width as shown by the selectivity graphs should be great enough to accommodate all the frequencies of the signal to be received.

The Response Curve. The process of selecting the carrier wave of a desired station is called *tuning.* This may be accomplished by adjusting one or more components of a series tuned circuit so that its resonant frequency will be equal to that of the desired carrier wave. The impedance of the tuned circuit at resonance will be at its minimum value, therefore, the current in the tuned circuit produced by the desired station will be at its maximum value. As the resonant frequency of the tuning circuit is varied, either above or below the frequency of the desired station, the impedance of the circuit will increase and the signal current of the desired station will therefore decrease. A graph showing the current flow in a tuned circuit at resonance and the decrease in current flow at frequencies off resonance is referred to as a *response curve.* A typical response curve is shown in Fig. 6-1.

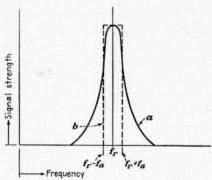

FIG. 6-1.—Relation between actual and ideal response curves. (*a*) Actual response curve, (*b*) ideal response curve.

Ideal Response Curve. A transmitted wave is made up of the carrier wave modulated by two side bands whose frequencies are equal to the frequency of the carrier wave plus or minus the frequency of the audio signal. For ordinary broadcast transmission, the maximum frequency of the audio signal is generally accepted as 5 kilocycles, and for high-fidelity transmission it is generally 10 kilocycles. The side bands of a modulated carrier wave will therefore vary up to 5 kc above and below its carrier frequency for ordinary broadcast signals and up to 10 kc for high-fidelity transmission. For example, an ordinary broadcasting station operating on a carrier frequency of 1000 kc will have side-band frequencies ranging from 995 to 1005 kc; for high-fidelity transmission the frequency of the side bands will vary from 990 to 1010 kc.

In order to reproduce the signals as transmitted, the ideal response curve should have a flat top and straight sides, so that it may pass a 10-kc band for ordinary broadcast and a 20-kc band for the reception of high-fidelity signals (Fig. 6-1). Although it is impossible to obtain this ideal, it can be closely approximated by the proper use of resonant circuits. Three methods of increasing the fidelity, sensitivity, and selectivity of a receiver are: (1) increasing the circuit Q, (2) using two or more tuned circuits, (3) use of a band-pass amplifier. Increasing the circuit Q is accomplished by decreasing the circuit resistance and thereby increasing the slope of the resonant curve (see Figs. 2-38 and 3-14). This is one of the many principles of resonant circuits as described in Arts. 2-19 to 2-24 and taken up in detail in Chap. XI of the authors' *Electrical Essentials of Radio*. The circuit actions of the two other methods are discussed later in this chapter.

Radio Channels. It is evident from the above discussion that each transmitting station requires a band 10 kc wide for ordinary broadcasting

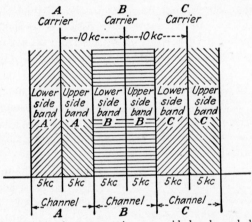

Fig. 6-2.—Relation between carrier wave, side bands, and channels.

stations and 20 kc wide for high-fidelity transmitters. This band is referred to as a *radio channel.* In order to prevent interference between two stations operating on adjacent channels there should be a difference of at least 10 kc between their carrier frequencies (Fig. 6-2). For the same reason, the tuning circuit of a receiver should be capable of selecting signals from stations approximately 10 kc apart without any interference. In the broadcasting range extending from 550 to 1600 kc, 106 channels are available. At present there are approximately 900 stations assigned to these channels. Under this crowded condition more than one station may be operating on the same frequency; also, the side bands from adjacent channels may overlap the signals of more than one station. This interference between stations transmitting on the same frequency or operating partly within the same channel may produce a hum, whistle, or crosstalk in the receiver.

In order to prevent this annoying interference between stations, the Federal Communications Commission has set up a zoning system and accordingly assigns the carrier frequency to broadcasting stations so that the interference is reduced to a minimum. Furthermore, stations are licensed as to the amount of power they may use, and in some cases they are also limited as to the hours during which they may broadcast. For example, only four stations are at present assigned to the 710-kc channel, namely, WOR at New York, KIRO at Seattle, KMPC at Los Angeles, and WFTL at Ft. Lauderdale, Fla. All four stations employ high-power transmitters, the first two operating with 50,000 watts and the last two with 10,000 watts, but because of the great distance between these stations they do not interfere with one another and may therefore operate on a continuous time schedule. On the other hand, there are at present more than 80 stations assigned to the 1240-kc channel, with as many as five stations in the same state assigned to the same channel. The licensed power of these stations varies from 50 watts to 250 watts and some of the stations are restricted to operating at only certain hours of the day.

The ability of a receiver to minimize this interference will depend on the selectivity of its tuned circuits. In order to eliminate the interference from adjacent stations, the selectivity will have to be increased. This reduces the width of the response curve and may decrease the fidelity of the receiver, since the high notes may not be reproduced. For example, if the selectivity is increased so that the width of the response curve is reduced to 8 kc, only 4 kc of the 5-kc side bands as transmitted are reproduced. Under this condition all audio signals of frequencies between 4000 and 5000 cycles will not be reproduced by this receiver. By decreasing the sensitivity of the receiver the strength of the interfering signals can be reduced so that they will not be heard, providing the strength of the desired signal is from 20 to 50 times greater than the strongest undesired signal.

6-2. Circuit Elements. *Types of Variable Capacitors.* Although tuning can be accomplished by varying either the value of the inductance or capacitance of the tuning circuit, the method most commonly used is by varying the capacitance. Three types of variable capacitors are used in tuning. These are referred to as *straight-line-capacity, straight-line-wavelength,* and *straight-line-frequency;* they are commonly abbreviated as SLC, SLW, and SLF respectively.

With a capacitor of the *straight-line-capacity* type, the capacitance increases in a direct ratio with the amount of rotation of its movable plates (see Fig. 6-3a). For example, if such a capacitor is rotated so that the rotor plates are one-quarter in mesh with the stator, its capacitance will be one-quarter of its total value; if the rotor plates are one-half in mesh with the stator, its capacitance will be one-half of its total value, etc.   If an SLC capacitor is used in the tuning circuit of a broadcast receiver, most of the stations to be tuned in will appear on one-half of the dial (see Fig. 6-3a).   This is so because the resonant frequency of a tuned circuit does not vary in a direct ratio with changes in its capacitance. It will also be observed that the upper half of the frequency band (1075 to 1600 kc) will appear on approximately only one-eighth of the dial. Furthermore, when this type of capacitor is used it is very difficult to separate the signals from adjacent stations in the upper half of the frequency band.

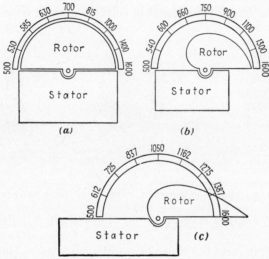

Fig. 6-3.—Frequency distribution obtained with three types of variable capacitors (a) Straight-line-capacity, (b) straight-line-wavelength, (c) straight-line-frequency.

The first attempt to remedy this condition was the use of the *straight-line-wavelength* capacitor.   In this type of capacitor the area of the rotor plates is reduced on the side that first enters into mesh with the stator plates, so that the wavelength of the tuned circuit increases in a direct ratio with the amount of rotation of the movable plates.   With this type of rotor plate the capacitance increases very slowly at first but increases at a faster rate as the plates go further into mesh.   If an SLW capacitor is used in the tuning circuit of a broadcast receiver, most of the stations to be tuned in will appear on approximately three-fourths of the dial (see Fig. 6-3b).   Furthermore, the stations in the upper half of the frequency band will appear on approximately one-third of the dial.

While the SLW capacitor made it possible to attain better selectivity than with the SLC capacitor, it was still difficult to separate signals from stations of carrier frequencies greater than 1100 kc. This difficulty was overcome by the use of rotor plates shaped so that the resonant frequency of the tuned circuit would vary directly with the amount of rotation of the capacitor. Such capacitors are called *straight-line-frequency* capacitors. The rate of increase in capacitance at the high frequencies is decreased by cutting off the side of the rotor plate that first enters into mesh with the stator at a sharper angle than was done with the SLW capacitor. The rate of increase at the low frequencies was accelerated by tapering the opposite side of the rotor plate (see Fig. 6-3c). With this type of capacitor the resonant frequency of the tuned circuit varies in direct proportion to the amount of rotation of the variable capacitor.

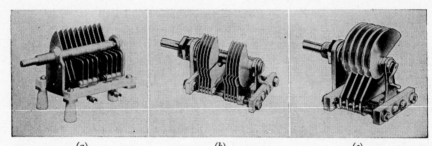

(a)　　　　　　　　　　(b)　　　　　　　　　　(c)

Fig. 6-4.—Commercial types of capacitors. (a) Straight-line-capacity, (b) straight-line-wavelength, (c) straight-line-frequency. (*Courtesy of National Company, Inc.*)

All the preceding discussion of variable capacitors is based on 180 degrees of rotation of the rotor plates. By increasing the amount of rotation to 270 degrees the capacitor can be made more compact. The selectivity obtainable is also improved as the 1100-kc range (500 to 1600 kc) is spread over 270 mechanical degrees instead of 180 degrees. A commercial form of this type of capacitor is shown in Fig. 6-4c. Three additional methods commonly used to obtain compactness for SLF capacitors are: (1) using a greater number of rotor plates of a smaller surface area, (2) using thinner plates and a smaller air gap, (3) using semicircular rotor plates and varying the design of the stator plates. Practically all the tuning circuits of a radio receiver now use a compact form of variable capacitor.

R-F Tuning Coils. The secondary winding of an r-f transformer provides the fixed inductance that is used with the variable capacitor to form the tuned circuit of a radio receiver. In this type of circuit the input signal flows through the primary winding of the r-f transformer and by means of the mutual inductance between the two windings the signal is transferred to the secondary. The variable capacitor and the secondary winding form a series resonant circuit, which must be tuned to the frequency of the desired station. The value of the inductance required in the secondary winding will depend on the frequency range desired and the value of the capacitance of the variable capacitor that is used. From Art. 2-20 it can be seen that increasing the inductance of the secondary coil increases the amount of voltage developed across this winding, thus increasing the gain of the tuned circuit. Furthermore, it has been shown in Art. 2-23 that increasing the inductance of the coil also increases the circuit Q (if the resistance remains constant), which in turn also increases the selectivity of the tuned circuit. It was also shown in Art. 2-23 that the selectivity of the series tuned circuit is dependent on the LC ratio.

The amount of inductance that should be used is such a value that when combined with the distributed capacitance of the secondary winding and the minimum capacitance of the tuning capacitor it will form a resonant circuit whose frequency of resonance is equal to or greater than the highest frequency desired. For ordinary broadcast reception this frequency is approximately 1600 kc. The maximum value of the variable capacitor must be equal to the amount of capacitance required to decrease the frequency of resonance of the tuned circuit to the minimum desired frequency. For ordinary broadcast reception this frequency is approximately 550 kc.

Example 6-1. It is desired to determine the inductance required in the secondary winding of an r-f transformer and it is assumed that the distributed capacitance of the winding and the circuit wiring is 23 $\mu\mu$f (considered acting in parallel with the tuning capacitor). (*a*) What value of inductance is required in order to obtain resonance at 1600 kc if the minimum value of the variable capacitor is 17 $\mu\mu$f? (*b*) What value of capacitance must the capacitor have if it is desired to tune in stations as low as 550 kc with the coil used in part (*a*)?

Given:

$C_D = 23\ \mu\mu$f
$C_V = 17\ \mu\mu$f (min.)
$f = 1600$ kc (*a*)
$f = 550$ kc (*b*)

Find:

(*a*) $L = ?$
(*b*) $C_V = ?$

Solution:

(*a*) $L = \dfrac{25{,}300}{f_r{}^2 C} = \dfrac{25{,}300}{1600^2 \times (17 + 23)10^{-6}} = 246\ \mu$h

(*b*) $C_T = \dfrac{25{,}300}{f_r{}^2 L} = \dfrac{25{,}300}{550^2 \times 246} = 0.0003399\ \mu$f or 340 $\mu\mu$f

$C_V = C_T - C_D = 340 - 23 = 317\ \mu\mu$f

Variable capacitors used for only broadcast reception generally have a maximum capacitance of 350 $\mu\mu$f. The above example shows that the inductance of the secondary winding used with this capacitor would have to be approximately 250 μh in order to be able to tune in a signal of 550 kc. The inductance of an r-f coil whose length is considerably greater than its diameter will vary in direct proportion to the square of the number of turns, to the square of the diameter, and in an inverse proportion to its length (see Art. 2-3). From this statement it would seem that the inductance required for an r-f coil can best be obtained by using a short coil having a large diameter and a great number of turns. In the early stages of radio development the r-f coils were designed along these lines. These early coils had a diameter ranging from three to five inches, a length of approximately three-quarters of an inch, and approximately 75 turns. Further study and experimentation have shown that the

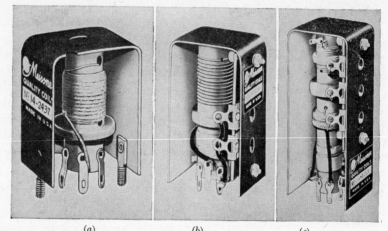

(a)   (b)   (c)

FIG. 6-5.—Commercial types of r-f coils. (a) Single-band coil, (b) dual-band coil, (c) triple-band coil. (*Courtesy of Meissner Manufacturing Division Maguire Industries, Inc.*)

physical dimensions of r-f coils should be as small as possible. This fact led to the development of coils whose length and diameter were approximately equal. This is the type of coil that is generally used and its diameter will vary from a half-inch to one inch. A few of the different types of commercial coils are shown in Fig. 6-5. The theory of inductance and r-f coils is taken up in detail in Chap. VIII of the authors' *Electrical Essentials of Radio*.

6-3. Short Waves. *Frequency Ranges.* Short-wave radio communication makes use of waves whose frequencies are higher than those employed in ordinary broadcast transmission and reception. Thus stations operating on frequencies above 1600 kc are commonly referred to as short-wave stations. Their carrier waves are generally expressed in either megacycles or meters; for example, a station operating at 30,000 kc may be referred to as operating on either the 30-mc band or on the 10-meter band. For frequencies above 1600 kc, various bands are allocated to the different types of communication service, such as amateur, aircraft, ship to shore, police, point to point, and long-distance commercial telephony. The wavelengths and frequencies for the various types of short-wave communication services are shown on the chart illustrated in Fig. 1-9.

Characteristics of Short-wave Communication. In general, the operating characteristics of short-wave and broadcast communication are similar. However, there are features of short-wave communication that are not common to those used in broadcast. These characteristics are: (1) less power is required to transmit high-frequency signals over great distances than is needed for low-frequency signals; (2) the distances reached by short-wave signals during the daylight hours will become greater as the frequency of transmission is increased; (3) nighttime reception is very poor, especially for signals of frequencies greater than 13 mc; (4) the reception in terms of signal strength is very irregular, that is, it may be strong one day and weak the next or it may even vary during the same day; (5) short-wave signals may be received perfectly at distant points from the transmitter and not be received at all at certain localities that may be near the transmitter, this phenomenon being known as *skipping.*

Short-wave Bands. If a portion of the short-wave range extending from 1600 to 60,000 kc is considered, it will be seen that this range covers a span of 58,400 kc. If this span were to provide channels of 10-kc width, there would be 5841 channels for this span alone, as compared to 106 channels for the broadcast range. This is one of the many reasons for using the short-wave channels for the transmission of frequency modulation and television signals.

For broadcast reception, it is possible to use a single coil and capacitor for each stage of tuning. Because of the width of the frequency range to be covered and the large number of stations that can be accommodated, a system employing a single coil and capacitor is not practical for short-wave reception. If a short-wave receiver were to cover a range of from 1.6 to 60 mc with a single range and had a dial marked with 100 divisions to cover 180 degree of rotation of the variable capacitor, it would mean that for an SLF capacitor each division would represent 584 kc. It can readily be seen that if such a system were used to tune stations operating on a 10-kc channel, 58 channels may be tuned in or out by moving the dial just one division. It is obvious that such a condition is not practical. Furthermore, it is impossible to design a combination of a single fixed coil and a variable capacitor to cover this entire range. Every variable capacitor has some amount of capacitance even when the rotor plates are completely unmeshed from the stator.   This minimum capacitance of the capacitor, plus the distributed capacitance of the coil and the stray capacitances existing in the tuned circuit, makes it impossible to design a single combination of coil and capacitor that will tune the high- and low-frequency bands satisfactorily.

In order to correct this condition, the short-wave frequency span is divided into a number of bands.   The frequency limits of each of these bands will vary with the type of radio and the manufacturer.   This variation is illustrated in Table VI-I, which lists the frequency limits for each band of two popular makes of radio receivers.   A separate coil

TABLE VI-I

Band	Set A	Set B
Broadcast	530 to 1550 kc	550 to 1600 kc
1	1.5 to 4.2 mc	1.5 to 5.5 mc
2	4.0 to 11.5 mc	5.4 to 15.5 mc
3	11 to 23 mc	15 to 42 mc

designed to cover the frequency range for each band desired is generally used with a common variable capacitor.

6-4. All-wave Receivers.   *Variable Inductance.*   Radio receivers may be made to tune the broadcast band and one or more short-wave

Fig. 6-6.—Set of plug-in coils.   (*Courtesy of Insuline Corporation of America.*)

bands.   In order to obtain such a tuning range, the capacitor and inductor used in the tuning circuit are constructed so that either one or both can be adjusted to the value required for the band desired.   One method of varying the inductance is accomplished by use of a series of plug-in coils (see Fig. 6-6), each coil being designed for a definite frequency range. The value of inductance required for these coils is determined by the maximum capacitance of the tuning capacitor and the lowest frequency of the desired band, as illustrated in the following examples.

Example 6-2.   A 320-$\mu\mu$f variable capacitor having a minimum capacitance of 13.5 $\mu\mu$f is used in the tuning circuit of the all-wave receiver listed as set A in Table VI-I.   (a) If the distributed capacitance of the coil is neglected, find the inductance of the secondary for each of the coils required.   (b) What is the highest resonant frequency obtainable for each band?

Given:

$C_{max} = 320\ \mu\mu f$

$C_{min} = 13.5\ \mu\mu f$

Find:

(a) L_S for each coil

(b) Max f_r for each band

Solution:

(a) $L_S = \dfrac{25{,}300}{f_{min}{}^2 C_{max}}$

$L_{S \cdot B} = \dfrac{25{,}300}{530^2 \times 320 \times 10^{-6}} = 281\ \mu h$

$L_{S \cdot 1} = \dfrac{25{,}300}{1.5^2 \times 10^6 \times 320 \times 10^{-6}} = 35.1\ \mu h$

$L_{S \cdot 2} = \dfrac{25{,}300}{4.0^2 \times 10^6 \times 320 \times 10^{-6}} = 4.93\ \mu h$

$L_{S \cdot 3} = \dfrac{25{,}300}{11^2 \times 10^6 \times 320 \times 10^{-6}} = 0.653\ \mu h$

(b) $f_{max} = \dfrac{159}{\sqrt{L C_{min}}}$

$f_{B \cdot max} = \dfrac{159}{\sqrt{281 \times 13.5 \times 10^{-6}}} = 2581\ kc$

$f_{1 \cdot max} = \dfrac{159}{\sqrt{35.1 \times 13.5 \times 10^{-6}}} = 7.30\ mc$

$f_{2 \cdot max} = \dfrac{159}{\sqrt{4.93 \times 13.5 \times 10^{-6}}} = 19.2\ mc$

$f_{3 \cdot max} = \dfrac{159}{\sqrt{0.653 \times 13.5 \times 10^{-6}}} = 53.5\ mc$

From the above example it can be seen that the maximum frequency for each band is much greater than that listed for set A in Table VI-I. This is to be expected as the distributed capacitance of the coil and the circuit have been neglected.   How much this stray capacitance affects the frequency range of the tuned circuit may be seen from the results of the following example.

Example 6-3.   If the tuning circuit used in Example 6-2 has a distributed circuit capacitance of 20 $\mu\mu$f, what will the minimum and the maximum frequencies be for each band of the receiver?

Given: Find:
$$C_{max} = 320 \ \mu\mu f$$ f_{min} and f_{max} for each band
$$C_{min} = 13.5 \ \mu\mu f$$
$$C_D = 20 \ \mu\mu f$$

Solution:

$$f_{min} = \frac{159}{\sqrt{L(C_{max} + C_D)}}$$

$$f_{max} = \frac{159}{\sqrt{L(C_{min} + C_D)}}$$

Broadcast band:

$$f_{min} = \frac{159}{\sqrt{281 \times (320 + 20) \times 10^{-6}}} = 514 \ kc$$

$$f_{max} = \frac{159}{\sqrt{281 \times (13.5 + 20) \times 10^{-6}}} = 1639 \ kc$$

Band 1:

$$f_{min} = \frac{159}{\sqrt{35.1 \times (320 + 20) \times 10^{-6}}} = 1.45 \ mc$$

$$f_{max} = \frac{159}{\sqrt{35.1 \times (13.5 + 20) \times 10^{-6}}} = 4.63 \ mc$$

Band 2:

$$f_{min} = \frac{159}{\sqrt{4.93 \times (320 + 20) \times 10^{-6}}} = 3.88 \ mc$$

$$f_{max} = \frac{159}{\sqrt{4.93 \times (13.5 + 20) \times 10^{-6}}} = 12.4 \ mc$$

Band 3:

$$f_{min} = \frac{159}{\sqrt{0.653 \times (320 + 20) \times 10^{-6}}} = 10.9 \ mc$$

$$f_{max} = \frac{159}{\sqrt{0.653 \times (13.5 + 20) \times 10^{-6}}} = 34 \ mc$$

From the above example it can be seen that the frequency limits of each band are approximately the same as those listed for set A in Table VI-I. The values of capacitance and inductance used in these problems do not necessarily represent the values actually used in the construction of the set referred to. The values used have been selected in order to illustrate their application in obtaining the various frequency bands.

It can also be seen that the maximum value of the tuning capacitor is too high for the receiver to be able to tune high frequencies if a practical coil with a reasonable number of turns is to be used. Tuning capacitors having a lower value of maximum capacitance are made with fewer plates and therefore also have a lower value of minimum capacitance. For this reason a smaller capacitor, generally about 140 $\mu\mu f$ or less, is used in the tuning circuits of short-wave receivers.

Band Switching with Inductors. In the early type of all-wave receiver, changing from one band of frequencies to another was accomplished by interchanging the plug-in-type coils. This was a rather complicated process, for in many types of receivers it required opening the cabinet of the receiver and substituting the proper plug-in coils for the ones

inserted in the set at the time. This method was not simple enough to become very popular. The all-wave receiver of today uses a much simpler process for changing from one frequency band to another. With this method, the primary and secondary windings for each band are wound on a single coil form (see Fig. 6-5). By means of a band selector switch, any set of primary and secondary windings may be connected into or out of the tuning circuit; two types of band selector switches are shown

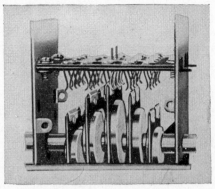

FIG. 6-7.—Commercial band switch. (*Courtesy of Hammarlund Manufacturing Company, Inc.*)

in Figs. 6-7 and 6-8. These switches are designed so that the amount of coupling introduced between the tuned circuits of the different stages is negligible. The switch contacts are usually arranged so that the unused coils are short-circuited. If the coils not actually in use are not short-

FIG. 6-8.—Multigang circuit selector switch. (*Courtesy of P. R. Mallory & Co., Inc.*)

circuited, the distributed capacitance of these coils may cause them to become resonant at some frequency, each within its own band, thereby coupling impedances into the coils that are being used. The construction of the switch should provide a low-resistance contact and should also provide some means whereby the connections between the coils and the switch are made as short as possible.

Although the wiring of a band selector switch becomes rather complicated, especially when more than one tuning circuit is used, it greatly simplifies the operation of the all-wave receiver. The change from one band to another is accomplished by merely turning the band selector switch to the band desired.

Band Switching with Capacitors. If a single coil is to be used to cover the entire frequency range, it is necessary to adjust the capacitance of the tuned circuit for each band desired. This can be accomplished by connecting a fixed capacitor in series with the tuning capacitor (see Fig. 6-9). The effect of the fixed capacitance is to reduce the capacitance

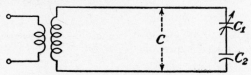

Fig. 6-9.—Increasing the frequency range of a tuned circuit by use of a fixed capacitor.

of the circuit, thereby increasing its resonant frequency. The value of the inductance required may be found by the following equations:

$$L = \frac{25,300}{f_1^2 C_1} \tag{6-1}$$

$$L = \frac{25,300}{f_2^2 C} \tag{6-2}$$

where L = inductance of the tuning circuit, microhenries

f_1 = frequency to which the circuit will tune without the fixed series capacitor, kilocycles

f_2 = frequency to which the circuit will tune with the fixed series capacitor, kilocycles

C_1 = capacitance of the tuning capacitor, microfarads

C = capacitance of the series circuit formed by the tuning capacitor and the fixed capacitor, microfarads

As the inductance is the same in Eqs. (6-1) and (6-2), then

$$\frac{25,300}{f_1^2 C_1} = \frac{25,300}{f_2^2 C} \tag{6-3}$$

dividing both sides by 25,300

$$\frac{1}{f_1^2 C_1} = \frac{1}{f_2^2 C} \tag{6-4}$$

and

$$C = \frac{f_1^2 C_1}{f_2^2} \qquad (6\text{-}5)$$

NOTE: C_1 and C may be expressed in either μf or $\mu\mu$f providing both are in the same units. Also, f_1 and f_2 may be expressed in cycles, kc, or mc providing both are in the same units.

Equation (6-5) is very useful in solving for the amount of capacitance necessary for any desired frequency range when only one value of inductance is to be used. The value of capacitance C_2 that must be connected in series with the original tuning capacitor C_1 in order to obtain the required capacitance C may be determined by the use of the equation

$$C_2 = \frac{CC_1}{C_1 - C} \qquad (2\text{-}24b)$$

Example 6-4. A certain tuned circuit using a 200-$\mu\mu$f tuning capacitor tunes from 500 kc to 1500 kc. What value of series capacitance C_2 (see Fig. 6-9) is required in order to provide a second band whose minimum frequency will be 1500 kc?

Given: Find:

$f_1 = 500$ kc $C_2 = ?$

$f_2 = 1500$ kc

$C_1 = 200$ $\mu\mu$f

Solution:

$$C = \frac{f_1^2 C_1}{f_2^2} = \frac{500 \times 500 \times 200}{1500 \times 1500} = 22.22 \ \mu\mu\text{f}$$

$$C_2 = \frac{CC_1}{C_1 - C} = \frac{22.22 \times 200}{200 - 22.22} = 25 \ \mu\mu\text{f}$$

From Example 6-4, it can be seen that in order to obtain resonance at 1500 kc the capacitance of this tuned circuit must be 22.22 $\mu\mu$f. Therefore, in order for the circuit to be resonant at 1500 kc without the series capacitor, the minimum capacitance of the tuning capacitor must be 22.22 $\mu\mu$f. The maximum resonant frequency obtainable when the series capacitor is used will depend on the value of the inductance, which remains constant, and the capacitance of the series circuit formed by the minimum capacitance of the tuning capacitor C_1 and the fixed capacitor C_2 (Fig. 6-9).

Example 6-5. The tuning circuit of Example 6-4 is capable of tuning from 500 kc to 1500 kc with its tuning capacitor alone, the capacitor having a maximum capacitance of 200 $\mu\mu$f and a minimum capacitance of 22.22 $\mu\mu$f. The frequency range of the circuit may be extended by connecting the capacitor C_2 of Fig. 6-9 into the circuit as indicated in Example 6-4. (a) What value of inductance is required for this circuit? (b) What is the minimum resonant frequency of the circuit when a 25-$\mu\mu$f capacitor is connected in series with the tuning capacitor (see Fig. 6-9)? (c) What is the maximum resonant frequency of the circuit when a 25-$\mu\mu$f capacitor is connected in series with the tuning capacitor? (*d*) What is the frequency range of the tuning circuit for both bands?

Given:
$$C_{1 \cdot max} = 200 \ \mu\mu f$$
$$C_{1 \cdot min} = 22.22 \ \mu\mu f$$
$$f_r\text{-band 1} = 500 \text{ to } 1500 \text{ kc}$$
$$C_2 = 25 \ \mu\mu f$$

Find:
(*a*) $L = ?$
(*b*) $f_{r \cdot min}$ band 2
(*c*) $f_{r \cdot max}$ band 2
(*d*) frequency range of both bands

Solution:

(*a*) $\quad L = \dfrac{25{,}300}{f_{min}^2 C_{1 \cdot max}} = \dfrac{25{,}300}{500 \times 500 \times 200 \times 10^{-6}} = 506 \ \mu h$

(*b*) $\quad C_{max} = \dfrac{C_{1 \cdot max} C_2}{C_{1 \cdot max} + C_2} = \dfrac{200 \times 25}{200 + 25} = 22.22 \ \mu\mu f$

$\qquad f_{min} = \dfrac{159}{\sqrt{LC_{max}}} = \dfrac{159}{\sqrt{506 \times 22.22 \times 10^{-6}}} = 1500 \text{ kc}$

(*c*) $\quad C_{min} = \dfrac{C_{1 \cdot min} C_2}{C_{1 \cdot min} + C_2} = \dfrac{22.22 \times 25}{22.22 + 25} = 11.76 \ \mu\mu f$

$\qquad f_{max} = \dfrac{159}{\sqrt{LC_{min}}} = \dfrac{159}{\sqrt{506 \times 11.76 \times 10^{-6}}} = 2061 \text{ kc}$

(*d*) frequency range = 500 to 2061 kc

Effect of Distributed Capacitances. In the preceding examples and discussion the distributed capacitance of the coil and the tuning circuit was neglected in order to simplify the explanations and the examples. In actual practice these capacitances must be taken into consideration because they increase the minimum and maximum capacitance of the tuning circuit and hence change its frequency range.

Example 6-6. What is the frequency range of each band of the tuning circuit of Example 6-5 if the distributed capacitance of the coil and circuit is to be considered and its value is 20 $\mu\mu$f? (NOTE: Use the value of inductance found in part (*a*) of Example 6-5.)

Given:
$$C_{1 \cdot max} = 200 \ \mu\mu f$$
$$C_{1 \cdot min} = 22.22 \ \mu\mu f$$
$$C_2 = 25 \ \mu\mu f$$
$$C_D = 20 \ \mu\mu f$$
$$L = 506 \ \mu h$$

Find:
frequency range, Band 1
frequency range, Band 2

Solution:

Band 1:

$$C_{max} = C_{1 \cdot max} + C_D = 200 + 20 = 220 \ \mu\mu f$$

$$f_{min} = \frac{159}{\sqrt{LC_{max}}} = \frac{159}{\sqrt{506 \times 220 \times 10^{-6}}} = 476 \text{ kc}$$

$$C_{min} = C_{1 \cdot min} + C_D = 22.22 + 20 = 42.22 \ \mu\mu f$$

$$f_{max} = \frac{159}{\sqrt{LC_{min}}} = \frac{159}{\sqrt{506 \times 42.22 \times 10^{-6}}} = 1088 \text{ kc}$$

Band 2:

$$C_{max} = C_{max \cdot 2} + C_D = 22.22 + 20 = 42.22 \ \mu\mu f$$

$$f_{min} = \frac{159}{\sqrt{LC_{max}}} = \frac{159}{\sqrt{506 \times 42.22 \times 10^{-6}}} = 1088 \ kc$$

$$C_{min} = C_{min \cdot 2} + C_D = 11.76 + 20 = 31.76 \ \mu\mu f$$

$$f_{max} = \frac{159}{\sqrt{LC_{min}}} = \frac{159}{\sqrt{506 \times 31.76 \times 10^{-6}}} = 1254 \ kc$$

From the above example it can be seen that a small amount of distributed capacitance in the tuned circuit will decrease its frequency range considerably. It is therefore important that the stray capacitances in a tuned circuit be kept at a minimum.

By using several fixed capacitors of different values and a rotary switch, a number of different frequency bands can be obtained. A circuit using this system is shown in Fig. 6-10.

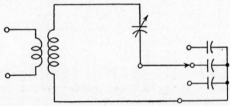

FIG. 6-10.—Use of a rotary switch and several fixed capacitors to obtain several frequency bands.

Band Switching Using Both Inductors and Capacitors. Although the frequency range of a tuned circuit may be increased by changing the amount of either its capacitance or its inductance, a number of receivers change both. This method is much more expensive, since a greater number of parts is required and the wiring of the selector switch becomes quite complex. With this type of receiver it is possible to obtain straight-line-frequency reception on all bands. Figure 6-11 illustrates an all-wave coil assembly that uses separate coils and capacitors for each band. A rotary switch is used to connect the proper units into the circuit for the particular band selected.

6-5. Bandspread. *Frequency Range of the Individual Bands.* The use of separate coils or fixed capacitors provided a means whereby it was possible to cover the broadcast band and a number of short-wave bands with one receiver. To eliminate the possibility of a gap between two adjacent bands, the coils are usually designed to overlap the extreme frequencies of the adjacent bands. Generally, the maximum resonant frequency of each band is chosen as some multiple of its minimum frequency. Broadcast receivers use a ratio of 3 to 1, while for high-frequency bands ratios of less than 1.5 to 1 are sometimes used.

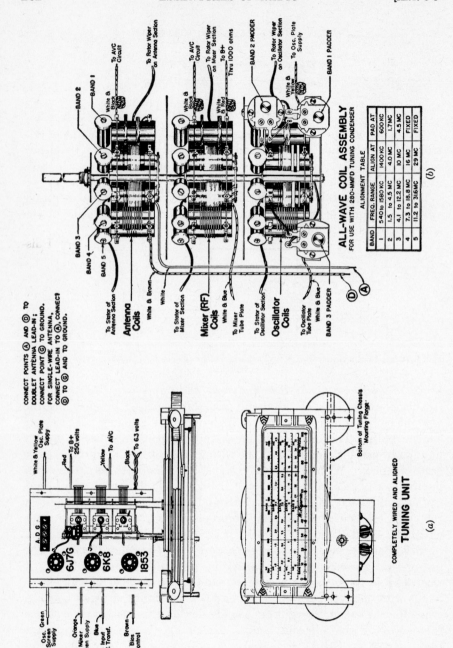

CONNECT POINTS Ⓐ AND Ⓓ TO
DOUBLET ANTENNA LEAD-IN;
CONNECT POINT Ⓖ TO GROUND,
FOR SINGLE-WIRE ANTENNA,
CONNECT LEAD-IN TO Ⓐ, CONNECT
Ⓓ TO Ⓖ AND TO GROUND.

ALL-WAVE COIL ASSEMBLY
FOR USE WITH 280-MMFD TUNING CONDENSER

ALIGNMENT TABLE

BAND	FREQ. RANGE	ALIGN AT	PAD AT
1	540 to 1580 KC	1400 KC	600 KC
2	1.5 to 4.5 MC	4.0 MC	1.7 MC
3	4.1 to 12.2 MC	10 MC	4.5 MC
4	7.3 to 18.8 MC	16 MC	FIXED
5	11.2 to 31.6 MC	29 MC	FIXED

(b)

COMPLETELY WIRED AND ALIGNED
TUNING UNIT

(a)

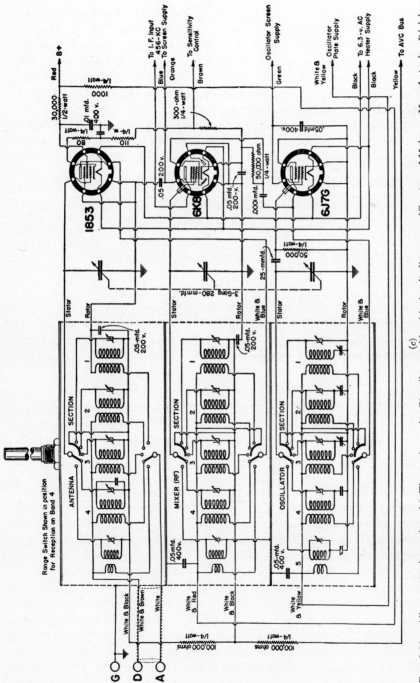

(c)

FIG. 6-11.—All-wave tuning unit.   (a) The tuning unit, (b) coil assembly, (c) circuit diagram.   (Courtesy of Meissner Manufacturing Division
Maguire Industries, Inc.)

To facilitate tuning, it is essential that the tuning range for each band occupy practically the entire scale of the dial. Because of the varying widths of these bands, special tuning circuits are used to obtain the correct maximum-minimum capacitance ratio for each band. This process is called *bandspreading* and is accomplished by connecting a small adjustable capacitor in series, parallel, or combination with the main tuning capacitor, as shown in Fig. 6-12.

Trimmers. The operation of these auxiliary capacitors is based on the principle that the capacitance of a circuit is increased by connecting capacitors in parallel and decreased by connecting them in series.

Example 6-7. A 20-$\mu\mu$f auxiliary capacitor, C_2 of Fig. 6-12a, is connected in parallel with a tuning capacitor C_1 having a range of 10 $\mu\mu$f to 100 $\mu\mu$f. What is the range of capacitance of the combined circuit?

Given: Find:
$$C_2 = 20 \ \mu\mu\text{f}$$ $C_{\min}$ to $C_{\max}$
$$C_{1 \cdot \min} = 10 \ \mu\mu\text{f}$$
$$C_{1 \cdot \max} = 100 \ \mu\mu\text{f}$$

Solution:

$$C_{\min} = C_{1 \cdot \min} + C_2 = 10 + 20 = 30 \ \mu\mu\text{f}$$
$$C_{\max} = C_{1 \cdot \max} + C_2 = 100 + 20 = 120 \ \mu\mu\text{f}$$
$$\text{Range} = 30 \ \mu\mu\text{f} \text{ to } 120 \ \mu\mu\text{f}$$

Example 6-8. What is the range of the combined circuit of **Example 6-7** if a 100-$\mu\mu$f auxiliary capacitor is used in place of the 20-$\mu\mu$f capacitor?

Given: Find:
$$C_2 = 100 \ \mu\mu\text{f}$$ $C_{\min}$ to $C_{\max}$
$$C_{1 \cdot \min} = 10 \ \mu\mu\text{f}$$
$$C_{1 \cdot \max} = 100 \ \mu\mu\text{f}$$

Solution:

$$C_{\min} = C_{1 \cdot \min} + C_2 = 10 + 100 = 110 \ \mu\mu\text{f}$$
$$C_{\max} = C_{1 \cdot \max} + C_2 = 100 + 100 = 200 \ \mu\mu\text{f}$$
$$\text{Range} = 110 \ \mu\mu\text{f} \text{ to } 200 \ \mu\mu\text{f}$$

From Example 6-7 it can be seen that adding a 20-$\mu\mu$f auxiliary capacitor in parallel with the 10- to 100-$\mu\mu$f tuning capacitor increases its range to 30 to 120 $\mu\mu$f. Also, from Example 6-8 it can be seen that adding a 100-$\mu\mu$f auxiliary capacitor in parallel with the tuning capacitor increases the range to 110 to 200 $\mu\mu$f. It should be noted that in each case the greatest per cent of increase occurs at the minimum value of capacitance. If the auxiliary capacitor is made adjustable between the values of 20 $\mu\mu$f and 100 $\mu\mu$f, then a large number of minimum and maximum values of capacitance can be obtained to produce a corresponding bandspread. Such an adjustable capacitor is generally referred to as a *trimmer*. Trimmers have the same effect on a tuned circuit as does distributed capacitance. The effectiveness of the trimmer capacitor can therefore be seen by referring to Examples 6-2 and 6-3, where the effect of including a distributed capacitance of 20 $\mu\mu$f showed a change in the broadcast frequency limits from 530 to 2581 kc to 514 to 1639 kc.

Padders.   In order that a desired frequency range may be obtained, it is sometimes desirable to restrict the maximum capacitance of the tuning circuit without greatly changing its minimum value.   To accomplish this, an auxiliary capacitor, C_2 of Fig. 6-12b, is connected in series

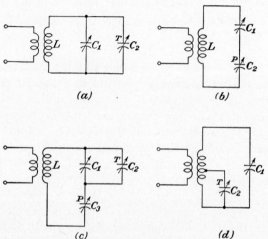

Fig. 6-12.—Trimmer and padder capacitors connected to produce bandspread and band-compression.

with the secondary coil L and the tuning capacitor C_1.   This capacitor is called a *padder* and is also made adjustable so that the minimum capacitance of the tuning circuit can be kept fairly constant.

Example 6-9.   A 20-$\mu\mu$f to 200-$\mu\mu$f adjustable capacitor, C_2 of Fig. 6-12b, is connected in series with the tuning capacitor C_1, having a range of 10 $\mu\mu$f to 100 $\mu\mu$f. What is the range of capacitance of the combined circuit if the adjustable capacitor is set at 20 $\mu\mu$f?

Given: Find:
$$C_2 = 20 \ \mu\mu f$$ C_{min} to C_{max}
$$C_{1\cdot min} = 10 \ \mu\mu f$$
$$C_{1\cdot max} = 100 \ \mu\mu f$$
Solution:

$$C_{min} = \frac{C_{1\cdot min}C_2}{C_{1\cdot min} + C_2} = \frac{10 \times 20}{10 + 20} = 6.66 \ \mu\mu f$$

$$C_{max} = \frac{C_{1\cdot max}C_2}{C_{1\cdot max} + C_2} = \frac{100 \times 20}{100 + 20} = 16.66 \ \mu\mu f$$

Range = 6.66 $\mu\mu$f to 16.66 $\mu\mu$f

Example 6-10.   What is the range of the combined circuit of Example 6-9 if the padder capacitor is set at 200 $\mu\mu f$?

Given:
$$C_2 = 200 \ \mu\mu f$$
$$C_{1\cdot min} = 10 \ \mu\mu f$$
$$C_{1\cdot max} = 100 \ \mu\mu f$$

Find:
$$C_{min} \text{ to } C_{max}$$

Solution:

$$C_{min} = \frac{C_{1\cdot min}C_2}{C_{1\cdot min} + C_2} = \frac{10 \times 200}{10 + 200} = 9.52 \ \mu\mu f$$

$$C_{max} = \frac{C_{1\cdot max}C_2}{C_{1\cdot max} + C_2} = \frac{100 \times 200}{100 + 200} = 66.66 \ \mu\mu f$$

$$\text{Range} = 9.52 \ \mu\mu f \text{ to } 66.66 \ \mu\mu f$$

From Example 6-9 it can be seen that adding a 20-$\mu\mu f$ capacitance in series with the 10–100 $\mu\mu f$ tuning capacitor decreases its range to 6.66–16.66 $\mu\mu f$.   Also, from Example 6-10 it can be seen that adding a 200-$\mu\mu f$ capacitance in series with the tuning capacitor decreases the range to 9.52–66.66 $\mu\mu f$.   It should be noted that in each case the greatest per cent of decrease occurs at the maximum value of capacitance, hence the padding capacitor has comparatively little effect on the minimum capacitance of the tuning circuit but definitely controls its maximum capacitance.

Radio receivers sometimes employ both trimmers and padders in order to obtain the desired bandspread; such a circuit is shown in Fig. 6-12c.   The desired frequency limits are obtained by adjusting these two capacitors to the correct values.   Another method sometimes used is to connect the trimmer across only part of the secondary coil L as shown in Fig. 6-12d.   The amount of bandspread increases as the tap is made closer to the bottom of the coil.

Example 6-11.   The tuning circuit of the oscillator section of a superheterodyne receiver is to be adjusted so that it will always tune 465 kc higher than the tuning circuit of the receiver, whose frequency limits are to be 530 kc and 1550 kc.   A circuit similar to that shown in Fig. 6-12c is to be used and the circuit elements are to have the following values: $L = 200 \ \mu h$, $C_{1\cdot min} = 12.5 \ \mu\mu f$, $C_{1\cdot max} = 250 \ \mu\mu f$, and $C_2 = 6.5 \ \mu\mu f$. The distributed capacitance of the circuit is 15 $\mu\mu f$.   (a) What value of padder capacitor C_3 is required when the tuning circuit is adjusted to its minimum frequency? (b) Using the padder capacitance as calculated in part (a), what is the resonant frequency of the oscillator section when the tuning circuit is adjusted to its maximum frequency?

Given:
$$f = 530 \text{ kc to } 1550 \text{ kc}$$
$$C_1 = 12.5 \text{ to } 250 \ \mu\mu f$$
$$C_2 = 6.5 \ \mu\mu f$$
$$C_D = 15 \ \mu\mu f$$
$$L = 200 \ \mu h$$

Find:
(a) $C_3 = ?$
(b) $f_{osc\cdot max}$

Solution:

(a)　$f_{osc\cdot min} = f_{min} + 465 = 530 + 465 = 995$ kc

$$C_{f\cdot min} = \frac{25{,}300}{(f_{osc\cdot min})^2 L} = \frac{25{,}300}{995^2 \times 200} = 127.7 \ \mu\mu f$$

$$C_3 = \frac{(C_{1\cdot max} + C_2)(C_{f\cdot min} - C_D)}{(C_{1\cdot max} + C_2) - (C_{f\cdot min} - C_D)} = \frac{256.5 \times 112.7}{256.5 - 112.7} = 201 \ \mu\mu f$$

(b)　$C_{min} = \dfrac{(C_{1\cdot min} + C_2)C_3}{(C_{1\cdot min} + C_2) + C_3} + C_D = \dfrac{19 \times 201}{19 + 201} + 15 = 32.35 \ \mu\mu f$

$$f_{osc\cdot max} = \frac{159}{\sqrt{LC_{min}}} = \frac{159}{\sqrt{200 \times 32.35 \times 10^{-6}}} = 1976 \text{ kc}$$

The maximum frequency of the oscillator as calculated in Example 6-11 is equal to 1976 kc instead of 2015 kc (1550 + 465). By properly adjusting the trimmer capacitor C_2, the correct value of maximum frequency can be obtained. As any change in the value of trimmer capacitance will have only a slight effect on the maximum value of capacitance of the entire circuit, the minimum frequency will remain practically the same. Adjusting the trimmers and padders in order to obtain the correct oscillator frequency will be taken up in greater detail in Chap. XIV.

Bandspread Tuning. Dials used for tuning generally have a rotation of 180 mechanical degrees. With such a dial, the amount of change in kc for each degree of rotation will vary with the amount of bandspread. On the broadcast band, 550 to 1600 kc, each degree would represent a change of 1650 divided by 180, or approximately 5 kc. As there should be at least a 10-kc difference between adjacent stations, there is no problem in tuning a desired station on the broadcast band.

On the short-wave bands, tuning a desired station becomes quite difficult and increases in difficulty as the frequency of the band is increased. This can be seen by observation of the frequency bands in set A of Table VI-I. For this receiver the approximate kilocycle change for each degree of rotation will be 15 kc for band 1, 41.6 kc for band 2, and 66.6 kc for band 3. Two methods are used to spread the amount of kilocycle change over a greater portion of the dial, one mechanical and the other electrical.

The mechanical method employs a geared dial that causes the variable capacitor to move at a slower rate than the dial. The greater the ratio between the two gears, the slower will be the movement of the variable capacitor. However, there is a limit to the amount the gear ratio can be increased without producing a backlash. In general, this method is not very efficient as in order for it to be really effective a precision dial must be used and its cost is prohibitive for the average set.

The electrical method utilizes the principle of the trimmer capacitor to obtain bandspread. A midget or micro variable capacitor, depending on the frequency band, is substituted for C_2 (Fig. 6-12). This small capacitor is usually referred to as a *bandspread capacitor*. In order to receive signals from a station transmitting at 16.28 mc, the main tuning capacitor C_1 would be adjusted to approximately 16 mc and the bandspread capacitor would be used to tune the circuit to 16.28 mc. The main tuning capacitor is used to adjust the tuning circuit to approximately the desired frequency. The bandspread capacitor is used to obtain the exact frequency, as a considerable movement of this capacitor will only change the resonant frequency by a small fraction of a kilocycle.

These two methods of bandspread tuning are usually found only in receivers specially built for radio amateurs' use. The average all-wave receiver generally does not have this feature. The better receivers, as built for radio amateurs, may use both of these methods.

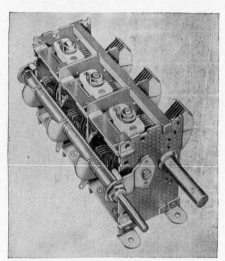

Fig. 6-13.—Bandspread tuning capacitor. (*Courtesy of Meissner Manufacturing Division Maguire Industries, Inc.*)

6-6. Multiple Stages. *Selectivity of Multiple Stages.* Up to now all the tuning circuits have been considered as having only one stage, that is, they use only one tuning capacitor and coil to select the desired signal. A single tuning stage does not always provide sufficient selectivity for satisfactory reception, hence in order to obtain the desired selectivity a number of similar tuning stages are sometimes used. The selectivity of the receiver will then be dependent on the selectivity of each stage and the number of stages used. The manner in which the selectivity is improved by increasing the number of tuned circuits can be seen by observation of Fig. 6-14. The frequency of resonance for each tuned circuit is 1000 kc. The signal output at the resonant frequency is assumed to be 100 per cent. The signal output at all other frequencies will therefore be a definite percentage of this output. Assuming that the characteristics of each tuning circuit are the same, the percentage of the input signal, for all frequencies above and below resonance, can be represented by the response curve for the first stage of tuning. For example, at 5 kc off resonance, that is, 995 kc or 1005, the input signal is reduced to 92 per cent as represented by the response curve for the first stage of tuning. The output from the second stage for this frequency would be equal to 92 per cent of 92 per cent, or 84.6 per cent. The output from the third stage for the same frequency would be 92 per cent of 84.6 per cent, or 77.8 per cent, and that for the fourth stage would be 92 per cent of 77.8 per cent, or 71.6 per cent.   This procedure can be followed for any value of frequency.

Number of Tuning Stages to Be Used.   From the preceding discussion and reference to Fig. 6-14, it can be seen that increasing the number of stages of tuning definitely increases the over-all selectivity of a receiver. Theoretically, it would seem that any number of tuning stages could be added but practically this is not true, as other factors must be taken into consideration.   In order to obtain good fidelity from general broadcast

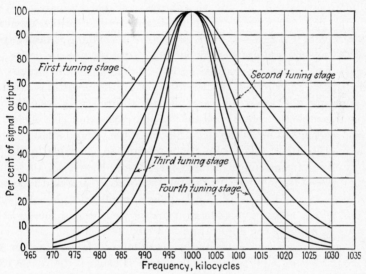

FIG. 6-14.—Graph illustrating the manner in which the selectivity of a receiver increases with additional stages of tuning.

stations, the width of the band passed (measured at 0.707 of the maximum value) should not be less than 10 kc.   Adding too many stages may decrease the width of the band passed below this value, thus decreasing the fidelity of reception.

In modern receivers, the tuning circuit forms a definite part of each stage of radio-frequency amplification and the complete unit is generally referred to as a stage of r-f amplification.   There are a number of methods employed to couple one stage of r-f amplification to another, and the choice of which one to use will depend on the type of r-f amplifier tube and circuit used.   Radio-frequency amplification and methods of coupling will be considered in detail in Chap. VII.   The total amplification desired and its relation to the amplification produced by each tube, coupling device, and tuning circuit must also be considered.

The circuit used is another factor to be considered. The simple tuned-radio-frequency (trf) receiver, which was popular for a number of years, generally used two stages of r-f amplification before the detector. Superheterodyne receivers do not depend on the r-f stages to obtain the necessary amplification before detection, as the intermediate frequency (i-f) amplifiers are used for this purpose. Although the number of r-f tuning circuits in superheterodyne receivers will vary with the make and model, it is general practice to use one or more tuning circuits in addition to the oscillator section.

6-7. Single Control Tuning. *Ganged Tuning.* In the early types of radio receivers each tuning circuit was controlled separately by an individual dial. This procedure made tuning quite difficult, since most of the receivers had three or more controls, thus making it impossible to adjust the circuits simultaneously with only two hands.

As the coil, capacitor, and wiring for each of the tuning circuits were usually similar to one another, the dial setting for a given station was approximately the same for each of the controls. It was therefore possible to couple the rotors of all the variable capacitors with one another by some mechanical means so that they could be rotated simultaneously with a single control; this is sometimes referred to as *ganged tuning*.

A number of mechanical arrangements have been used to turn the rotors of all the tuning capacitors simultaneously. Among the arrangements used were a system of gears, pulleys, racks and pinions, parallel arms and levers, and use of a common shaft. Only one of these methods is now used, namely, the application of a common shaft.

Multiple Capacitors. A multiple capacitor consists of two or more separate capacitors built into a single frame so that all the rotors can be operated from a common shaft. Such a capacitor is called a *multiple* or *gang capacitor* (see Fig. 6-15). In order to reduce the capacitance between adjacent stator sections, a flat metal plate is mounted between each section. This plate is connected to ground and thus acts as an electrostatic shield.

For certain positions of the rotor all its weight would be concentrated on one side. If the rotor contains a large number of plates this unequal distribution of weight will tend to move the rotor out of the position to which it had been adjusted. To overcome this difficulty the rotor is balanced mechanically by mounting half of the stator and rotor plates 180 mechanical degrees from each other (see Fig. 6-15).

Multiple capacitors are more efficient, less bulky, and less expensive than the other systems of obtaining ganged tuning. They are therefore the most commonly used method.

(a)   (b)

(c)

FIG. 6-15.—Commercial types of multiple, or gang capacitors. (a) Two-gang capacitor, (b) three-gang capacitor, (c) capacitor with opposed rotor and stator for perfect
counterbalancing. (a and b, *courtesy of Meissner Manufacturing Division Maguire Industries, Inc.; c, courtesy of Hammarlund Manufacturing Company, Inc.*)

6-8. Equalizing the Tuning Circuits. *Tracking.* Although the
single-control tuning system rotated each tuning capacitor by the same
amount, the electrical adjustment, while approximately equal, was not
exactly the same for each tuning circuit. This electrical difference was
due to the slight mechanical differences in the capacitors, coils, and wiring of the tuning circuits. In order to obtain the maximum fidelity,
selectivity, and sensitivity for a receiver, it is necessary that all the
tuning circuits track together over the entire range of the receiver.
This means that the resonant frequency for each of the tuning circuits
must be exactly the same for all positions of the tuning control. To
obtain perfectly matched coils and capacitors and to have the wiring for
each tuning circuit exactly the same requires precision manufacture.
This procedure is too expensive and also is impractical for mass produc-

tion.   It was therefore necessary to employ some means of adjusting each circuit.

Methods Used to Align the Tuning Circuits.   The inductance of the coils and of the wiring for all the tuning circuits in a receiver is constant in value for all positions of the tuning control.   It is therefore possible to assemble and wire each tuning circuit so that their values of inductance, for all practical purposes, are close enough to each other to be considered as being the same.   Thus it was only necessary to make adjustments for differences in capacitance between each circuit.   There have been numerous systems used to compensate for differences in capacitance but only two are in common use at the present time.

The more common of these two methods uses a small adjustable trimmer capacitor that is connected in parallel with the main tuning capacitor (see Fig. 6-15).   In this system the trimmer capacitors can be adjusted for only general capacitance differences between each tuning circuit but cannot be used to align each section for all positions of the tuning control.   It is general practice to adjust the capacitor sections for three positions, namely, the approximate center and each end of the frequency band.   Adjustments are made at these three positions and are then rechecked in order that all circuits track as closely as possible for all positions.

Fig. 6-16.—A slotted rotor plate.

A more accurate method is to cut slots in the end rotor plates, as shown in Figs. 6-15 and 6-16.   These plates generally have four or more sections and the capacitance for each section can be changed by bending the plate at that section.   If it is bent toward the stator the capacitance is increased and if bent away from the stator the capacitance will be decreased.   The tuning control is adjusted for some frequency within a section of the rotor plate and that section is adjusted to obtain maximum signal response for that frequency.   As any adjustments made for one value of frequency will not affect other frequency adjustments, maximum signal response can be obtained for as many positions as there are rotor plate sections.   Using this system, the tuning circuits can be made to track for all positions of the tuning control.

Some receivers use a combination of both of these methods.   In these receivers the trimmers are used to compensate for general differences in capacitance and the slotted rotor plates are used to align the capacitor sections for various positions of the tuning control.

6-9. Automatic Tuning.   In the methods of tuning described in the preceding discussion, the selecting of stations on a receiver is accomplished by rotating the tuning dial to the desired position by hand.   This is sometimes referred to as *manual tuning*.   Another method of tuning a receiver is by merely pushing a button or a lever. With this system, the receiver may automatically be tuned to the stations predetermined for each tuning button. This is called *automatic tuning* and it is used extensively in the medium- and high-priced sets. The number of tuning buttons on a receiver varies from four to as many as nineteen, depending on the manufacture and model of the receiver. In the majority of cases, however, the automatic tuning control provides five or six tuning buttons.

Methods of Obtaining Automatic Tuning Control. Although numerous systems have been devised for obtaining automatic tuning (see reference in bibliography), they may be roughly classified into three general types, namely, (1) mechanically operated manual types, (2) tuned-circuit substitution types, (3) motor-operated types.

Mechanically Operated Manual Types. In these types of automatic tuning, the shaft of the tuning capacitor is turned to the preset desired position by pressing a button, key, or some type of lever. This type of tuning may be further subdivided into five common methods of operation, namely, linear, rocker bar, rotary, indent, and flash. The *linear* method employs a series of cams and levers to obtain the station selection. Pushing a button produces motion in about the same manner as pushing on a typewriter key and thereby causes the shaft of the tuning capacitor to be rotated to its preset position. The *rocker-bar* method employs a series of push buttons, which translate the motion to preset positions of the tuning capacitor. The *rotary* type uses a dial similar in appearance to the dial of the modern telephone. The *indent* method, also known as *spot tuning*, uses a steel ball that is pressed in a groove of a soft metal cylinder at preset positions and thereby provides indents to aid the manual tuning. The *flash* method, also known as *light-indicator tuning*, does not use any button arrangement but is tuned by the ordinary manual tuning. When the tuning dial is in a position corresponding to one of the preset flash-tuned stations, a dial light is caused to light up in back of a transparent marker indicating the station to which the receiver is tuned.

Tuned-circuit Substitution Types. In these types of automatic tuning, a number of precalibrated tuned circuits are connected to a push-button type of selector switch. The precalibrated tuned circuits are generally tuned by means of mica trimmer capacitors, permeability tuned coils, or a combination of both. In most cases where the tuned-circuit substitution method of automatic tuning is used, the ordinary manual tuning is also provided. However, in a few instances, the manual type of tuning is omitted and such receivers can only be tuned to those stations for which specific tuned circuits are provided.

Motor-operated Types. In these types of automatic tuning, the shaft of the tuning capacitor is turned to the position required for a desired station by means of a small electric motor. The tuning of desired stations is obtained by a station selector switch or a number of push buttons and generally requires the use of a selecting commutator or some other device for stopping the motor at the desired point.

Auxiliary Controls Required with Automatic Tuning. Adding automatic tuning to a receiver generally requires including a number of extra auxiliary circuits or controls, the most important of which are (1) transfer circuit or mechanism to change from continuous or manual tuning to automatic tuning, (2) an audio silencing or muting provision that will silence the receiver when the automatic tuning mechanism is changing the receiver from one station to another, (3) a station selecting commutator mechanism for stopping the motor at the correct position for station reception with the motor-operated types.

BIBLIOGRAPHY

Automatic Tuning, *MYE Technical Manual*, P. R. Mallory & Co., Inc., Indianapolis, Ind.

GHIRARDI, A. A., *Radio Physics Course*, Murray Hill Books, Inc., New York.

MANLY, H. P., *Drake's Cyclopedia of Radio and Electronics*, Frederick J. Drake & Co., Chicago.

The Radio Amateur's Handbook, The American Radio Relay League, Inc., West Hartford, Conn.

QUESTIONS

1. What is meant by tuning? How is it accomplished?

2. Name and explain the three functions generally performed by tuning circuits.

3. What are side bands? How do the side bands of the signals transmitted by a high-fidelity station compare with those sent out on ordinary broadcast?

4. What is meant by an ideal response curve? How does the fidelity of transmission affect the width of this ideal curve?

5. What four methods are used to approximate the ideal response curve?

6. What is meant by a radio channel?

7. How does increasing the selectivity of a receiver beyond a certain point decrease its fidelity?

8. What factors in radio transmission may produce crosstalk in a receiver? How can this interference be minimized?

9. How does the frequency vary with the amount of rotation for each of the following types of variable capacitors: (a) SLC? (b) SLW? (c) SLF?

10. Explain the methods used to obtain compactness in variable capacitor construction.

11. What factors determine the inductance of the secondary of a tuned r-f transformer?

12. Is it desirable to use a small capacitor and a large inductance, or a large capacitor and a small inductance, in the tuning circuit? Explain.

13. Should the physical dimensions of an r-f coil be large or small? Explain.

14. What types of radio service use the short-wave bands?

15. What five characteristics of short-wave communication are not found in ordinary broadcast communication?

16. Why is it not practical to use a single coil and capacitor to cover the entire short-wave band?

17. What factors determine the frequency limits for each band?

18. What is meant by an all-wave receiver? What methods may be used to obtain the required tuning range?

19. If a single variable capacitor is to be used for tuning, what factors determine the value of inductance for each coil used?

20. Is it practical in an all-wave receiver to use a variable capacitor whose maximum value is similar to that used for ordinary broadcast reception? Explain.

21. What are the advantages of using a band selector switch in place of plug-in coils for changing the frequency band to be tuned?

22. What factors must be taken into consideration in designing a band switch?

23. Explain the method of obtaining the frequency range for each of the bands desired by using a single inductance coil and varying the capacitance.

24. What effect does the distributed capacitance of a tuning circuit have on the frequency limits for each band?

25. What advantages are obtained by changing both the capacitance and inductance for each frequency band?

26. Why is it necessary to use bandspread coils for tuning short-wave receivers?

27. What is the difference between the construction of a bandspread coil and the usual type of r-f coil?

28. What is the difference between the construction and application of trimmer and padder capacitors?

29. In bandspread coils, what is the purpose of (a) trimmers? (b) Padders?

30. What is meant by bandspread tuning? Where is it used? Why is it necessary?

31. Explain the mechanical method of obtaining bandspread tuning. What are its advantages?

32. Explain the electrical method of obtaining bandspread tuning. What are its advantages?

33. Explain how the selectivity of a receiver is increased by using multiple-stage tuning.

34. What factors determine the number of stages of tuning to be used?

35. What are the advantages of single-control tuning?

36. What is a multiple variable capacitor? What are its advantages?

37. What is meant by tracking?

38. What are equalizing capacitors? Where are they used? Why are they used?

39. How are slotted rotor plates used to align the tuning circuit? What are their advantages?

40. What is meant by automatic tuning?

41. What are the three basic methods of obtaining automatic tuning? Describe each.

PROBLEMS

1. A tuning circuit whose minimum frequency is to be 550 kc uses a 300-$\mu\mu$f variable capacitor whose minimum capacitance is 16 $\mu\mu$f. (a) What is the value of inductance that the secondary winding must possess? (b) What is the highest frequency obtainable with the inductance as calculated in part (a)?

2. How is the frequency range of the tuning circuit in Prob. 1 affected by a distributed circuit capacitance of (a) 10 $\mu\mu$f? (b) 20 $\mu\mu$f?

3. A tuning circuit whose minimum frequency is to be 530 kc uses a 150-$\mu\mu$f variable capacitor whose minimum capacitance is 13 $\mu\mu$f. (a) What is the value of inductance that the secondary winding must possess? (*b*) What is the highest frequency obtainable with the inductance as calculated in part (*a*)?

4. How is the frequency range of the tuning circuit in Prob. 3 affected by a distributed circuit capacitance of (*a*) 12 $\mu\mu$f? (*b*) 18 $\mu\mu$f?

5. The inductance of the secondary winding of a certain tuning circuit is 41.5 μh. The distributed capacitance of the circuit is 12 $\mu\mu$f. (*a*) What is the maximum value required of the capacitor if the minimum frequency is to be 1500 kc? (*b*) What is the highest frequency obtainable if the minimum capacitance of the variable capacitor is 16 $\mu\mu$f?

6. A variable capacitor and an inductor (secondary winding of a transformer) having an inductance of 14.4 μh are to be used to tune a frequency band whose limits are to be 4 mc and 9 mc. The distributed capacitance of the circuit is 10 $\mu\mu$f. What are the maximum and minimum values required of the variable capacitor?

7. A 300-$\mu\mu$f variable capacitor having a minimum capacitance of 16 $\mu\mu$f is used in the tuning circuit of the all-wave receiver listed as set A in Table VI-I. If the distributed capacitance of the tuning circuit is neglected, what value of inductance is required of the secondary winding of each of the four coils in order to tune the lower frequency of their respective bands?

8. Using the values of inductance found in Prob. **7**, what is the highest resonant frequency obtainable for each band?

9. If the tuning circuit of Prob. **7** has a distributed capacitance of 15 $\mu\mu$f and the same coils are used, what are the frequency limits of each band if the distributed capacitance is considered?

10. A 200-$\mu\mu$f variable capacitor having a minimum capacitance of 11 $\mu\mu$f is used in the tuning circuit of the all-wave receiver listed as set B in Table VI-I. If the distributed capacitance of the tuning circuit is neglected, what value of inductance is required of the secondary winding of each of the four coils in order to tune the lower frequency of their respective bands?

11. Using the values of inductance found in Prob. **10**, what is the highest resonant frequency obtainable for each band?

12. If the tuning circuit of Prob. **10** has a distributed capacitance of 12 $\mu\mu$f and the same coils are used, what are the frequency limits of each band if the distributed capacitance is considered?

13. A certain tuned circuit using a 300-$\mu\mu$f variable capacitor tunes from 530 to 1550 kc. What value of series capacitance is required in order to increase the minimum frequency from 530 to 1500 kc?

14. What is the frequency range of the tuning circuit of Prob. 13 when the series capacitor as calculated in Prob. 13 is connected in the circuit? (Assume the minimum capacitance of the tuning capacitor to be 35.1 $\mu\mu$f.)

15. What is the frequency range of each band of the tuning circuit of Prob. 13, if the distributed capacitance of the coil and circuit is equal to 15 $\mu\mu$f?

16. A two-band receiver uses a 335-$\mu\mu$f variable capacitor to tune the broadcast band to a minimum frequency of 530 kc. A fixed capacitor is connected in series with the variable capacitor to adjust the tuning circuit for the short-wave band whose minimum frequency is to be 1.5 mc. The variable capacitor has a minimum capacitance of 12 $\mu\mu$f. (*a*) What value of series capacitance is required for the short-wave band? (*b*) What are the frequency limits of each band?

17. What are the frequency limits of each band of the receiver of Prob. 16, if the distributed capacitance of the tuned circuit is equal to 12 $\mu\mu$f and the values of all the circuit elements are the same as those of Prob. 16?

18. A two-band receiver uses a variable tuning capacitor whose maximum capacitance is 500 $\mu\mu$f and whose minimum capacitance is 16 $\mu\mu$f. The distributed capacitance is 10 $\mu\mu$f. The minimum frequencies of the two bands are 550 kc and 1.6 mc respectively. (a) What value of inductance is required of the secondary in order to obtain the minimum frequency for the broadcast band? (b) What value of series capacitance is required in order to obtain the minimum frequency for the short-wave band using the same inductor as in part (a)? (c) What is the maximum resonant frequency of each band?

19. A tuning circuit using a variable capacitor that has a maximum capacitance of 250 $\mu\mu$f and a minimum capacitance of 10 $\mu\mu$f has a frequency range of from 500 to 1800 kc. The distributed capacitance of the circuit is 10 $\mu\mu$f. (a) What is the value of the trimmer capacitor required to decrease the higher limit of the frequency range to 1600 kc? (b) What effect does the use of this trimmer capacitor have on the lower limit of the frequency band?

20. The upper and lower limits of a frequency band are 11.8 mc and 3.88 mc respectively. The maximum and minimum capacitances of the tuning capacitor are 140 $\mu\mu$f and 6 $\mu\mu$f. The distributed capacitance of the circuit is 10 $\mu\mu$f. (a) What is the value of the trimmer capacitor required to decrease the higher limit of the frequency range to 10 mc? (b) What effect does the use of this trimmer capacitor have on the lower limit of the frequency band?

21. The tuning circuit of the oscillator section of a superheterodyne receiver is to be adjusted so that it will always tune 175 kc higher than the tuning circuit of the receiver whose frequency limits are 550 and 1610 kc. A circuit similar to that shown in Fig. 6-12c is used and the circuit elements have the following values: $L = 150$ μh, $C_{1\cdot\text{max}} = 320$ $\mu\mu$f, $C_{1\cdot\text{min}} = 13.5$ $\mu\mu$f, and $C_2 = 20$ $\mu\mu$f. The distributed capacitance of the circuit is 20 $\mu\mu$f. (a) What value is required of the padder capacitor when the tuning circuit is adjusted to its minimum frequency? (b) Using the padder capacitor as calculated in part (a), what is the resonant frequency of the oscillator section when the tuning circuit is adjusted to its maximum frequency?

22. Neglecting the distributed capacitance of the circuit of Prob. 21, (a) what value of padder capacitance would appear to be required when the tuning circuit is adjusted to its minimum frequency? (b) Using the padder capacitance as calculated in part (a), what would the resonant frequency of the oscillator section appear to be when the tuning circuit is adjusted to its maximum frequency?

23. The tuning circuit of the oscillator section of a superheterodyne receiver is to be adjusted so that it will always tune 265 kc higher than the tuning circuit of the receiver, whose frequency limits are 550 and 1625 kc. A circuit similar to that shown in Fig. 6-12c is used and the circuit elements have the following values: $L = 135$ μh, $C_{1\cdot\text{max}} = 320$ $\mu\mu$f, $C_{1\cdot\text{min}} = 13.5$ $\mu\mu$f, and $C_2 = 20$ $\mu\mu$f. The distributed capacitance of the circuit is 20 $\mu\mu$f. (a) What value is required of the padder capacitor when the tuning circuit is adjusted to its minimum frequency? (b) Using the padder capacitor as calculated in part (a), what is the resonant frequency of the oscillator section when the tuning circuit is adjusted to its maximum frequency?

24. The tuning circuit of the oscillator section of a superheterodyne receiver is to be adjusted so that it will always tune 175 kc higher than the tuning circuit of the receiver, whose frequency limits are 550 and 1600 kc. A circuit similar to that shown in Fig. 6-12c is used and the circuit elements have the following values: $L = 180$ μh, $C_{1\cdot\text{max}} = 260$ $\mu\mu$f, $C_{1\cdot\text{min}} = 10$ $\mu\mu$f, and $C_2 = 20$ $\mu\mu$f. The distributed capacitance of the circuit is 15 $\mu\mu$f. (a) What value is required of the padder capacitor when the tuning circuit is adjusted to its minimum frequency? (b) Using the padder capacitor as calculated in part (a), what is the resonant frequency of the oscillator section when the tuning circuit is adjusted to its maximum frequency?

CHAPTER VII

RADIO-FREQUENCY AMPLIFIER CIRCUITS

Amplification is the process of increasing the amplitude of a signal. An amplifier is a device that increases the power or voltage of an input signal, with the aid of vacuum tubes, by furnishing additional power supplied by a separate source. The input signal, which is used to control the output power of the amplifier, may come from the antenna, the output of a previous stage of amplification, the output of a detector circuit, a microphone, a phonograph pickup, a photocell, or a transmission line. A radio-frequency amplifier is one designed to increase the amplitude of signals at radio frequencies. Because vacuum tubes form a definite part of all amplifiers, it is essential that the amplifying properties of vacuum tubes be thoroughly understood.

7-1. The Vacuum Tube As an Amplifier. *Voltage and Power Amplifiers.* The amplifying action of a vacuum tube has been described in Chap. IV. This action may be utilized in radio circuits in a number of ways, the method used depending upon the results that are to be obtained. Fundamentally there are two types of amplifiers, namely, the voltage amplifier and the power amplifier. In a similar manner, there are fundamentally two types of amplifier tubes, voltage amplifiers and power amplifiers. Because the power output of practically all amplifier tubes will be greater than the input power applied to the grid, strictly speaking all amplifiers are power amplifiers. However, the primary objective of a voltage amplifier is to increase the voltage of the input signal without regard to the output power. The primary objective of a power amplifier is to increase the energy of the input signal without regard to the output voltage.

Radio-frequency Voltage and Power Amplifiers. The sensitivity of a radio receiver can be increased by amplifying the incoming signal, as received by the antenna, before applying it to the input of the detector circuit. The primary objective of these amplifiers is to increase the voltage in the r-f circuits and they are called *r-f voltage amplifiers.* R-f amplifiers are also used in transmitters to increase the amplitude of the high-frequency modulated signal before it is sent out into space from the antenna. The primary objective of these amplifiers is to increase the energy of the modulated signal before it is transmitted, and they are called *r-f power amplifiers.*

R-f amplifiers are used in superheterodyne receivers to amplify the voltage of a narrow band of intermediate values of frequencies and are called *i-f amplifiers*. These amplifiers are very efficient because they can be designed to operate on a definite narrow frequency band. The frequency at which an i-f amplifier operates varies with the circuit design and generally ranges from 175 to 465 kc. The width of the band that it is required to amplify is generally 10 kc. Thus an i-f amplifier designed to operate at 465 kc will be expected to amplify all signals whose frequencies lie between 465 plus 5, or 470 kc, and 465 minus 5, or 460 kc. The signals of all frequencies outside of this 10-kc band should be reduced to a negligible value. I-f amplifiers will be taken up in greater detail under band-pass amplifiers later in this chapter.

The operating characteristics and the circuit actions of r-f voltage amplifiers are taken up in this chapter, while the r-f power amplifiers will be presented with the study of transmitters in Chap. XIII.

7-2. Classification of Amplifiers.   *Class A Amplification.*   In the preceding discussion amplifiers have been described as being either voltage or power amplifiers. They have also been described as being radio-frequency or intermediate-frequency amplifiers; they may appear in additional classifications, such as audio-frequency, video-frequency, and direct-current amplifiers.

Another commonly used classification of amplifiers is based upon their operating characteristics. On this basis they are known as Class A, Class B, Class AB, or Class C amplifiers (see Fig. 7-1). A *Class A amplifier* is one in which the grid bias and the alternating input signal voltages are of such values that the plate current will flow in the output circuit at all times. A *Class B amplifier* is one in which the grid bias is made approximately equal to the cutoff value. In this case the plate current will be approximately zero for zero signal input, and plate current will flow for only approximately one-half of the input cycle. A *Class AB amplifier* is one in which the grid bias and the alternating signal input voltages are of such values that plate current will flow for appreciably more than half but less than the complete time of the alternating input cycle. A *Class C amplifier* is one in which the grid bias is considerably greater than cutoff value so that the plate current is zero for zero signal input, and plate current will flow appreciably less than one-half the time of the alternating input cycle.

A further designation is sometimes made by adding the subscript 1 or 2, in which 1 indicates that grid current does not flow during any part of the time of an alternating input cycle, while 2 indicates that grid current does flow during some part of the alternating input cycle. Thus an AB_1 amplifier does not draw any grid current at any time while an

AB₂ amplifier does take grid current during some part of the time of the alternating input cycle.

Most r-f, i-f, and a-f amplifiers used in the average radio receiver are voltage amplifiers and operate as Class A; hence only this type will be considered at this time.   The remaining classes of amplifiers are generally used as power amplifiers and will be taken up in a later chapter.

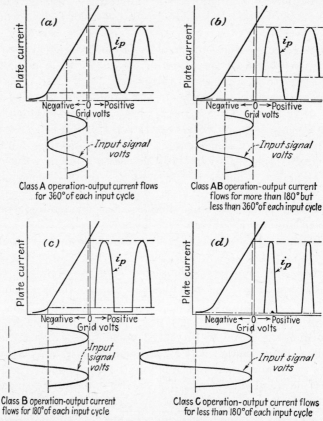

FIG. 7-1.—Curves showing the relation between the current flow in the output circuit and the input signal for various classifications of amplifier operation.

Class A Amplifiers.   A Class A amplifier is one in which the grid bias and the alternating input signal voltages are of such values that plate current will flow in the output circuit at all times (see Figs. 7-1 and 7-2). A radio tube may be operated as Class A in order to reproduce faithfully the variations in the input signal, the reproduced signals appearing across the impedance in the plate or output circuit.   In the elementary voltage amplifier circuit shown in Fig. 7-3, the variations in voltage across the output impedance Z_o will be a reproduction of the variations in the input signal voltage e_g impressed across the grid but of increased amplitude.

Operating Grid Bias for a Class A Amplifier. The value of grid bias required for Class A operation will depend upon the operating characteristics of the tube used and the voltage of the input signal. This can be seen by observation of the operating characteristics of a Class A amplifier as shown in Fig. 7-2. The grid bias should be of a value that will cause

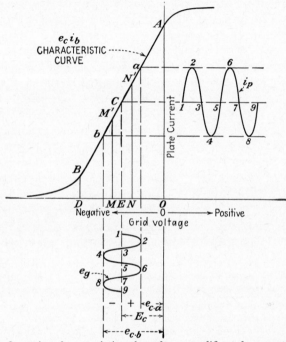

Fig. 7-2.—Operating characteristics of a voltage amplifier tube operated Class A.

the tube to operate on only the straight portion AB of the grid-plate transfer characteristic curve. The output current in the plate circuit will then be an exact enlarged reproduction of the input signal variations that were applied to the grid. The impedance of the output circuit remains constant for a definite value of frequency, and as the radio-frequency component of any input signal is constant, the variations in voltage developed across the plate load will vary in the same manner as the variations in plate current.

Since driving the grid positive will cause distortion, the maximum value of permissible input signal voltage will depend on the extreme limits of negative grid voltage that will cause the tube to operate on the straight portion of its characteristic curve. In order that the maximum input signal voltage may be applied to a tube, the value of grid bias at which it is operated should be at the mid-point between the limits of the grid bias.

The limits of negative grid voltage for the tube whose operating characteristics are shown in Fig. 7-2 are represented by the points D and O. For maximum signal input the tube should be operated at point E. Increasing the value of grid bias as at M or decreasing it as at N will shift the operating point to M' or N' on the characteristic curve. In either case the amount of grid-voltage swing will be reduced, thus decreasing the amount of input signal voltage that can be applied to the grid of the tube without causing distortion.

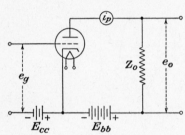

FIG. 7-3.—Elementary voltage amplifier circuit.

The maximum value of input signal voltage that should be applied to a tube will be equal to either the amount of grid bias used, indicated by the distance OE on Fig. 7-2, or the difference between the maximum amount of negative grid voltage that will cause the tube to operate on the straight portion of its curve and the grid-bias voltage at which the tube is operated, indicated by the distance DE on Fig. 7-2. The smaller of these two values will be the maximum amount of input signal voltage that can be applied without producing distortion.

Example **7-1.** A type 6C5 tube is to be operated as a Class A amplifier with 300 volts applied to its plate. What is the maximum amount of input signal voltage that can be applied without producing distortion when the tube is operated with a grid bias of (*a*) 8 volts? (*b*) 6 volts? (*c*) 4 volts?

NOTE: Assume that the straight portion of the curve (Fig. 4-21) extends beyond a grid bias of zero volts. This assumption will hold true for the characteristic curves of practically all Class A triode amplifier tubes.

Given:

$E_b = 300$ volts
(*a*) $E_c = -8$ volts
(*b*) $E_c = -6$ volts
(*c*) $E_c = -4$ volts

Find:

(*a*) $E_{g \cdot m} = ?$
(*b*) $E_{g \cdot m} = ?$
(*c*) $E_{g \cdot m} = ?$

Solution:

From the curve for $E_b = 300$ volts (Fig. 4-21), it can be seen that the straight portion of the curve ends when the grid bias is approximately 12 volts. Thus

(*a*) $E_{g \cdot m} = 12 - 8 = 4$ volts
(*b*) $E_{g \cdot m} = 12 - 6 = 6$ volts
(*c*) $E_{g \cdot m} = 4 - 0 = 4$ volts

Method of Obtaining Grid Bias. It was shown in Art. 5-4 that the grid bias required for the desired operating conditions of a detector tube could be obtained by means of a cathode-bias resistor. In a similar manner, it is also possible to obtain the proper grid bias for the desired operating conditions of a tube in an r-f amplifier circuit.

When a tube is used as an amplifier the amount of direct current flowing in the plate circuit with zero signal input can be obtained for any value of plate voltage and grid bias from either the plate characteristic or grid-plate transfer characteristic curves. The zero signal plate current for one or two recommended values of plate voltage and grid bias may be obtained from Appendix XV or from a standard tube manual. It is also always desirable to use a by-pass capacitor, generally in the order of 0.1 μf, in conjunction with the cathode-bias resistor in r-f circuits.

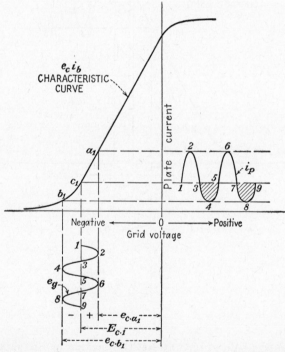

Fig. 7-4.—Distortion in a Class A operated voltage amplifier tube caused by using too large a bias.

7-3. Distortion in Class A Amplifiers. *Distortion Caused by Operating the Tube on the Curved Portion of Its Characteristic Curve.* When the tube whose operating characteristics are illustrated in Fig. 7-2 is operated with a grid bias whose value is E_c, the variation in input signal voltage e_g will produce a grid-voltage swing whose limits are $e_{c·a}$ and $e_{c·b}$. This variation in grid voltage causes the tube to operate on the straight

portion of the curve between a and b. The varying plate current i_p will therefore change in the same manner as the input voltage e_g.

If the tube is operated with a grid bias whose value is too near the negative bend of the curve it will cause distortion of the output signal. This can be seen by referring to the operating characteristics for this condition as illustrated in Fig. 7-4. The grid bias $E_{c.1}$ causes the tube to operate about point c_1 on the curve. The input signal voltage e_g will produce a grid-voltage swing whose limits are $e_{c.a_1}$ and $e_{c.b_1}$. This variation in grid

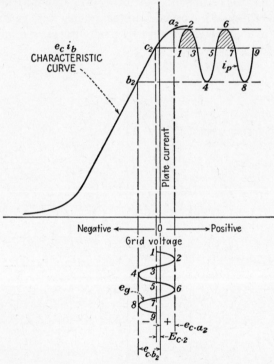

Fig. 7-5.—Distortion in a Class A operated voltage amplifier tube caused by using too small a bias.

voltage causes the tube to operate on the portion of the curve between a_1 and b_1. The negative halves of each cycle of the alternating input signal voltage will operate on the curved portion of the curve between b_1 and c_1. The plate current resulting from each of the negative half-cycles will therefore be distorted as illustrated by the shaded area (Fig. 7-4).

If a tube is operated with a grid bias whose value is too near the positive bend of the curve it will also cause distortion. This can be seen by referring to the operating characteristics for this condition as illustrated in Fig. 7-5.   The grid bias $E_{c.2}$ causes the tube to operate about point c_2 on the curve.   The input signal e_g will produce a grid-voltage swing whose limits are $e_{c.a_2}$ and $e_{c.b_2}$.   This variation in grid voltage causes the tube to operate on the portion of the curve between a_2 and b_2.   The positive halves of each cycle of the alternating input signal voltage will operate on the curved portion of the curve between c_2 and a_2.   The plate current resulting from each of the positive half-cycles will therefore be distorted as illustrated by the shaded area (Fig. 7-5).

Distortion Caused by Driving the Grid Positive.   When the grid is made positive with respect to the cathode it will act in the same manner as the plate.   Some of the electrons emitted by the cathode will be attracted to the grid, causing a current i_g to flow in the external grid circuit (Fig. 7-6).   This current is forced to flow through the resistance R_g or any other circuit element connected in this path, such as the secondary of a coupling transformer.   The grid current i_g in flowing through the resistance

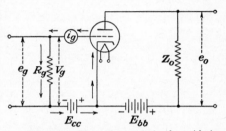

Fig. 7-6.—Flow of current in the grid circuit when the grid is positive with respect to its cathode.

of the grid circuit R_g produces a voltage drop V_g in this circuit.   This voltage drop is developed in the grid circuit during each instant that the grid is positive.   The effective grid voltage at these instants will be equal to the applied voltage e_g minus the voltage drop V_g.   The characteristic curves for the two operating conditions shown in Figs. 7-7 and 7-8 illustrate how the input signal is distorted when the voltage on the grid is made positive.   This distortion of the input signal voltage will there-fore produce distortion in the plate current as illustrated by these diagrams.

Distortion of this type is produced by operating the tube with an incorrect value of grid bias (Fig. 7-7) or by applying too large a signal to the input circuit (Fig. 7-8).   For purposes of comparison the two characteristic curves used in Figs. 7-7 and 7-8 are the same as the one used in Fig. 7-2.

Distortion Caused by Operating the Tube with an Incorrect Grid Bias. When the tube is operated with a grid bias whose value is less than the maximum value of the input signal voltage, the grid voltage will be driven positive during the portion of each cycle in which the positive value of the input signal is greater than the grid bias.   The manner in which the output signal is distorted for this type of operation can be seen by exami-nation of its operating characteristics as illustrated in Fig. 7-7.   With a grid-bias voltage as indicated at $E_{c.3}$, the input signal e_g causes the tube to operate on the straight portion of the curve between a_3 and b_3. It can be seen that under this condition the grid is made positive at some instants. The voltage drop due to the current flowing in the grid circuit during these intervals reduces the effective grid voltage during these instants, thus reducing the maximum positive grid voltage from $e_{c.a_3}$ to $e_{c.a}$. This distortion of the input signal voltage causes the tube to operate between b_3 and a on the curve. The output current will therefore be

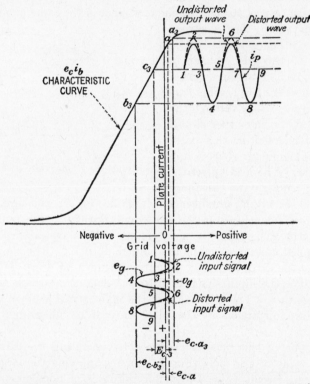

Fig. 7-7.—Distortion in a Class A voltage amplifier tube when operated with incorrect grid bias so that the grid is driven positive during part of each cycle.

distorted in a similar manner, as is illustrated by the distorted output wave resulting from this incorrect operation (Fig. 7-7).

Distortion Caused by Applying Too Large an Input Signal. When the tube is operated with its correct value of grid bias but the applied input signal is too large, either half or both halves of the output signal may be distorted. The manner in which this type of operation causes distortion can be seen by examination of Fig. 7-8. The variation in input signal voltage, $3e_g$ produces a grid-voltage swing whose limits are $e_{c \cdot a_4}$ and $e_{c \cdot b_4}$. This variation in grid voltage causes the tube to operate on the curve between points a_4 and b_4. Each negative half-cycle causes the tube to operate on the negative bend of the curve, thus causing the plate current flowing during these half-cycles to be distorted. During a part of each positive half-cycle of the input signal the grid is driven positive. The voltage drop due to the current flowing in the grid circuit reduces the effective grid voltage, thus reducing the maximum positive

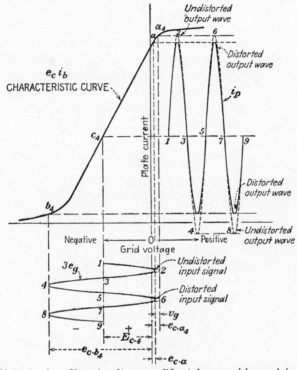

FIG. 7-8.—Distortion in a Class A voltage amplifier tube caused by applying too large an input signal.

grid-voltage swing from $e_{c \cdot a_4}$ to $e_{c \cdot a}$. This distortion of the input signal causes the tube to operate, for each positive half-cycle, between c_4 and a on the curve. The current flowing in the plate circuit during each positive half-cycle will therefore be distorted. It can thus be seen that for this operating condition some distortion occurs during both the negative and positive half-cycles.

7-4. Voltage Amplification Produced by a Class A Amplifier. *Equivalent Amplifier Circuits Using Triodes.* In the study of vacuum tubes

(Chap. IV), it was shown that the grid of a tube is μ times as effective in controlling the plate current as is the plate. When an alternating signal voltage e_g is applied to the grid of a tube, the plate circuit may be considered as a circuit containing a generator of $-\mu e_g$ volts in series with the plate resistance r_p and the output circuit impedance z_o. This principle is very important, as it is a basis for calculating the operating characteristics of an amplifier circuit. The output voltage $-\mu e_g$ is designated as negative because of the phase reversal, as explained in Art. 4-6.

The vacuum tube used in an amplifier can therefore be considered as a generator whose output voltage is equal to $-\mu e_g$. An equivalent electrical circuit can be drawn for an amplifier circuit by substituting a generator for the vacuum tube. The equivalent electrical circuit for the elementary amplifier of Fig. 7-3 is shown in Fig. 7-9a. This type of equivalent circuit is referred to as the *constant-voltage-generator* form and is very convenient for use in studying the operating characteristics of amplifier circuits using triodes. The alternating-current component of the plate current flowing in this circuit is

$$i_p = \frac{\mu e_g}{Z_o + r_p} \tag{7-1}$$

The voltage developed across the load impedance by this current will then be

$$e_p = i_p Z_o \tag{7-2}$$

Substituting Eq. (7-1) in (7-2)

$$e_p = \frac{\mu e_g Z_o}{Z_o + r_p} \tag{7-3}$$

The voltage amplification of the circuit then becomes

$$VA = \frac{e_p}{e_g} = \frac{\dfrac{\mu e_g Z_o}{Z_o + r_p}}{e_g} \tag{7-4}$$

and

$$VA = \frac{\mu Z_o}{Z_o + r_p} \tag{7-5}$$

When the output impedance is made up only of resistors, resistance-capacitance-coupled amplifier circuits, or a tuned amplifier circuit in which the reactive effects cancel one another so that the resultant impedance is only resistance, the output impedance Z_o will be equal to R_o. Under these conditions, Eqs. (7-1), (7-3), and (7-5) become

$$i_p = \frac{\mu e_g}{R_o + r_p} \tag{4-8}$$

$$e_p = \frac{\mu e_g R_o}{R_o + r_p} \tag{4-9}$$

$$\text{VA} = \frac{\mu R_o}{R_o + r_p} \tag{4-10}$$

Equivalent Amplifier Circuit Using Pentodes.   The maximum voltage amplification of a circuit using a triode amplifier can be made almost equal to its amplification factor.   This is possible because of the comparatively low values of plate resistance obtainable in triode amplifier tubes.   In amplifier circuits using high-mu tubes such as tetrodes and

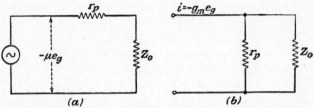

Fig. 7-9.—Equivalent circuit for the elementary amplifier circuit of Fig. 7-3.   (a) Constant-voltage-generator form, (b) constant-current-generator form.

pentodes the values of plate resistance are so high that the amount of voltage amplification obtainable is but a fraction of the amplification factor of the tube used.   The large difference between the voltage amplification of the circuit and the amplification factor of the tube is due to the high values of the plate resistance of the tetrodes and pentodes and the comparatively low values of plate-load impedance that must be used for practical amplifier circuits.   When the ratio between the plate resistance and the load impedance becomes great, the transconductance of the output circuit approaches the value obtained when the load impedance is practically zero.   The voltage amplification of the circuit will then be dependent on the value of the tube's transconductance rather than on its amplification factor.   This can be seen if Eqs. (7-1), (7-3), and (7-5) are expressed in terms of transconductance instead of amplification factor.   Substituting Eq. (4-5) in Eq. (7-1) and regrouping the terms

$$i_p = g_m e_g \frac{r_p}{Z_o + r_p} \tag{7-6}$$

Substituting Eq. (4-5) in Eq. (7-3) and regrouping, the voltage across the load impedance then becomes

$$e_p = g_m e_g \frac{r_p Z_o}{Z_o + r_p} \tag{7-7}$$

Substituting Eq. (4-5) in Eq. (7-5) and regrouping, the voltage amplification of the circuit then becomes

$$VA = g_m \frac{r_p Z_o}{Z_o + r_p} \tag{7-8}$$

By rearranging the terms in Eq. (7-8), the output impedance required to produce a definite value of voltage amplification may be found by

$$Z_o = \frac{VA r_p}{g_m r_p - VA} \tag{7-9}$$

From Eq. (7-7) it can be seen that the effect of applying a signal voltage e_g to the input circuit of a tube may be considered the same as though the tube generated a current of a value equal to $-g_m e_g$ that is caused to flow through a parallel impedance formed by the plate resistance r_p and the load impedance Z_o. It may thus be concluded that an amplifier circuit may also be considered in the form shown in Fig. 7-9b, which is generally referred to as the *constant-current-generator* form. This type of circuit is very convenient for use in studying the operating characteristics of amplifier circuits using tetrodes, pentodes, and beam power tubes.

The impedance of a tuned circuit at its resonant frequency has the effect of only resistance. When the load in the plate circuit of an r-f amplifier tube is a tuned circuit, the effective output impedance Z_o at resonance will have the effect of only resistance and can therefore be added arithmetically to the plate resistance r_p in Eqs. (7-6), (7-7), and (7-8).

Applications of Equations (7-1) *to* (7-9). All the equations developed in this article are interrelated, and the following examples will serve to illustrate their applications.

Example 7-2. A type 6SF5 triode, used as a voltage amplifier, has a plate resistance of 85,000 ohms and an amplification factor of 100 when operated with 100 volts on its plate and a grid bias of 1 volt. What is the voltage amplification of an amplifier stage using such a tube under these operating conditions when the load resistance is 65,000 ohms?

Given: Find:
$\quad r_p = 85,000$ ohms $\quad$ VA $= ?$
$\quad R_o = 65,000$ ohms
$\quad \mu = 100$
Solution:

$$VA = \frac{\mu R_o}{R_o + r_p} = \frac{100 \times 65,000}{65,000 + 85,000} = 43.3$$

Example 7-3. A 1-volt a-c signal (maximum value) is applied to the input side of the tube and amplifier circuit of Example 7-2. (a) What amount of variation will this produce in the plate current?   (b) What amount of voltage will be developed across the output load resistor?

Given: Find:

e_g = 1 volt (max)   (a) i_p = ?
μ = 100   (b) e_p = ?
r_p = 85,000 ohms
R_o = 65,000 ohms

Solution:

(a) $$i_p = \frac{\mu e_g}{R_o + r_p} = \frac{100 \times 1}{65,000 + 85,000} = 0.666 \text{ ma (max)}$$

(b) $e_p = \text{VA} \times e_g = 43.3 \times 1 = 43.3$ volts (max)

or

$$e_p = i_p R_o = 0.666 \times 10^{-3} \times 65,000 = 43.3 \text{ volts (max)}$$

Example 7-4.   A type 6SJ7 tube is operated as a Class A voltage amplifier. The transconductance of the tube is 1575 micromhos and the plate resistance is 700,000 ohms when the tube is operated with 100 volts on its plate, 100 volts on the screen grid, and with a grid bias of 3 volts.   (a) If the plate load is a tuned circuit, what must its effective impedance be in order to obtain a voltage amplification per stage of 90? (b) How much will the plate current vary when a 20-mv a-c signal is applied to the grid circuit of the tube?   (c) What amount of voltage will be developed across the output load resistor?

Given: Find:

g_m = 1575 μmhos   (a) Z_o = ?
r_p = 700,000 ohms   (b) i_p = ?
VA = 90   (c) e_p = ?
e_g = 20 mv

Solution:

(a) $$Z_o = \frac{\text{VA } r_p}{g_m r_p - \text{VA}} = \frac{90 \times 700,000}{(1575 \times 10^{-6} \times 700,000) - 90} = 62,222 \text{ ohms}$$

(b) $$i_p = g_m e_g \frac{r_p}{Z_o + r_p} = \frac{1575 \times 10^{-6} \times 20 \times 10^{-3} \times 7 \times 10^5}{62,222 + 7 \times 10^5} = 28.9 \ \mu\text{a}$$

(c) $e_p = i_p Z_o = 28.9 \times 10^{-6} \times 62,222 = 1.798$ volts

or

$$e_p = \text{VA } e_g = 90 \times 20 \times 10^{-3} = 1.8 \text{ volts}$$

7-5. Radio-frequency Amplifier Circuits. *Classification of Radio-frequency Amplifier Circuits.*   Amplifier circuits are generally classified according to the method used to couple the output circuit of the amplifier tube to the input circuit of the tube in the following stage.   Thus an amplifier may be either a *resistance-capacitance-coupled*, *impedance-coupled*, or *transformer-coupled* circuit. R-f amplifiers are generally either transformer-coupled or impedance-coupled. Resistance-capacitance coupling is used occasionally for r-f amplifiers when an untuned amplifier circuit is desired.

Voltage Amplification of Tuned-radio-frequency Amplifier Circuits. From Eq. (7-5) it can be seen that theoretically the voltage amplification, or gain per stage, can be increased by (1) using a tube with a higher amplification factor but with approximately the same value of plate resistance, (2) using a tube with a lower value of plate resistance but with the same amplification factor, (3) increasing the value of the load impedance.

Practically, these considerations will hold only for triodes. High-gain r-f amplifiers very seldom use triodes because of the undesired coupling produced by the interelectrode capacitances, hence pentodes are generally used for r-f amplifiers.

The plate resistance of r-f pentode voltage amplifier tubes is very high, some of these tubes having a plate resistance in the order of a mil-

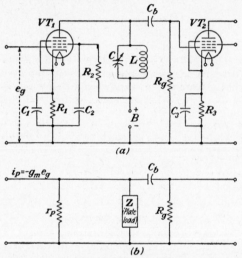

Fig. 7-10.—R-f amplifier circuit using tuned-impedance coupling. (a) Actual circuit (b) equivalent circuit.

lion ohms. The amplification factor is likewise very high, some tubes having an amplification factor in the order of one thousand. The construction of these tubes is such that there is practically complete electrostatic shielding between the plate and the control grid. The net result of all these factors is that greater amplification can be obtained with a pentode r-f voltage amplifier than with any other type of tube.

The plate load of a transformer-coupled r-f amplifier consists of the primary winding of the r-f transformer and the impedance coupled from its tuned secondary circuit (see Fig. 7-14a). For impedance-coupled r-f voltage amplifiers the plate load consists of only the tuned circuit (see Fig. 7-10a). In actual practice the load impedance of these circuits will be only a small fraction of the value of the plate resistance, therefore when r_p and Z_o are considered as being in parallel with one another

(Fig. 7-9*b*), the resultant impedance will be practically equal to the value of the load impedance.   Equations (7-7) and (7-8) may then be simplified as

$$e_p = g_m e_g Z_o \tag{7-10}$$

$$\mathrm{VA} = g_m Z_o \tag{7-11}$$

From these two equations it can be seen that the output voltage and the voltage amplification will increase with an increase in the value of the output load impedance.   As parallel tuned circuits offer a high impedance at their resonant frequency they are generally used as the plate load in r-f circuits.

Tuned Impedance-coupled Radio-frequency Amplifiers.   This type of circuit is ordinarily used in transmitters but is also occasionally used in receivers.   An r-f amplifier circuit using impedance coupling is shown in Fig. 7-10*a*.   The coupling element consists of the tuned *LC* circuit, which is also the plate load.   When the tuned circuit is adjusted so that it is in resonance with a desired signal, the maximum voltage will be developed across the tuned circuit.   This voltage will vary in accordance with the r-f modulated input signal voltage.   The varying voltage is applied to the grid circuit of the next stage through the coupling capacitor C_b, which allows the varying signal current to flow through it and at the same time keeps the B voltage out of the grid circuit.

Because of the low d-c resistance of the inductor L, the d-c voltage drop across the inductor will be very small.   The voltage applied to the plate of the tube will therefore be practically equal to the voltage of the B power supply.   At resonance the impedance of the parallel tuned circuit will be at its maximum value and will be equal to the product of the circuit Q and the inductive reactance [Eq. (2-56)].   The resultant reactance at this frequency $(X_L - X_C)$ will be practically zero, therefore the impedance will not only be high but will offer a pure resistance load to the plate of the tube.

Voltage Amplification of a Tuned Impedance-coupled Radio-frequency Amplifier.   The constant-current-generator form of equivalent circuit for the tuned impedance-coupled amplifier circuit of Fig. 7-10*a* is shown in Fig. 7-10*b*.   In actual circuits the value of the grid-leak resistance is made much higher than the parallel impedance of the resonant circuit.   The plate resistance of pentodes is of the order of one megohm.   The impedance of the output circuit, with a fair degree of approximation, can therefore be considered as being equal to the parallel impedance of the tuned circuit.   Thus from Eq. (2-56)

$$Z_o \cong Z_{T \cdot r} = 2\pi f L Q \tag{7-12}$$

An approximate value of the voltage amplification at resonance may then be obtained by substituting Eq. (7-12) in Eq. (7-11)

$$\text{VA} \cong g_m 2\pi f L Q \tag{7-13}$$

Substituting Eq. (2-58) in Eq. (7-13)

$$\text{VA} \cong \frac{g_m X_L{}^2}{R_L} \tag{7-13a}$$

Substituting Eq. (2-8) in Eq. (7-13a)

$$\text{VA} \cong \frac{g_m (2\pi f L)^2}{R_L} \tag{7-14}$$

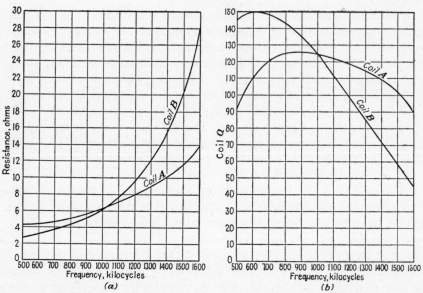

Fig. 7-11.—Effect of frequency on the characteristics of a coil. (a) Variation of coil resistance with frequency, (b) variation of coil Q with frequency.

In the above equations R_L represents the high-frequency resistance of the inductor L. The exact resistance value of this coil is very difficult to calculate, as it is dependent in a complex manner upon the physical characteristics of the coil and the frequency of the current. It is desirable that the voltage amplification of an amplifier be fairly uniform for the entire range of frequencies in any one band. In order to obtain this condition it is necessary that the coil be of the correct size and shape and that it be wound with the correct size of wire, so that the high-frequency resistance of the circuit will vary in such a manner as to produce fairly uniform amplification for the band of frequencies being considered. The curves in Fig. 7-11a illustrate the variation of resistance with frequency for two coils having the same value of inductance but with different physical characteristics.   The curves in Fig. 7-11b illustrate the variation of coil Q with frequency for these two coils.

The ratio of the effective Q of the amplifier circuit to the Q of the tuned circuit will depend upon the value of plate resistance for the tube used. The plate resistance of pentodes is very high, therefore the Q of the amplifier circuit employing pentodes will be practically equal to the Q of the tuned circuit.   The plate resistance of triodes is low, therefore the effective Q of amplifier circuits employing triodes will normally be much lower than the actual Q of the tuned circuit.

Example 7-5.   A tuned impedance-coupled r-f amplifier similar to the circuit shown in Fig. 7-10a uses a type 1N5-GT tube.   For the conditions under which the tube is being operated the value of g_m is 750 micromhos.   The coil has an inductance of 280 μh and its resistance at 1000 kc is 11.2 ohms.   What is the voltage amplification of the circuit when the frequency of the input signal is 1000 kc?

Given: Find:
$$g_m = 750 \times 10^{-6} \text{ mhos} \qquad\qquad \text{VA} = ?$$
$$L = 280 \times 10^{-6} \text{ henry}$$
$$R = 11.2 \text{ ohms}$$
$$f = 10^6 \text{ cycles}$$

Solution:

$$\text{VA} = \frac{g_m(2\pi f L)^2}{R_L} = \frac{750 \times 10^{-6}(6.28 \times 10^6 \times 280 \times 10^{-6})^2}{11.2} = 207$$

Example 7-6.   The inductance of an impedance-coupled r-f amplifier is 125.6 μh. The high-frequency characteristics of the coil used are illustrated by the curves drawn for coil B (Fig. 7-11).   The transconductance of the tube used is 1575 micromhos. What is the voltage amplification of the circuit at (a) 500 kc? (b) 1000 kc? (c) 1500 kc?

Given: Find:
$$L = 125.6 \ \mu\text{h} \qquad\qquad (a) \ \text{VA at 500 kc}$$
$$g_m = 1575 \text{ micromhos} \qquad (b) \ \text{VA at 1000 kc}$$
$$\text{Curves, Fig. 7-11} \qquad\qquad (c) \ \text{VA at 1500 kc}$$

Solution:
$$\text{VA} = g_m 2\pi f L Q$$
$$Q_{500} = 145, \qquad Q_{1000} = 125, \qquad Q_{1500} = 58, \text{ from Fig. 7-11b}$$

(a) $\text{VA} = 1575 \times 10^{-6} \times 6.28 \times 500 \times 10^3 \times 125.6 \times 10^{-6} \times 145 = 90$

(b) $\text{VA} = 1575 \times 10^{-6} \times 6.28 \times 1000 \times 10^3 \times 125.6 \times 10^{-6} \times 125 = 155$

(c) $\text{VA} = 1575 \times 10^{-6} \times 6.28 \times 1500 \times 10^3 \times 125.6 \times 10^{-6} \times 58 = 108$

Untuned Radio-frequency Amplifier Circuits.   Untuned r-f amplifier circuits do not have the high selectivity or the high amplifying qualities that are characteristic of the tuned circuit.   The only reason for using untuned circuits would be to prevent the selectivity of an r-f amplifier from becoming too great.   Because of the high-frequency discriminating qualities of a tuned amplifier, the selectivity may become too critical when several stages of r-f amplification are used.   An untuned amplifier may be added to reduce the degree of selectivity; untuned impedance-coupled amplifiers are generally used for this purpose.   An r-f amplifier circuit using untuned impedance coupling is shown in Fig. 7-12a.   The circuit of such an amplifier is similar to the tuned impedance r-f amplifier, illustrated in Fig. 7-10a, except for the r-f choke that is used as the coupling element in place of the tuned circuit.   The constant-current-generator form of equivalent circuit for the untuned impedance-coupled amplifier circuit of Fig. 7-12a is shown in Fig. 7-12b.

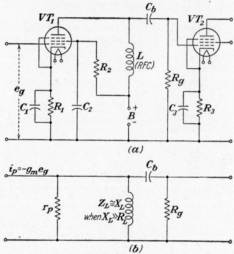

Fig. 7-12.—R-f amplifier circuit using untuned-impedance coupling.   (a) Actual circuit, (b) equivalent circuit.

Resistance-capacitance-coupled Radio-frequency Amplifier Circuits.   A resistance-capacitance-coupled r-f amplifier is another form of untuned r-f amplifier.   A typical resistance-capacitance-coupled r-f amplifier circuit is shown in Fig. 7-13a.   The variation in the plate current flowing through the coupling resistor R_c will produce a variation in the voltage drop across this resistor, thus varying the voltage applied to the grid of the next tube.   The high d-c plate voltage is isolated from the grid circuit by means of the blocking capacitor C_b and the grid-leak resistor R_g. The resistor R_g provides a path for discharging the capacitor C_b, which might otherwise block the action of the tube when the capacitor becomes charged.

The equivalent circuits for this type of amplifier are shown in Figs. 7-13b and 7-13c.   The interelectrode capacitance between the plate and cathode and the stray capacitance of the wiring between the plate circuit and the blocking capacitor C_b is represented by the capacitor C_p.   The interelectrode capacitance between the grid and cathode of the following tube and the stray capacitance of the wiring between the blocking capacitor and this grid circuit is represented by the capacitor C_g.

The capacitance C_p shunts the resistor R_c, thus causing some of the alternating output current from the plate of the tube to be by-passed through this capacitance. Since the voltage applied to the grid of the following tube is dependent on the voltage developed across R_c and as this voltage is dependent on the amount of current flowing through it,

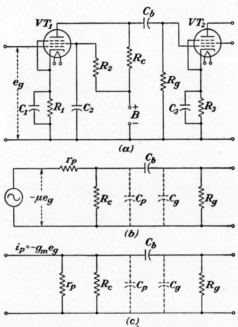

Fig. 7-13.—R-f amplifier circuit using resistance-capacitance coupling. (a) Actual circuit, (b) constant-voltage-generator form of equivalent circuit, (c) constant-current-generator form of equivalent circuit.

the efficiency of this arrangement is decreased because of the capacitance C_p. The capacitance C_g shunts the resistor R_g, thus further decreasing the efficiency of this type of coupling. The impedance of the capacitances C_p and C_g will vary inversely with the frequency, therefore at radio frequencies these impedances will be small and the amount of current by-passed will be large. The efficiency of this type of amplifier will therefore be low when used in r-f circuits and for this reason it is not generally used in such circuits.

The circuit elements required for a resistance-capacitance-coupled amplifier are small and their cost is comparatively low. High resistance values required for the coupling resistance are easily obtained, thus enabling pentode-type amplifier tubes to be operated at high gain. The interelectrode capacitances have very little effect at the usual audio frequencies. Because of these features resistance-capacitance coupling is used extensively for a-f amplifiers. Resistance-capacitance-coupled amplifiers will therefore be considered in greater detail in the following chapter.

Another reason for not using resistance-capacitance coupling in r-f circuits is that modern receivers generally employ more than one stage of tuning in order to obtain the desired selectivity. The transformers required to obtain this selectivity are also used to couple one circuit to another. Resistance-capacitance coupling does not contribute anything to the gain and selectivity of the amplifier, whereas the transformer does.

Resistance-capacitance-coupled amplifiers will amplify signals over a wide range of frequencies without the necessity of making adjustments to any of its component parts. This feature is especially adapted to a-f amplifier circuits, and to f-m and television r-f circuits.

Resistance-capacitance-coupled r-f amplifiers are sometimes used in receivers employing mechanical or electrical push-button tuning. By this means it becomes possible to overcome the difficulty of equalizing all sections of the multiple tuning capacitor.

Radio-frequency Amplifier Circuits Having a Tuned Secondary. R-f amplifiers with a tuned secondary are used extensively in radio receivers. A great deal of selectivity, fidelity, and amplification of the incoming signal will depend on the design of the r-f amplifier. The schematic wiring of a typical tuned-secondary r-f amplifier circuit is shown in Fig. 7-14a. This circuit differs from the impedance-coupled amplifier only in the manner in which the tuned circuit is connected to the plate of the tube. With the transformer-coupled amplifier the tuned circuit is coupled inductively to the plate, and with impedance coupling the tuned circuit is connected directly to the plate. For this reason the circuit shown in Fig. 7-10a is sometimes referred to as being *directly coupled.* Although differing in details of analysis, the actions of both of these will be the same.

For all practical purposes the equivalent circuit may be considered in the constant-voltage-generator form as shown in Fig. 7-14b or in the constant-current-generator form of Fig. 7-14c. In either case the equivalent circuit is a simple coupled circuit whose output load impedance may be found by applying the rules for analyzing coupled circuits. For the constant-voltage-generator form, the load impedance will be

$$Z_o = \frac{2\pi f M Q}{1 + \frac{(2\pi f M)^2}{R_s r_p}} \tag{7-15}$$

where $M = K \sqrt{L_P L_s}$.

Substituting this value of Z_o in Eq. (7-11)

$$VA = g_m \frac{2\pi f M Q}{1 + \dfrac{(2\pi f M)^2}{R_s r_p}} \qquad (7\text{-}16)$$

When the amplifier tube is of the pentode type, its plate resistance is so high that the voltage amplification, to a fair degree of approximation,

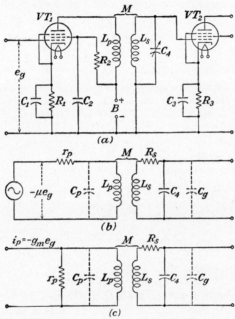

Fig. 7-14.—R-f amplifier circuit having a tuned secondary.   (*a*) Actual circuit, (*b*) constant-voltage-generator form of equivalent circuit, (*c*) constant-current-generator form of equivalent circuit.

can be simplified as follows

$$VA \cong g_m 2\pi f M Q \qquad (7\text{-}17)$$

The maximum amount of amplification will be obtained when the coupled impedance $\dfrac{(2\pi f M)^2}{R_s}$ (at resonance) and the plate resistance r_p are equal to each other.   This seems to contradict the thought expressed earlier in this chapter that the voltage amplification increases continuously as the load impedance is made larger than the plate resistance. However, in circuits employing a transformer the output voltage is obtained at its secondary terminals and will be at its maximum value when the maximum amount of energy is transferred from the primary to the secondary.   From Arts. 2-28, 2-29, and 2-30, it can be seen that maximum energy transfer, and hence maximum voltage amplification, occurs when $\dfrac{(2\pi fM)^2}{R_S}$ is equal to r_p. It is only possible to obtain this condition for amplifier circuits using triodes. When triodes are used, transformer coupling provides a means of matching the output impedance Z_o with the plate resistance r_p in order that maximum voltage amplification may be obtained. In the case of pentodes, the plate resistance is so high that it is impossible to obtain a load impedance whose reactance is anywhere near this value. For amplifier circuits using pentodes the amplification will be dependent upon the amount of coupling. This can be seen by observation of Eqs. (7-17) and (2-6).

Example 7-7. A tuned-secondary r-f amplifier, similar to Fig. 7-14a, uses a type 1E5-GT tube, and the voltages applied to its elements produce a transconductance of 650 micromhos. The values of the circuit elements are as follows: $L_P = 30\ \mu h$, $L_S = 300\ \mu h$, $R_S = 5$ ohms, $K = 0.3$, $f = 1000$ kc. What is the voltage amplification of the circuit?

Given:
$$g_m = 65 \times 10^{-5}\ \text{mhos}$$
$$L_P = 3 \times 10^{-5}\ \text{henry}$$
$$L_S = 30 \times 10^{-5}\ \text{henry}$$
$$R_S = 5\ \text{ohms}$$
$$f = 10^6\ \text{cycles}$$
$$K = 0.3$$

Find:
$$VA = ?$$

Solution:

$$VA = g_m 2\pi fMQ$$

$$= g_m 2\pi fK \sqrt{L_P L_S}\ \frac{2\pi f L_S}{R_S}$$

$$= 65 \times 10^{-5} \times 6.28 \times 10^6 \times 0.3 \sqrt{3 \times 10^{-5} \times 30 \times 10^{-5}}$$

$$\frac{6.28 \times 10^6 \times 30 \times 10^{-5}}{5} = 43.7$$

7-6. Intermediate-frequency Amplifier Circuits. *Advantages of Intermediate-frequency Amplifiers.*

An intermediate-frequency amplifier is an r-f amplifier circuit designed to amplify signals of a definite narrow band of frequencies instead of a wide band of frequencies. This type of amplifier is more efficient than the usual r-f amplifier as it can be designed to produce optimum Q for the frequency at which it is to operate, thus producing maximum amplification.

In most radio receivers the i-f amplifier has a tuned primary and a tuned secondary. This type of amplifier circuit improves both the selectivity and fidelity of reception. The advantage of having both the primary and secondary circuits tuned can be seen from Fig. 7-15. Curve A shows the response of an amplifier having only one tuned circuit and curve B shows the response of an amplifier with two tuned circuits. It is quite evident that curve B more nearly approaches the ideal response shown by curve C. Because of these features the i-f amplifier is used in the majority of modern radio receivers.

Band-pass Amplifiers. In order to obtain high fidelity and high selectivity the ideal response curve should have a flat top and straight sides. Although it is impossible to obtain this ideal, it can be closely

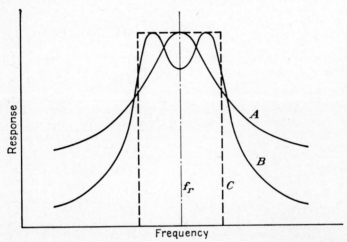

Fig. 7-15.—Response curves of typical amplifier circuits. Curve A, amplifier with a single tuned circuit. Curve B, amplifier with two tuned circuits that are tightly coupled. Curve C, the ideal response curve.

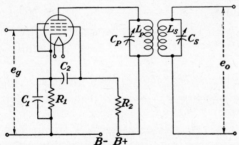

Fig. 7-16.—Typical band-pass amplifier circuit as used for the i-f amplifier in superheterodyne receivers.

approximated by using two resonant circuits tuned to the same frequency and coupled to each other (see Fig. 7-16). Such a circuit is called a *band-pass amplifier* and is used as an i-f amplifier in superheterodyne receivers.

Variable-coupling Intermediate-frequency Transformers. The width of the frequency band that will be passed will vary with the amount of coupling existing between the primary and secondary windings (see Art.

2-30). The effect of the coefficient of coupling upon the width of the band passed is expressed by

$$\text{Width of band pass} = Kf_r \qquad (2\text{-}84)$$

The average low-cost receiver uses coils having a fixed amount of coupling, while the more expensive receivers use i-f transformers that are provided with a means of varying the amount of coupling between the primary and secondary windings. Figure 7-17a illustrates a type of

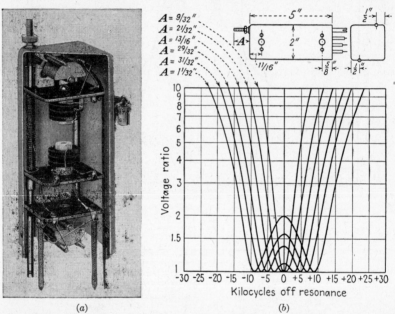

(a)	(b)

Fig. 7-17.—Illustration of variable coupling used for an i-f stage. (a) A variable coupling i-f transformer, (b) effect of various coupling values on the transmission characteristics of a single transformer as shown in (a). (*Courtesy of Hammarlund Manufacturing Company, Inc.*)

variable-coupling i-f transformer. This type of transformer has provisions for varying the mutual inductance between the primary and secondary windings throughout a wide range of values without otherwise affecting the circuit constants. Its approximate range is from one-third of critical coupling to more than three times critical coupling. Continuous variation between these limits may be controlled from the receiver panel by providing some form of mechanical arrangement for adjusting the relative positions of the coils. Where continuous variation is not desired, the coupling may be adjusted to the desired value and locked at that point. The width of the band pass should be equal to twice the value of the highest audio frequency being transmitted. The maximum values of audio frequencies used are approximately 5 kc for general broadcast transmission and 10 kc for high-fidelity transmission.

The slope of the sides of the response curve will vary with the value of Q for the circuit. Increasing the value of Q will make the slope of the curve steeper and will provide greater attenuation of the signal for frequencies outside of the desired band. The slope of the response curve will also increase with the number of i-f transformers used (see Art. 6-6 and Fig. 6-14). In a single-stage i-f amplifier (Fig. 7-19) two transformers are used and in a two-stage i-f amplifier three transformers would be used. The curves shown in Fig. 7-17b indicate the variation in the ratio of input to output voltage with changes in frequency and also show the effect of varying the coupling by changing the spacing between the primary and secondary windings. Figure 7-18 is an enlargement of the curve of Fig. 7-17b for the case when A is $\frac{13}{16}$ inch. As a single stage of i-f amplification requires the use of a tube and two i-f transformers, the over-all selectivity of the stage must include the effect of both trans-

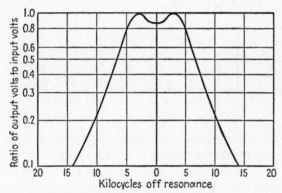

Fig. 7-18.—Curve showing variation of the ratio of output volts to input volts with changes in frequency.

formers. The attenuation of the output voltage at frequencies off resonance, which is a measure of the selectivity, may be found for a single transformer at various conditions of coupling from the curves of Fig. 7-17b. If the two transformers used in a single-stage i-f amplifier are similar, the overall attenuation in voltage can be found by squaring the value of the ordinate obtained from the response curve. In the case of a two-stage i-f amplifier using three identical transformers, the attenuation can be found by raising the value of the ordinate to the third power.

Example 7-8. A single-stage i-f amplifier uses two identical transformers with such a value of coupling that produces a response curve similar to Fig. 7-18. (*a*) What is the per cent of voltage output of the stage at 5 kc off resonance when the effect of coupling is considered? (b) What is the per cent of voltage output of the stage at 7.5 kc off resonance when the effect of coupling is considered?

Given: Find:

    Curve, Fig. 7-18   (a) Per cent of voltage

    (a) f off resonance = 5 kc   (b) Per cent of voltage

    (b) f off resonance = 7.5 kc

Solution:

(a)   Per cent of voltage at 5 kc off resonance for one transformer = 80 (from curve, Fig. 7-18)

     Per cent of voltage for the stage = $(0.8 \times 0.8) \times 100 = 64$ per cent

(b)   Per cent of voltage at 7.5 kc off resonance for one transformer = 40 (from curve, Fig. 7-18)

     Per cent of voltage for the stage = $(0.4 \times 0.4) \times 100 = 16$ per cent

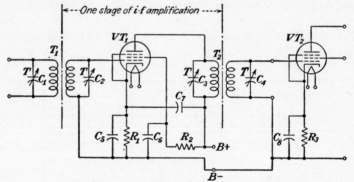

FIG. 7-19.—A single-stage i-f amplifier circuit.

Choice of the Intermediate-frequency Value. Various values of frequency are used for the i-f amplifiers of radio receivers. A frequency of 175 kc had been used for the broadcast band for a number of years but was found unsatisfactory. Most modern receivers, both single-band and multiband, use an i-f frequency of between 450 and 465 kc. Frequencies in the region between 250 and 270 kc are also used to a limited extent. In order to prevent image reception the choice of i-f frequency will depend on the number of tuned circuits in the receiver. I-f amplifiers form a definite part of all superheterodyne receivers, therefore the factors affecting the choice of i-f frequency will be considered in greater detail in Chap. XIV.

Voltage Amplification of a Band-pass Amplifier. The extensive use of band-pass amplifier circuits in the i-f stages of superheterodyne receivers makes it desirable to understand the factors that affect the voltage amplification or gain of this type of circuit. As the mathematics and circuit analysis involved in deriving the equation for the voltage amplification are quite difficult, the equation will be presented here without the derivation. However, the derivation is presented at the end of this article for those whose mathematical knowledge will enable them to follow the procedure. Thus, the voltage amplification of a band-pass amplifier circuit at a common resonant frequency for the two tuned circuits is

$$VA = g_m K \frac{2\pi f_r \sqrt{L_P L_S}}{K^2 + \dfrac{1}{Q_P Q_S}} \tag{7-18}$$

Example 7-9.   An i-f amplifier stage is to operate at 460 kc and its coils are adjusted so that the coefficient of coupling is 0.02. The circuit employs a type 6D6 tube, whose transconductance is 1500 micromhos. The inductance of the primary and secondary windings are each 800 μh. The Q of the primary circuit is 100 and that of the secondary is 120. What is the voltage amplification of the circuit?

Given: Find:
f_r = 460 kc   VA = ?
K = 0.02
g_m = 1500 micromhos
L_P = 800 μh
L_S = 800 μh
Q_P = 100
Q_S = 120

Solution:

$$VA = g_m K \frac{2\pi f_r \sqrt{L_P L_S}}{K^2 + \dfrac{1}{Q_P Q_S}}$$

$$= \frac{1500 \times 10^{-6} \times 0.02 \times 6.28 \times 460 \times 10^3 \sqrt{800 \times 10^{-6} \times 800 \times 10^{-6}}}{0.02^2 + \dfrac{1}{100 \times 120}} = 143$$

Examination of Eq. (7-18) will show that the voltage amplification is dependent upon the value of K. The maximum voltage amplification will occur when the coefficient of coupling is of such a value that will produce the maximum transfer of energy. This amount of coupling is called the *critical coupling* and occurs when the resistance coupled into the primary by the secondary is equal to the resistance of the primary, or from Eq. (2-69)

$$R_P = R_{P-S'} = \frac{(2\pi f M)^2 R_S}{Z_S^2} \tag{7-19}$$

But, at resonance $Z_S^2 = R_S^2$, hence

$$R_P = \frac{(2\pi f_r M)^2}{R_S} \tag{7-19a}$$

and

$$R_P R_S = K_c^2 (2\pi f_r)^2 L_P L_S \tag{7-19b}$$

$$R_P R_S = K_c^2 X_{L.P} X_{L.S} \tag{7-19c}$$

$$K_c^2 = \frac{R_P R_S}{X_{L.P} X_{L.S}} \tag{7-19d}$$

$$K_c^2 = \frac{1}{Q_P Q_S} \tag{7-19e}$$

$$K_c = \frac{1}{\sqrt{Q_P Q_S}} \tag{2-85}$$

The maximum possible amplification of the band-pass amplifier at its resonant frequency can then be found by substituting Eq. (2-85) in Eq. (7-18), which then becomes

$$VA_{max} = g_m \frac{1}{\sqrt{Q_P Q_S}} \frac{2\pi f_r \sqrt{L_P L_S}}{\left(\dfrac{1}{Q_P Q_S} + \dfrac{1}{Q_P Q_S} \right)} \tag{7-20}$$

By regrouping and simplifying

$$VA_{max} = g_m \pi f_r \sqrt{L_P L_S Q_P Q_S} \tag{7-21}$$

Example 7-10. What is the maximum possible voltage amplification of the amplifier circuit of Example 7-9?

Given:
$f_r = 460$ kc
$g_m = 1500$ micromhos
$L_P = 800$ μh
$L_S = 800$ μh
$Q_P = 100$
$Q_S = 120$

Find:
$VA_{max} = ?$

Solution:

$VA_{max} = g_m \pi f_r \sqrt{L_P L_S Q_P Q_S}$
$= 1500 \times 10^{-6} \times 3.14 \times 460 \times 10^3$
$\sqrt{800 \times 10^{-6} \times 800 \times 10^{-6} \times 100 \times 120} = 190$

When the primary and secondary circuit Q's are equal, in addition to their values of inductance being equal, Eq. (7-21) may be further simplified, as

$$VA_{max} = g_m \pi f_r L_P Q_P \tag{7-21a}$$

By comparing Eqs. (7-21a) and (7-13) it can be seen that the voltage amplification of a band-pass amplifier circuit is only one-half that produced by an amplifier stage containing but a single tuned circuit. However, the advantage gained in the selectivity with the band-pass amplifier generally outweighs the disadvantage of reduced voltage amplification.

Derivation of Equation for Voltage Amplication of a Band-pass Amplifier Circuit. The following is the derivation of Eq. (7-18) and is intended for those students whose mathematical and electrical circuit knowledge enables them to follow this complex solution. For those students with less mathematical training it is suggested that they accept the validity of Eq. (7-18) and proceed immediately to the following article, 7-7.

The circuit diagram of a band-pass amplifier is shown in Fig. 7-20a. This may be redrawn in its equivalent constant-current-generator form as shown in Fig. 7-20b. This may be further simplified by means of

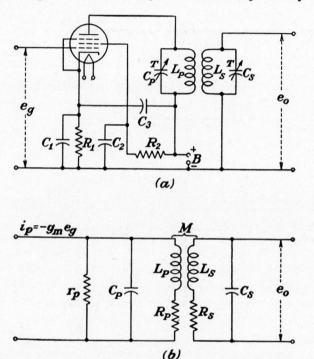

FIG. 7-20.—Single-stage i-f amplifier.   (a) Actual circuit, (b) equivalent circuit.

Thévenin's theorem. According to this theorem, when switch S (Fig. 7-21a) is open and the generator is considered as an open circuit, the circuit ac may be replaced by an equivalent series resistance and reactance, R_{eq} and X_{eq}, whose impedance will be equal to Z_{ac}. The generator voltage E is replaced by an equivalent voltage E_{eq} that is equal to the voltage E_{ac} when no load is applied.

The impedance of the parallel circuit Z_{ac} of Fig. 7-21b can be found by

$$Z_{ac} = \frac{E_{cct.}}{I_{cct.}} = \frac{E}{\sqrt{\left(\frac{E}{r_p}\right)^2 + \left(\frac{E}{X_c}\right)^2}} = \frac{r_p X_c}{\sqrt{r_p^2 + X_c^2}} \qquad (7\text{-}22)$$

The phase relation between the line current and line voltage is shown in Fig. 7-21c and is expressed by

$$\cos \theta = \frac{I_{r_p}}{I_{\text{cct.}}} = \frac{\dfrac{E}{r_p}}{\sqrt{\left(\dfrac{E}{r_p}\right)^2 + \left(\dfrac{E}{X_c}\right)^2}} = \frac{X_c}{\sqrt{r_p{}^2 + X_c{}^2}} \qquad (7\text{-}23)$$

$$\sin \theta = \frac{I_{X_c}}{I_{\text{cct.}}} = \frac{\dfrac{E}{X_c}}{\sqrt{\left(\dfrac{E}{r_p}\right)^2 + \left(\dfrac{E}{X_c}\right)^2}} = \frac{r_p}{\sqrt{r_p{}^2 + X_c{}^2}} \qquad (7\text{-}24)$$

An equivalent series circuit must offer the same impedance to the flow of current and must produce the same phase relation between the line

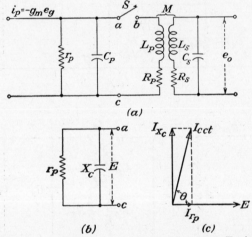

FIG. 7-21.—Band-pass amplifier circuit characteristics. (a) Equivalent circuit, constant-current-generator form, (b) parallel portion of the equivalent circuit, (c) vector relation of the currents and voltages of the circuit shown in (b).

current and line voltage. From the vector relation between the resistance, reactance, and impedance of a series circuit (Fig. 7-22a), it can be seen that

$$R_{\text{eq}} = Z \cos \theta \qquad (7\text{-}25)$$
$$X_{\text{eq}} = Z \sin \theta \qquad (7\text{-}26)$$

Substituting Eqs. (7-22), (7-23), and (7-24) in Eqs. (7-25) and (7-26). then

$$R_{\text{eq}} = \frac{r_p X_c}{\sqrt{r_p{}^2 + X_c{}^2}} \cdot \frac{X_c}{\sqrt{r_p{}^2 + X_c{}^2}} = \frac{r_p X_c{}^2}{r_p{}^2 + X_c{}^2} \qquad (7\text{-}25a)$$

$$X_{\text{eq}} = \frac{r_p X_c}{\sqrt{r_p{}^2 + X_c{}^2}} \cdot \frac{r_p}{\sqrt{r_p{}^2 + X_c{}^2}} = \frac{r_p{}^2 X_c}{r_p{}^2 + X_c{}^2} \qquad (7\text{-}26a)$$

As the voltage E is to be replaced by an equivalent voltage E_{eq} that is equal to the voltage across ac (Fig. 7-21a) when no load is applied, then

$$E_{eq} = \frac{E}{\sqrt{R_{eq}^2 + X_{eq}^2}} X_c \qquad (7\text{-}27)$$

The circuit of Fig. 7-21b may thus be replaced by the circuit of Fig. 7-22b, and the circuit of Fig. 7-21a may be replaced by that of Fig. 7-22c.

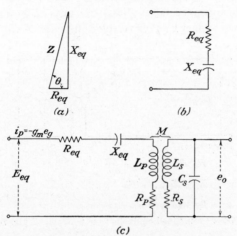

(a)   (b)

(c)

FIG. 7-22.—Band-pass amplifier circuit characteristics.   (a) Vector relation of the equivalent series circuit substituted for the circuit of Fig. 7-21b, (b) the equivalent series circuit of Fig. 7-21b, (c) simplified equivalent circuit of Fig. 7-21a.

However, in band-pass amplifier circuits, particularly those using pentodes, r_p is much greater than X_C and hence Eqs. (7-25a), (7-26a), and (7-27) are approximately equal to

$$R_{eq} \cong \frac{X_c^2}{r_p} \qquad (7\text{-}25b)$$

$$X_{eq} \cong X_c \qquad (7\text{-}26b)$$

$$E_{eq} \cong E \qquad (7\text{-}27a)$$

The circuit may now be drawn in its simplest form as shown in Fig. 7-23. The voltage amplification of any circuit is expressed by the equation

$$VA = \frac{e_p}{e_g} \qquad (4\text{-}6)$$

In this case the voltage e_p will be

$$e_p = I_S X_{C.s} \qquad (7\text{-}28)$$

In the explanation of coupled impedance (Art. 2-29) it was shown that

$$I_S = \frac{(2\pi f M) I_P}{Z_S} \tag{2-66}$$

As it is desired to determine the voltage amplification at only the resonant frequency, then Eq. (2-66) becomes

$$I_S = \frac{(2\pi f_r M) I_P}{R_S} \tag{7-29}$$

The primary current will be equal to the applied voltage divided by the impedance of the primary circuit plus the impedance coupled into the primary by the secondary. This coupled impedance will be

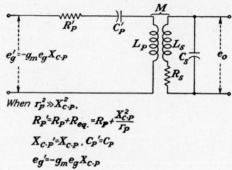

When $r_p^2 \gg X_{C \cdot P}^2$,

$$R_P{}' = R_P + R_{eq.} = R_P + \frac{X_{C \cdot P}^2}{r_p}$$

$$X_{C \cdot P}{}' = X_{C \cdot P}, \ C_P{}' = C_P$$

$$e_g{}' = -g_m e_g X_{C \cdot P}$$

Fig. 7-23.—Simplified equivalent series circuit of Fig. 7-20.

$$R_{P-S'} = \frac{(2\pi f M)^2 R_S}{Z_S{}^2} \tag{2-69}$$

and at resonance becomes

$$R_{P-S'} = \frac{(2\pi f_r M)^2}{R_S} \tag{7-30}$$

From Fig. 7-23 it can be seen that the primary current may be expressed as

$$I_P = \frac{g_m e_g X_{C \cdot P}}{Z_P + \dfrac{(2\pi f_r M)^2}{R_S}} \tag{7-31}$$

Substituting Eq. (7-31) in (7-29)

$$I_S = \frac{(2\pi f_r M)}{R_S} \cdot \frac{g_m e_g X_{C \cdot P}}{Z_P + \dfrac{(2\pi f_r M)^2}{R_S}} \tag{7-32}$$

$$I_S = \frac{(2\pi f_r M) g_m e_g X_{C \cdot P}}{Z_P R_S + (2\pi f_r M)^2} \tag{7-32a}$$

Also

$$VA = \frac{e_p}{e_g} = \frac{I_S X_{C \cdot S}}{e_g} \tag{7-33}$$

Substituting Eq. (7-32a) in (7-33)

$$VA = \frac{(2\pi f_r M) g_m e_g X_{C \cdot P} X_{C \cdot S}}{e_g [Z_P R_S + (2\pi f_r M)^2]} \qquad (7\text{-}33a)$$

Dividing both the numerator and denominator by e_g, regrouping the terms, and observing that $Z_P = R_{P'}$ (at resonance),

$$(2\pi f_r M) = K(2\pi f_r \sqrt{L_P L_S}), \text{ and } (2\pi f_r M)^2 = K^2 X_{L \cdot P} X_{L \cdot S}$$

$$VA = \frac{g_m K (2\pi f_r \sqrt{L_P L_S}) X_{C \cdot P} X_{C \cdot S}}{R_{P'} R_S + K^2 X_{L \cdot P} X_{L \cdot S}} \qquad (7\text{-}33b)$$

Dividing both the numerator and denominator by $X_{L \cdot P} X_{L \cdot S}$ and noting that at resonance $X_{L \cdot P} = X_{C \cdot P}$, $X_{L \cdot S} = X_{C \cdot S}$,

$$\frac{R_{P'}}{X_{L \cdot P}} = \frac{1}{Q_P}, \text{ and } \frac{R_S}{X_{L \cdot S}} = \frac{1}{Q_S}$$

$$VA = \frac{g_m K (2\pi f_r \sqrt{L_P L_S})}{\frac{1}{Q_P Q_S} + K^2} \qquad (7\text{-}33c)$$

Regrouping these terms

$$VA = g_m K \frac{2\pi f_r \sqrt{L_P L_S}}{K^2 + \frac{1}{Q_P Q_S}} \qquad (7\text{-}18)$$

Example 7-11. An i-f amplifier stage is made to operate at 460 kc by adjusting the coupling between the primary and secondary circuits to 0.02. The capacitance of each circuit is set at 119 $\mu\mu$f. The inductance of each coil is 1 mh and the high-frequency resistance of each coil is 24 ohms. A type 6K7 tube is used and is operated with 250 volts applied to its plate, 125 volts to the screen grid, and with a grid bias of 3 volts. What is the voltage amplification of this amplifier stage?

Given: Find:
$\quad f_r = 460$ kc $\quad VA = ?$
$\quad K = 0.02$
$\quad C_P = C_S = 119 \ \mu\mu$f
$\quad L_P = L_S = 1$ mh
$\quad R_P = R_S = 24$ ohms
$\quad$Tube — —6K7

Solution:

$$VA = g_m K \frac{2\pi f_r \sqrt{L_P L_S}}{K^2 + \frac{1}{Q_P Q_S}}$$

$g_m = 1650 \ \mu$mhos (from Appendix XV)

$r_P = 600,000$ ohms (from Appendix XV)

$Q_S = \frac{2\pi f_r L_S}{R_S} = \frac{6.28 \times 460 \times 10^3 \times 10^{-3}}{24} = 120.4$

$R_{eq} = \frac{X_c^2}{r_p} = \frac{10^{12}}{600,000(6.28 \times 460 \times 10^3 \times 119 \times 10^{-6})^2} = 14.1$ ohms

$$Q_P = \frac{2\pi f_r L_P}{R_P + R_{eq}} = \frac{6.28 \times 460 \times 10^3 \times 10^{-3}}{24 + 14.1} = 75.82$$

$$VA = g_m K \frac{2\pi f_r \sqrt{L_P L_S}}{K^2 + \dfrac{1}{Q_P Q_S}}$$

$$= \frac{1650 \times 10^{-6} \times 20 \times 10^{-3} \times 6.28 \times 460 \times 10^3 \sqrt{10^{-3} \times 10^{-3}}}{(20 \times 10^{-3})^2 + \dfrac{1}{75.82 \times 120.4}} = 187$$

Example 7-12. What is the maximum amount of voltage amplification that can be obtained from the amplifier circuit of *Example* 7-11?

Given: Find:
   $f_r = 460$ kc $VA_{max} = ?$
   $L_P = L_S = 1$ mh
   $g_m = 1650$ micromhos
   $Q_P = 75.82$
   $Q_S = 120.4$

Solution:

$$VA = g_m \pi f_r \sqrt{L_P L_S Q_P Q_S}$$
$$= 1650 \times 10^{-6} \times 3.14 \times 460 \times 10^3 \sqrt{10^{-3} \times 10^{-3} \times 75.82 \times 120.4} = 227$$

7-7. Multistage Radio-frequency Amplifier Circuits. *Need for Multistage Radio-frequency Amplifier Circuits.* In order to obtain the selectivity and amplification required in modern radio receivers it is desirable to employ more than one stage of r-f amplification. In the previous chapter it was shown that a single stage of tuning does not provide sufficient selectivity for satisfactory reception and hence multiple-stage tuning is used (see Art. 6-6). Each tuning circuit generally also accomplishes some amount of r-f amplification, therefore if two or three stages of tuning are used the receiver will consequently have two or three stages of r-f amplification.

Amplification of the desired signal can be accomplished before it reaches the detector, as in the case of r-f amplification, or after it leaves the detector, as in the case of a-f amplification. In the early stages of radio development, receivers used both r-f and a-f amplification. This practice was necessary because only triodes were available for r-f amplifier circuits and it was therefore impossible to produce sufficient r-f amplification without causing feedback. Furthermore, a strong signal could not be applied to the detector circuit without causing distortion. The development of high-gain pentode r-f amplifier tubes, power detectors, and pentode power tubes made it possible to employ a greater amount of r-f amplification and less a-f amplification. Audio-frequency amplifiers amplify static and other undesired noises in the same proportion that they amplify the audio signal, thus causing the final output of the receiver to be noisy if a great amount of a-f amplification is used.

The frequency of static is so low that its effect is comparatively small in r-f amplifiers. Because of this, and also because r-f amplifiers are essential to all receivers, the tendency in modern radio design is to use a greater amount of r-f amplification and less a-f amplification.

Multiple-stage Radio-frequency Amplifier Circuits. A multiple-stage amplifier circuit consists of two or more single-stage amplifier circuits

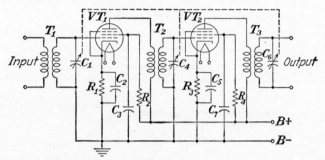

Fig. 7-24.—A two-stage tuned transformer-coupled r-f amplifier circuit.

coupled to each other. When more than two stages of r-f amplification are used, it is not necessary that they employ the same method of coupling throughout. A simple two-stage tuned transformer-coupled circuit is shown in Fig. 7-24. An r-f amplifier circuit using both impedance and transformer coupling is shown in Fig. 7-25.

Feedback. Feedback occurs when a portion of the current present in

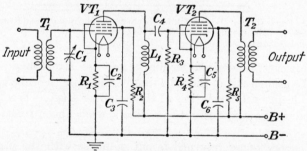

Fig. 7-25.—An r-f amplifier circuit using both impedance coupling and transformer coupling.

one circuit is fed back to a preceding circuit. Feedback may take place through any of the various types of coupling such as capacitive, inductive, or resistive coupling. In amplifier circuits containing two or more stages, coupling may exist in each of these three types. Capacitive coupling may take place through capacitors, stray capacitance, or through the interelectrode capacitance of tubes. Inductive coupling may take place through the windings of coils, transformers, or chokes. Resistive coupling may take place through the amplifier resistors, the resistance of the wiring, or the resistance of the power supply.

Regeneration and Degeneration. When two circuits operate at the same frequency and have a common impedance, feedback may result. The energy that is fed back may have a regenerative or degenerative effect, depending upon the phase relation between the current in the input circuit and the current being returned.

If the energy being returned is in phase with the input signal energy of the amplifier stage, regeneration will result and the output energy will be increased because of the additional amplification. A certain amount of regeneration can be used as an aid in obtaining an increase in ampli-

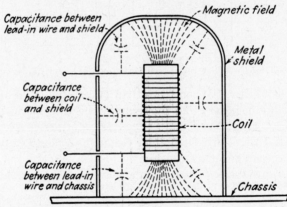

Fig. 7-26.—Illustration of the capacitance between the coil and its lead-in wires and the shield and chassis. The manner in which the magnetic lines from the coil cut the shield and chassis is also shown.

cation. However, undesired feedback may so strengthen the input signal at the grid circuit of the tube that it will cause the tube to oscillate and result in unstable operation of the amplifier stage. Feedback that is controlled can be very useful to amplifiers, while uncontrolled feedback is harmful.

If the energy being returned is out of phase with the input signal energy of the amplifier stage, degeneration will result and the output energy will be decreased. Ordinarily the effects of degeneration are not harmful unless they become excessive. In this case an additional stage of amplification may have to be added.

Methods Used to Control Undesired Regeneration. At radio frequencies, inductive and capacitive coupling between the tuned circuits of different stages is a common cause of regeneration. This cause of feedback is ordinarily controlled by shielding the various sections of the tuning capacitor from each other and by enclosing each coil in a copper or aluminum can (see Fig. 7-26). Extreme care must be exercised in using shields, for unless shielding is properly employed the output of the amplifier circuit will be reduced considerably. This can be seen from Fig. 7-26, in which the winding and the shield form the plates of a capacitor and the space between them acts as a dielectric. This capacitor acts in the same manner as the distributed capacitance of the coil, thus increasing the minimum capacitance of the tuning circuit and thereby decreasing its effective tuning range.

Another effect of shielding that must be taken into consideration is that produced by the magnetic field when a current flows in coils adjacent to shields. The magnetic lines set up by the current flowing in the coil cut the metal shield and set up eddy currents in the shield. These eddy currents produce a loss of energy and act in the same manner as increasing the resistance of the coil.

BIBLIOGRAPHY

BRAINERD, J. G., KOEHLER, G., REICH, H. J., and WOODRUFF, L. F., *Ultra-high-frequency Techniques*, D. Van Nostrand Company, Inc., New York.

EASTMAN, A. V., *Fundamentals of Vacuum Tubes*, McGraw-Hill Book Company, Inc., New York.

GLASGOW, R. S., *Principles of Radio Engineering*, McGraw-Hill Book Company, Inc., New York.

HENNEY, K., *Principles of Radio*, John Wiley & Sons, Inc., New York.

REICH, H. J., *Theory and Applications of Electron Tubes*, McGraw-Hill Book Company, Inc., New York.

TERMAN, F. E., *Fundamentals of Radio*, McGraw-Hill Book Company, Inc., New York.

TERMAN, F. E., *Radio Engineers' Handbook*, McGraw-Hill Book Company, Inc., New York.

Receiving Tube Manual, various tube manufacturers.

QUESTIONS

1. What is meant by amplification?

2. What is an r-f amplifier?

3. Name and define two fundamental types of amplifiers. Where is each used?

4. What are i-f amplifiers? What are the frequencies commonly used for i-f amplifiers?

5. Name and define four classifications of amplifiers based upon their operating characteristics.

6. What is the fundamental difference between a Class AB_1 and a Class AB_2 amplifier?

7. Which class of amplifier operation is most commonly used for r-f and i-f amplifiers in radio receivers?

8. At what value of grid bias should a tube be operated when being used in a Class A amplifier?

9. What is the maximum value of input signal voltage that should be applied to a tube in terms of the grid bias and the shape of the characteristic curve?

10. What is meant by distortion in an amplifier circuit?

11. What are the causes of distortion of the positive portion of the input signal?

12. What are the causes of distortion of the negative portion of the input signal?

13. Describe the constant-voltage-generator form of equivalent vacuum-tube circuit. When is this type of equivalent circuit most useful?

14. Describe the constant-current-generator form of equivalent vacuum-tube circuit. When is this type of equivalent circuit most useful?

15. Express the voltage amplification of a Class A voltage amplifier employing a triode in terms of the amplification factor of the tube, the plate-load impedance, and the plate resistance.

16. Express the voltage amplification of a Class A voltage amplifier employing a pentode in terms of the transconductance of the tube, the plate-load impedance, and the plate resistance.

17. Name three methods of coupling amplifier circuits. Give an application of each.

18. Why are pentodes more commonly used in voltage amplifier circuits than triodes?

19. Why are parallel tuned circuits generally used as the plate load of an r-f amplifier circuit employing a pentode?

20. What is the relation among the factors [Eq. (7-14)] affecting the voltage amplification of a tuned impedance-coupled r-f amplifier?

21. Why is it important to have the coils used for impedance-coupled amplifiers designed so that the coil Q remains nearly constant over the frequency range of the amplifier?

22. Where are untuned r-f amplifiers used?

23. Are resistance-capacitance-coupled amplifiers commonly used in r-f amplifier circuits of radio receivers? Why?

24. What are the advantages obtained with an r-f amplifier circuit having a tuned secondary? How does this circuit differ from the impedance-coupled amplifier?

25. What is meant by a direct-coupled amplifier?

26. What is the relation of the factors affecting the voltage amplification of an amplifier stage with a tuned secondary, employing a pentode, and as expressed by Eq. (7-17)?

27. Under what condition may the maximum voltage amplification be obtained from an amplifier with a tuned secondary? Is this attainable with triodes, pentodes, or both?

28. What are the advantages of using an i-f amplifier circuit over the usual r-f amplifiers?

29. What is meant by a band-pass amplifier?

30. How does the response curve of a band-pass amplifier compare with the ideal response curve?

31. What is the purpose of variable-coupling i-f transformers? How is variable coupling accomplished?

32. What are the factors that affect the voltage amplification of a band-pass amplifier?

33. Under what condition does the maximum voltage amplification of a band-pass amplifier occur?

34. How does the voltage amplification of a band-pass amplifier compare with that of an amplifier containing only one tuned circuit? What is the advantage of using a band-pass amplifier?

35. Why are multistage r-f amplifier circuits used?

36. Under what conditions does feedback occur?

37. How is regenerative feedback produced? What is its effect?

38. How is degenerative feedback produced? What is its effect?

39. How can undesired regeneration be controlled?

40. Why is it necessary to exercise care in the use of shields?

PROBLEMS

1. A type 6C5 tube is to be operated as a Class A amplifier with 250 volts applied to its plate. What is the maximum amount of signal voltage that can be applied without producing distortion when the tube is operated with a grid bias of (a) 8 volts? (b) 6 volts? (c) 4 volts? (Use Fig. 4-21.)

2. What is the maximum signal that can be applied to the tube of Prob. 1 without distortion if it is operated with 200 volts applied to its plate? Use the same amounts of grid bias.

3. It is desired to obtain grid bias for the tube of Prob. 1 by means of a cathode-bias resistor. What is the value of resistance required and the amount of power consumed by the resistor for each value of grid bias?

4. It is desired to obtain grid bias for the tube of Prob. 2 by means of a cathode-bias resistor. What is the value of resistance required and the amount of power consumed by the resistor for each value of grid bias?

5. A type 6U7-G tube is to be operated as an amplifier with a plate supply of 250 volts and screen-grid supply of 100 volts. (a) What value of grid bias is recommended (from Appendix XV)? (b) What are the plate current and screen-grid current under these operating voltages? (c) If grid bias is to be obtained by means of a cathode resistor, what value of resistance should be used to provide the recommended value of grid bias? (d) What amount of power is consumed by this resistor?

6. A type 6SF5 tube is to be operated as a voltage amplifier with 250 volts supplied to its plate and operating through a load resistance of 65,000 ohms. (a) What is the voltage amplification of the circuit? (b) What value of grid bias is recommended for these operating conditions? (c) If a signal with a maximum value of 2 volts is applied to the grid circuit, what value of output voltage is produced? (d) What is the maximum value of the varying component of the plate current?

7. A type 6K5-G tube is to be operated as a voltage amplifier with 250 volts supplied to its plate and operating through a load resistance of 50,000 ohms. (a) What is the voltage amplification of the circuit? (b) What value of grid bias is recommended for these operating conditions? (c) If a signal with a maximum value of 3 volts is applied to the grid circuit, what value of output voltage is produced? (d) What is the maximum value of the varying component of the plate current?

8. If it is desired to have the tube and circuit of Prob. 6 produce an output of 80 volts (maximum value) with the same values of plate voltage, grid bias, and input signal voltage, what value of resistance is required at the load?

9. If it is desired to have the tube and circuit of Prob. 7 produce an output of 75 volts (maximum value) with the same values of plate voltage, grid bias, and input signal voltage, what value of resistance is required at the load?

10. A type 12SK7 tube is to be operated as an r-f voltage amplifier with 250 volts supplied to its plate, 100 volts to the screen grid, and a grid bias of 3 volts. The load impedance is a tuned circuit that is resonant at the frequency being considered, thus producing a resistive effect of 40,000 ohms. What voltage amplification is produced by this circuit at its resonant frequency?

11. A type 12SK7 tube is to be operated as an r-f voltage amplifier with 100 volts supplied to its plate, 100 volts to the screen grid, and a grid bias of 1 volt. The load impedance is a tuned circuit that is resonant at the frequency being considered, thus producing a resistive effect of 40,000 ohms. (*a*) What voltage amplification is produced by this circuit at its resonant frequency? (*b*) If a signal with a maximum value of 0.8 volt is applied to the grid circuit, what value of output voltage is produced? (*c*) What is the maximum value of the varying component of the plate current?

12. A type 1T4 tube is to be operated as an r-f voltage amplifier with 90 volts supplied to its plate, 67.5 volts to the screen grid, and with zero grid bias. What impedance should the load have if it is desired to obtain a voltage amplification of 40 from the circuit?

13. A tuned impedance-coupled r-f amplifier uses a type 7A7 tube operated with 250 volts on its plate, 100 volts on the screen grid, and 3 volts grid bias. The coil has an inductance of 100 μh and its high-frequency resistance is 10 ohms at 1500 kc. What is the voltage amplification of the circuit at 1500 kc?

14. A tuned impedance-coupled r-f amplifier uses a type 7A7 tube operated with 100 volts on its plate, 100 volts on the screen grid, and 1 volt grid bias. The coil has an inductance of 100 μh and its high-frequency resistance is 10 ohms at 1500 kc. What is the voltage amplification of the circuit at 1500 kc?

15. The inductance of Coil B (Fig. 7-11) is 125.6 μh. If the coil is used in an r-f amplifier circuit with a type 6D6 tube whose transconductance is 1600 μmhos, what is the voltage amplification of the circuit at (*a*) 500 kc? (*b*) 800 kc? (*c*) 1200 kc? (*d*) 1600 kc?[NOTE: Use Eq. (7-13).]

16. The inductance of coil A (Fig. 7-11) is 125.6 μh. If the coil is used in an r-f amplifier circuit with a type 6D6 tube whose transconductance is 1600 μmhos, what is the voltage amplification of the circuit at (*a*) 500 kc? (*b*) 800 kc? (*c*) 1200 kc? (*d*) 1600 kc? [NOTE: Use Eq. (7-13).]

17. The transformer used in the r-f amplifier circuit (Fig. 7-14*a*) of a tuned-radio-frequency receiver has the following values: $L_P = 50$ μh, $L_S = 250$ μh, $K = 0.2$. The tube used with the amplifier stage is a pentode with a transconductance of 2000 μmhos. The high-frequency resistance of the coil varies in such a manner that the coil Q is 92 at 500 kc, 125 at 1000 kc, and 100 at 1500 kc. If it is assumed that the plate resistance of the tube is much greater than the coupled impedance, what is the approximate voltage amplification at (*a*) 500 kc? (*b*) 1000 kc? (*c*) 1500 kc?

18. The transformer used in the r-f amplifier circuit (Fig. 7-14*a*) of a tuned-radio-frequency receiver has the following values: $L_P = 100$ μh, $L_S = 250$ μh, $K = 0.3$, $R_S = 4$ ohms at 550 kc, $R_S = 8.5$ ohms at 1000 kc, and $R_S = 20$ ohms at 1600 kc. The tube used is a type 1N5-GT with a transconductance of 750 μmhos. If it is assumed that the plate resistance of the tube is much greater than the coupled impedance, what is the voltage amplification of a stage at (*a*) 550 kc? (*b*) 1000 kc? (*c*) 1600 kc?

19. An r-f amplifier stage, using transformer coupling with untuned primary and tuned secondary, uses a type 6SK7 tube whose transconductance is 2350 μmhos and whose plate resistance is 120,000 ohms. The transformer constants are $L_P = 200$ μh, $L_S = 340$ μh, $R_S = 14.5$ ohms at 1000 kc, $K = 0.4$. What is the voltage amplification of the stage at 1000 kc?

20. At what value of coefficient of coupling will the circuit of Prob. 19 produce the maximum amount of voltage amplification? (NOTE: This occurs when the coupled impedance at resonance is equal to the plate resistance of the tube.)

21. What is the voltage amplification of the circuit in Prob. 19 when the coefficient of coupling is (*a*) 0.7? (*b*) 0.8? (*c*) 0.9?

22. The curve of Fig. 7-18 shows that for a certain i-f transformer the attenuation at 5 kc off resonance reduces the output to 80 per cent of its maximum value. At 8 kc off resonance the output is only 35 per cent of its maximum value. What is the per cent output voltage of a stage using two identical transformers at (a) 5 kc off resonance? (b) 8 kc off resonance?

23. The attenuation of a certain i-f transformer reduces the output voltage to 90 per cent at 5 kc off resonance and to 60 per cent at 7.5 kc off resonance. If three such transformers are used in a two-stage i-f amplifier, what is the per cent of reduction due to the transformers at (a) 5 kc off resonance? (b) 7.5 kc off resonance?

24. A certain 456-kc i-f amplifier stage uses a type 6SK7 tube whose transconductance is 2000 micromhos. The constants of the i-f transformer are $L_P = L_S = 500$ µh, $Q_P = Q_S = 80$, $K = 0.025$. What is the voltage amplification of the circuit?

25. (a) At what value of coupling will the voltage amplification of the circuit of Prob. 24 be maximum? (b) What is the maximum voltage amplification?

26. A certain 465-kc i-f amplifier stage uses a type 6S7 tube whose transconductance is 1750 micromhos. The constants of the i-f transformer are $L_P = 700$ µh, $L_S = 600$ µh, $Q_P = 70$, $Q_S = 100$, $K = 0.02$. What is the voltage amplification of the circuit?

27. (a) At what value of coupling will the voltage amplification of the circuit of Prob. 26 be maximum? (b) What is the maximum voltage amplification?

28. An automobile radio designed for an i-f of 262 kc uses a pentode tube whose transconductance is 1750 micromhos and whose plate resistance is 1 megohm. The constants of the i-f transformer are $L_P = L_S = 1.6$ mh, $R_P = R_S = 30$ ohms at 262 kc, $K = 0.03$. The value of capacitance across the primary and secondary is 230 µµf each. What is the value of Q for (a) the secondary circuit? (b) the primary circuit? (c) What is the voltage amplification of the circuit?

29. (a) At what value of coupling will the voltage amplification of the circuit of Prob. 28 be maximum? (b) What is the maximum voltage amplification?

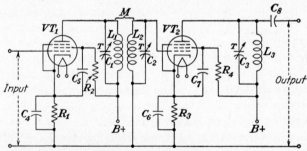

VT_1 and VT_2 .... $g_m = 1650$ µ mhos, $r_p = 600,000$ ohms
$L_1 = L_2 = 600$ µh, $Q_1 = Q_2 = 150$, $K = 0.035$, $f_r = 500$ kc
z_3 (L_3C_3 resonant at 500 kc) = 40,000 ohms

FIG. 7-27.

30. The two-stage amplifier shown in Fig. 7-27 uses a double-tuned circuit in the first stage and a single-tuned circuit in the second stage to provide more uniform response at its output. The amplifier is to operate at 500 kc and the values of its circuit elements are indicated on the diagram. (a) What voltage amplification is produced by the first stage? (b) What voltage amplification is produced by the second stage? (c) What is the overall voltage amplification of the amplifier?

CHAPTER VIII

AUDIO-FREQUENCY VOLTAGE AMPLIFIER CIRCUITS

The signal delivered to a radio receiver by its antenna is generally in the order of only a few microvolts and its energy may be only a few micromicrowatts. The signal delivered to the loudspeaker may, however, be several volts and the energy may be several watts. It can be seen from these two statements that the ratio of the strength of the signal sent through the loudspeaker to the strength of the signal from the antenna may be of the order of more than a billion (10^9). It can also be seen that the signal has to be increased both in voltage and in power. In order to obtain this large increase without producing distortion, or picking up and amplifying extraneous signals, several stages of amplification must be used. Radio-frequency amplifier circuits, as discussed in the previous chapter, are most commonly used to obtain voltage amplification. Audio-frequency amplifier circuits are designed to increase either the voltage, the power, or both. As voltage amplifiers, they are always operated as Class A. Power amplifiers are operated either as Class AB or Class B. Audio amplifiers are commonly classified according to the method of coupling that is used and hence are known as *resistance-capacitance-coupled, transformer-coupled, or impedance-coupled a-f amplifiers.*

8-1. Requirements of the Audio Amplifier. *Audio Frequencies.* Audio frequencies cover a band between 20 cycles and 20,000 cycles. An *audio-frequency amplifier* is one that will amplify signals whose frequencies lie within this band. The frequency range of various audible sound waves and their relation to broadcasting and receiving apparatus are illustrated by the chart shown in Fig. 8-1.

Frequency Requirements of the Audio-frequency Amplifier. The sounds produced by a symphonic orchestra contain practically all the frequencies that are likely to be produced by any type of radio program. In order to obtain perfect fidelity of reproduction of the music produced by such an orchestra, sounds from 20 to 20,000 cycles may have to be reproduced. For the average receiver such accuracy of reproduction is neither obtainable nor necessary. A study of the frequency ranges of the various units used in radio transmitters and receivers, as illustrated in Fig. 8-1, indicates that the limits of frequency reproduction for the average high-quality receiver will range from 50 to 5500 cycles.

320

The sounds reproduced by the radio receiver should be essentially the same as those produced by the artists in the studio of the transmitting

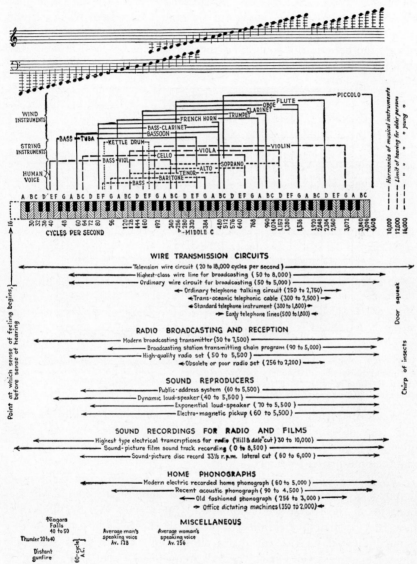

FIG. 8-1.—The audio spectrum and its relation to broadcasting.   (*Courtesy of Electronics.*)

station. The more nearly the frequency range reproduced by the receiver approaches the frequency range of the sound waves as transmitted, the higher will be its *fidelity of reception*.   The reception from a radio receiver that reproduces all frequencies from 60 to 8000 cycles in correct proportion is quite realistic and the quality of reproduction is considered to be high. Because of certain characteristics of the human ear some changes in the quality of the sound may take place without being detected by the average listener. For the average listener the correct reproduction of sounds having frequencies between 50 and 5000 cycles is quite satisfactory.

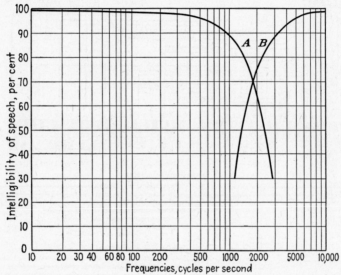

FIG. 8-2.—Curves showing variations in intelligibility of speech with frequency. Curve A—intelligibility when frequencies below the values indicated on the curve are eliminated. Curve B—intelligibility when frequencies above the values indicated on the curve are eliminated. (*Courtesy of Jensen Manufacturing Company.*)

Audio-frequency amplifiers form only a part of the radio receiver. This type of amplifier is usually designed to reproduce only those frequencies between 50 and 5000 cycles, which is the range used in low- and medium-priced receivers.

Effect of Frequency Elimination on Speech Intelligibility. The intelligibility of speech sounds is affected when some of the component frequencies of the sound are eliminated. Curve A of Fig. 8-2 illustra'es how the intelligibility is affected when all the frequencies below any value indicated on the curve are eliminated. Curve B of the same illustration shows the effect when all frequencies above any value indicated on the curve are eliminated. From these two curves it can be seen that speech becomes unintelligible when a small band of frequencies is eliminated at the low-frequency end of the band, while almost all the high frequencies must be eliminated to produce the same result. From these two curves it can also be seen that the intelligibility of speech sounds is not affected to any great extent by the failure to reproduce all sounds having frequencies below 400 cycles or above 5000 cycles. The resultant sound, however, will not seem natural.

Intensity Required to Produce Audible Sounds. The intensity required to produce an audible sound will vary with its frequency. In order to produce all audible sounds with equal loudness, the intensity required will vary as shown in Fig. 8-3. The ordinates of these curves indicate

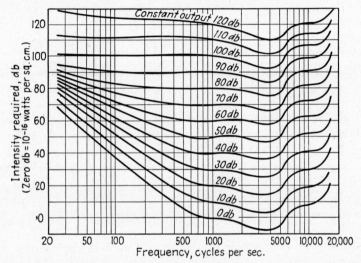

FIG. 8-3.—Curves illustrating how the relative amount of power required to produce a sound of equal intensity varies with the frequency. (*Courtesy of Jensen Manufacturing Company.*)

the intensity required to produce a sound of any frequency whose loudness will be equal to that produced by a 1000-cycle reference intensity level. The lowest curve (marked 0 db) indicates the intensity required to produce a sound that is barely audible. This curve is sometimes referred to as the *threshold of audibility*. The uppermost curve (marked 120 db) indicates the intensity at which sound is not only heard but also felt. This curve is sometimes referred to as the *threshold of feeling*. The numbers on each curve indicate the intensity of a signal in db above the minimum audible sound over the range of frequency indicated by the abscissa. It can be seen from these curves that when the strength of the sound is comparatively high, the intensity required to produce sounds of equal loudness will be comparatively uniform. When the strength of the sound is comparatively low, the intensity required will be fairly uniform between 1000 and 5000 cycles and increases rapidly as the frequency drops below 1000 cycles or rises above 5000 cycles. This relationship between intensity and frequency is very important in determining the amount of power that an amplifier must supply to the loudspeaker. An amplifier designed to amplify low-frequency sounds (under 500 cycles) must therefore have a higher power rating than one designed to amplify only those sounds having frequencies between 500 and 5000 cycles.

8-2. Use of Logarithms in Sound Measurements. *Relation of Sound Energy to Ear Response.* The operating characteristics of an audio amplifier are generally expressed in terms of its gain or loss in volume. The unit used to express this change is based on the ability of the human ear to respond to these changes.

In the rendition of a musical program, a symphonic orchestra will produce varying amounts of sound energy. The amount of energy used in producing the loudest note may be many thousand times as great as that used to produce the lowest note. However, the ear does not respond to these sounds in proportion to the energy used; the loudest note is not heard many thousands of times as loud as the lowest note. Research has shown that the response will vary logarithmically. In radio terminology, the ratio of any two levels of power is expressed in a unit called the *decibel*, commonly abbreviated db. The number of decibels is equal to 10 times the logarithm of the ratio of the two levels or values of power. A knowledge of logarithms is therefore essential in order to understand problems involving sound as related to amplifiers, speakers, microphones, etc.

Logarithms. Logarithms are commonly used in engineering mathematics to facilitate mathematical computations. Although numerous systems (or bases) of logarithms can be used, the common logarithm, that is, the logarithm to the base 10, is used most frequently and is the system used with the decibel. By definition, *a common logarithm of a number is the exponent* (or power) *to which* 10 (called the base) *must be raised to produce the number*. The logarithm of 100 will therefore be equal to 2, as 10^2 equals 100. This may be expressed as

$$\log_{10} 100 = 2$$

As only the common system of logarithms is used in sound-level calculations, the reference to the base 10 can therefore be omitted. The expression may then be written as

$$\log 100 = 2$$

As the logarithm of 10 is equal to 1 and the logarithm of 100 is equal to 2 it is evident that the logarithm of any number between 10 and 100 must be greater than 1 and less than 2. Consequently the logarithm of a number will consist of two parts: (1) a whole number called the *characteristic*, and (2) a decimal called the *mantissa*. For example, the logarithm of 50, which is equal to 1.699, is made of the characteristic whose value is 1 and the mantissa whose value is 0.699.

The characteristic of any number greater than 1 is always positive; numerically it is equal to 1 less than the number of figures to the left of the decimal point. The characteristic of any number less than 1 is always negative; numerically it is equal to 1 more than the number of zeros between the decimal point and the first significant figure.

Example 8-1. What is the characteristic of the following numbers; (*a*) 18.3, (*b*) 183, (*c*) 18,300, (*d*) 1.83, (*e*) 0.183, (*f*) 0.00183?

Given: Find:
    18.3; 183; 18,300   Characteristic = ?
    1.83; 0.183; 0.00183

Solution:

	Number	Characteristic
(*a*)	18.3	1
(*b*)	183	2
(*c*)	18300	4
(*d*)	1.83	0
(*e*)	0.183	−1
(*f*)	0.00183	−3

The mantissa or decimal part of a logarithm is found by reference to a table of logarithms. A logarithmic table is a tabulation of mantissas. The mantissa is always a positive number and is determined from the significant digits in the number. A table of the common logarithms of numbers is provided in Appendix XIII. It should be understood that a decimal point is assumed in front of each of the values of mantissas in the table of Appendix XIII.

Example 8-2. What is the logarithm of (*a*) 18,300? (*b*) 18.3? (*c*) 650,000? (*d*) 1.25?

Given: Find:
    18,300; 18.3;   Logarithm = ?
    650,000; 1.25.

Solution:

Number	Characteristic	Mantissa (from Appendix XIII)	Logarithm
(*a*) 18,300	4	.2625	4.2625
(*b*) 18.3	1	.2625	1.2625
(*c*) 650,000	5	.8129	5.8129
(*d*) 1.25	0	.0969	0.0969

It should be observed that the numbers used in Example 8-2 contain not more than three significant figures and that Appendix XIII provides mantissas for numbers up to three significant figures only. In cases where a number has more than three significant figures the mantissa can be obtained by interpolation. Interpolation is the process of estimating missing values between two values that are known. This process is illustrated in the following examples. In radio calculations it is usually permissible to take a mantissa corresponding to the nearest first three significant figures, thereby eliminating the need of interpolating.

Example 8-3. What is the logarithm of (a) 17.25? (b) 8522? (c) 4.578? (Solve by interpolation and compare the answer with the nearest three-place number.)

Given:
(a) 17.25
(b) 8522
(c) 4.578

Find:
Logarithm = ?
1. By interpolation
2. By nearest 3-place number

Solution:

(a) 1.

Characteristic	Mantissa	Logarithm
1	173...... .2380 172...... .2355 difference. .0025 1725..... .2355 + $\frac{5}{10}$ × .0025 = .23675	1.23675

2. This lies midway between 17.2 and 17.3 hence the nearest logarithm for a 3-place number would be either 1.2380 or 1.2355.

(b) 1.

Characteristic	Mantissa	Logarithm
3	853...... .9309 852...... .9304 difference. .0005 8522..... .9304 + $\frac{2}{10}$ × .0005 = .9305	3.9305

2. The nearest logarithm for a 3-place number is 3.9304.

(c) 1.

Characteristic	Mantissa	Logarithm
0	458...... .6609 457...... .6599 difference. .0010 4578..... .6599 + $\frac{8}{10}$ × .0010 = .6607	0.6607

2. The nearest logarithm for a 3-place number is 0.6609.

It is sometimes necessary to find the number corresponding to a logarithm when the logarithm is known. The number corresponding to a logarithm is known as the antilogarithm or *antilog* and may be found by working in the reverse order of finding the logarithm of a number.   For example, the common logarithm of 100 is 2 and hence it may be said that the antilog of 2 is 100.

Example 8-4.   What is the antilog of the common logarithm (*a*) 3.8751?   (*b*) 0.0645?

Given:	Find:
(*a*) Log = 3.8751	Antilog = ?
(*b*) Log = 0.0645	

Solution:

(*a*)   Antilog of 3.8751

The logarithm should be divided into its characteristic (3) and its mantissa (.8751). From Appendix XIII it can be found that the mantissa .8751 corresponds to the number 750.   The characteristic 3 indicates that the number will have $3 + 1$ or 4 figures to the left of the decimal point.   Combining these two facts, the antilog of 3.8751 is found to be 7500.

(*b*)   Antilog of 0.0645

Characteristic = 0
Mantissa = .0645
Number corresponding to the mantissa = 116 (from Appendix XIII)
Number of places to the left of the decimal point = $0 + 1 = 1$
Thus, the antilog of 0.0645 is 1.16

Example 8-5.   What is the antilog of the common logarithm 4.3353 (*a*) by inter-polation?   (*b*) without interpolation?

Given:	Find:
Log = 4.3353	Antilog = ?

Solution:

Antilog 4.3353
(*a*)   Characteristic = 4
Mantissa = .3353
(from Appendix XIII)

Number	Mantissa
217	.3365
216	.3345
Difference	.0020

$$\text{Number} = 216 + \frac{.3353 - .3345}{.3365 - .3345} = 216 + .4 = 216.4$$

Number of places to the left of the decimal point = $4 + 1 = 5$
Thus, the antilog of 4.3353 is 21,640
(*b*)   If the accuracy required permits disregarding interpolation, the nearest number to the mantissa is 216 and the antilog would be taken as 21,600.

8-3. Sound Measurements.   *The Decibel.*   The operating character-istics of an audio amplifier are generally expressed in terms of its gain or loss in volume. The unit used to express this change in volume is based on the ability of the human ear to respond to these changes. The unit most frequently used is the *bel*, named in honor of Alexander Graham Bell. The bel is defined as the common logarithm of the ratio between two quantities. Another unit called the *neper* is sometimes used. The neper is similar to the bel and is equal to the Naperian logarithm of the ratio between two quantities. Both of these units are relative units of measurement and do not specify any definite amount of sound, power, voltage, or current. The bel is too large a unit for general use and hence the *decibel*, which is one-tenth of a bel, is commonly used. The decibel may be used to express the ratio between two values of either sound, power, voltage, or current. The change in volume in any circuit, expressed in decibels, abbreviated *db*, can be found by the equation

$$db = 10 \log \frac{P_l}{P_s} \tag{8-1}$$

where P_l = larger amount of power, watts

P_s = smaller amount of power, watts

The ratio of the two powers will always be greater than one if the larger power is placed in the numerator. The characteristic of the logarithm of the ratio will therefore always be equal to zero or some higher positive value. The use of the negative characteristic is thereby eliminated, thus simplifying the solution of problems involving power loss. If there is a loss of power, a negative sign ($-$) should be placed before the decibel value. A gain in power or volume is indicated by a plus sign ($+$). The solution of the problem will indicate whether there is a decrease or an increase in the power for the particular case being considered.

The decibel is a logarithmic unit and therefore represents a logarithmic change. As the response of the human ear to sounds of varying intensity is logarithmic, regardless of the power level, the decibel provides a good means of expressing variations in sound measurements. The smallest change in sound intensity that can be detected by the human ear is approximately one decibel, although the average person does not ordinarily detect changes under two or three decibels.

Example 8-6. A type 6A3 tube is used in a radio receiver to deliver a maximum undistorted power output of 3.2 watts to its loudspeaker. What db gain in undistorted power will be obtained when each of the following types of tubes is substituted for the 6A3: (*a*) a type 6F6 having a maximum undistorted power output of 4.8 watts? (*b*) A type 6L6 having a maximum undistorted power output of 6.4 watts?

Given: Find:
    $P - 6A3$ = 3.2 watts   (*a*) Decibel gain with 6F6
    $P - 6F6$ = 4.8 watts   (*b*) Decibel gain with 6L6
    $P - 6L6$ = 6.4 watts

Solution:

(a)   db $= 10 \log \dfrac{P_l}{P_s} = 10 \log \dfrac{4.8}{3.2} = 10 \log 1.5$

   $\log 1.5 = 0.1761$ (from Appendix XIII)
   db $= 10 \times 0.1761 = +1.761$

(b)   db $= 10 \log \dfrac{P_l}{P_s} = 10 \log \dfrac{6.4}{3.2} = 10 \log 2$

   $\log 2 = 0.301$ (from Appendix XIII)
   db $= 10 \times 0.301 = +3.01$

From the results obtained in Example 8-6 it can be seen that doubling the power increases the volume by only 3 db.   This change is barely perceptible to the average listener, therefore it would not be practical to substitute either of the two tubes suggested in 'Example 8-6 in order to obtain a gain in volume.

Example 8-7.   What output power would be required in order to produce a gain of 14 db over the volume obtained with the 6A3 tube of Example 8-6?

Given:	Find:
$P_s = 3.2$ watts	$P_o = ?$
Gain $= 14$ db	

Solution:

$$db = 10 \log \frac{P_o}{P_s}$$

$$\log \frac{P_o}{P_s} = \frac{db}{10} = \frac{14}{10} = 1.4$$

Antilog of $1.4 = 25.1$ (from Appendix XIII)

Thus

$$\frac{P_o}{P_s} = 25.1$$

$$P_o = P_s \times 25.1 = 3.2 \times 25.1 = 80.32 \text{ watts}$$

A power output as large as 80 watts cannot be obtained by using a single power output tube.   Power outputs as large as this are generally obtained in receiver circuits by using a powerful push-pull amplifier.

Voltage and Current Ratios.   The decibel is fundamentally a measure of power ratio; however, as voltage and current are functions of power, Eq. (8-1) can be transformed to express the change in volume in db for two different values of voltage or current output.

Substituting $\dfrac{E^2}{R}$ for P in Eq. (8-1), then

$$db = 10 \log \frac{\dfrac{E_1{}^2}{R_1}}{\dfrac{E_2{}^2}{R_2}} = 10 \log \left(\frac{E_1}{E_2}\right)^2 \frac{R_2}{R_1} \tag{8-2}$$

or

$$db = 10 \log \left(\frac{E_1}{E_2}\right)^2 + 10 \log \frac{R_2}{R_1} \tag{8-2a}$$

or
$$db = 20 \log \frac{E_1}{E_2} + 10 \log \frac{R_2}{R_1} \qquad (8\text{-}2b)$$

or
$$db = 20 \log \frac{E_1 \sqrt{R_2}}{E_2 \sqrt{R_1}} \qquad (8\text{-}2c)$$

Substituting I^2R for P in Eq. (8-1), then

$$db = 10 \log \frac{I_1^2 R_1}{I_2^2 R_2} \qquad (8\text{-}3)$$

or
$$db = 10 \log \left(\frac{I_1}{I_2}\right)^2 + 10 \log \frac{R_1}{R_2} \qquad (8\text{-}3a)$$

or
$$db = 20 \log \frac{I_1}{I_2} + 10 \log \frac{R_1}{R_2} \qquad (8\text{-}3b)$$

or
$$db = 20 \log \frac{I_1 \sqrt{R_1}}{I_2 \sqrt{R_2}} \qquad (8\text{-}3c)$$

For conditions where the impedances are equal, Eqs. (8-2c) and (8-3c) can be simplified as

$$db = 20 \log \frac{E_1}{E_2} \qquad (8\text{-}4)$$

$$db = 20 \log \frac{I_1}{I_2} \qquad (8\text{-}5)$$

Example 8-8. The characteristics of a certain audio amplifier are such that a voltage amplification of 5 is obtained at 50 cycles, 15 at 1500 cycles, and 30 at 5000 cycles. Assuming the voltage amplification at 1500 cycles as the reference level, what is the loss or gain in decibels at the other frequencies?

Given: Find:

     $f_1 = 50$ cycles   db @ 50 cycles = ?

     VA = 5   db @ 5000 cycles = ?

     $f_2 = 1500$ cycles

     VA = 15

     $f_3 = 5000$ cycles

     VA = 30

Solution:

$$db \text{ (loss) @ 50 cycles} = 20 \log \frac{VA \ @ \ f_2}{VA \ @ \ f_1} = -20 \log \frac{15}{3} = 20 \log 3$$

$$= 20 \times 0.4771 = -9.542 \ db$$

$$db \text{ (gain) @ 5000 cycles} = 20 \log \frac{VA \ @ \ f_3}{VA \ @ \ f_2} = 20 \log \frac{30}{15}$$

$$= 20 \log 2 = 20 \times 0.301 = +6.02 \ db$$

The results of Example 8-8 indicate that this amplifier has poor fidelity. There is a loss of approximately 9.5 db at the low frequencies and a gain of 6 db at the high frequencies. Such differences in volume are easily detected by the average listener.

Zero Reference Level.   The decibel is an indication of the ratio between two quantities. As a unit of measurement, it does not express any definite amount of power, volume, voltage, or current but only denotes the ratio between two magnitudes of any one of these quantities of measurement. For this reason it is therefore only a relative unit of measurement.

In order to have some definite comparison of volume changes a zero reference level is arbitrarily chosen. Unfortunately there is no single value that is used as a zero reference level by all manufacturers. However, it is general practice in radio and telephone applications to assume a power of six milliwatts as zero db. This means that any power level less than 6 mw will indicate a negative db and power levels greater than 6 mw will indicate positive db. Unless some other level is indicated as zero db, the level 6 mw is to be assumed.

Using 6 mw as a zero db reference level is a convenient method of rating the output of an amplifier, microphone, or loudspeaker. Thus, the statement that an amplifier delivers zero db to its load is taken to mean that it has an output of 6 mw.

In order to avoid some of the confusion caused by the lack of a standard reference level for zero decibel, the *volume unit*, abbreviated v-u, has been introduced. The volume unit uses one milliwatt as a reference level; hence, the volume level when expressed in v-u is equal to the number of decibels above (or below) one milliwatt. For example, an amplifier rated at +40 v-u has a volume level 40 db above 1 mw.

In the rating of microphones, both the v-u and the 6-mw zero decibel reference levels are used. In addition to these, particularly in the case of crystal microphones, the rating may be given as a voltage rating in decibels below one volt per bar. This type of rating in which zero decibel is equal to one volt per bar is used chiefly in connection with microphones and is explained more fully in a later chapter (see Art. 12-3).

Example 8-9.   A certain amplifier circuit is rated at +40 db.   (a) What is the power output in watts?   (b) What is its rating in v-u?

Given:
     db = +40

Find:
  (a) P_o = ?
  (b) v-u = ?

Solution:

(a) $db = 10 \log \dfrac{P_o}{P_R}$

     $\log \dfrac{P_o}{P_R} = \dfrac{db}{10} = \dfrac{40}{10} = 4$

     $P_o = P_R \text{ Antilog } 4 = 0.006 \times 10^4 = 60 \text{ watts}$

(b) $v\text{-}u = 10 \log \dfrac{60}{0.001} = 10 \log 60{,}000 = 10 \times 4.7782 = 47.7 \text{ v-u}$

Example 8-10. What is the power output in watts of a microphone that has an output of −40 db?

Given: Find:
$$db = -40$$ $$P_o = ?$$
Solution:

$$db = 10 \log \frac{P_R}{P_o}$$

$$\log \frac{P_R}{P_o} = \frac{db}{10} = \frac{40}{10} = 4$$

$$P_o = \frac{P_R}{\text{antilog } 4} = \frac{0.006}{10^4} = 0.6 \times 10^{-6} \text{ watt or } 0.6 \ \mu w$$

Example 8-11. The power output of a type 50L6-GT beam power amplifier tube is 4.3 watts when operated at the recommended electrode voltages. What is its output rating in decibels?

Given: Find:
$$\text{Tube} = 50L6\text{-}GT$$ $$db = ?$$
$$P_o = 4.3 \text{ watts}$$
Solution:

$$db = 10 \log \frac{P_o}{P_R} = 10 \log \frac{4.3}{0.006} = 10 \log 716$$

$$\log 716 = 2.8549 \text{ (from Appendix XIII)}$$
$$db = 10 \times 2.8549 = 28.549$$

8-4. Methods of Coupling. *Audio Amplifiers.* Any system used to couple the output of one tube to the input of another tube must provide some means of preventing the high voltage at the plate of one tube from affecting the grid bias of the next tube. In order to obtain a high degree of fidelity and sensitivity, the coupling system used should pass the audio signal currents with a minimum amount of change in frequency, amplitude, or phase.

The methods used to couple audio-amplifier stages include iron-core transformers; combinations of resistors and a capacitor; resistor, capacitor, and an inductor; and inductors and a capacitor. Each of these methods of coupling will cause the audio signal to be distorted to some degree. Each problem must be considered individually in order to determine which coupling method is best to use.

8-5. Resistance-capacitance-coupled Amplifier. *Basic Circuit Action.* Resistance-capacitance coupling is obtained by connecting the plate circuit and grid circuit of two successive stages by means of two resistors and a capacitor, as shown in Figs. 8-4 and 8-7. The varying plate current output of tube 1 will flow through the *coupling resistor* R_c. A varying voltage corresponding to the plate current variations will therefore be produced across this resistor. This varying voltage is applied to the grid of tube 2.

The *blocking capacitor* C_b is used to prevent the high voltage that is applied to the plate of tube 1 from being applied to the grid of tube 2. If it were not for this capacitor, the grid of tube 2 would operate at a high positive voltage, thus causing a high current to flow in both the grid and plate circuits of the tube. A tube operating under these overload conditions will become damaged very quickly.

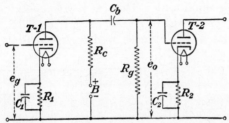

FIG. 8-4.—Resistance-capacitance-coupled amplifier circuit using triodes.

If this capacitor were used by itself, that is, without the resistor R_g, the operation of the second tube would become blocked because the negative charges on the grid side of the capacitor would increase the bias sufficiently to cause the tube to operate beyond cutoff. To prevent this blocking action a high resistance R_g, called a *grid leak*, is connected between the grid and cathode to provide a path for the accumulated electrons to leak off. The choice of the resistance value of R_g is based largely on the principle of time constants, as was presented in Art. 2-31 and as was further illustrated in the study of detectors.

Frequency Characteristics. An important characteristic of the resistance-capacitance-coupled amplifier is the manner in which the amplification varies with the frequency. Although the gain is not uniform for the entire audio-frequency range, it is practically constant over a fairly wide range of frequencies, decreasing very rapidly at both the very low and very high frequencies (see Fig. 8-5). This variation in gain is due to the changes in impedance with frequency of the blocking capacitor C_b and the interelectrode capacitances C_{pk} (plate-cathode) of tube 1, and C_{gk} (grid-cathode) of tube 2. To determine the characteristics of this type of amplifier it is therefore necessary to study the circuit actions at the low, intermediate, and high audio-frequency ranges.

Equivalent Electrical Circuit of the Amplifier. Resistance-capacitance coupling consists of a network of two resistors and a capacitor connected as shown in Figs. 8-4 and 8-7. The impedance of the resistors will remain practically constant over the entire range of audio frequencies, while the impedance of the capacitors will vary inversely with frequency changes. Therefore, the only variable factor is the capacitive reactance of the circuit.

The effects of a capacitor in a circuit are dependent on its impedance and the manner in which it is connected. At low frequencies, the impedance of a capacitor will be high, and its effect in a series circuit will become important while its effect in a parallel circuit will become negligible. At high frequencies, the impedance of a capacitor will be low and its effect in a series circuit will become negligible while its effect in a parallel circuit will become important. Thus, at low frequencies only the series-connected capacitances need be considered, while at high frequencies only the parallel-connected capacitances need be considered.

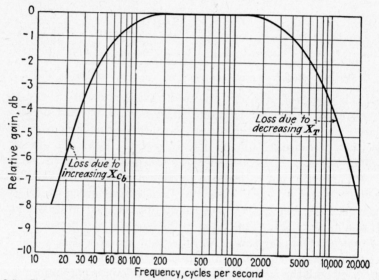

Fig. 8-5.—Relative gain vs frequency characteristics for a typical resistance-capacitance-coupled audio-frequency amplifier.

The basic equivalent electrical circuit for a resistance-capacitance-coupled amplifier will therefore be the same for all audio frequencies (see Fig. 7-13). The only variations are the capacitances whose effects must be considered at the frequency range being studied. The characteristics of audio amplifiers are generally considered for low, intermediate, and high audio frequencies. For calculating purposes, a single representative frequency of each of these ranges is used. Although these frequencies are not standardized, it is common practice to use 100 cycles for the low-frequency range, 1000 cycles for the intermediate-frequency range, and 10,000 cycles for the high-frequency range.

Equivalent Amplifier Circuits for the Three Audio-frequency Ranges. The interelectrode capacitance C_{pk} between the plate and cathode of tube 1 (Figs. 8-6c and 8-8c) acts as a shunt across the coupling resistor R_c.

The interelectrode capacitance C_{gk} between the grid and cathode of tube 2 acts as a shunt across the grid-leak resistor R_g; the capacitance C_{gk} is a part of the input capacitance C_i shown in Figs. 8-6c and 8-8c.   The values of these capacitances are very small; therefore their impedances at low and intermediate frequencies are normally very high.   The portion of the

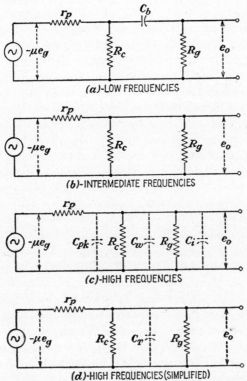

FIG. 8-6.—Equivalent electrical circuits at various audio frequencies for a resistance-capacitance-coupled amplifier circuit using triodes.

plate current that is by-passed by the interlectrode capacitances C_{pk} and C_{gk} at the low and intermediate audio frequencies is therefore very small. Because of this small loss the effect of these capacitances need only be considered at the high audio frequencies.

The blocking action of the capacitor C_b is determined by its value of capacitance and the frequency of the signal being applied.   Referring to Figs. 8-4 and 8-7, it can be seen that the signal voltage across the grid-leak resistor R_g will be equal to the voltage across the coupling resistor R_c minus the voltage drop across the blocking capacitor C_b.   At the low audio frequencies the impedance of the blocking capacitor may become appreciable and therefore the voltage drop across it will also be appreciable. This will cause a reduction in the voltage across the grid-leak resistor R_g and hence result in a reduction of the voltage applied to the grid of tube 2. The effect of the blocking capacitor must therefore be considered at the low audio frequencies because its impedance will be highest at these low values of frequency.

The capacitance of the blocking capacitor C_b is generally of such a value that its impedance at 1000 cycles is negligible in comparison to the resistance of R_g. Practically all the signal voltage developed across the coupling resistor R_c will then be applied to the grid of the next tube. The effects of the blocking capacitor can therefore be ignored for the intermediate and high frequencies.

Knowing these facts it is now possible to draw an equivalent electrical circuit of a stage of amplification for each frequency range. Figures 8-6 and 8-8 show the equivalent electrical circuits for the triode and pentode amplifiers of Figs. 8-4 and 8-7 respectively. At the high frequencies the interelectrode capacitances C_{pk} and C_i, together with the stray capacitance C_w due to the wiring (see Figs. 8-6c and 8-8c), may be considered as a single capacitance C_T shunting the resistors as shown in Figs. 8-6d and 8-8d.

Factors to Be Considered in Determining the Values of R_c, R_g, and C_b. In order to obtain the maximum voltage gain the value of the coupling (or plate load) resistor R_c should be high. However, it should be observed that the voltage at the plate of tube 1 will be equal to the voltage of the B supply minus the voltage drop $I_b R_c$ across the coupling resistor R_c. Increasing the value of R_c increases this voltage drop, thus decreasing the voltage at the plate of tube 1. In order to maintain the plate voltage at its required value, the voltage of the B supply would have to be increased. If the value of the coupling resistor is made too high the B supply voltage required will become prohibitive; hence the value of R_c is limited to a large extent by the plate supply voltage.

Another factor limiting the extent to which R_c may be increased is the reduction in the gain of the amplifier at the high audio frequencies. At these frequencies the effect of the series capacitance C_b may be ignored, but the effect of the shunting capacitance C_T (fully described in Art. 8-8) becomes important. This shunting capacitance will have a low impedance at the high audio frequencies and will cause a reduction in the impedance of the parallel circuit formed by the coupling resistor R_c, the grid-leak resistor R_g, and the shunting capacitance C_T. A reduction in the value of this impedance will cause a reduction in the voltage at this parallel circuit, thereby causing a loss in the amplification at the high frequencies. It may further be observed that the division of current in the parallel combination depends on the impedance of its various members. Increasing the value of the coupling resistor as a means of increasing the amplification of the circuit does not produce the gain anticipated but instead results in a decrease in current through the coupling resistor, thereby decreasing the overall gain of the circuit.

The low-frequency characteristics of a resistance-capacitance-coupled amplifier depend largely upon the ratio between the impedance of the blocking capacitor C_b and the resistance of grid-leak resistor R_g. Increasing the capacitance of the blocking capacitor decreases its impedance, thus lowering the value of resistance required for the grid-leak resistor. The higher the value of the grid-leak resistor, the higher will be the overall amplification. It has previously been shown that at the high frequencies part of the signal current will be by-passed by the interelectrode capacitance C_{gk} between the grid and cathode of tube 2. The portion of the signal current by-passed will depend upon the ratio between the resistance of the grid-leak resistor and the impedance of the interelectrode capacitance C_{gk}.

Practical Values of R_c, R_g, and C_b. The values of the coupling resistor, grid-leak resistor, and the blocking capacitor will depend upon the tube used, the operating plate and grid voltages, and the frequency characteristics desired. The resistance of the coupling resistor, sometimes called the *plate resistor* or *load resistor*, will range from 50,000 ohms to 500,000 ohms. The plate resistance of triodes is of a comparatively low value and the coupling resistor used will generally have a resistance of from two to five times the value of the plate resistance. Pentodes have a comparatively high value of plate resistance and the value of the coupling resistor used with this type tube will seldom exceed 500,000 ohms and hence will be only a fraction of the tube's plate resistance.

The resistance of the grid-leak resistor, sometimes referred to as the *grid resistor*, will range from one-tenth megohm to one megohm. This value is dependent on the values of the coupling resistor and blocking capacitor and its resistance is generally from two to five times the value of the coupling resistor.

The capacitance of the blocking capacitor, sometimes called the *coupling capacitor*, will depend upon the frequency characteristics desired and will range from 0.003 μf to 0.03 μf. This capacitor should have a high dielectric strength in order to prevent any of the plate voltage being applied to tube 1 from leaking to the grid of tube 2. Mica-dielectric capacitors are recommended for the coupling capacitor, although paper-dielectric capacitors having a high value of equivalent-parallel resistance are also used.

These values and rules for determining the resistance of the coupling and grid-leak resistors and the capacitance of the blocking capacitor are very general. Recommended values for these circuit elements for the various types of amplifier tubes are listed in the Resistance-coupled Amplifier Chart of Appendix XVI. Observation of these listings indicates that the choice of plate supply voltage and the value of the coupling resistor determines the values of the other circuit elements. The desired amount of voltage gain and the desired frequency characteristics are the factors that determine the amount of plate supply voltage and the value of the coupling resistor to be used.

In order that the tube used will operate with the correct grid bias and screen-grid voltage, the proper values of cathode resistor, screen resistor,

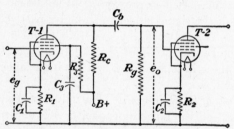

FIG. 8-7.—Resistance-capacitance-coupled amplifier circuit using pentodes.

cathode by-pass capacitor, and screen by-pass capacitor must be used. The values required for commonly used tubes at various amounts of plate-supply voltage are also listed in the Resistance-capacitance-coupled Amplifier Chart of Appendix XVI.

8-6. Voltage Amplification for the Intermediate-frequency Range. Resistance-capacitance-coupled audio amplifiers are generally designed to give the maximum voltage gain for the intermediate frequencies. The voltage amplification for this frequency range will therefore be considered first.

For amplifiers using triodes, the equivalent circuit for intermediate frequencies will be as shown in Fig. 8-6b. From this equivalent circuit diagram it can be seen that the impedance of the output load is equal to the impedance of the parallel circuit formed by the coupling resistor R_c and the grid-leak resistor R_g, or

$$Z_o = \frac{R_c R_g}{R_c + R_g} \tag{8-6}$$

The voltage amplification at intermediate audio frequencies for a triode amplifier can be found by substituting this value of impedance [Eq. (8-6)] in the basic equation for the voltage amplification of a triode as was expressed by Eq. (7-5).

$$VA = \frac{\mu Z_o}{Z_o + r_p} \tag{7-5}$$

Equation (7-5) may be rearranged to read

$$VA = \frac{\mu}{\dfrac{r_p}{Z_o} + 1} \tag{8-7}$$

Substituting Eq. (8-6) for Z_o in Eq. (8-7)

$$VA_M = \frac{\mu}{\dfrac{r_p(R_c + R_g)}{R_c R_g} + 1} \tag{8-8}$$

For amplifiers using pentodes, the equivalent circuit for intermediate frequencies will be as shown in Fig. 8-8b. The impedance of the load, that is, exclusive of the plate resistance r_p, is equal to the impedance of the parallel circuit formed by the coupling resistor R_c and the grid leak resistor R_g and is expressed by Eq. (8-6). This may also be expressed as

$$\frac{1}{Z_o} = \frac{1}{R_c} + \frac{1}{R_g} \tag{8-6a}$$

The voltage amplification at intermediate audio frequencies for a pentode amplifier can be found by substituting Eq. (8-6) or (8-6a) in the basic equation for the voltage amplification of a pentode as was expressed by Eq. (7-8).

$$VA = g_m \frac{r_p Z_o}{Z_o + r_p} \tag{7-8}$$

Equation (7-8) may be rearranged to read

$$VA = \frac{g_m}{\dfrac{1}{Z_o} + \dfrac{1}{r_p}} \tag{8-9}$$

Substituting Eq. (8-6) for Z_o in Eq. (8-9)

$$VA_M = \frac{g_m}{\dfrac{R_c + R_g}{R_c R_g} + \dfrac{1}{r_p}} \tag{8-10}$$

If Eq. (8-6a) is substituted for $\dfrac{1}{Z_o}$ in Eq. (8-9)

$$VA_M = \frac{g_m}{\dfrac{1}{R_c} + \dfrac{1}{R_g} + \dfrac{1}{r_p}} \tag{8-10a}$$

or
$$VA_M = g_m R_{eq} \qquad\qquad (8\text{-}10b)$$

where
$$R_{eq} = \cfrac{1}{\dfrac{1}{R_c} + \dfrac{1}{R_g} + \dfrac{1}{r_p}} \qquad \text{[from Eq. (2-32)]}$$

Example 8-12. The resistance-capacitance-coupled amplifier of a certain radio receiver uses the triode unit of a 6SQ7 tube operated with 250 volts on its plate and a coupling resistor of 500,000 ohms. If the recommended values (Appendix XVI) are used for the other circuit elements of the coupling network, what is the voltage amplification for the intermediate-frequency range?

Given: Find:
    Tube $= 6$SQ7 $VA_M = ?$
    $E_b = 250$ volts
    $R_c = 0.5$ megohm

Solution:

    $r_p = 91,000$ ohms (from Appendix XV)
    $\mu = 100$ (from Appendix XV)
    $R_g = 1$ megohm (from Appendix XVI, use 300-volt listing assuming that
$$E_b = E_{bb} - I_b R_o = 250 \text{ volts})$$

$$VA_M = \cfrac{\mu}{\dfrac{r_p(R_c + R_g)}{R_c R_g} + 1} = \cfrac{100}{\dfrac{91,000(0.5 \times 10^6 + 10^6)}{0.5 \times 10^6 \times 10^6} + 1} = 78.55$$

Example 8-13. The resistance-capacitance-coupled amplifier of a certain radio receiver uses a type 6J7 tube operated as a pentode Class A amplifier with 250 volts on its plate and a coupling resistor of 250,000 ohms. If the recommended values (Appendix XVI) are used for the other circuit elements of the coupling network, what is the voltage amplification for the intermediate-frequency range?

Given: Find:
    Tube $= 6$J7 $VA_M = ?$
    $E_b = 250$ volts
    $R_c = 0.25$ megohm

Solution:

    $r_p = 1$ megohm (from Appendix XV)
    $g_m = 1225$ μmhos (from Appendix XV)
    $R_g = 0.5$ megohm (from Appendix XVI)

$$VA_M = g_m R_{eq} = 1225 \times 10^{-6} \times \frac{10^6}{7} = 175$$

where
$$R_{eq} = \cfrac{1}{\dfrac{1}{R_c} + \dfrac{1}{R_g} + \dfrac{1}{r_p}} = \cfrac{1}{\dfrac{1}{0.25 \times 10^6} + \dfrac{1}{0.5 \times 10^6} + \dfrac{1}{10^6}} = \frac{10^6}{7}$$

8-7. Voltage Amplification for the Low-frequency Range. The voltage gain for the low audio frequencies will be less than that obtained for the intermediate-frequency range because of the voltage drop at the blocking capacitor C_b. For most practical purposes, the factor by which the gain is reduced is dependent upon the ratio of the resistance of the grid-leak resistor to the impedance of the series circuit consisting of the blocking capacitor and the grid-leak resistor as expressed by Eq. (8-11b). This factor is expressed mathematically as

$$K_L = \frac{1}{\sqrt{1 + \left(\dfrac{X_c}{R}\right)^2}} \qquad (8\text{-}11)$$

where K_L = low frequency factor of voltage amplification
$\quad X_c$ = reactance of the coupling capacitor C_b, ohms

$$R = R_g + \frac{r_p R_c}{r_p + R_c} = R_g + \frac{R_c}{1 + \dfrac{R_c}{r_p}}$$

However, when r_p is small compared to R_c and R_g as is the case with

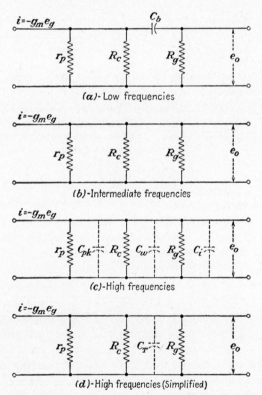

(a)- Low frequencies

(b)-Intermediate frequencies

(c)-High frequencies

(d)-High frequencies (Simplified)

Fig. 8-8.—Equivalent electrical circuits at various audio frequencies for a resistance-capacitance-coupled amplifier circuit using pentodes.

triodes, R may be taken as equal to R_g without causing any great error in the low-frequency factor K_L.   Hence

$$K_L \cong \frac{1}{\sqrt{1 + \left(\dfrac{X_c}{R_g}\right)^2}} \tag{8-11a}$$

or

$$K_L \cong \frac{R_g}{\sqrt{R_g{}^2 + X_c{}^2}} \tag{8-11b}$$

$$K_L \cong \frac{R_g}{\sqrt{R_g{}^2 + \left(\dfrac{1}{2\pi f C_b}\right)^2}} \tag{8-11c}$$

The voltage amplification at low audio frequencies for triode amplifiers can now be found by combining Eqs. (8-11b) and (8-8), as

$$VA_L = K_L \, VA_M \tag{8-12}$$

or

$$VA_L \cong \frac{\mu R_g}{\sqrt{R_g{}^2 + X_c{}^2} \left(\dfrac{r_p(R_c + R_g)}{R_c R_g} + 1\right)} \tag{8-12a}$$

The voltage amplification at low audio frequencies for pentode amplifiers can be found by combining Eqs. (8-11) and (8-10b), as

$$VA_L = K_L \, VA_M \tag{8-12}$$

or

$$VA_L = \frac{1}{\sqrt{1 + \left(\dfrac{X_c}{R}\right)^2}} g_m R_{eq} \tag{8-13}$$

Examination of Eqs. (8-11), (8-11a), and (8-13) will show that when the frequency of the audio signal is such that the reactance of the blocking capacitor is equal to the resistance value, the voltage gain will be 70.7 per cent of the voltage amplification obtained for the intermediate-frequency range. When the frequency of the audio signal decreases so that the reactance of the blocking capacitor is twice the resistance value, the voltage gain will be less than 50 per cent of the voltage amplification obtained for the intermediate frequency. When expressed in db, this would indicate -3 db when X_c is equal to R and -7 db when X_c is twice the value of R. As changes in volume greater than 3 db are readily detected, it becomes apparent that the values of the resistances and the blocking capacitor should be carefully selected in order to obtain good sound reproduction.

Example 8-14. What is the voltage amplification of the amplifier circuit used in Example 8-12 for a low audio frequency signal of 100 cycles by use of the low-frequency factor expressed in (*a*) Eq. (8-11)?   (*b*) Eq. (8-11a)?

Given: Find:
$$f = 100 \text{ cycles}$$ $$VA_L = ?$$
$$VA_M = 78.55$$
$$R_c = 0.5 \text{ megohm}$$
$$r_p = 91,000 \text{ ohms}$$
$$R_g = 1 \text{ megohm}$$

Solution:
$$C_b = 0.004 \ \mu f \text{ (from Appendix XVI)}$$

(a) $VA_L = K_L VA_M = 0.938 \times 78.55 = 73.68$

$$K_L = \frac{1}{\sqrt{1 + \left(\dfrac{X_c}{R}\right)^2}} = \frac{1}{\sqrt{1 + \left(\dfrac{397,500}{1,076,988}\right)^2}} = 0.938$$

$$X_C = \frac{159,000}{fC} = \frac{159,000}{100 \times 0.004} = 397,500 \text{ ohms}$$

$$R = R_g + \frac{r_p R_c}{r_p + R_c} = 10^6 + \frac{91,000 \times 500,000}{91,000 + 500,000} = 1,076,988 \text{ ohms}$$

(b) $VA_L = K_L VA_M = 0.929 \times 78.55 = 72.97$

$$K_L = \frac{1}{\sqrt{1 + \left(\dfrac{X_c}{R_g}\right)^2}} = \frac{1}{\sqrt{1 + \left(\dfrac{397,500}{1,000,000}\right)^2}} = 0.929$$

$$X_C = \frac{159,000}{fC} = \frac{159,000}{100 \times 0.004} = 397,500 \text{ ohms}$$

$$R = R_g = 1,000,000 \text{ ohms}$$

Example 8-15.   What is the voltage amplification of the amplifier circuit used in Example 8-13 for a low audio-frequency signal of 100 cycles, by use of the low-frequency factor expressed in (a) Eq. (8-11)?   (b) Eq. (8-11a)?

Given: Find:
$$f = 100 \text{ cycles}$$ $$VA_L = ?$$
$$VA_M = 175$$
$$R_c = 0.25 \text{ megohm}$$
$$r_p = 1 \text{ megohm}$$
$$R_g = 0.5 \text{ megohm}$$

Solution:
$$C_b = 0.005 \ \mu f \text{ (from Appendix XVI)}$$

(a) $VA_L = K_L VA_M = 0.910 \times 175 = 159.25$

$$K_L = \frac{1}{\sqrt{1 + \left(\dfrac{X_c}{R}\right)^2}} = \frac{1}{\sqrt{1 + \left(\dfrac{318,000}{700,000}\right)^2}} = 0.910$$

$$X_C = \frac{159,000}{fC} = \frac{159,000}{100 \times 0.005} = 318,000 \text{ ohms}$$

$$R = R_g + \frac{r_p R_c}{r_p + R_c} = 500,000 + \frac{1,000,000 \times 250,000}{1,000,000 + 250,000} = 700,000 \text{ ohms}$$

(b) $VA_L = K_L VA_M = 0.843 \times 175 = 147.5$

$$K_L = \frac{1}{\sqrt{1 + \left(\dfrac{X_c}{R_g}\right)^2}} = \frac{1}{\sqrt{1 + \left(\dfrac{318,000}{500,000}\right)^2}} = 0.843$$

$$X_C = \frac{159,000}{fC} = \frac{159,000}{100 \times 0.005} = 318,000 \text{ ohms}$$

$$R = R_g = 500,000 \text{ ohms}$$

From the results of Examples 8-14 and 8-15 it can be seen that the voltage gain at low frequencies of audio amplifiers using triodes can be calculated by use of the approximate low-frequency factor of Eq. (8-11a) without introducing any appreciable error. However, the low-frequency gain for amplifiers using pentodes should be determined by use of Eq. (8-11) for more accurate results.

8-8. Voltage Amplification for the High-frequency Range. The voltage gain for the high audio frequencies will be less than that obtained for the intermediate-frequency range because of the by-pass path provided by the capacitance C_T (see Figs. 8-6d and 8-8d). For most practical purposes, the factor by which the voltage gain is reduced is dependent upon the ratio of the equivalent resistance of the parallel circuit formed by the plate resistance, coupling resistor, and grid-leak resistor to the reactance of the capacitance C_T that shunts these resistors. This factor is expressed mathematically as

$$K_H = \frac{1}{\sqrt{1 + \left(\dfrac{R_{eq}}{X_T}\right)^2}} \qquad (8\text{-}14)$$

or

$$K_H = \frac{1}{\sqrt{1 + (R_{eq}2\pi f C_T)^2}} \qquad (8\text{-}14a)$$

The voltage amplification at high audio frequencies for amplifiers using triodes can be found by combining Eqs. (8-14a) and (8-8)

$$VA_H = K_H \, VA_M \qquad (8\text{-}15)$$

or

$$VA_H = \frac{\mu}{\sqrt{1 + (R_{eq}2\pi f C_T)^2}\left(\dfrac{r_p(R_c + R_g)}{R_c R_g} + 1\right)} \qquad (8\text{-}15a)$$

The voltage amplification at high audio frequencies for amplifiers using pentodes can be found by combining Eqs. (8-14a) and (8-10b)

$$VA_H = K_H \, VA_M \qquad (8\text{-}15)$$

or

$$VA_H = \frac{g_m R_{eq}}{\sqrt{1 + (R_{eq}2\pi f C_T)^2}} \qquad (8\text{-}16)$$

Examination of the high-frequency factor expressed in Eq. (8-14) will show that, when the frequency of the audio signal is such that the reactance of the shunting capacitance C_T is equal to the equivalent resistance of the parallel circuit formed by the plate resistance, the coupling resistor, and the grid-leak resistor, the voltage gain will be 70.7 per cent of the voltage amplification obtained for the intermediate-frequency range. When the frequency of the audio signal increases so that the reactance of the shunting capacitance is reduced to one-half the value of the equivalent resistance, the voltage gain will be less than 50 per cent of the voltage amplification obtained at the intermediate audio frequencies. Expressed in decibels, these reductions in gain represent -3 db and -7 db respectively. From this, it is apparent that the interelectrode capacitances of the tube and the stray capacitance of the wiring have an important bearing on the fidelity of sound reproduction.

Factors Affecting the Value of the Shunting Capacitance. The total shunting capacitance C_T (see Figs. 8-6d and 8-8d) is equal to the sum of the three separate shunting capacitances indicated on Figs. 8-6c and 8-8c. Thus the value of C_T may be expressed as

$$C_T = C_w + C_{pk} + C_i \qquad (8\text{-}17)$$

where C_T = total shunting capacitance
$\quad C_w$ = stray capacitance of the wiring
$\quad C_{pk}$ = interelectrode capacitance between the plate and cathode of the first tube
$\quad C_i$ = effective input capacitance of the load, which in this case is the second tube

The stray capacitance due to the wiring is usually quite low in value and is generally under 10 $\mu\mu$f. The plate-cathode capacitance of the first tube may be obtained from a standard tube manual. The effective input capacitance of the load when the output is fed into a second tube is the combined effect of the grid-cathode and grid-plate capacitances of the second tube. These two capacitances are in effect the same as two capacitors connected in parallel with one another. However, their combined effect is not equal to their arithmetic sum, as is the usual case with capacitors connected in parallel. This is so because the voltage is not the same at each capacitance owing to the normal amplifying action that takes place between the grid and plate circuits.

The effective input capacitance can best be explained by studying the charges at these two capacitances. The charge on any capacitor is equal to the product of the capacitance and the voltage. Therefore, the charge accumulated due to the grid-cathode interelectrode capacitance of tube 2 is

$$Q_{gk} = C_{gk}e_o \qquad (8\text{-}18)$$

The charge accumulated due to the grid-plate interelectrode capacitance of tube 2 is

$$Q_{gp} = C_{gp}e_{gp} \qquad (8\text{-}19)$$

However, the difference of potential between the grid and plate is

$$e_{gp} = e_o - \text{VA } e_o \qquad (8\text{-}20)$$

But, as the plate voltage change of a tube is 180 degrees out of phase with its grid voltage change, Eq. (8-20) may be expressed as

$$e_{gp} = e_o + \text{VA } e_o \qquad (8\text{-}20a)$$

or
$$e_{gp} = e_o(1 + \text{VA}) \qquad (8\text{-}20b)$$

where e_{gp} = difference of potential between the grid and plate

e_o = voltage at the grid of the second tube

VA = voltage amplification of the circuit

VA e_o = difference of potential between the plate and cathode

Substituting Eq. (8-20b) in (8-19)

$$Q_{gp} = C_{gp}e_o(1 + \text{VA}) \qquad (8\text{-}19a)$$

The total effective charge at the input of the second tube is equal to the sum of the grid-cathode and the grid-plate charges, or

$$Q_i = Q_{gk} + Q_{gp} \qquad (8\text{-}21)$$

also
$$C_ie_o = C_{gk}e_o + C_{gp}e_o(1 + \text{VA}) \qquad (8\text{-}22)$$

and
$$C_i = C_{gk} + C_{gp}(1 + \text{VA}) \qquad (8\text{-}23)$$

It should be noted that in Eq. (8-23) the voltage amplification represents that of the circuit and cannot exceed the amplification factor of the tube. It will normally be equal to approximately one-half the amplification factor of the tube.

Example 8-16. The stray capacitance of the wiring of the amplifier circuit used in Example 8-12 is 5 $\mu\mu$f, and the interelectrode capacitance C_{pk} of the first tube (6SQ7) is 3.2 $\mu\mu$f. The interelectrode capacitances of the second tube (6A3) are $C_{gk} = 7.5$ $\mu\mu$f, $C_{gp} = 16.5$ $\mu\mu$f and the amplification factor of the tube is 4.2. What is the total shunting capacitance C_T of the circuit?

Given:
$C_w = 5$ $\mu\mu$f
$C_{pk} = 3.2$ $\mu\mu$f
$C_{gk} = 7.5$ $\mu\mu$f
$C_{gp} = 16.5$ $\mu\mu$f
$\mu = 4.2$

Find:
$C_T = ?$

Solution:
$$C_i = C_{gk} + C_{gp}(1 + \text{VA}) = 7.5 + 16.5(1 + 2.1) = 58.65$$
Note: VA $= 0.5 \times \mu = 0.5 \times 4.2 = 2.1$
$$C_T = C_w + C_{pk} + C_i = 5 + 3.2 + 58.65 = 66.85 \ \mu\mu f$$

Example 8-17. What is the voltage amplification of the circuit used in Example 8-12 for a high audio frequency of 5000 cycles if the shunt capacitance is 66.85 $\mu\mu$f?

Given:
$f = 5000$ cycles
$C_T = 66.85\mu\mu$f
VA$_M = 78.55$

Find:
VA$_H = ?$

Solution:

$$VA_H = K_H \, VA_M = 0.989 \times 78.55 = 77.68$$

where $K_H = \dfrac{1}{\sqrt{1 + (R_{eq}2\pi f C_T)^2}}$

$$= \dfrac{1}{\sqrt{1 + \left(\dfrac{10^6}{14} \times 6.28 \times 5000 \times 66.85 \times 10^{-12}\right)^2}} = 0.989$$

$$R_{eq} = \dfrac{1}{\dfrac{1}{r_p} + \dfrac{1}{R_c} + \dfrac{1}{R_g}} = \dfrac{1}{\dfrac{1}{91,000} + \dfrac{1}{500,000} + \dfrac{1}{1,000,000}} = \dfrac{10^6}{14} \text{ ohms}$$

Example 8-18.   What is the voltage amplification of the circuit used in Example 8-13 for a high audio frequency of 5000 cycles if the shunt capacitance is 315 $\mu\mu$f?

Given: Find:
$\qquad f = 5000$ cycles $\qquad VA_H = ?$
$\qquad C_T = 315 \ \mu\mu$f
$\qquad VA_M = 175$
$\qquad R_{eq} = \dfrac{10^6}{7}$ ohms

Solution:

$$VA_H = K_H \, VA_M = 0.577 \times 175 = 100.9$$

where $K_H = \dfrac{1}{\sqrt{1 + (R_{eq}2\pi f C_T)^2}}$

$$= \dfrac{1}{\sqrt{1 + \left(\dfrac{10^6}{7} \times 6.28 \times 5000 \times 315 \times 10^{-12}\right)^2}} = 0.577$$

Example 8-19.   The results of Examples 8-12, 8-14, and 8-17 indicate that the voltage amplification of the triode resistance-capacitance-coupled amplifier circuit using the triode section of a 6SQ7 is 78.55 at 1000 cycles, 73.68 at 100 cycles, and 77.68 at 5000 cycles.   Assuming the voltage amplification at 1000 cycles as the reference level, what is the loss in decibels at the other frequencies?

Given: Find:
$\qquad VA_M = 78.55$ @ 1000 cycles $\qquad$ (a) Decibel loss @ 100 cycles
$\qquad VA_L = 73.68$ @ 100 cycles $\qquad$ (b) Decibel loss @ 5000 cycles
$\qquad VA_H = 77.68$ @ 5000 cycles.

Solution:

(a)   Loss @ 100 cycles $= 20 \log \dfrac{VA_M}{VA_L} = 20 \log \dfrac{78.55}{73.68} = 0.554$ db

(b)   Loss @ 5000 cycles $= 20 \log \dfrac{VA_M}{VA_H} = 20 \log \dfrac{78.55}{77.68} = 0.094$ db

Example 8-20.   The results of Examples 8-13, 8-15, and 8-18 indicate that the voltage amplification of the pentode resistance-capacitance-coupled amplifier circuit using a 6J7 tube is 175 at 1000 cycles, 159.25 at 100 cycles, and 100.9 at 5000 cycles. Assuming the voltage amplification at 1000 cycles as the reference level, what is the loss in decibels at the other frequencies?

Given:

    VA_M = 175 @ 1000 cycles

    VA_L = 159.25 @ 100 cycles

    VA_H = 100.9 @ 5000 cycles

Find:

    (a) Decibel loss @ 100 cycles

    (b) Decibel loss @ 5000 cycles

Solution:

(a)   Loss @ 100 cycles $= 20 \log \dfrac{VA_M}{VA_L} = 20 \log \dfrac{175}{159.25} = 0.812$ db

(b)   Loss @ 5000 cycles $= 20 \log \dfrac{VA_M}{VA_H} = 20 \log \dfrac{175}{100.9} = 4.78$ db

8-9. Circuit Characteristics of Resistance-capacitance-coupled Amplifiers. From the results obtained in Examples 8-12 to 8-18 it can be seen that the voltage amplification of the resistance-capacitance-coupled amplifier circuit using either a high-mu triode or a pentode is fairly uniform for the entire audio-frequency range that is transmitted by the average broadcast station. From the results obtained in Examples 8-19 and 8-20 it can be seen that the decibel variation with either the triode or pentode is much less than the variation in voltage amplification and the resulting change in volume is so small that it cannot be detected by the average listener.

One of the outstanding characteristics of resistance-capacitance-coupled amplifiers is that they have good fidelity over a comparatively wide frequency range. The results obtained for the two amplifier circuits in Examples 8-12 to 8-20 can therefore be considered as being typical of resistance-capacitance-coupled amplifiers.

All the gain in this type of amplifier circuit is provided by the tube. The associated circuit elements do not add to the gain but rather reduce the effective gain of the circuit so that the resulting voltage amplification is considerably less than the amplification factor of the tube used. However, the overall amplification of a resistance-capacitance-coupled amplifier circuit is generally higher than can be obtained by using any one of the other coupling methods. This is possible because the high values of resistance required to match the high values of plate resistance of high-mu triodes and pentode tubes are easily obtained.

Other advantages of this type of amplifier circuit are: (1) the parts are low in cost and occupy very little space; (2) as there are no coils or transformers in the circuit, there is very little pickup of undesirable currents from any a-c leads, thus the amount of nonlinear distortion is minimized.

A disadvantage of this type of amplifier is that a higher B supply voltage must be used in order to compensate for the voltage drop across the coupling resistor.

Because of the many advantages of resistance-capacitance coupling it is commonly used in audio amplifier circuits.   The theory of this type of amplifier circuit has been considered in great detail because of this fact and also because its principle of operation is basic and is the one most easily understood.   It therefore can serve as a comparison and can be used in the explanation of the operation of other types of amplifier circuits.   If the theory of operation of this type of amplifier is clearly understood, the theory of the others can more easily be followed.

8-10. Impedance-coupled Amplifier. *Basic Circuit Action.* One method of eliminating the high voltage drop between the B power supply and the plate of the tube is to replace the coupling resistor of the resist-

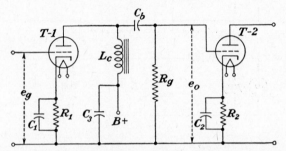

Fig. 8-9.—Impedance-coupled amplifier circuit using triodes.

ance-capacitance-coupled amplifier with an iron-core choke coil having a high value of inductance and a low value of resistance.   Amplifier circuits using this method of coupling are called *impedance-coupled amplifiers* and are similar to the resistance-capacitance-coupled amplifier except for the substitution of the inductance coil L_c for the coupling resistor R_c (Fig. 8-9).

The voltage drop across the coupling impedance is dependent on the ohmic resistance of the coil and the plate current; this voltage drop will be comparatively small.   The voltage of the B power supply need then be only slightly higher than the required plate voltage of the tube used.

The impedance that the coupling coil offers to the signal current is dependent on its value of inductance and the frequency of the audio signal.   In order to obtain a high value of impedance at the low audio frequencies, the inductance of the coupling coil is made as high as is practicable.   A high value of impedance is desired in order to obtain a high value of voltage amplification.   The inductance of choke coils used as coupling impedances for audio amplifiers have a wide range of values and will vary from 10 to 800 henries.

Frequency Characteristics. The frequency response of impedance-coupled amplifiers is not so good as that obtained with resistance-capacitance-coupled amplifiers (see Fig. 8-11).   The decrease in gain is greater at both the low and high audio frequencies than for resistance-capacitance-coupled amplifiers.   This is due to the fact that the impedance of a resistor is fairly uniform at all frequencies and its distributed capacitance is negligible, while the impedance of a coil varies directly with the frequency change and has an appreciable amount of distributed capacitance owing to the large number of turns required.   At low audio frequencies

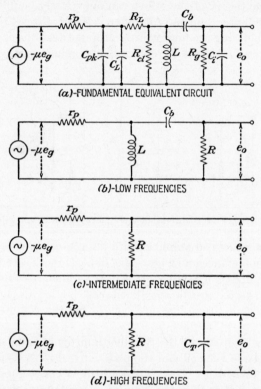

Fig. 8-10.—Equivalent electrical circuits at various audio frequencies for an impedance-coupled amplifier circuit using triodes.

the impedance of the coupling coil will be decreased, thus causing a decrease in the voltage gain at these frequencies.   The distributed capacitance of the coil increases the shunt capacitance of the circuit and at the high audio frequencies this increase in shunting capacitance will cause more of the output current to be by-passed, thus further decreasing the voltage gain at these frequencies.

Voltage Amplification of the Impedance-coupled Amplifier.   The method of determining the voltage amplification produced by the impedance-coupled amplifier is similar to that used in determining the voltage amplification of the resistance-capacitance-coupled amplifier circuit, which has already been presented in detaii. The circuit characteristics are again observed at the low, intermediate, and high frequencies of the audio range. The equivalent electrical circuits for the three frequency ranges are given in Fig. 8-10. In these circuits R_L represents the resistance of the coupling impedance, C_L represents the distributed capacitance of the coupling unit, and R_{cl} is used to represent the core loss of the coupling impedance. All other designations are the same as before.

At the low and intermediate frequencies, the reactance of the shunting capacitances is so high in comparison to R that it may be disregarded at these frequencies. At the intermediate and high frequencies, the reactance of the inductor is much greater than R and hence it may be disregarded at these frequencies. Thus the voltage amplification of the circuit at the intermediate frequencies [Eq. (8-24)] is dependent largely upon the values of resistances in the circuit because the effects of all the reactances are negligible at these frequencies. The voltage amplification at the low frequencies [Eq. (8-25)] decreases because of the reduction in the reactance of the inductor L shunting the load and the increase in the reactance of the blocking capacitor C_b connected in series with the resistor R_g. The voltage amplification at the high frequencies [Eq. (8-26)] decreases because the reactance of the shunting capacitances becomes relatively low at these frequencies, thereby causing a decrease in the voltage amplification. The equations for expressing the approximate voltage amplification at the various frequencies are

$$\text{VA}_M \cong \frac{\mu R}{r_p + R} \tag{8-24}$$

also
$$\text{VA}_M \cong g_m R_{eq} \tag{8-10b}$$

$$\text{VA}_L \cong \frac{1}{\sqrt{1 + \left[\dfrac{R_{eq}}{X_L}\right]^2 + \left[\dfrac{R_{eq}X_C}{r_p R_g}\right]^2}} g_m R_{eq} \tag{8-25}$$

$$\text{VA}_H \cong \frac{1}{\sqrt{1 + \left(\dfrac{R_{eq}}{X_T}\right)^2}} g_m R_{eq} \tag{8-26}$$

or
$$\text{VA}_H \cong \frac{g_m R_{eq}}{\sqrt{1 + (R_{eq}2\pi f C_T)^2}} \tag{8-26a}$$

where $R = \dfrac{R_c R_g}{R_c + R_g} \cong R_g$ when R_c becomes so high that its effect is negligible

$R_{eq} = \dfrac{r_p R_{cl} R_g}{r_p R_{cl} + r_p R_g + R_{cl} R_g} \cong \dfrac{r_p R_g}{r_p + R_g}$ when R_{cl} is very high

R_{cl} = resistance which would produce an effect equivalent to the core loss, ohms

X_C = reactance of the blocking capacitor C_b, ohms

X_T = reactance of the total shunting capacitance C_T, ohms

$C_T = C_{pk} + C_L + C_i + C_w$

Comparing Eqs. (8-24), (8-25), and (8-26a) with Eqs. (8-7), (8-13), and (8-16) will show that the equations for the voltage amplification of impedance-coupled amplifiers are very much similar to those of resistance-capacitance-coupled amplifiers.

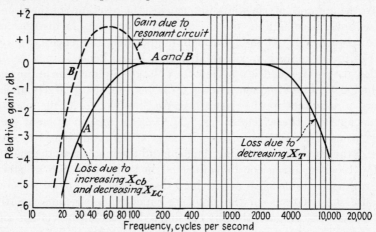

Fig. 8-11.—Relative gain vs. frequency characteristics for an impedance-coupled audio-frequency amplifier. Curve A for a simple impedance-coupled circuit (Fig. 8-9), curve B for a circuit with a resonant section (Figs. 8-12a and 8-12b).

Example 8-21. The coupling coil of an impedance-coupled amplifier circuit similar to Fig. 8-9 has an inductance of 150 henries and a resistance of 3500 ohms. Tube 1 is a type 6C5 operated with 250 volts at its plate and with 8 volts grid bias. A 500,000-ohm resistor is used at R_g and the blocking capacitor C_b has a value of 0.01 μf. The total shunting capacitance of the circuit is 200 $\mu\mu f$. Assume the core loss of the coupling unit to be so low that R_{cl} may be ignored. (a) What is the impedance of the coupling coil at 50, 1000, and 10,000 cycles (neglecting the effect of its resistance and distributed capacitance)? (b) What voltage is required of the B power supply? (c) What is the voltage amplification of the circuit at 50, 1000, and 10,000 cycles? (d) What is the gain in decibels at 50, 1000, and 10,000 cycles? (e) What is the decibel variation over a range of 50 to 10,000 cycles?

Given:	Find:
$L = 150 \ h$	(a) X_L
$R_L = 3500$ ohms	(b) E_{bb}
$T_1 = 6C5; \ E_b = 250$ volts	(c) VA
$E_c = -8$ volts	(d) Decibel gain
$R_g = 500,000$ ohms	(e) Decibel variation
$C_b = 0.01 \ \mu f$	
$C_T = 200 \ \mu\mu f$	

Solution:

(a) $X_L = 2\pi fL = 6.28 \times 50 \times 150 = 47,100$ ohms (at 50 cycles)

$X_L = 2\pi fL = 6.28 \times 1000 \times 150 = 942,000$ ohms (at 1000 cycles)

$X_L = 2\pi f L = 6.28 \times 10,000 \times 150 = 9,420,000$ ohms (at 10,000 cycles)

(b) $E_{bb} = E_b + I_b R_L = 250 + 0.008 \times 3500 = 278$ volts

where $I_b = 8$ ma (from Appendix XV)

(c) $VA_{50} = \dfrac{1}{\sqrt{1 + \left(\dfrac{R_{eq}}{X_L}\right)^2 + \left(\dfrac{R_{eq}X_c}{r_p R_g}\right)^2}} \, g_m R_{eq}$

$= \dfrac{2000 \times 10^{-6} \times 9800}{\sqrt{1 + \left(\dfrac{9800}{47,100}\right)^2 + \left(\dfrac{9800 \times 318,000}{10,000 \times 500,000}\right)^2}} = 16.4$

where $R_{eq} = \dfrac{r_p R_g}{r_p + R_g} = \dfrac{10,000 \times 500,000}{10,000 + 500,000} = 9800$ ohms

$r_p = 10,000$ ohms (from Appendix XV)

$X_L = 2\pi f L = 6.28 \times 50 \times 150 = 47,100$ ohms

$X_C = \dfrac{159,000}{fC} = \dfrac{159,000}{50 \times 0.01} = 318,000$ ohms

$g_m = 2000 \times 10^{-6}$ mho (from Appendix XV)

$VA_{1000} = g_m R_{eq} = 2000 \times 10^{-6} \times 9800 = 19.6$

$VA_{10,000} = \dfrac{1}{\sqrt{1 + (R_{eq} 2\pi f C_T)^2}} \, g_m R_{eq}$

$= \dfrac{2000 \times 10^{-6} \times 9800}{\sqrt{1 + (9800 \times 6.28 \times 10^4 \times 200 \times 10^{-12})^2}} = 19.4$

(d) decibel $= 20 \times \log 16.4 = 20 \times 1.2148 = 24.296$ (at 50 cycles)

decibel $= 20 \times \log 19.6 = 20 \times 1.2923 = 25.846$ (at 1000 cycles)

decibel $= 20 \times \log 19.4 = 20 \times 1.2878 = 25.756$ (at 10,000 cycles)

(e) decibel variation $= 25.8 - 24.3 = 1.5$ db

Double-impedance Coupling. One of the methods used to increase the gain of the impedance-coupled amplifier at the low audio frequencies is to replace both the coupling resistor and the grid-leak resistor with low-frequency choke coils. Such an arrangement is shown in Fig. 8-12a and is called a *double-impedance-coupled amplifier circuit.* The inductances of both coils are generally of the same value and when combined with the blocking capacitor C_b they form a series tuned circuit that is resonant at some low value of audio frequency. The voltage amplification at this frequency will thus be increased.

A disadvantage of this circuit is that the use of two coils in parallel doubles the amount of distributed capacitance, thus further increasing the shunt capacitance of the circuit. The gain at the high audio frequencies will therefore be further decreased.

Parallel Plate Feed. In the impedance-coupled amplifier circuits shown in Figs. 8-9 and 8-12a the direct current from the B power supply must flow through the coupling impedance coil. The flow of direct current through a coil having an iron core will decrease the permeability of the magnetic circuit, thus causing the inductance of the coil to decrease. Although this decrease in inductance causes a decrease in the voltage gain over the entire audio-frequency range, it is only at the low audio frequencies that any appreciable difference is obtained.

In order to prevent decreases in voltage gain due to changes in the inductance of the coil, it is necessary to provide a means of isolating the direct current from the coupling impedance.   This is accomplished by providing two parallel paths for the plate current (see Fig. 8-12b).   The resistor R_B provides the path for the d-c component or steady value of plate current, and the coupling coil L_c and the blocking capacitor C_3 will then carry only the signal or varying component of the plate current. This type of circuit is called an *impedance-coupled parallel-plate-feed*

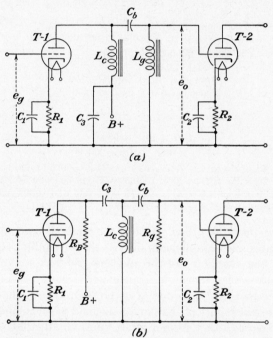

FIG. 8-12.—Applications of impedance-coupled amplifier circuits.   (a) Double-imped-ance-coupled amplifier circuit, (b) impedance-coupled amplifier circuit with parallel-plate-feed.

amplifier circuit and is used whenever it becomes desirable to keep the d-c plate current out of the coupling impedance.   The resonant frequency of the series tuned circuit formed by the blocking capacitor C_3 and the coupling coil L_c is the frequency at which the capacitive reactance equals the inductive reactance.   The voltage gain at this frequency will be increased since the voltage across the coupling coil will be comparatively high.   Thus the voltage gain at any audio frequency can be increased by using values of C_3 and L_c that will make the series tuned circuit resonant for that frequency.

The response at frequencies above and below the resonant frequency will attenuate either slowly or rapidly depending on the amount of resistance at R_B.   Increasing the value of the resistor R_B decreases the rate of attenuation, thus broadening the peak of the response curve. Decreasing this resistance will increase the rate of attenuation, thus making the peak of the response curve sharp.   The curve of Fig. 8-11 shows the variation in voltage gain over the audio-frequency range. The curve shown in the dashed line represents the effect of the series tuned portion of the circuit.   By choosing the proper resonant frequency for this series tuned circuit it is possible to improve the frequency response characteristics of the amplifier.   It should be evident that by choosing suitable values for R_B, L_c, and C_3 (Fig. 8-12b), it is possible to improve the response at low audio frequencies and to broaden the entire response curve of the circuit.

Example 8-22.   The coupling coil used in an impedance-coupled audio-amplifier circuit similar to Fig. 8-12 has an inductance of 300 henries.   What value of blocking capacitor is required to cause the tuned circuit to be resonant at (*a*) 82 cycles?   (*b*) 820 cycles?   (*c*) 8200 cycles?

Given:
$$L_c = 300 \text{ henries}$$

Find:
    (*a*) C at 82 cycles
    (*b*) C at 820 cycles
    (*c*) C at 8200 cycles

Solution:

(*a*) $C = \dfrac{25,300}{f_r^2 L} = \dfrac{25,300}{(82 \times 10^{-3})^2 \times 300 \times 10^6} = 0.0125 \ \mu\text{f}$

(*b*) $C = \dfrac{25,300}{f_r^2 L} = \dfrac{25,300}{(820 \times 10^{-3})^2 \times 300 \times 10^6} = 125 \ \mu\mu\text{f}$

(*c*) $C = \dfrac{25,300}{f_r^2 L} = \dfrac{25,300}{(8200 \times 10^{-3})^2 \times 300 \times 10^6} = 1.25 \ \mu\mu\text{f}$

Circuit Characteristics.   In comparison with resistance-capacitance-coupled audio amplifiers, the impedance-coupled audio amplifier requires less voltage for the B supply, usually has a slightly greater gain per stage, but its response over the entire audio-frequency range is not so uniform. However, its disadvantage is sometimes offset by the fact that it is possible to peak the response of an impedance-coupled amplifier at any desired audio frequency.

Impedance coupling is generally used with triodes where relatively high values of plate current make the use of load resistors impractical since higher power supply voltages would be required.   This method of coupling has not been used very much since the introduction of specially designed tubes for resistance-capacitance-coupled amplifiers.

8-11. Transformer-coupled Amplifier.   *Basic Circuit Connections.* Audio amplifier circuits using a low-frequency (iron-core) transformer as the coupling unit between two successive stages are called *transformer-*

coupled audio amplifiers. As with the impedance-coupled amplifier circuit, connections can be made to produce either series or parallel feed. Connecting one side of the primary winding to the plate of the first tube and the other side to the B power supply will produce series feed (Fig. 8-13a). Parallel feed is obtained by connecting a resistor R_B between the plate and B power supply; the primary winding, in series with the blocking capacitor C_b, is then connected in parallel with this resistor (Fig. 8-15).

Frequency Characteristics. Transformer-coupled audio-amplifier circuits generally employ triodes such as the 1H4-G, 6C5, 6J5, and 6L5-G. The plate resistance of these tubes is usually less than 12,000 ohms and the amplification factor very seldom exceeds 20. The equivalent electrical circuit can therefore be considered in the constant-voltage-generator form as shown in Fig. 8-13b. A complete analysis of this circuit is quite difficult because of the many factors that vary with the frequency such as the primary and secondary impedance, the shunting effect due to the distributed capacitance of the windings, the shunting effect of the core loss, and the coupled impedance effect. However, an approximate solution can be obtained by omitting the shunting effects of the distributed capacitance and the core loss and also omitting the effects of coupled impedance. The equivalent electrical circuit may then be reduced to the form shown in Fig. 8-13c. In addition to the factors shown on Fig. 8-13c, the voltage amplification is also dependent upon the coefficient of coupling between the primary and secondary windings of the transformer. In well-designed a-f transformers, the coefficient of coupling is very close to unity and hence this factor may be disregarded. The voltage amplification for any audio frequency may then be expressed as

$$\text{VA} = \mu n \frac{Z_P}{Z_P + r_p} \tag{8-27}$$

where n = transformer secondary to primary turns ratio
   Z_P = total equivalent impedance of the primary winding

Voltage Amplification for the Intermediate-frequency Range. At the low- and intermediate-frequency values, the reactances of all of the shunting capacitances shown in Fig. 8-13b are so high that their effects may be disregarded. The core loss in well-designed transformers is generally so low that its effective resistance R_{cl} may also be disregarded; the equivalent circuit may then be further simplified as shown in Figs. 8-14a and 8-14b. The output voltage will then be

$$e_o = \mu e_g \frac{X_{LP}}{\sqrt{R_1^2 + X_{LP}^2}} n \tag{8-28}$$

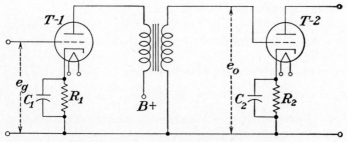

(a)-Simple transformer-coupled amplifier circuit

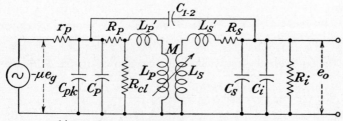

(b)-Complete equivalent plate circuit of Fig. *(a)*

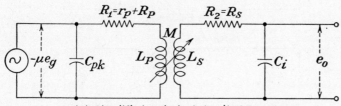

(c)-Simplified equivalent circuit of Fig. *(a)*

where r_p = Plate resistance of **T-1**

C_{pk} = Plate-cathode capacitance of **T-1**

C_P = Distributed capacitance of the primary winding

R_P = Resistance of the primary winding

R_{cl} = Equivalent resistance of the transformer's core loss

L_P' = Leakage inductance of the primary

L_P = Inductance of the primary

C_{1-2} = Distributed capacitance between the primary and secondary windings

L_S = Inductance of the secondary

L_S' = Leakage inductance of the secondary

R_S = Resistance of the secondary winding

C_S = Distributed capacitance of the secondary winding

C_i = Input capacitance of **T-2**, see Eq. (8-23)

R_i = Input resistance of **T-2**

Fig. 8-13.—Simple transformer-coupled amplifier circuit using triodes.

and the voltage amplification becomes

$$VA_M = \mu n \frac{X_{LP}}{\sqrt{R_1{}^2 + X_{LP}{}^2}} \tag{8-29}$$

where X_{LP} = reactance of the primary winding

R_1 = equivalent primary circuit resistance = $\dfrac{r_p R_{cl}}{r_p + R_{cl}} + R_P$

NOTE: $R_1 \cong r_p + R_P$ when R_{cl} is large compared to r_p

R_{cl} = resistance producing an effect equal to the core loss

In well-designed transformers, the value of X_{LP} is much greater than R_1 and hence

$$VA_M \cong \mu n \tag{8-30}$$

Voltage Amplification for the Low-frequency Range. At low frequencies, the equivalent circuit conditions as shown in Fig. 8-14*a* are the

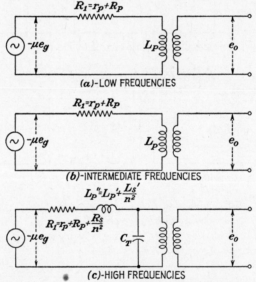

FIG. 8-14.—Simplified equivalent electrical circuits at various audio frequencies for a transformer-coupled amplifier using triodes.

same as for the intermediate frequencies. The voltage amplification will therefore be the same as expressed by Eq. (8-29). This may also be expressed as

$$VA_L = K_L VA_M \tag{8-12}$$

where

$$K_L = \frac{X_{LP}}{\sqrt{R_1{}^2 + X_{LP}{}^2}} \tag{8-31}$$

Well-designed transformers provide uniform response (± 2 db) for frequencies as low as 100 cycles with series-plate-feed circuits and as low as 30 cycles with parallel-plate-feed circuits. In order to obtain such uniform response, X_{LP} must be much greater than R_1—even at the low frequencies. It therefore becomes necessary for the transformer to have a high value of inductance.

Voltage Amplification for the High-frequency Range. At the high frequencies, the effects of the shunting capacitances and the leakage inductances can no longer be disregarded. Under these conditions, the equivalent circuit will be as shown in Fig. 8-14c. The voltage amplification of the circuit will then be

$$VA_H = K_H \, VA_M \qquad (8\text{-}15)$$

where

$$K_H = \frac{X_T}{\sqrt{R_{1\text{-}2}^2 + (X_P'' - X_T)^2}} \qquad (8\text{-}32)$$

X_T = total equivalent shunting reactance referred to the primary
$R_{1\text{-}2}$ = total equivalent resistance referred to the primary
X_P'' = total equivalent leakage reactance referred to the primary

Examination of Eq. (8-32) will show that K_H will be maximum when X_P'' is equal to X_T. From Eqs. (8-32) and (2-48), it can be shown that

$$K_{H\text{-}\max} = \frac{10^6 \sqrt{\dfrac{L_P''}{C_T}}}{R_{1\text{-}2}} \qquad (8\text{-}32a)$$

where L_P'' = inductance, henries
C_T = capacitance, micromicrofarads

Comparison of the low-and high-frequency amplification factors of the transformer-coupled amplifier circuits with those of the resistance-capacitance-coupled circuits will show that they are similar in form.

Example 8-23. A transformer-coupled a-f amplifier circuit similar to Fig. 8-13a is to be used to couple the output of a type 6J5 tube to a type 6L6 tube. The 6J5 tube is to be operated with a grid bias of 8 volts and with 250 volts at its plate; its plate-cathode capacitance is 3.6 $\mu\mu$f. The operating voltages and load impedance of the 6L6 tube are such that the tube presents 10-$\mu\mu$f capacitance at its input. The constants of the transformer are: $n = 3$; $L_P = 100$ henries; $L_S = 900$ henries; $R_P = 100$ ohms; $R_S = 900$ ohms; $L_P' = 0.15$ henry; $L_S' = 1.35$ henries; total distributed capacitance referred to the primary = 60 $\mu\mu$f; assume the core-loss effect to be negligible. The total stray capacitance of the circuit wiring referred to the primary is 10 $\mu\mu$f. What voltage amplification is produced by the stage, 6J5 tube and transformer, at (a) 1000 cycles? (b) 50 cycles? (c) 10,000 cycles? (d) At what frequency will the maximum amplification occur? (e) What is the voltage amplification at this frequency?

Given:

T-1 = 6J5; C_{pk} = 3.6 $\mu\mu$f;

T-2 = 6L6; C_i = 10 $\mu\mu$f;

n = 3; L_P = 100 henries; L_S = 900 henries;

R_P = 100 ohms; R_S = 900 ohms;

L_P' = 0.15 henry; L_S' = 1.35 henries;

C_D = 60 $\mu\mu$f; C_w = 10 $\mu\mu$f;

Find:

(a) VA @ 1000 cycles

(b) VA @ 50 cycles

(c) VA @ 10,000 cycles

(d) f for VA_{max}

(e) VA_{max}

Solution:

(a) $\text{VA}_{1000} = \mu n = 20 \times 3 = 60$

   where μ = 20 (from Appendix XV)

(b) $\text{VA}_{50} = \dfrac{X_{LP}\,\text{VA}_M}{\sqrt{R_1^2 + X_{LP}^2}} = \dfrac{31{,}400 \times 60}{\sqrt{7800^2 + 31{,}400^2}} = 58.2$

   where $R_1 \cong r_p + R_P = 7700 + 100 = 7800$ ohms

   r_p = 7700 ohms (from Appendix XV)

   $X_{LP} = 2\pi f L_P = 6.28 \times 50 \times 100 = 31{,}400$ ohms

(c) $\text{VA}_{10{,}000} = \dfrac{X_T\,\text{VA}_M}{\sqrt{R_{1-2}^2 + (X_{P}'' - X_T)^2}} = \dfrac{97{,}333 \times 60}{\sqrt{7900^2 + (18{,}840 - 97{,}333)^2}} = 74$

   where $X_T = \dfrac{1}{2\pi f C_T} = \dfrac{1}{6.28 \times 10^4 \times 163.6 \times 10^{-12}} = 97{,}333$ ohms

   $C_T = C_{pk \cdot 1} + C_D + C_w + n^2 C_i = 3.6 + 60 + 10 + 9 \times 10 = 163.6$ $\mu\mu$f

   $R_{1-2} = r_p + R_P + \dfrac{R_S}{n^2} = 7700 + 100 + \dfrac{900}{9} = 7900$ ohms

   $X_P'' = 2\pi f L_P'' = 6.28 \times 10^4 \times 0.3 = 18{,}840$ ohms

   $L_P'' = L_P' + \dfrac{L_S'}{n^2} = 0.15 + \dfrac{1.35}{9} = 0.3$ h

(d) $f_r = \dfrac{1}{2\pi\sqrt{L_P'' C_T}} = \dfrac{1}{6.28\sqrt{0.3 \times 163.6 \times 10^{-12}}} = 22{,}747$ cycles

(e) $\text{VA}_{max} = \dfrac{10^6\sqrt{\dfrac{L_P''}{C_T}}\,\text{VA}_M}{R_{1-2}} = \dfrac{10^6\sqrt{\dfrac{0.3}{163.6}} \times 60}{7900} = 325$

The low and high audio-frequency response of transformer-coupled amplifiers will decrease in the same manner and for similar reasons as the double-impedance-coupled amplifier. By using parallel feed instead of series, the frequency response curve can be peaked at either the low or high frequencies to obtain a more uniform response. The shape of the frequency response curve will, therefore, like the impedance coupled amplifier, have a number of variations (see Fig. 8-16).

8-12. Audio-frequency Transformers. Audio transformers are used primarily to increase the voltage of audio-frequency signals. The increase in voltage produced by a transformer will be in direct proportion to the turns ratio of the secondary and primary windings. This ratio may vary from unity or 1 to 1 ratio to as high as 6 to 1. In addition to the turns ratio, the voltage gain of a transformer-coupled audio amplifier circuit will depend on the impedance of the primary winding. In order to obtain maximum voltage amplification, the impedance of the primary circuit should be high so that the ratio of primary impedance to plate resistance is high.

The impedance of the primary winding is dependent on its inductance and the frequency of the audio signal.   In order to obtain a high inductance a large number of turns must be wound on a soft iron core having a high permeability.   Increasing the number of turns on the primary increases the number of turns required on the secondary.   This in turn increases the size of the transformer and also increases its cost.   The size

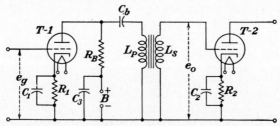

FIG. 8-15.—Transformer-coupled amplifier circuit with parallel-plate-feed.

of the transformer is generally kept at a minimum by winding both the primary and secondary with a small size (about No. 40) enamel-covered copper wire.   As the current flow in the transformer windings is usually only a few milliamperes, it is safe to use wire as small as No. 40.   Because of the large number of turns on the primary and secondary windings their distributed capacitance will be quite high.   The shunting effect of this capacitance will decrease the gain, particularly at the high audio frequencies.

Decreasing the number of turns on both the primary and secondary windings and keeping their turns ratio high is another method used to decrease the size and cost of the transformer.   The primary winding of transformers of this type have a low value of inductance.   The impedance of the primary winding for the low audio-frequency signals will therefore be very low compared to the high plate resistance of the tube.   The voltage gain for these frequencies are thus reduced considerably.

From the above discussion it can be seen that the frequency response of the transformer must be considered in addition to its turns ratio. The maximum voltage amplification of a transformer-coupled audio amplifier cannot be obtained unless the transformer that is used is well designed.   To obtain high fidelity, the design and constructional considerations limit the turns ratio to approximately 3 to 1.   At present, this ratio is the one most commonly used.

Example 8-24.   A transformer-coupled audio amplifier circuit similar to that shown in Fig. 8-13a uses a type 6L5-G tube operated so that its plate resistance is

10,000 ohms and its amplification factor is 17. The transformer has a turns ratio of 2 to 1 and the impedance of the primary winding is 15,000 ohms at 50 cycles and 30,000 ohms at 100 cycles. (a) What is the voltage amplification at the intermediate frequency? (b) What is the voltage amplification at 50 cycles? (c) What is the voltage amplification at 100 cycles?

Given:

$n = 2$

$\mu = 17$

$r_p = 10,000$ ohms

$Z_P = 15,000$ ohms @ 50 cycles

$Z_P = 30,000$ ohms @ 100 cycles

Find:

(a) VA_M

(b) VA @ 50 cycles

(c) VA @ 100 cycles

Solution:

(a) $VA_M = \mu n = 17 \times 2 = 34$

(b) $VA_{50} = \mu n \dfrac{Z_P}{Z_P + r_p} = 34 \dfrac{15,000}{\sqrt{15,000^2 + 10,000^2}} = 28.3$

(c) $VA_{100} = \mu n \dfrac{Z_P}{Z_P + r_p} = 34 \dfrac{30,000}{\sqrt{30,000^2 + 10,000^2}} = 32.2$

Example 8-25. A transformer having a 3 to 1 turns ratio is substituted for the transformer used in Example 8-24. The impedance of this transformer is 7500 ohms at 50 cycles and 15,000 ohms at 100 cycles. (a) What is the voltage amplification at the intermediate frequency? (b) What is the voltage amplification at 50 cycles? (c) What is the voltage amplification at 100 cycles?

Given:

$n = 3$

$\mu = 17$

$r_p = 10,000$ ohms

$Z_P = 7500$ ohms at 50 cycles

$Z_P = 15,000$ ohms at 100 cycles

Find:

(a) VA_M

(b) VA_{50}

(c) VA_{100}

Solution:

(a) $VA_M = \mu n = 17 \times 3 = 51$

(b) $VA_{50} = \mu n \dfrac{Z_P}{Z_P + r_p} = 51 \dfrac{7500}{\sqrt{7500^2 + 10,000^2}} = 30.6$

(c) $VA_{100} = \mu n \dfrac{Z_P}{Z_P + r_p} = 51 \dfrac{15,000}{\sqrt{15,000^2 + 10,000^2}} = 42.5$

Example 8-26. What is the db loss at 50 cycles and 100 cycles for (a) the amplifier circuit used in Example 8-24? (b) The amplifier circuit used in Example 8-25?

Given:

(a) $VA_M = 34$

$VA_{50} = 28.3$

$VA_{100} = 32.2$

(b) $VA_M = 51$

$VA_{50} = 30.6$

$VA_{100} = 42.5$

Find:

(a) Decibel loss @ 50 cycles

Decibel loss @ 100 cycles

(b) Decibel loss @ 50 cycles

Decibel loss @ 100 cycles

Solution:

(a) $\text{Loss}_{50} = 20 \log \dfrac{VA_M}{VA_{50}} = 20 \log \dfrac{34}{28.3} = 20 \times 0.0797 = 1.59 \text{ db}$

$\text{Loss}_{100} = 20 \log \dfrac{VA_M}{VA_{100}} = 20 \log \dfrac{34}{32.2} = 20 \times 0.0236 = 0.472 \text{ db}$

(b) $\text{Loss}_{50} = 20 \log \dfrac{VA_M}{VA_{50}} = 20 \log \dfrac{51}{30.6} = 20 \times 0.2219 = 4.43 \text{ db}$

$\text{Loss}_{100} = 20 \log \dfrac{VA_M}{VA_{100}} = 20 \log \dfrac{51}{42.5} = 20 \times 0.0792 = 1.58 \text{ db}$

From the results obtained in Examples 8-24 and 8-25 it can be seen that increasing the turns ratio of the transformer increases the voltage amplification at the intermediate audio frequencies. However, if the

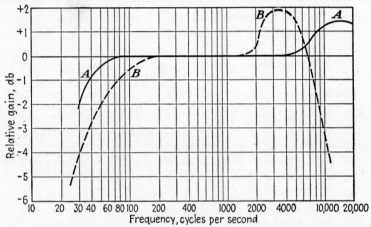

Fig. 8-16.—Relative gain vs frequency characteristics for a transformer-coupled audio-frequency amplifier. Curve *A* is for a circuit using a high-grade transformer, curve *B* is for a circuit using a low-grade transformer.

increase in turns ratio is obtained by decreasing the number of turns on the primary there will be very little change in amplification at the low audio frequencies. The results obtained in Example 8-26 for the amplifier circuit using the transformer having a 2 to 1 ratio indicates that the frequency response is fairly uniform as the changes in volume for the low audio frequencies are barely perceptible. On the other hand the frequency response for the amplifier circuit using the transformer having a 3 to 1 ratio is not as good because the decrease in inductance has made appreciable changes in volume at the low audio frequencies.

The curves shown in Fig. 8-16 illustrate how the voltage gain of a transformer-coupled audio-amplifier circuit varies with frequency. Curve *A* represents the voltage gain of the circuit when using a high-grade transformer and curve *B* shows the voltage gain of the same circuit when using a low-grade transformer. It can be observed that the response is fairly uniform over a large portion of the audio-frequency range when a high-grade transformer is used. However, using a low-grade transformer causes the response to fall off at both the high and low audio frequencies.

Advantages of Using a Transformer as a Coupling Element. Audio transformers are used as a coupling element whenever a greater voltage amplification is required than can be obtained from the tube alone. By using a well-designed transformer, the voltage amplification for the intermediate audio frequencies will be approximately equal to the product of the amplification factor of the tube and turns ratio. The frequency response can be made to be fairly uniform by using a transformer having a comparatively high value of inductance and limiting its distributed capacitance so that when combined with the transformer's inductance it will produce resonance at a high audio frequency (see Fig. 8-16).

Another advantage of this type of coupling is that the voltage drop across the transformer winding is negligible, thus making it possible to use a low voltage B power supply. Disadvantages are the large size and high cost of the transformers required to produce high fidelity.

8-13. Multistage Audio-frequency Amplifier Circuits. *Need for Multistage Amplifier Circuits.* The final stage of a radio receiver, that is, the one that feeds the loudspeaker, is usually an a-f power amplifier stage. Power amplifiers (taken up in Chap. IX) require a higher signal input voltage than is ordinarily available directly from the detector stage and hence an a-f voltage amplifier stage is needed. This voltage amplifier stage is also referred to as the *driving stage* or as the *driver* as its purpose is to raise the signal voltage to an amount sufficient to drive the final output stage.

If the input signal voltage is very low in value, as may be the case in public-address systems, it may become necessary to provide one or more additional stages of voltage amplification. When a number of stages of amplification are connected in series they may also be referred to as being connected in *cascade*.

Voltage Amplification of Multistage Amplifier Circuits. The overall voltage amplification of a multistage amplifier circuit is the ratio of the final output signal voltage to the input signal voltage at the first stage of the amplifier. In terms of the voltage amplification of each stage individually, the overall voltage amplification is equal to the product of the separate values, or

$$VA_T = VA_1 \times VA_2 \times VA_3, \cdots \qquad (8\text{-}33)$$

When the gain of a multistage amplifier circuit is expressed in decibels, the overall gain of the circuit in terms of the gain of each stage individually is equal to the sum of the separate values, or

$$db_T = db_1 + db_2 + db_3, \cdots \qquad (8\text{-}34)$$

For example, a three-stage amplifier circuit whose individual stages have voltage amplifications of 100, 50, and 10 respectively would have an overall amplification of 50,000. The gain in decibels of these three stages would be 40, 34, and 20 db respectively and the overall gain of the amplifier circuit would be 94 db.

Need for Decoupling Circuits with Multistage Amplifiers. When a common power supply is used for the various stages of a multistage amplifier circuit, the power supply acts as a common impedance to the various stages. Under this condition, coupling will exist between the various stages and may cause an appreciable amount of feedback. This feedback will be either regenerative or degenerative depending upon the phase relation of the feedback voltage, which to a large extent is governed by the number of stages employed. When an appreciable amount of feedback is present, especially at low frequencies, it may produce oscillations at the low frequencies, causing a disturbance in the loudspeaker commonly referred to as *motorboating*. In order to obtain satisfactory operation of multistage amplifiers it may therefore become necessary to provide special circuits to decouple one stage from another. The methods of decoupling and the characteristics of these decoupling circuits are presented in Art. 8-18.

8-14. Feedback Amplifiers. *Positive and Negative Feedback.* In the study of the regenerative detector circuit (Art. 5-8) it was shown that regeneration occurs when part of the energy of the output circuit is returned to the input circuit in such a manner that the energy returned increases the strength of the input signal. This principle is applied to an amplifier circuit by returning to its input circuit a voltage that has been obtained from its output circuit; this type of circuit is called a *feedback amplifier*. When the voltage returned to the input circuit is in phase with the signal voltage it will increase the strength of the signal input of the amplifier and the feedback is referred to as *positive feedback* or regeneration. When the voltage returned to the input circuit is 180 degrees out of phase with the signal voltage it will decrease the strength of the signal input of the amplifier and the feedback is referred to as *negative feedback*, inverse feedback, or degeneration.

Feedback amplifiers, as used in radio receivers, employ negative feedback. Although it seems undesirable to use an amplifier that does not produce the maximum possible gain for the circuit, the advantages of the negative feedback amplifier outweigh the disadvantage of reduced gain. Among the advantages are (1) higher fidelity, (2) improved stability, (3) less amplitude distortion, (4) less harmonic distortion, (5) less frequency distortion, (6) less phase distortion, (7) lower ratio of noise level. Furthermore, by use of high-mu tubes or by using an additional stage of amplification it becomes possible to still obtain the desired gain for the amplifier circuit.

Principles of Feedback Amplifiers. In the previous study of amplifiers, the voltage amplification of a single-stage amplifier circuit has been expressed as the ratio of the output signal voltage to the input signal voltage as indicated by Eq. (4-6). From this equation, the output voltage e_o for an input voltage e_s is therefore

$$e_o = \text{VA } e_s \qquad (8\text{-}35)$$

In the study of feedback amplifiers, it is necessary to consider the fact that in addition to the output voltage e_o, the output will also include a certain amount of noise, hum, and other forms of distortion. The distortion due to noise, hum, etc., causes an additional signal to be set up in the output circuit, this additional signal being some definite percentage of the output voltage (see Fig. 8-17a). The output of the amplifier circuit without feedback is then really equal to the sum of the output signal voltage and the distortion voltage, or

$$e_o + D = Ae_s + de_o \qquad (8\text{-}36)$$

where e_o = instantaneous value of the output signal without feedback, volts

D = amount of distortion without feedback, volts

A = voltage amplification of the circuit

e_s = instantaneous value of the input signal, volts

d = distortion without feedback, expressed as a decimal

Example 8-27. The input signal of an amplifier circuit having a voltage amplification of 80 is one volt, and the distortion due to noise and hum is 5 per cent. What are the values of the output signal and the noise and hum distortion voltages?

Given: Find:

$A = 80$ $e_o = ?$

$e_s = 1$ volt $de_o = ?$

$d = 0.05$

Solution:

$$e_o = Ae_s = 80 \times 1 = 80 \text{ volts}$$
$$de_o = 0.05 \times 80 = 4 \text{ volts}$$

The principle of feedback amplifiers is illustrated in Fig. 8-17b. In this type of amplifier, a portion of the output voltage is returned to the input circuit either in phase with the input voltage for positive feedback, or 180 degrees out of phase with the input voltage for negative feedback.

The amount of voltage that is fed back is generally expressed as a percentage of the output voltage. The decimal equivalent of this percentage is denoted by the Greek letter β. For positive feedback β is positive and for negative feedback it is a negative value. From the relation of the

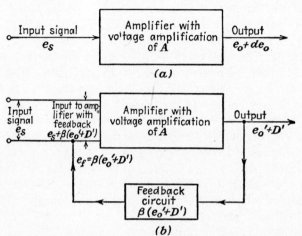

FIG. 8-17.—Block diagrams illustrating the principles of feedback. (a) Amplifier circuit without feedback, (b) amplifier circuit with feedback.

output and input signals as expressed in Eq. (8-36), the output of the feedback amplifier illustrated in Fig. 8-17b can be expressed as

$$e_o' + D' = A[e_s + \beta(e_o' + D')] + de_o' \qquad (8\text{-}37)$$

where e_o' = instantaneous value of the output signal with feedback, volts

D' = amount of distortion with feedback, volts

β = per cent of output voltage being fed back, decimal equivalent

NOTE: Terms marked ' indicate values when feedback has been considered.

Expanding and regrouping the terms of Eq. (8-37), then

$$Ae_s + de_o' = e_o' + D' - A\beta e_o' - A\beta D' \qquad (8\text{-}37a)$$

and $\quad Ae_s + de_o' = e_o'(1 - A\beta) + D'(1 - A\beta) \qquad (8\text{-}37b)$

From Eq. (8-37b) it can be seen that

$$Ae_s = e_o'(1 - A\beta) \qquad (8\text{-}38)$$

and $\qquad de_o' = D'(1 - A\beta) \qquad (8\text{-}39)$

By rearranging the terms of Eq. (8-38) the output voltage can now be expressed as

$$e_o' = e_s \frac{A}{1 - A\beta} \qquad (8\text{-}40)$$

Also, by rearranging the terms of Eq. (8-39) the distortion voltage can be expressed as

$$D' = e_o' \frac{d}{1 - A\beta} \tag{8-41}$$

Principles of Negative Feedback Amplifiers. From Eq. (8-40) it can be seen that when negative feedback is used, that is, when β is negative, the output voltage of the amplifier will be reduced by a factor whose value is equal to 1 divided by $(1 + A\beta)$. From Eq. (8-41) it can be seen that the distortion component of the output voltage is decreased by the same factor. By increasing the input signal voltage it is possible to restore the output voltage to its original value. Increasing the input signal will, however, also increase the distortion, but the distortion voltage will still be less than it was without negative feedback since it is always a definite percentage of the output voltage.

The quantity $A\beta$ is generally referred to as the *feedback factor.* This factor represents the ratio of the feedback voltage e_f to the input voltage at the amplifier, which is $e_s - e_f$ with negative feedback. This may be expressed mathematically as

$$A\beta = \frac{e_f}{e_s - e_f} \tag{8-42}$$

By rearranging the terms of this equation, it may be seen that

$$\frac{e_s}{e_f} = \frac{1 + A\beta}{A\beta} \tag{8-42a}$$

This indicates, for example, that if the feedback factor $A\beta$ has a value of 10, the feedback voltage e_f will then be 10 volts for each 11 volts of input signal e_s. This may be further interpreted as indicating that, for a circuit with a feedback factor of 10, it will require an input signal of 11 volts in order to produce the same output voltage as would be obtained from a 1-volt signal if the amplifier were used without feedback.

Example 8-28. A negative feedback circuit is added to the amplifier circuit of Example 8-27. The proportion of the output voltage that is returned by feedback is 0.01. What are the values of the output signal voltage and the distortion voltage?

Given: Find:
    $A = 80$ $e_o' = ?$
    $e_s = 1$ volt $D' = ?$
    $d = 0.05$
    $\beta = -0.01$

Solution:

$$e_o' = e_s \frac{A}{1 - A\beta} = 1 \frac{80}{1 - 80(-0.01)} = 44.44 \text{ volts}$$

$$D' = e_o' \frac{d}{1 - A\beta} = 44.44 \frac{0.05}{1 - 80(-0.01)} = 1.23 \text{ volts}$$

Example 8-29.   The results of Example 8-28 show that the addition of a feedback circuit to the amplifier of Example 8-27 has caused a reduction in the value of the output signal.   (*a*) To what value must the input signal of the amplifier of Example 8-28 be raised in order to obtain the same amount of output signal voltage as was obtained without feedback as in Example 8-27?   (*b*) Using the value of input signal obtained in part (*a*), what is the value of the distortion voltage?

Given:
$$e_o = 80 \text{ volts}$$
$$e_o' = 44.44 \text{ volts}$$
$$e_s = 1 \text{ volt}$$
$$A = 80$$
$$d = 0.05$$
$$\beta = -0.01$$

Find:
$$e_s' = ?$$
$$D' = ?$$

Solution:

(*a*) $e_s' = e_s \dfrac{e_o}{e_o'} = 1 \times \dfrac{80}{44.44} = 1.80 \text{ volts}$

(*b*) $D' = e_o'' \dfrac{d}{1 - A\beta} = 80 \times \dfrac{0.05}{1 - 80(-0.01)} = 2.22 \text{ volts}$

From the values of output voltage and distortion voltage obtained in Examples 8-27 and 8-29 it can be seen that, although the same output voltage is obtained with negative feedback as without it, the distortion voltage with feedback is reduced to approximately 50 per cent of its former value.   In a similar manner, the noise and hum voltages will also be reduced to about 50 per cent of their former values.

By increasing the value of the feedback factor, the proportion of the output voltage that is fed back is increased, thus further decreasing the magnitude of the distortion voltage.   It is therefore possible to reduce the magnitude of the distortion voltage to a negligible value by controlling the amount of feedback voltage.   As the overall voltage amplification of the circuit is also reduced by an increase in the amount of feedback voltage, it is necessary to compensate for the loss in overall voltage amplification if it falls below the value required of the amplifier.

8-15. Advantages and Limitations of Feedback Amplifiers.   *Nonlinear Distortion and Phase Distortion.*   Nonlinear distortion is caused by operating an amplifier tube over a nonlinear portion of its characteristic curve.   Phase distortion will occur owing to the introduction of phase shift caused when the input and output voltages of an amplifier are not exactly 180 degrees out of phase with each other.   The output of an amplifier having nonlinear distortion, phase distortion, or both can be considered as consisting of the amplified input signal voltage plus an added new signal voltage.   These two types of distortion also will be reduced by negative feedback; this is accomplished in the same manner as that already explained for the case of noise and hum.

Frequency Distortion. Frequency distortion occurs when the gain of an amplifier varies with changes of frequency of the signal applied to its grid circuit. Because β is generally independent of the frequency, the variation in the gain of an amplifier due to changes in frequency will be reduced when negative feedback is used. The relative effect of the fre-

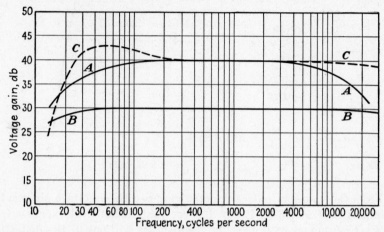

Fig. 8-18.—Variation of voltage gain with frequency. Curve A for an amplifier without feedback, curve B for a similar amplifier with negative feedback, curve C for an amplifier with balanced feedback.

quency upon the gain of an amplifier with and without feedback is shown in Fig. 8-18. By increasing the value of β, the gain of an amplifier can be made to be fairly uniform over a wide frequency range. Because of this feature, negative feedback amplifiers are used in video-amplifier circuits where a low-gain wide-band amplifier circuit is required.

Example 8-30. The voltage amplification of a certain amplifier is 100 for a 400-cycle signal and is only 10 for a 50-cycle signal. (a) What is the change in output volume, expressed in decibels? (b) If a negative feedback circuit designed to feed back 4 per cent of the output signal is added, what is the change in volume, expressed in decibels, under this condition?

Given: Find:

$A_{400} = 100$ (a) Decibel loss @ 50 cycles = ?

$A_{50} = 10$ (b) Decibel loss @ 50 cycles = ?

$\beta = -0.04$

Solution:

(a) Loss at 50 cycles $= 20 \log \dfrac{A_{400}}{A_{50}} = 20 \log \dfrac{100}{10} = 20 \times 1 = 20$ db.

(b) e_o' @ 400 cycles $= e_s \dfrac{A}{1 - A\beta} = e_s \dfrac{100}{1 - 100(-0.04)} = 20e_s$

e_o' @ 50 cycles $= e_s \dfrac{A}{1 - A\beta} = e_s \dfrac{10}{1 - 10(-0.04)} = 7.14e_s$

Loss at 50 cycles $= 20 \log \dfrac{A_{400}}{A_{50}} = 20 \log \dfrac{20}{7.14} = 20 \times 0.4473 = 8.94$ db.

Stability of Negative Feedback Amplifiers. The gain of an amplifier circuit may vary with (1) the particular tube used (even though of the same type), (2) the operating voltages, (3) the load impedance. A change in one or more of these variables may cause a change in the gain of the amplifier, thus affecting its stability. The stability of an amplifier can be improved by using negative feedback. The manner in which negative feedback affects the stability of an amplifier can be shown mathematically by rearranging the terms of Eq. (8-40) to express the voltage amplification of the circuit with feedback.

$$\text{VA}' = \frac{e_o{'}}{e_s} = \frac{A}{1 - A\beta} \tag{8-43}$$

or

$$\text{VA}' = -\frac{1}{\beta}\left(\frac{1}{1 - \dfrac{1}{A\beta}}\right) \tag{8-43a}$$

When the feedback factor $A\beta$ is much greater than 1, the gain of a negative feedback amplifier will then be approximately equal to

$$\text{VA}' \cong -\frac{1}{\beta} \tag{8-44}$$

From Eqs. (8-43) and (8-43a), it can be seen that when the feedback factor $A\beta$ is much greater than 1, the voltage amplification of the circuit is dependent on the percentage of the output voltage returned, β, rather than on the voltage amplification of the amplifier. The value of β is generally dependent upon a resistance network whose component values are independent of the frequency, the electrode voltages applied to the amplifier tube, and the tube's operating characteristics. The stability of negative feedback amplifiers can therefore be made to be comparatively high by adjusting the percentage of feedback to produce a high feedback factor.

Example 8-31. An amplifier circuit having a voltage amplification of 100 employs a negative feedback circuit whose feedback factor is -19. (a) What is the overall voltage amplification of the circuit as determined by use of Eq. (8-43)? (b) What is the approximate overall voltage amplification of the circuit as determined by use of Eq. (8-44)?

Given:	Find:
$A\beta = -19$	(a) VA = ?
$A = 10$	(b) VA $\cong$?

Solution:

(a) $\text{VA} = \dfrac{A}{1 - A\beta} = \dfrac{100}{1 - (-19)} = \dfrac{100}{20} = 5$

(b) $\text{VA} \cong -\dfrac{1}{\beta} \cong \dfrac{-1}{-0.19} \cong 5.26$

where $\beta = \dfrac{A\beta}{A} = \dfrac{-19}{100} = -0.19$

Limitations of Feedback Amplifiers. Any increase in the feedback factor to a value much greater than 1 will cause an increase in the proportion of the output voltage that is returned. The overall voltage amplification of the circuit will then be low compared to the voltage amplification of the same amplifier without feedback. In order to produce the same amplification as was obtained without feedback, it then becomes necessary to increase the input voltage e_s by an amount $A\beta$ times the voltage of the input signal e_s. This can be shown mathematically in the following manner. When the output with feedback, e_o', is to be equal to the output without feedback, e_o, then the input signal e_s will have to be increased to a value e_s'. The voltage amplification of the circuit with feedback may then be expressed as

$$\text{VA}' = \frac{e_o'}{e_s'} = \frac{e_o}{e_s'} \tag{8-45}$$

and

$$e_s' = \frac{e_o}{\text{VA}'} \tag{8-46}$$

Substituting Eq. (8-43) for VA′ in Eq. (8-46)

$$e_s' = \frac{e_o}{\dfrac{A}{1 - A\beta}} = \frac{e_o(1 - A\beta)}{A} \tag{8-46a}$$

Substituting $\dfrac{e_o}{e_s}$ for A in the denominator of Eq. (8-46a)

$$e_s' = \frac{e_o(1 - A\beta)}{\dfrac{e_o}{e_s}} = e_s(1 - A\beta) \tag{8-46b}$$

Thus, when β is negative, the input signal voltage must be increased by the factor $(1 + A\beta)$. This increased value of input signal voltage can be obtained by designing the preceding amplifier circuits to produce a higher voltage amplification or by using an additional amplifier stage. When the requirements of an amplifier are such that high fidelity is the paramount factor, any additional expense is warranted if the desired results are obtained.

In the preceding explanations of the actions of negative feedback it has been assumed that the feedback voltage was exactly 180 degrees out of phase with the input signal. In practical amplifier circuits, however, this condition is not obtained. The amount of lead or lag, with respect to the desired 180 degrees phase relation, is dependent upon the reactances of the coupling units, the interelectrode capacitances of the tubes, and the frequency of the input signal. If the angle of lead or lag attains a value of 180 degrees, the feedback becomes positive and the circuit becomes unstable.

The phase shift caused by the reactances of the coupling units and the interelectrode capacitances cannot exceed 90 degrees for one amplifier stage.   Even though the phase shifts of two stages is cumulative, it is unlikely that a 180-degree phase shift will be obtained in a two-stage amplifier.   However, it is possible to obtain such a condition in a three-stage amplifier.   Instability does not occur with positive feedback if the value of the feedback factor is kept less than 1.   Limiting the feedback factor to such a low value will, however, limit the amount of feedback voltage that it is possible to return.   The maximum amount of reduction of distortion, hum, and noise will therefore be decreased.   It can thus be seen that negative feedback may readily be employed with one or two amplifier stages, but becomes rather difficult for three or more amplifier stages.

8-16. Negative Feedback Amplifier Circuits.   Negative feedback can be applied to a single-stage or multistage amplifier in a number of ways. Basically, however, all the circuits that are used can be divided into three general classes: (1) voltage feedback circuits, that is, circuits that derive the feedback voltage directly from the output voltage of the amplifier; (2) current feedback circuits, that is, circuits that derive the feedback voltage from a voltage drop produced by the output current flowing through a resistor; (3) a combination of both voltage and current feedback.

Principle of Voltage-controlled Feedback.   When the feedback circuit is connected so that the voltage returned to the input circuit is proportional to the voltage across the output load, the feedback circuit is said to be *voltage controlled*.   A simple amplifier circuit using voltage-controlled feedback is illustrated in Fig. 8-19.   The feedback voltage of this circuit is applied to the input of the amplifier between the cathode and the input voltage e_s'.   The portion e_f of the output voltage e_o' that is added to the input circuit is controlled by the voltage dividing resistors, R_f and R_2, and the capacitor C_2.   The portion or fraction of the output voltage being fed back may be expressed mathematically as

$$\beta = \frac{R_f}{\sqrt{(R_f + R_2)^2 + X_c{}^2}} \qquad (8\text{-}47)$$

As the reactance of the capacitor C_2 is generally very low compared to $(R_f + R_2)$, the effect of the capacitor may be ignored; then

$$\beta \cong \frac{R_f}{R_f + R_2} \qquad (8\text{-}47a)$$

The capacitor C_2, connected in series with the resistors R_f and R_2 as shown in Fig. 8-19, is used as a blocking capacitor to prevent the high plate voltage from being applied to the input circuit. The polarity (and phase relation) of the feedback voltage e_f with respect to the input signal voltage e_s' can be determined by either of two methods of analysis: (1) by studying the a-c signal effect, (2) by observing the direction of electron flow in the circuit. In studying the a-c effect, it is most convenient to assume the conditions for one-half cycle of the input voltage, for example, the positive half cycle of the input signal voltage as indicated on Fig. 8-19. This

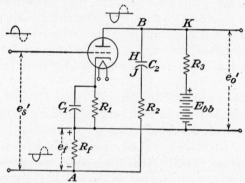

FIG. 8-19.—A voltage-controlled negative feedback circuit.

positive signal, upon being applied to the grid of the tube, causes an increase in the plate current. The increase in plate current causes an increase in the voltage drop at R_3, and as E_{bb} is constant, the voltage at the plate of the tube must decrease, as is indicated by the negative signal on the diagram. This negative signal will be transmitted through C_2 and R_2 to point A of the resistor R_f. The feedback voltage e_f, being equal to the voltage drop across the resistor R_f, will therefore be equivalent to adding a voltage source in series with the grid circuit. Furthermore, as the negative terminal A (that is, negative for the condition assumed above) is connected to the grid side of the grid-cathode circuit, the voltage e_f will be opposite in polarity to the input signal e_s' and hence the feedback is said to be negative. If the reactance of the capacitor C_2 is small compared to the combined resistance of R_2 and R_f, the voltage e_f will be practically 180 degrees out of phase with the input signal voltage e_s'. In determining the polarity of the feedback voltage by observing the electron flow, the method of analysis is similar to the a-c signal analysis in most of the details. For example, it will again be convenient to consider the conditions for a half cycle of the input signal e_s'. Using the positive half cycle, it can again be seen that a positive signal at the grid of the tube will produce a negative signal at the plate. Point B and

consequently point H (Fig. 8-19) will however always be positive as they are connected to the positive terminal of E_{bb} via R_3. The negative signal at the plate then merely means that plate H of capacitor C_2 will become less positive and hence C_2 must discharge some of its voltage. The path of electrons under this condition will be from J through R_2, R_f, C_1 (because the reactance of C_1 is small compared to R_1), cathode to plate B to H. As electrons travel from negative to positive, point A of the resistor R_f will be negative. By the same reasoning as before, it can be seen that the feedback is negative. In the case of a negative signal at e_s', the signal at B will be positive and the capacitor C_2 will take on a higher voltage charge. The electron path will be from H B K, through R_3, E_{bb}, R_f, R_2 to J. The polarity at point A will now be positive thus maintaining the condition of negative feedback.

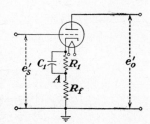

Fig. 8-20.—A current-
controlled negative feedback
circuit.

Principle of Current-controlled Feedback. When the feedback circuit is connected so that the voltage returned to the input circuit is propor-
tional to the current flowing through the output load, the feedback circuit is said to be *current controlled.* A simple amplifier circuit using current-controlled feedback is illustrated in Fig. 8-20. In this circuit, the feedback voltage is obtained by connecting the cathode by-pass capacitor C_1 so that it shunts only part of the cathode bias resistor or by eliminating the by-pass capacitor C_1 entirely. The a-f output current will then flow through the feedback resistor R_f, causing the grid bias to vary with the changes in plate current. When the input signal e_s' is positive, the plate current, and consequently the current in R_f, will increase. The voltage drop across R_f will increase and make point A more positive. This makes the cathode more positive with respect to ground, which is equivalent to making the grid more negative. Thus a positive signal on the grid produces the condition necessary for negative feedback. When the input signal is negative, the plate current will decrease and consequently the voltage drop at R_f will decrease. The cathode therefore becomes less positive, which is equivalent to making the grid less negative (or more positive) and hence fulfills the require-
ment for negative feedback.

Principle of Feedback for Multistage Amplifiers. Feedback circuits for more than one amplifier stage become quite complex. An example of a two-stage negative feedback amplifier is illustrated in Fig. 8-21. Examination of this circuit will show that both voltage-controlled and current-controlled feedback are present. However, by the choice of values for R_1, R_2, and R_f the voltage-controlled feedback is made the predominant source of feedback voltage and hence the circuit is commonly referred to as *voltage-controlled feedback*.   The polarity of the feedback voltage at R_f can readily be checked by tracing the a-c signal (for one-half cycle).   Thus, a positive signal at the grid of tube 1 will cause a negative signal at the plate of tube 1.   This negative signal is applied to the grid

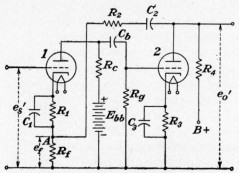

FIG. 8-21.—A two-stage amplifier circuit illustrating the application of a voltage-controlled feedback circuit.

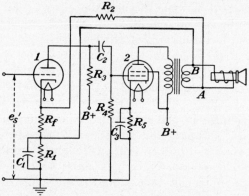

FIG. 8-22.—Negative feedback amplifier circuit with feedback voltage taken from the secondary of the output transformer.

of tube 2 via the capacitor C_b.   The negative signal at the grid of tube 2 causes a positive signal at the plate of tube 2.   This positive signal at the plate of tube 2 is transmitted to point A via C_2 and R_2.   This positive signal at point A raises the cathode potential, which is equivalent to applying a negative signal to the grid, hence satisfying the requirement of negative feedback.

Another method of obtaining negative feedback for an amplifier circuit is illustrated in Fig. 8-22.   In this circuit the feedback voltage is taken from the secondary side of the output transformer.   The resistors

R_f and R_2 form the voltage-divider network that controls the amount of feedback. The correct connection for the leads A and B is generally determined experimentally, that is, by first connecting them in one manner and then reversing them. One connection will produce degeneration and the other regeneration; the resulting output at the loudspeaker should indicate the correct connection.

Example 8-32. The resistors of the voltage-divider network of a voltage-controlled feedback amplifier circuit similar to that of Fig. 8-19 are $R_f = 5000$ ohms, $R_2 = 50,000$ ohms. What is the approximate value of β?

Given:
$R_f = 5000$ ohms
$R_2 = 50,000$ ohms

Find:
$\beta \cong ?$

Solution:

$$\beta \cong \frac{R_f}{R_f + R_2} = \frac{5000}{5000 + 50,000} = 0.0909$$

8-17. Balanced Feedback Amplifier. In the study of the resistance-capacitance-coupled amplifier, it was shown that the voltage amplification of the amplifier tends to decrease at the very low and very high audio fre-

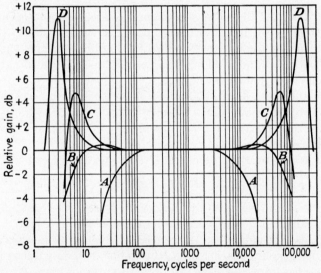

FIG. 8-23.—Relative gain vs frequency characteristics of a two-stage resistance-capacitance-coupled a-f amplifier with various amounts of feedback. Curve A, amplifier without feedback. Curve B, $A\beta$ equal to -2 at mid-frequency. Curve C, $A\beta$ equal to -10 at mid-frequency. Curve D, $A\beta$ equal to -50 at mid-frequency.

quencies. The loss in amplification at the low frequencies is due to the high reactance of the blocking (or coupling) capacitor C_b at the low frequencies, which reduces the voltage available at the output of the amplifier.   The loss in amplification at the higher frequencies is due to the low reactance of the shunting capacitance at these frequencies.   This shunting capacitance, consisting of the interelectrode capacitance of the tubes and the stray capacitance of the wiring, etc., provides undesired paths for a large portion of the high-frequency signal currents.   In addition to the reduction in the voltage amplification at the extreme frequencies, there will also be a large phase shift introduced at the low and high frequencies.

If the feedback factor $A\beta$ is large and the phase shift approaches 180 degrees, positive feedback will occur and the frequency response characteristics will be affected as is illustrated in Fig. 8-23.   From these representative curves it can be seen that while an increase in the amount

Fig. 8-24.—A feedback amplifier with equalizing filter networks for neutralizing the amplification peaks.

of feedback makes the voltage gain practically constant over a wider range of frequencies, it also produces peaks of voltage gain at the lower and upper ends of the frequency range.   When the effects of these peaks of amplification are great enough to warrant special consideration, two methods of correction are available.

One method of reducing the effect of the peaks is by means of filter circuits as shown in Fig. 8-24.   The RC filter network at the input side will neutralize the peaks that occur at the low frequency and the LR network at the output side will neutralize the high-frequency peaks.   This method, referred to as an *equalized circuit*, is useful only when the peaks are not too large.

A second method of reducing the effects of the peaks is by providing the amplifier with both positive and negative feedback.   An amplifier of this type, called a *balanced feedback amplifier*, is shown in Fig. 8-25.   By means of this type of circuit, a more nearly constant response is obtained for a multistage amplifier.   This is achieved by designing the first portion of the amplifier to provide practically uniform response to all frequencies and then applying both positive and negative feedback voltages.   The feedback voltages are generally of such proportions that the amount of positive feedback at the mid-frequency will cancel the negative feedback. At frequencies above and below this point, the amounts of positive and negative feedback will vary in such a manner that will tend to neutralize any variations from the optimum response of the first portion of the amplifier and thus provide practically uniform response over a wider range of frequency.

An advantage of the balanced feedback amplifier is that it provides practically uniform amplification over a wider range of frequency than an amplifier employing only negative feedback. A higher overall voltage gain is also obtained with the balanced feedback amplifier as is illustrated in Fig. 8-18.

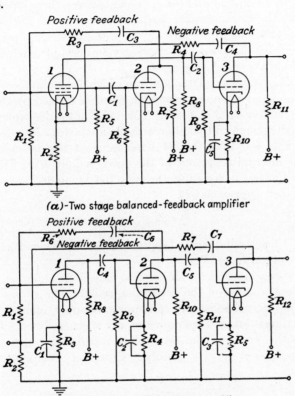

(a)-Two stage balanced-feedback amplifier

(b)-Three stage balanced-feedback amplifier

Fig. 8-25.—Several methods of obtaining balanced feedback.

8-18. Decoupling Circuits. *Need for Decoupling Circuits.* In the preceding article the discussion concerned circuits employing controlled feedback. However, it is possible that uncontrolled feedback, and therefore undesired feedback, may also be present in multistage amplifier circuits.

Coupling may exist between circuits operating at the same frequency and having a common impedance. In modern receivers, it is common practice to supply the plate voltage for all the tubes from a single source of d-c power. This power supply then acts as a common impedance for all the amplifier circuits. The coupling existing between these circuits may be either regenerative or degenerative, depending upon the phase relationship. In a two-stage amplifier circuit the plate currents are 180 degrees out of phase with each other and the coupling between these circuits is degenerative and therefore negative feedback will occur. The plate currents of the first and third stages of a three-stage amplifier are in phase with each other and the coupling between these circuits is regenerative and therefore positive feedback will occur. If this undesired feedback is sufficient to produce any appreciable effects upon the operation of the receiver it becomes necessary to decouple each stage of the amplifier from the other stages.

Decoupling Circuits. The manner in which decoupling is accomplished is illustrated by the simple decoupling network formed by the capacitor C_D and the resistor R_D (Fig. 8-26). The value of the decoupling capacitor must be high enough so that its reactance at the lowest audio frequency is considerably less than the total resistance of the decoupling resistor R_D and the internal resistance of the power supply R_B. The factor by which the undesired coupling through the common power supply is reduced is then approximately

$$K_D \cong \frac{X_D}{R_D + R_B} \tag{8-48}$$

where K_D = decoupling factor (approximate value when X_D is much less than $R_D + R_B$)

X_D = reactance of the decoupling capacitor, ohms

R_D = resistance of the decoupling resistor, ohms

R_B = internal resistance of the power supply, ohms

The internal resistance of the power supply is generally very low in comparison to the value of the decoupling resistor and therefore for all practical purposes can be ignored. Equation (8-48) may then be expressed as

$$K_D \cong \frac{X_D}{R_D} \tag{8-48a}$$

or

$$K_D \cong \frac{10^6}{2\pi f C_D R_D} \tag{8-48b}$$

From Eq. (8-48b), it can be seen that the decoupling factor can be made smaller by increasing the value of either the decoupling resistor or the decoupling capacitor. Increasing the value of the decoupling resistor will increase the voltage drop at this resistor and thereby decrease the voltage at the plate of the tube. In order to maintain the plate voltage at the required value, it becomes necessary to increase the voltage of the power supply to compensate for the drop in voltage at the decoupling resistor.

In a resistance-capacitance-coupled audio amplifier circuit the value of the decoupling resistor is generally about one-fifth the value of the plate coupling resistor R_c (Fig. 8-26). The value of the decoupling capacitor varies from about 0.25 μf to 8 μf. (For r-f and i-f circuits the value of the decoupling capacitor is approximately 0.01 μf and 0.1 μf respectively.)

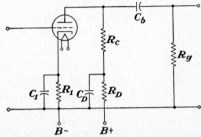

Fig. 8-26.—A simple plate decoupling circuit.

In some amplifier circuits the amount of resistance required to obtain sufficient decoupling causes the voltage drop across the decoupling resistor to become quite high. In such circuits, a choke coil may be substituted for the decoupling resistor R_D. In radio receivers this choke coil may be either a separate smoothing choke or the field coil of the loudspeaker. However, unless the increase in voltage drop at the resistor becomes too high, resistors are generally used, as they are less expensive and require less space than a separate choke.

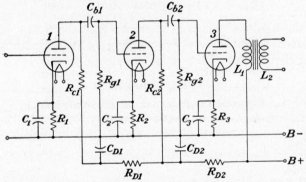

Fig. 8-27.—Application of plate decoupling circuits to a three-stage amplifier.

A three-stage audio amplifier using decoupling networks is shown in Fig. 8-27. The overall decoupling of a multistage amplifier is equal to the product of the decoupling factors of each of the networks used. Hence, the overall decoupling factor of a three-stage amplifier using two decoupling networks, similar to Fig. 8-27, becomes

$$K_{DT} = K_{D1}K_{D2} \tag{8-49}$$

or

$$K_{DT} \cong \frac{X_{D1}X_{D2}}{R_{D1}R_{D2}} \tag{8-49a}$$

$$K_{DT} \cong \frac{10^{12}}{(2\pi f)^2 C_{D1}C_{D2}R_{D1}R_{D2}} \tag{8-49b}$$

Example 8-33. A 1-μf capacitor and a 50,000-ohm resistor are connected to form a decoupling network. What is the approximate value of the decoupling factor for a 100-cycle a-f signal?

Given: Find:
$$C_D = 1 \ \mu f$$ $$K_D = \ ?$$
$$R_D = 50,000 \text{ ohms}$$
$$f = 100 \text{ cycles}$$

Solution:

$$K_D \cong \frac{10^6}{2\pi f C_D R_D} \cong \frac{10^6}{6.28 \times 100 \times 1 \times 50,000} \cong 0.0318$$

Example 8-34. Two identical decoupling networks are connected in a three-stage amplifier similar to the circuit shown in Fig. 8-27. The values of the resistors and capacitors are the same as those used in Example 8-33. What is the value of the overall decoupling factor for a 100-cycle a-f signal?

Given: Find:
$$C_{D1} = C_{D2} = 1 \ \mu f$$ $$K_{DT} = \ ?$$
$$R_{D1} = R_{D2} = 50,000 \text{ ohms}$$
$$f = 100 \text{ cycles}$$
$$K_{D1} = K_{D2} \cong 0.0318 \text{ (from Example 8-33)}$$

Solution:

$$K_{DT} = K_{D1}K_{D2} = 0.0318 \times 0.0318 = 0.001$$

From the results obtained in Examples 8-33 and 8-34 it can be seen that a greater amount of overall decoupling is obtained with a two-stage decoupling circuit than with a single decoupling section.

BIBLIOGRAPHY

Brainerd, J. G., Koehler, G., Reich, H. J., and Woodruff, L. F., *Ultra-high-frequency Techniques*, D. Van Nostrand Company, Inc., New York.

Eastman, A. V., *Fundamentals of Vacuum Tubes*, McGraw-Hill Book Company, Inc., New York.

Ghirardi, A. A., Practical Radio Course, *Radio News*, January, March, April, May, June, 1944.

Glasgow, R. S., *Principles of Radio Engineering*, McGraw-Hill Book Company, Inc., New York.

Henney, K., *Principles of Radio*, John Wiley & Sons, Inc., New York.

Reich, H. J., *Theory and Applications of Electron Tubes*, McGraw-Hill Book Company, Inc., New York.

Terman, F. E., *Fundamentals of Radio*, McGraw-Hill Book Company, Inc., New York.

Terman, F. E., *Radio Engineers' Handbook*, McGraw-Hill Book Company, Inc., New York.

Receiving Tube Manual, various tube manufacturers.

QUESTIONS

1. What is the purpose of an audio amplifier?

2. What audio-frequency range is generally considered acceptable in low-cost radio receivers? What audio-frequency range is desirable for high-fidelity reception?

3. What effect does attenuation of the lower frequencies have upon the reproduction of speech sounds? What effect does attenuation of the higher frequencies produce?

4. Is the same amount of energy required to produce sound waves at all audible frequencies? Explain. How does this affect the design of an audio amplifier?

5. In what manner does the human ear respond to sounds of various levels of energy? What unit is used to express such variations?

6. Define a common logarithm. How is the characteristic of a logarithm determined? How is its mantissa determined? What is an antilog?

7. Define the unit called the *bel*. Define the decibel. Explain the advantages of its use.

8. Explain how the decibel may be used to express ratios of voltage and current as well as power.

9. Why is the decibel only a relative unit of power measurement? What amount of power is generally used as the zero reference level in connection with radio receiver measurements?

10. Name three methods of coupling used with audio amplifiers. What precaution must be taken with regards to the plate and grid voltages?

11. Explain the basic action of the resistance-capacitance method of coupling amplifiers. In Fig. 8-4, what is the function of the resistor R_c, the capacitor C_b, and the resistor R_g? What is the function of resistor R_1 and the capacitor C_1 of Fig. 8-4?

12. Why is it necessary to consider the characteristics of the resistance-capacitance-coupled amplifier at various frequencies? What representative values of frequency are commonly used to show the characteristics of an amplifier circuit?

13. What is the advantage of drawing an equivalent electrical circuit for a resistance-capacitance-coupled amplifier stage? With the aid of circuit diagrams, explain the variation in the equivalent circuits at the intermediate, low, and high frequencies.

14. What factors affect the choice of values for R_c, R_g, and C_b? Give the approximate range of values for these circuit elements in practical resistance-capacitance-coupled amplifier circuits.

15. Derive the equation for the voltage amplification of an R-C-coupled triode amplifier for the intermediate-frequency range.

16. Derive the equation for the voltage amplification of an R-C-coupled pentode amplifier for the intermediate-frequency range.

17. Derive the equation for the approximate voltage amplification of an R-C-coupled triode amplifier for the low-frequency range.

18. Derive the equation for the approximate voltage amplification of an R-C-coupled pentode amplifier for the low-frequency range.

19. Derive the equation for the voltage amplification of an R-C-coupled triode amplifier for the high-frequency range.

20. Derive the equation for the voltage amplification of an R-C-coupled pentode amplifier for the high-frequency range.

21. Why is the maximum voltage amplification obtained at the intermediate frequency?

22. What is the cause of the attenuation or loss in amplification at the low frequencies?

23. What is the cause of the attenuation or loss in amplification at the high frequencies?

24. Is the attenuation the same for pentode amplifiers as for triode amplifiers at the low and the high frequencies? Explain.

25. Upon what factors does the effective value of the shunting capacitance of an *R-C*-coupled amplifier circuit depend?

26. What are the advantages of the *R-C*-coupled amplifier that justify its extensive use?

27. What is the advantage of the impedance-coupled amplifier over the *R-C*-coupled amplifier?

28. How does the frequency response of the impedance-coupled amplifier compare with that of the *R-C*-coupled amplifier?

29. How does the double-impedance-coupled amplifier compare with the *R-C*-coupled amplifier? What are its advantages and disadvantages?

30. What is meant by parallel-plate-feed? What are its advantages and disadvantages?

31. What factors affect the frequency response of impedance-coupled amplifiers?

32. Explain the difference in the connections for series feed and parallel feed as applied to a transformer-coupled amplifier circuit.

33. Do transformer-coupled amplifier circuits generally use triodes or pentodes? Why?

34. What factors affect the frequency response of a transformer-coupled audio amplifier? What factors are generally omitted for obtaining the approximate characteristics?

35. What is a simple expression for the approximate voltage gain at the mid-frequency range of a transformer-coupled audio amplifier? Why is this simple expression possible?

36. What purpose, in addition to coupling, is served by the audio transformer? What ratios of primary to secondary turns are used?

37. Why is it important that the impedance of the primary winding match the plate resistance of the tube with which it is associated? What are the constructional features of the transformer that make it possible to obtain sufficiently high impedance?

38. Is it desirable to obtain a high turns ratio for a transformer by decreasing the number of turns on the primary winding? Why?

39. What are the advantages of transformer coupling?

40. Why is it necessary to use a multistage a-f amplifier in a radio receiver?

41. What is meant by a driving stage?

42. What is the relation of the overall voltage amplification of a multistage amplifier circuit to the voltage amplification of its individual stages?

43. What is the relation of the overall decibel gain of a multistage amplifier circuit to the gain of its individual stages?

44. Why are decoupling circuits required with some multistage amplifier circuits?

45. What is meant by motorboating? What is its cause in multistage amplifiers?

46. What is meant by feedback? What is positive feedback? What is negative feedback?

47. What is meant by a feedback amplifier? What are its advantages?

48. What are some of the causes of distortion in the output of an amplifier? How is distortion reduced by negative feedback?

49. What is meant by the feedback factor? How may the value of the feedback factor be interpreted in terms of input signal required?

50. What is meant by nonlinear distortion and phase distortion? What are their causes? How may they be reduced?

51. What is frequency distortion? What is its cause? How is it reduced?

52. Describe the effect of negative feedback upon the stability of an amplifier.

53. What must be done with the input signal of a negative feedback amplifier if it is desired to obtain the same gain for the amplifier as without feedback?

54. What effect do the coupling units of a negative feedback amplifier have upon the phase relation of the feedback voltage? Is this effect more important in a single-stage, two-stage, or a three-stage amplifier? Why?

55. Describe three methods of applying negative feedback to an amplifier.

56. Describe the function of the resistors R_2 and R_f and the capacitor C_2 of Fig. 8-19.

57. What is the polarity of point A of Fig. 8-19 during the time that the input signal is going through its negative half cycle? Give proof for your answer.

58. Explain how negative feedback is obtained in the circuit of Fig. 8-20

59. Which circuit elements of Fig. 8-21 form the feedback circuit? Determine the polarity of the feedback signal being fed to point A during the negative half cycle of the input signal; give proof for your answer.

60. Describe how the correct connection for negative feedback can be determined for the circuit of Fig. 8-22.

61. Describe two methods of correcting the response of a circuit that has pronounced peaks of amplification at the frequency extremes.

62. What is meant by a balanced feedback amplifier? What are its advantages?

63. How many feedback paths are there in the circuit of Fig. 8-25? Identify the circuit elements of each feedback path. Determine the polarity of each feedback during the positive half cycle of the input signal; give proof.

64. What is meant by a decoupling circuit? Why are decoupling circuits necessary?

65. What determines the size of the decoupling capacitor? What range of values are commonly used?

66. What general proportion is sometimes used to determine the value of the decoupling resistor? Under what condition would it be advisable to substitute a choke coil for the decoupling resistor?

PROBLEMS

1. Find the logarithms of the following numbers: (*a*) 180, (*b*) 2750, (*c*) 8.75, (*d*) 12.5, (*e*) 5, (*f*) 98.5, (*g*) 35,000, (*h*) 30.7, (*i*) 18.3, (*j*) 98,600.

2. Find the logarithms of the following numbers by interpolation and compare the answer with the logarithm of the nearest three-place number: (*a*) 18.75, (*b*) 2537, (*c*) 9.852, (*d*) 67,230, (*e*) 3768.

3. Find the antilog of the following common logarithms: (*a*) 2.4771, (*b*) 5.8779, (*c*) 0.7782, (*d*) 1.0294, (*e*) 2.3385, (*f*) 3.7007, (*g*) 0.9834, (*h*) 2.6082, (*i*) 3.3186, (*j*) 1.3459.

4. What decibel gain is obtained if a type 25L6 tube that delivers 4.3 watts of power is substituted in an amplifier circuit for a type 43 tube that delivers 2.2 watts of power? Assume that all of the changes necessary in the circuit have been made.

5. A type 6K6 power amplifier tube when operated with 250 volts on its plate and screen grid, and with a grid bias of 18 volts can deliver 3.4 watts of power. If the plate and screen-grid voltages are reduced to 100 volts and the grid bias is reduced to 7 volts, the same tube can deliver only 0.35 watt. What is the corresponding decibel loss in power?

6. The power amplifier pentode unit of a type 1D8-GT tube is rated at 0.035 watt when its grid bias is 4.5 volts and with 45 volts applied to its plate and screen grid. The same tube is rated at 0.2 watt when its grid bias is 9 volts and 90 volts are applied to its plate and screen grid. What is the corresponding increase in decibels?

7. What is the decibel rating of a public-address system whose power output is (a) 8 watts? (b) 15 watts? (c) 30 watts? (d) 70 watts? (Use 6 mw as the reference level.)

8. A booster amplifier capable of delivering 100 watts of undistorted power has an overall gain of 17 db. What amount of driving power is required to obtain this output?

9. An amplifier has a signal current of 1 ma flowing through its 1000-ohm input resistance. The amplifier increases the signal strength so that a 100-volt signal appears across its 10,000-ohm output resistance. Find (a) the voltage gain in decibels, (b) the current gain in decibels, (c) the power gain in decibels, (d) the decibels output above 6 mw, (e) the rating of the amplifier in volume units.

10. The following are the characteristics of a commercial type of public-address system: gain (microphone input) 114 db, frequency response 65–9000 cycles ±2 db. (a) What is the overall voltage amplification of the amplifier at mid-frequency if it is assumed that the gain at mid-frequency is 114 db? (b) What is the overall voltage amplification at the extreme frequencies if the variation is ±2 db?

11. A certain transformer-coupled a-f amplifier produces a voltage amplification of 50 at 1000 cycles, 45 at 100 cycles, and 25 at 10,000 cycles. Using the mid-frequency as the reference level, what is the decibel gain or loss at (a) the low frequency? (b) the high frequency?

12. A certain resistance-capacitance-coupled a-f amplifier produces a voltage amplification of 50 at 1000 cycles, 48 at 100 cycles, and 32 at 10,000 cycles. Using the mid-frequency as the reference level, what is the decibel gain or loss at (a) the low frequency? (b) the high frequency?

13. A typical stage of resistance-capacitance-coupled a-f amplification is shown in Fig. 8-28. The effects of the cathode-bias resistor and its by-pass capacitor are to be

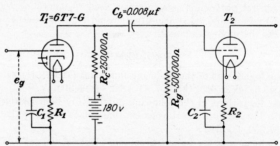

$T_1 - \mu = 65$, $r_p = 62{,}000\,\Omega$, $C_{gp} = 1.7\,\mu\mu f$, $C_{gk} = 1.8\,\mu\mu f$, $C_{pk} = 3.1\,\mu\mu f$
$T_2 - \mu = 120$, $C_{gp} = 1\,\mu\mu f$, $C_{gk} = 3.5\,\mu\mu f$, $C_{pk} = 7.5\,\mu\mu f$
$C_w = $ Stray capacitance of wiring, etc. $= 10\,\mu\mu f$

FIG. 8-28.

disregarded. What is the voltage amplification of the stage at (a) the intermediate frequency of 1000 cycles? (b) the low frequency of 100 cycles? (c) the high frequency of 10,000 cycles?

14. What is the decibel variation at the low and high audio frequencies over the intermediate frequency of the amplifier of Prob. 13?

15. A portion of the a-f amplifier of a battery-operated receiver is shown in Fig. 8-29. What is the voltage amplification of the stage at (a) the intermediate frequency of 1000 cycles? (b) the low frequency of 100 cycles? (c) the high frequency of 10,000 cycles?

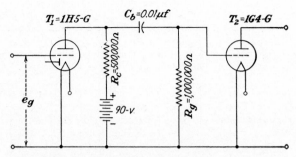

$T_1 = 1H5\text{-}G$ $C_b = 0.01\mu f$ $T_2 = 1G4\text{-}G$

$T_1\text{-}\mu = 65$, $r_p = 240,000\,\Omega$, $C_{gp} = 1\,\mu\mu f$, $C_{gk} = 1.1\,\mu\mu f$, $C_{pk} = 5.8\,\mu\mu f$
$T_2\text{-}\mu = 8.8$, $r_p = 10,700\,\Omega$, $C_{gp} = 2.8\,\mu\mu f$, $C_{gk} = 2.2\,\mu\mu f$, $C_{pk} = 3.4\,\mu\mu f$
$C_w = $ Stray capacitance of wiring, etc. $= 5\,\mu\mu f$

FIG. 8-29.

16. What is the decibel gain of the amplifier stage of Prob. 15 at the intermediate frequency?

17. A portion of the a-f amplifier of an automobile receiver is shown in Fig. 8-30. What is the voltage amplification of the first stage at (a) the intermediate frequency of 1000 cycles? (b) the low frequency of 100 cycles? (c) the high frequency of 10,000 cycles?

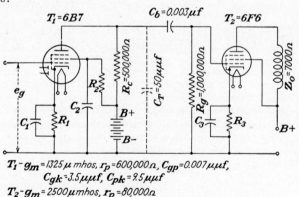

$T_1 = 6B7$ $C_b = 0.003\mu f$ $T_2 = 6F6$

$T_1\text{-}g_m = 1325\,\mu\,mhos$, $r_p = 600,000\,\Omega$, $C_{gp} = 0.007\,\mu\mu f$,
$C_{gk} = 3.5\,\mu\mu f$, $C_{pk} = 9.5\,\mu\mu f$
$T_2\text{-}g_m = 2500\,\mu mhos$, $r_p = 80,000\,\Omega$

FIG. 8-30.

18. What is the decibel variation at the low and high frequencies over the intermediate frequency of the amplifier stage in Prob. 17?

19. The plate load of the type 6F6 tube in the amplifier of Fig. 8-30 has an impedance of 7000 ohms. (a) If the load impedance has unity power factor, what voltage amplification is produced by the second stage of the amplifier? (b) What is the approximate value of voltage amplification when calculated by means of Eq. (7-11)?

20. (a) What is the overall voltage amplification of the amplifier of Fig. 8-30 at 1000 cycles? (b) What is the overall decibel gain of this amplifier at 1000 cycles?

21. A high-gain two-stage amplifier circuit is shown in Fig. 8-31. What is the voltage amplification of the first stage at (a) 1000 cycles? (b) 100 cycles? (c) 10,000 cycles? (d) What is the voltage amplification of the second stage at the same three values of frequency?

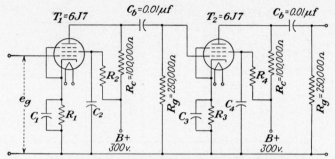

T_1 and T_2-g_m=1225µ mhos, r_p=1,000,000Ω, C_{gp}=0.005µµf, C_{gk}=7µµf, C_{pk}=12µµf
C_w= Stray capacitance of wiring, etc. = 10µµf (at each tube)

FIG. 8-31.

22. What is the decibel variation at the low and high frequencies over the intermediate frequency of one stage of amplification in the amplifier of Prob. 21?

23. What is the overall voltage amplification of the two-stage amplifier of Prob. 21 at (a) 1000 cycles? (b) 100 cycles? (c) 10,000 cycles?

24. What is the overall decibel gain of the two-stage amplifier of Prob. 21 at (a) 1000 cycles? (b) 100 cycles? (c) 10,000 cycles?

25. The resistance and capacitance values given in Prob. 21 have been taken from Appendix XVI. The values recommended for the other resistors and capacitors shown on Fig. 8-31 can also be obtained from Appendix XVI. What values are recommended for (a) R_1? (b) R_2? (c) R_3? (d) R_4? (e) C_1? (f) C_2? (g) C_3? (h) C_4?

26. The voltage amplification of the amplifier in Prob. 21 can be increased by increasing the value of the coupling resistor R_c. (a) If R_c is increased to 250,000 ohms, what are the recommended values for R_g, R_1, R_2, R_3, R_4, C_b, C_1, C_2, C_3, and C_4. (b) What is the voltage amplification per stage at 1000, 100, and 10,000 cycles? (c) What is the overall decibel gain of the amplifier at 1000, 100, and 10,000 cycles?

27. The amplifier of Prob. 26 has a loss of approximately 1.7 db at 100 cycles. At what frequency will its loss be approximately 2 db?

Hint 1. Rearranging the terms of Eq. (8-11c) will produce a satisfactory equation namely

$$f_{min} = \frac{K_L}{2\pi R C_b \sqrt{1 - K_L^2}}$$

Hint 2. For -2 db, $K_L \cong 0.8$ for a single stage amplifier. For a two-stage amplifier $K_L \cong \sqrt{0.8} \cong 0.895$ per stage.

28. The amplifier of Prob. 26 has a loss of approximately 0.6 db at 10,000 cycles. At what frequency will its loss be approximately 2 db?

Hint 1. Rearranging the terms of Eq. (8-14a) will produce a satisfactory equation, namely

$$f_{max} = \frac{\sqrt{1 - K_H^2}}{2\pi K_H R_{eq} C_T}$$

Hint 2. Same as Hint 2 for Prob. 27.

29. A single stage of a high-gain amplifier is shown in Fig. 8-32. (a) From Appendix XVI determine the recommended values for R_g, C_b, R_1, C_1, R_2, and C_2. (b)

What is the voltage amplification produced by the stage at 1000, 100, and 10,000 cycles? (*c*) What is the decibel gain at each of these frequencies?

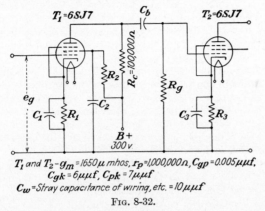

T_1 and T_2 - g_m = 1650 μ mhos, r_p = 1,000,000 Ω, C_{gp} = 0.005 $\mu\mu f$.
C_{gk} = 6 $\mu\mu f$, C_{pk} = 7 $\mu\mu f$
C_w = Stray capacitance of wiring, etc. = 10 $\mu\mu f$

Fig. 8-32.

30. What is the frequency range of the amplifier stage of Prob. 29 if ±2 db variation is permissible?

31. A single stage of an impedance-coupled amplifier is shown in Fig. 8-33. The input tube is to be operated with 250 volts at its plate and with a grid bias of 8 volts. The total shunting capacitance of the circuit is 350 $\mu\mu f$. Assume the core-loss effect

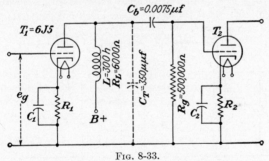

Fig. 8-33.

to be negligible. (*a*) What voltage is required of the B power supply? (*b*) What is the voltage amplification of the stage at 50, 1000, and 10,000 cycles? (*c*) What is the decibel variation over a frequency range of 50 to 10,000 cycles?

32. A type 6J7 tube is substituted for the type 6J5 tube in the amplifier shown in Fig. 8-33. Assume that all necessary socket wiring changes are made; also that the screen grid is supplied with 100 volts and that the grid bias is reduced to 3 volts. Use 1 megohm as the value of the plate resistance. (*a*) What voltage is required of the B power supply? (*b*) What is the voltage amplification of the stage at 50, 1000, and 10,000 cycles? (*c*) What is the decibel variation over a frequency range of 50 to 10,000 cycles? (*d*) Would this change be recommended and why? (*e*) Discuss the possibility of using the type 6J7 tube in this circuit as a triode by connecting the screen and suppressor grids to the plate.

33. The audio reactor used as the coupling element in an impedance-coupled a-f amplifier circuit similar to Fig. 8-9 has an inductance of 300 henries. Its resistance is 6250 ohms and its maximum current capacity is 10 ma. (*a*) What is the voltage drop at the reactor when it is used with a type 6C5 tube with 8 ma of plate current flowing? (*b*) What voltage is required of the B power supply if it is desired to maintain 250 volts at the plate of the tube? (*c*) What is the reactance of the choke to 100, 1000, and 5000 cycles if its distributed capacitance is disregarded? (*d*) What is the reactance of the choke to 100, 1000, and 5000 cycles if its distributed capacitance is 50 $\mu\mu f$?

34. The audio choke used as the coupling unit in an impedance-coupled a-f amplifier circuit similar to Fig. 8-9 has an inductance of 150 henries, a resistance of 3500 ohms, and a current rating of 10 ma. (*a*) What is the voltage drop at the choke when it is used with a type 6P5 tube with 5 ma of plate current flowing? (*b*) What voltage is required of the B power supply if it is desired to maintain 250 volts at the plate of the tube? (*c*) What is the reactance of the choke to 100, 1000, and 5000 cycles if its distributed capacitance is disregarded? (*d*) What is the reactance of the choke to 100, 1000, and 5000 cycles if its distributed capacitance is 20 $\mu\mu f$?

35. The audio reactor used as the coupling coil of an impedance-coupled a-f amplifier circuit similar to Fig. 8-12 has an inductance of 320 henries. What value of blocking capacitor is required to make the tuned circuit resonant at (*a*) 100 cycles? (*b*) 1000 cycles? (*c*) 5000 cycles?

36. The audio reactor used as the coupling coil of an impedance-coupled a-f amplifier circuit similar to Fig. 8-12 has an inductance of 150 henries. What value of blocking capacitor is required to make the tuned circuit resonant at (*a*) 100 cycles? (*b*) 1000 cycles? (*c*) 5000 cycles?

37. A single stage of a transformer-coupled amplifier with its circuit constants is given in Fig. 8-34. (*a*) What voltage is required at the B power supply in order to

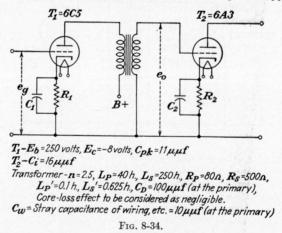

T_1-E_b =250 volts, E_c =−8 volts, C_{pk} =11 $\mu\mu f$
T_2-C_i =16 $\mu\mu f$
Transformer-*n* = 2.5, L_P =40 h., L_S =250 h., R_P =80 Ω, R_S =500 Ω,
L_P' =0.1 h., L_S' =0.625 h., C_D =100 $\mu\mu f$ (at the primary),
Core-loss effect to be considered as negligible.
C_W = Stray capacitance of wiring, etc. = 10 $\mu\mu f$ (at the primary)

FIG. 8-34.

provide 250 volts at the plate of the first tube? (*b*) What is the voltage amplification at 50, 1000, and 10,000 cycles? (*c*) At what frequency will the maximum voltage amplification occur? (*d*) What is the maximum voltage amplification? (*e*) What is the decibel variation at 50 cycles compared to 1000 cycles? (*f*) What is the decibel variation at 10,000 cycles compared to 1000 cycles?

38. A certain a-f amplifier is designed to produce an overall voltage amplification of 4500 with an input signal of 5 mv. The distortion in the amplifier is 5 per cent.

(a) What is the output voltage? (b) What is the distortion in volts? (c) If a feedback circuit with $\beta = -0.01$ is added, what is the value of the feedback factor? (d) What is the output voltage with feedback added? (e) What is the distortion in volts with feedback added? (f) With this feedback, what value of input signal will be required in order to restore the output to its original value? (g) What is the distortion in volts with feedback and the increased input signal as found in part f?

39. A certain a-f amplifier has a voltage amplification of 16 and an input signal of 2.5 volts. (a) What is the output voltage? (b) If a feedback circuit with $\beta = -0.05$ is added, what is the value of the feedback factor? (c) What is the output voltage if no change is made in the input voltage? (d) What value of input signal will be required in order to restore the output voltage to its original value?

40. The voltage amplification of a certain amplifier circuit is 160 at a frequency of 1000 cycles but drops to 20 at a frequency of 30 cycles. (a) What is the change in gain expressed in decibels? (b) If a feedback circuit with a value of $\beta = -0.10$ is added, what is the decibel change in gain between 1000 cycles and 30 cycles?

41. The resistors of the voltage divider network of a feedback circuit similar to Fig. 8-19 are: $R_f = 10,000$ ohms, and $R_2 = 90,000$ ohms. (a) What is the approximate value of β? (b) If the voltage amplification of the circuit is 160 without feedback, what is its amplification with feedback? (c) What is the approximate value of voltage amplification with feedback, using Eq. (8-44)?

42. It is desired to add a feedback circuit, similar to Fig. 8-19, to an output tube being worked through a 7000-ohm load. (a) What minimum resistance should the feedback network have if the ratio of feedback circuit impedance to load impedance is to be approximately 20 to 1? (b) If a feedback factor of 3 is desired, what standard resistance values should the two resistors have? (Assume $A = 20$.) (c) What standard size capacitor is recommended if $(R_f + R_2)$ should be approximately 20 times the reactance of the capacitor at a minimum frequency of 50 cycles?

43. An a-f amplifier circuit using a 250,000-ohm resistor as its plate load also has a decoupling resistor of 30,000 ohms and a decoupling capacitor of 0.25 μf. (a) What is the decoupling factor to a 50-cycle signal? (b) What is the overall decoupling factor for two such stages?

CHAPTER IX

POWER AMPLIFIER CIRCUITS

The prime purpose of voltage amplifier circuits, presented in the two previous chapters, is to produce a substantial increase in the output voltage for a given input voltage. The amplified voltage is then applied to the input circuit of a power amplifier stage. Audio-frequency power amplifiers are used to furnish the power required to operate a loudspeaker. Radio-frequency power amplifiers are used to produce the power required at the antenna of a transmitter.

9-1. Power Amplifier Circuits. *Classifications.* Power amplifier circuits are used in both a-f and r-f circuits and are generally classified according to the frequency at which they are operated, namely, *a-f power amplifiers* or *r-f power amplifiers.* Whereas the tubes used in voltage amplifier circuits are generally operated as Class A, the tubes used in power amplifier circuits may be operated either as Class A, Class B, Class AB, or Class C. Each of the two classifications of power amplifiers can therefore be subdivided according to the manner in which the tube is operated. All classes of tube operation may be used in r-f and a-f power amplifier circuits; however, Class C is used primarily in r-f power amplifiers.

Triodes, pentodes, and beam power tubes are used as power amplifiers. These tubes may be operated singly, in parallel, or in push-pull, depending upon the amount of power output required of the amplifier circuit. Although the principle of operation and the general construction of the vacuum tubes used as power amplifiers are similar to those used as voltage amplifiers, their operating characteristics are quite different. Voltage amplifier tubes are operated with a comparatively high value of impedance in the plate circuit in order to obtain a high output voltage. In this type of amplifier, voltage gain is the paramount factor and the power output is comparatively small. Power amplifier tubes are operated with a lower value of plate-load impedance than voltage amplifier tubes because the plate resistance of these tubes is lower and also in order to obtain a larger power output. In this type of amplifier, power output is the paramount factor and the value of output voltage is not important. Tubes used as power amplifiers must therefore be capable of carrying more current than voltage amplifier tubes.

Effect of a Varying Input Signal on the Plate Voltage. The static characteristics of a tube are obtained by varying the voltage applied to one of the tube's electrodes while keeping all other electrode voltages constant.   These characteristics are obtained without any impedance connected into the plate circuit of the tube, as any impedance in this circuit will cause the voltage at the plate of the tube to vary with the variations in plate current.   This can be seen by reference to the elementary amplifier circuit diagram shown in Fig. 9-1a.   With zero signal input, the voltage on the grid of the tube will be equal to the steady grid bias E_c. The plate current I_b, being dependent on the grid bias, will therefore also be steady.   The voltage E_b at the plate of the tube will then be equal to the plate supply voltage E_{bb} minus the voltage drop across the output resistor R_o, or

$$E_b = E_{bb} - I_b R_o \qquad (9\text{-}1)$$

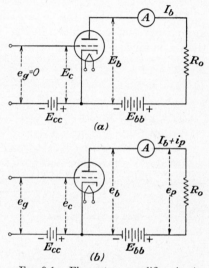

FIG. 9-1.—Elementary amplifier circuit. (a) With zero signal input, (b) with an a-c signal input.

When an alternating signal voltage e_g is applied to the input circuit of the amplifier, the voltage on the grid of the tube will become more negative during the negative half cycles of the input signal and less negative during the positive half cycles. This change in grid bias causes a variation in the plate current, represented by i_p in Fig. 9-1b, flowing through the output resistor R_o. It can be seen from Fig. 9-1 that any change in plate current will change the voltage drop at the output resistor, thus causing the voltage at the plate of the tube to vary.

The variation in plate current of a voltage amplifier tube is usually very small, hence the change in plate voltage will also be small.   It is thus possible, for all practical purposes, to obtain the operating characteristics of a voltage amplifier tube from its static characteristic curves. The variation in plate current of a power amplifier tube is comparatively high, thus causing the plate voltage variations to be high.   A new set of curves that will approximate the performance of a tube under actual working conditions must therefore be used.   This set of curves is called the *dynamic characteristics* and indicates the performance capabilities of a tube when it is operating with an input signal and with a load impedance connected into its plate circuit.

9-2. Dynamic Characteristics of a Vacuum Tube. *Load Line of a Vacuum Tube.* The dynamic characteristics of a tube can be obtained graphically from the tube's static plate characteristic curves with the aid of a load line. The load line is drawn on the static characteristic curves and represents the variation of plate current with voltage for the type of load impedance used. If the output load is resistive, the variation of plate current with voltage will be linear and the load line will therefore be a straight line. If the output load is inductive or capacitive, the variation of plate current with voltage will be nonlinear and the load line will be an ellipse (see Fig. 9-14). Resistive loads may be an actual noninductive resistor as shown in Fig. 9-2 or may be the reflected load from the secondary of an output transformer as shown in Fig. 9-3.

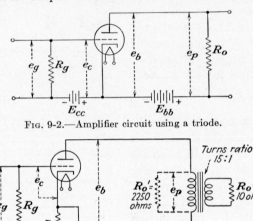

Fig. 9-2.—Amplifier circuit using a triode.

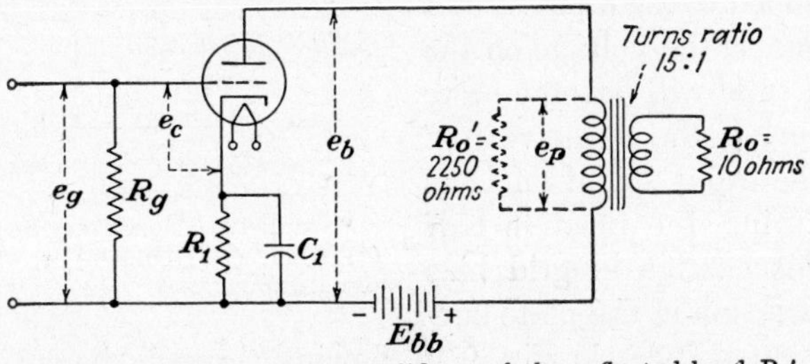

Fig. 9-3.—Triode power amplifier and the reflected load R_o'.

Method of Plotting the Load Line for a Single Triode Class A Power Amplifier with a Resistive Load. The alternating plate current output of a Class A power amplifier should have approximately the same wave form as that of the alternating voltage impressed on the input circuit of the tube. In order to obtain this type of output, the dynamic transfer characteristic curves (Fig. 9-8) must be nearly a straight line for the complete range of the variable grid voltage. As the operating characteristics of a tube will vary with the resistance of the plate load and the voltage of the B power supply, the load line of a tube will therefore be dependent on both of these variables. The method of drawing the load line on the static plate characteristic curves can best be explained by the following example.

Example 9-1.   A type 6J5 tube is connected as shown in Fig. 9-2.   Draw the load line for this tube when being operated with a resistive load of 40,000 ohms and a B supply of 200 volts.

Given: Find:
   Tube $= 6J5$ Draw the load line
      $E_{bb} = 200$ volts
      $R_o = 40,000$ ohms

Solution:

If the voltage drop across R_o should become equal to 200 volts, the voltage between the plate and cathode would be zero.   The plate current for this condition would then be

$$i_{b.\text{max}} = \frac{E_{bb}}{R_o} = \frac{200}{40,000} = 0.005 \text{ amp, or 5 ma}$$

This locates point A, $e_{b.\text{min}} = 0$ volts and $i_{b.\text{max}} = 5$ ma, on the static plate characteristic curves of Fig. 9-4.

When the plate current is zero, the voltage drop across the output resistor R_o will be zero and the voltage between the plate and cathode will be equal to the B supply

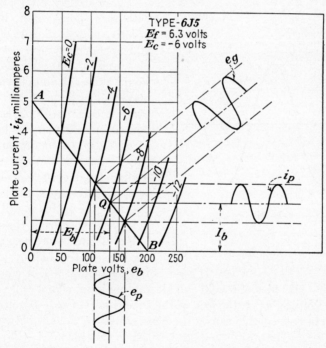

Fig. 9-4.—Method of plotting the load line and of obtaining the dynamic operating characteristics.

voltage, or 200 volts.   This locates point B, $e_{b.\text{max}} = 200$ volts and $i_{b.\text{min}} = 0$ ma, on the static plate characteristic curves of Fig. 9-4.

A straight line connecting points A and B will represent the load line of the type 6J5 tube for an output resistive load of 40,000 ohms and a B supply of 200 volts.

The intersection of the load line and the curve for the grid bias to be used determines the *quiescent* or *operating point*. Thus for a grid bias of 6 volts, point Q (Fig. 9-4) will be the operating point. From this diagram, it can be seen that with zero signal input a steady current I_b (equal to 1.625 ma) will flow in the plate circuit. This steady current of 1.625 ma flowing through the 40,000-ohm resistance produces a 65-volt drop across the output resistor R_o, thereby causing the voltage between the plate and cathode to be reduced to 135 volts.

Summarizing, a type 6J5 tube with zero signal input, having a resistive plate load of 40,000 ohms and operating with a 6-volt grid bias and a 200-volt B supply, would have 135 volts between the plate and cathode of the tube and a steady current of 1.625 ma would flow through the output load.

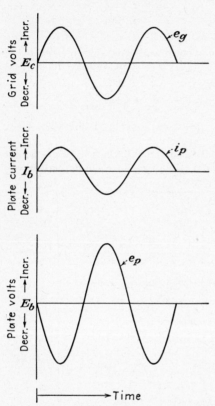

FIG. 9-5.—Phase relations between the a-c grid voltage, the a-c component of the plate current, and the a-c component of the plate voltage.

Effect of Input Signal Voltage on e_c, e_b, and i_b. When an alternating signal voltage e_g (Fig. 9-2) is applied to the input circuit of the tube, the grid bias will become less negative during the positive half cycles and more negative during the negative half cycles. Referring to Fig. 9-4, it can be seen that with a grid bias of 6 volts, an alternating input signal of 2 volts will vary the voltage, e_c, on the grid of the tube from -4 to -8 volts. This variation in grid voltage causes the plate current i_b to vary between 1 ma and 2.25 ma. The output voltage e_p will then vary between -25 and $+25$ volts causing the voltage at the plate e_b to vary between 110 and 160 volts.

It can thus be seen that when the voltage on the grid is increased—that is, made less negative—the current in the plate circuit will increase. This increase in plate current causes the voltage drop across the output resistor to increase, thus decreasing the voltage between the plate and

cathode of the tube.   In a similar manner, it can be seen that a decrease
in grid voltage will decrease the current in the plate circuit, thus decreasing the voltage drop across the output resistor, and thereby increase the
voltage at the plate of the tube.   The phase relation between the grid
voltage, plate current, and the plate voltage for an amplifier circuit whose
load contains only resistance is shown in Fig. 9-5.   From these diagrams
it can be seen that, with only resistance in an amplifier circuit, the grid-
voltage variations are in phase with the variations in plate current, and

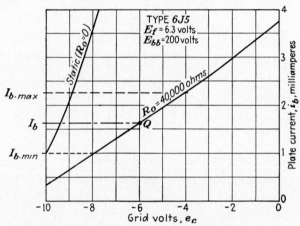

Fig. 9-6.—Dynamic and static characteristic curves.

the plate-voltage variations are 180 degrees out of phase with the grid-
voltage variations.   As all amplifier circuits contain at least a small
amount of undesired capacitance and inductance, this in-phase and 180-
degree out-of-phase relationship is very seldom obtained.   The amount
of phase difference from these theoretical conditions will depend upon the
amount of capacitance and inductance present in the circuit and in some
cases may be so small that it can be ignored.

Dynamic Characteristic Curves.   Although the operating characteristics of a tube can be obtained from the static plate characteristic curves
with the aid of a load line, a more complete interpretation can be acquired
from a family of dynamic characteristic curves.   A single dynamic characteristic curve represents the actual operating characteristics of a tube
for a definite type and value of load impedance.   The dynamic characteristic curve of a tube will therefore vary with the value and type of load
impedance.   Thus, a family of curves can be plotted from values obtained
from the static plate characteristic curves and the load lines.   Values of
grid volts and plate current for the dynamic characteristic curve shown
in Fig. 9-6 were obtained from Fig. 9-4 at the points where the load line
intersects the static curves.

It can readily be seen from this curve that a steady plate current of 1.625 ma will flow when the B supply is 200 volts and the tube is operated with a grid bias of 6 volts.   It can also be seen that a 2-volt alternating current signal input varies the grid voltage from -4 to -8 volts, thus

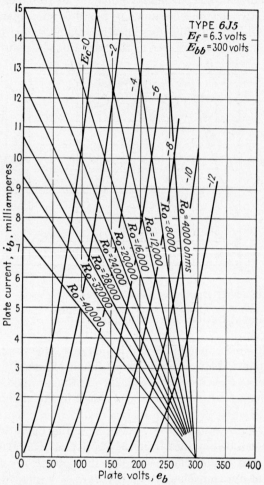

FIG. 9-7.—Load lines for a type 6J5 tube.

causing the plate current to vary between 1 and 2.25 ma.   These are the same values that were obtained from the series of static characteristic curves and the load line of Fig. 9-4.

For purposes of comparison, the transfer static curve $(R_o = 0)$ has been drawn on the same graph.   Values of grid volts and plate current were obtained from Fig. 9-4 at the points where the line representing 200 volts on the plate intersects each static curve. It can be observed that the dynamic curve is much flatter than the static curve. This means that the plate-current variations for dynamic conditions would be smaller than the plate-current variations for static conditions, assuming that the grid-voltage variations are the same.

A series of dynamic curves for a type 6J5 tube, operating with a 300-volt B supply on its plate, for various values of load resistance are

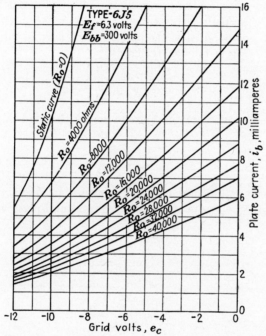

FIG. 9-8.—Dynamic characteristics for a type 6J5 tube.

shown in Fig. 9-8. Values of grid volts and plate current for these curves were obtained at the points where the various load lines (Fig. 9-7) intersect the static plate characteristic curves. Zero load condition is represented by the static transfer characteristic curve plotted for a 300-volt B supply. From this family of curves, it can be seen that the slope of the transfer characteristic curve becomes steeper with a decrease in the plate load and flatter with an increase in the plate load. Thus, increasing the plate load will decrease the plate-current output. However, increasing the plate load also lengthens the straight portion of the transfer characteristic curve, thus making it possible to apply a larger signal voltage to the input circuit of the tube without producing distortion.

9-3. Power Amplification. *Power Output.* The current that flows through the plate circuit of a tube consists of two parts: (1) a steady or d-c component I_b; (2) a varying or a-c component i_p (see Fig. 9-1). The useful part of the plate current is the varying component as only variations in plate current produce sounds at the loudspeaker. The steady plate current I_b will not cause the loudspeaker to produce any sound and therefore does not contribute directly toward the useful output of an amplifier circuit. This portion of the plate current does, however, contribute toward the power loss of the circuit as it produces heat at both the load impedance and the plate of the tube.

The varying component of the plate current flowing through the output resistor R_o (Fig. 9-1) is expressed as

$$i_p = \frac{\mu e_g}{R_o + r_p} \tag{4-8}$$

The varying component of the voltage across the load impedance R_o is equal to

$$e_p = \frac{\mu e_g R_o}{R_o + r_p} \tag{4-9}$$

The instantaneous value of the a-c power output p_o is equal to the product of the varying components of the plate current and plate voltage, or

$$p_o = i_p e_p \tag{9-2}$$

Substituting Eqs. (4-8) and (4-9) for i_p and e_p in Eq. (9-2)

$$p_o = \frac{\mu e_g}{R_o + r_p} \times \frac{\mu e_g R_o}{R_o + r_p} \tag{9-2a}$$

or

$$p_o = \frac{(\mu e_g)^2 R_o}{(R_o + r_p)^2} \tag{9-2b}$$

Maximum Power Output. It has previously been shown that the voltage amplification of a circuit increases with an increase in the value of the load impedance. Thus, for a voltage amplifier, maximum voltage amplification can be approached only by making the value of the load impedance many times greater than the plate resistance. However, although a great increase in the output voltage e_p is obtained, the useful power output of the voltage amplifier circuit is quite low. This can be seen by an analysis of Eqs. (4-8) and (4-9). Examination of these two equations indicates that for constant values of amplification factor and input signal, the output voltage e_p will vary according to the factor $\frac{R_o}{R_o + r_p}$, and the plate current i_p will vary according to the factor

$\dfrac{1}{R_o + r_p}$. Further analysis will show that, with a fixed value of r_p, any increase in R_o will increase the output voltage e_p and decrease the output current i_p; conversely, a decrease in R_o will decrease the output voltage e_p and increase the output current i_p.   It can also be seen that e_p and i_p do not change at the same rate and consequently the power output may either increase or decrease with a change in R_o depending upon whether R_o is smaller or larger than r_p.   The maximum power output will be obtained when R_o is equal to r_p which may be proved experimentally, or mathematically as in the following example.

Example 9-2.   Prove that the maximum amount of power output is obtained at the load of an amplifier circuit when the load resistance R_o is equal to the plate resistance r_p.   Assume the tube to have a plate resistance of 8000 ohms, a constant amplification factor of 20, and an input signal of 1 volt.   Establish the proof by determining the power output with load resistance values of 4000, 6000, 8000, 10,000, and 12,000 ohms.

<table>
<tr><td>Given:</td><td>Find:</td></tr>
<tr><td>r_p = 8000 ohms</td><td>$p_{o\cdot\text{max}}$ = ?</td></tr>
<tr><td>μ = 20</td><td></td></tr>
<tr><td>e_g = 1 volt</td><td></td></tr>
<tr><td>R_o = 4000, 6000, 8000, 10,000 and 12,000 ohms</td><td></td></tr>
</table>

Solution:

R_o, ohms	$R_o + r_p$ ohms	e_p Eq. (4-9) volts	i_p Eq. (4-8) ma	p_o	
				Eq. (9-2) mw	Eq. (9-2b) watts
4,000	12,000	6.666	1.666	11.11	0.01111
6,000	14,000	8.571	1.428	12.23	0.01224
8,000	16,000	10	1.25	12.5	0.0125
10,000	18,000	11.11	1.111	12.34	0.01234
12,000	20,000	12	1	12	0.012

From the tabular results listed above, it can be seen that the maximum power output is obtained when R_o = 8000 ohms, which is also the value of r_p.

The principle illustrated in Example 9-2 can be applied to any type of power source and load and is referred to as the principle of *maximum power transfer*.

Graphical Analysis of Maximum Power Output.   The power output characteristics of an amplifier circuit (see Fig. 9-9) illustrates the principle of maximum power transfer.   The values of power output used in plotting this curve were obtained by the use of Eq. (9-2b); some of the values also are listed in the solution of Example 9-2. It can be seen from this curve that the output power increases rapidly as the load resistance is increased from zero and reaches its maximum value when the load and plate resistances are equal. Further increases in load resistance cause the output power to decrease, although at a much slower rate.

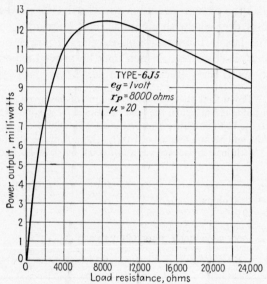

FIG. 9-9.—Power-output characteristics for a type 6J5 tube.

When R_o is equal to r_p, the instantaneous value of the power output [Eq. (9-2b)] then becomes

$$p_{o \cdot m} = \frac{(\mu e_g)^2}{4 r_p} \tag{9-3}$$

If the effective value of the input signal is substituted for the instantaneous value in Eq. (9-3), the a-c power output of the circuit may then be found by use of the equation

$$P_{o \cdot m} = \frac{(\mu E_g)^2}{4 r_p} \tag{9-4}$$

If the maximum value of the input signal is substituted for the effective value in Eq. (9-4), then

$$P_{o \cdot m} = \frac{(\mu E_{g \cdot m})^2}{8 r_p} \tag{9-4a}$$

where $p_{o \cdot m}$ = instantaneous value of power output with maximum power transfer, watts

$P_{o \cdot m}$ = maximum a-c power output of the amplifier circuit, watts

e_g = instantaneous value of the input signal, volts

E_g = effective value of the input signal, volts

$E_{g \cdot m}$ = maximum or peak value of the input signal, volts

Example 9-3.   An amplifier circuit uses a type 6A3 tube operated Class A with 250 volts on its plate and with a grid bias of 45 volts.   What is the maximum power output that can be obtained from this amplifier circuit with an input signal whose peak value is 20 volts?

Given: Find:

    Tube = 6A3 $P_{o \cdot m}$ = ?

      E_b = 250 volts

      E_c = −45 volts

      $E_{g \cdot m}$ = 20 volts

Solution:

From Appendix XV: μ = 4.2, r_p = 800 ohms

$$P_{o \cdot m} = \frac{(\mu E_{g \cdot m})^2}{8 r_p} = \frac{(4.2 \times 20)^2}{8 \times 800} = 1.102 \text{ watts}$$

9-4. Distortion in Power Amplifiers.   *Nonlinear Distortion.*   Every tube's transfer characteristic curve can be divided into three parts: (1) the curve formed at the upper bend, (2) the curve formed at the lower bend, (3) the portion joining these two parts.   The line joining the upper and lower bends, although generally considered as being straight, actually is curved.   The degree of curvature of this portion of the transfer characteristic curve depends upon the value of the load impedance.   The effect of the load impedance on the curvature of the transfer characteristic can be seen by reference to the dynamic characteristics of the type 6J5 tube (Fig. 9-8).   From this figure, it can also be seen that increasing the value of the load impedance tends to lengthen the curve, thus making it more nearly a straight line.   Although a considerable amount of curvature exists at the no-load or static condition, this decreases to a very small amount as the value of the load impedance is increased.

Nonlinear distortion is caused by operating a tube on any curved portion of its transfer characteristic curve.   Thus, a Class A power amplifier will produce some distortion, since even the best operating portion of its characteristic curve is not actually a straight line.   This distortion is caused mainly by the second harmonic, and the per cent of distortion can be calculated by use of the equation

Per cent of second harmonic distortion

$$= \frac{\dfrac{i_{b \cdot \max} + i_{b \cdot \min}}{2} - I_b}{i_{b \cdot \max} - i_{b \cdot \min}} \times 100 \quad (9\text{-}5)$$

or

Per cent of second harmonic distortion

$$= \frac{(i_{b \cdot \max} + i_{b \cdot \min}) - 2I_b}{2(i_{b \cdot \max} - i_{b \cdot \min})} \times 100 \quad (9\text{-}5a)$$

where $i_{b \cdot \max}$ = maximum value of total plate current

$i_{b \cdot \min}$ = minimum value of total plate current

I_b = average or quiescent value of plate current

Example 9-4. A type 6J5 triode is operated from a 300-volt B power supply and it is desired to obtain maximum power output. The grid bias is 6 volts and the plate resistance of the tube is 8000 ohms. What is the per cent of second harmonic distortion when a signal having a maximum value of 4 volts is applied to the input circuit?

Given: Find:

Tube = 6J5   Per cent of second harmonic distortion

E_{bb} = 300 volts

E_c = −6 volts

r_p = 8000 ohms

$E_{g \cdot m}$ = 4 volts

Solution:

$$R_o = r_p = 8000 \text{ ohms (for maximum power output)}$$

From the dynamic characteristic curves of the type 6J5 tube (Fig. 9-8)

$$i_{b \cdot \max} = 16 \text{ ma}$$
$$i_{b \cdot \min} = 5.2 \text{ ma}$$
$$I_b = 10 \text{ ma}$$

Per cent of second harmonic distortion $= \dfrac{(i_{b \cdot \max} + i_{b \cdot \min}) - 2I_b}{2(i_{b \cdot \max} - i_{b \cdot \min})} \times 100$

$$= \frac{(16 + 5.2) - 2 \times 10}{2(16 - 5.2)} \times 100 = 5.55 \text{ per cent}$$

Maximum Undistorted Power Output. When operating a tube as a power amplifier it becomes necessary to consider the per cent of distortion as well as the power output. Maximum power output is obtained when the load and plate resistances are equal. Increasing the value of the load resistance will decrease the curvature of the characteristic curve and thus decrease the amount of distortion. It is common practice to sacrifice some of the output power in order to use a load resistance that will produce a satisfactory minimum amount of distortion. Undistorted power output, as used in reference to audio amplification, means that the amount of distortion is small enough that it cannot be noticed by the average person. A distortion of 5 per cent can be distinguished by the average listener. The recommended maximum allowable distortion of an audio amplifier has been taken as 5 per cent. A rule generally used for single-tube triode power amplifiers is to use a load resistor whose value is approximately equal to twice the value of the plate resistance.

Substituting E_g for e_g, and $2r_p$ for R_o in Eq. (9-2b)

$$P_{\text{o·m·u}} = \frac{2(\mu E_g)^2}{9r_p} \qquad (9\text{-}6)$$

and

$$P_{\text{o·m·u}} = \frac{(\mu E_{g·m})^2}{9r_p} \qquad (9\text{-}6a)$$

where $P_{\text{o·m·u}}$ = maximum undistorted power output, watts

Example 9-5.   The type 6J5 triode of Example 9-4 is operated with the same electrode potentials and a-c input signal as used in Example 9-4.   What is the per cent of second harmonic distortion if the plate load is increased to the value at which the circuit will produce its maximum amount of undistorted power output?

Given: Find:
   Tube = 6J5   Per cent of second harmonic distortion
    E_{bb} = 300 volts
    E_c = −6 volts
    r_p = 8000 ohms
   $E_{g·m}$ = 4 volts

Solution:

   $R_o = 2r_p$ = 16,000 ohms (for maximum undistorted power output)

From the dynamic characteristic curves of the type 6J5 tube (Fig. 9-8).

$$i_{b·\text{max}} = 10 \text{ ma}$$
$$i_{b·\text{min}} = 3.5 \text{ ma}$$
$$I_b = 6.6 \text{ ma}$$

Per cent of second harmonic distortion $= \dfrac{(i_{b·\text{max}} + i_{b·\text{min}}) - 2I_b}{2(i_{b·\text{max}} - i_{b·\text{min}})} \times 100$

$$= \frac{(10 + 3.5) - 2 \times 6.6}{2(10 - 3.5)} \times 100 = 2.30 \text{ per cent}$$

Examination of the results obtained in Example 9-4 indicates that the per cent of second harmonic distortion exceeds the recommended maximum when the plate load is selected to produce maximum power output. However, when the plate load is increased to twice the value of the plate resistance, as in Example 9-5, the per cent of distortion is reduced considerably and is well below the recommended maximum.

Although some power is sacrificed by increasing the value of the load resistance, the amount is very small, as can be observed from the power output curve (Fig. 9-9).   From this curve, it can be seen that the decrease in power output does not become appreciable until the value of the plate load becomes several times that of the plate resistance.

9-5. Ratings of Power Amplifiers.   *Power Amplification.*   Amplifier tubes generally are operated with a grid bias high enough to prevent any current from flowing in the grid circuit.   Under this condition the current flowing in the input circuit of the amplifier is practically zero.   When the input signal is fed into an amplifier tube through a resistor, the power used by this input resistor represents the input power of the amplifier; this is sometimes called the *driving power*. In such a circuit, the ratio of the a-c power output to the a-c power consumed in the grid circuit is called the *power amplification* of the amplifier circuit. The power amplification ratio may be infinite in certain types of power amplifiers since the vacuum tube is capable of releasing additional power from the local power supply.

In contrast to the high power amplification obtained from a power amplifie/ circuit, the voltage amplification obtained is very low. It can be seen, by observation of the power output equations for a vacuum-tube amplifier circuit, that the output power varies as the square of the input signal voltage. Thus, if the value of the input signal voltage is tripled the output power will be increased to nine times its former value. For this reason, the input voltage to power amplifier tubes should be comparatively high. Power amplifier tubes are therefore designed to operate with large input signal voltages without producing distortion.

Example 9-6. A type 6F6 tube is operated as a Class A_1 triode power amplifier to produce maximum undistorted power output. The plate resistance of the tube is 2500 ohms and its amplification factor is 6.8. At 1000 cycles, a signal current with an effective value of 70 μa flows through the 200,000-ohm grid leak resistor. (a) What is the voltage amplification at this frequency? (b) What is the power amplification at this frequency?

Given:
$$r_p = 2500 \text{ ohms}$$
$$R_g = 200,000 \text{ ohms}$$
$$\mu = 6.8$$
$$I_g = 70 \ \mu a$$

Find:
(a) VA = ?
(b) PA = ?

Solution:

(a) $\quad E_g = I_g \times R_g = 7 \times 10^{-5} \times 2 \times 10^5 = 14 \text{ volts}$
$$R_o = 2r_p = 2 \times 2500 = 5000 \text{ ohms}$$
$$\text{VA} = \frac{\mu R_o}{R_o + r_p} = \frac{6.8 \times 5000}{5000 + 2500} = 4.53$$

(b) $\quad P_{\text{o·m·u}} = \frac{2(\mu E_g)^2}{9r_p} = \frac{2(6.8 \times 14)^2}{9 \times 2500} = 0.805 \text{ watt}$
$$P_{\text{input}} = I_g{}^2 R_g = (70 \times 10^{-6})^2 \times 0.2 \times 10^6 = 0.00098 \text{ watt}$$
$$\text{PA} = \frac{P_{\text{o·m·u}}}{P_{\text{input}}} = \frac{0.805}{0.00098} = 821$$

Plate Circuit Efficiency. The efficiency of any power supplying device is usually expressed as a percentage and represents the ratio of its power output to its power input. The vacuum tube itself does not contribute any power to the output circuit but by its action power is released from a local power supply. The power supplied to the plate circuit of a tube can thus be represented by the power that the tube releases from its B power supply. The power released from the B power supply is equal to the product of the plate supply voltage and the average plate current at maximum signal input. The average plate current flow at maximum signal input may be slightly higher than that at zero signal input. This increase in current is produced by the nonlinear or rectifying action of the tube. For most practical purposes, this difference in plate current can be ignored. The average plate current can then be taken as equal to the quiescent or operating plate current I_b. The efficiency of the plate circuit can then be expressed as

$$\text{Plate circuit efficiency} = \frac{P_o}{E_{bb}I_b} \times 100 \qquad (9\text{-}7)$$

where P_o = a-c power output, watts

E_{bb} = voltage of B power supply, volts

I_b = average value of plate current, amperes

Example 9-7. What is the plate circuit efficiency of the type 6F6 power output tube of Example 9-6, if the average plate current is 32 ma and the B power supply is 410 volts?

Given: Find:
$P_o = 0.805$ watt   Plate circuit efficiency
$E_{bb} = 410$ volts
$I_b = 32$ ma

Solution:

$$\text{Plate circuit efficiency} = \frac{P_o \times 100}{E_{bb}I_b} = \frac{0.805 \times 100}{410 \times 0.032} = 6.13 \text{ per cent}$$

Plate Efficiency. In the rating of power amplifiers, the plate circuit efficiency is very seldom used. The term generally used is the plate efficiency of the power amplifier tube. The ratio of the a-c power output to the product of the average values of plate voltage and plate current at maximum signal input is called the *plate efficiency*.

$$\text{Plate efficiency} = \frac{P_o}{E_b I_b} \times 100 \qquad (9\text{-}8)$$

In Class A amplification (Fig. 9-4) maximum efficiency will be obtained when the maximum negative values of the varying components of the plate voltage e_p and the plate current i_p produce the lowest possible values of plate voltage e_b and plate current i_b, namely, zero. Under this condition, the maximum value of e_b will be twice the value of the operating plate voltage E_b and the maximum value of i_b will be twice the value of the operating plate current I_b. The peak values of E_p and I_p will thus be equal to E_b and I_b respectively. As the a-c power output (for resistive loads) is equal to the product of the effective values of E_p and I_p, then

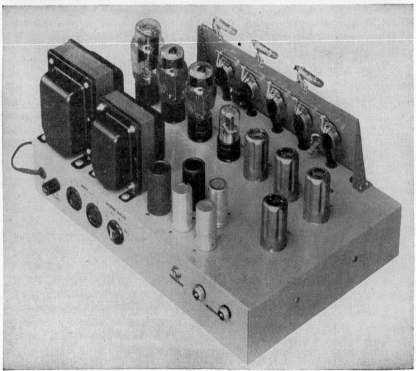

FIG. 9-10.—Commercial audio-frequency power amplifier.   (*Courtesy of Radio News.*)

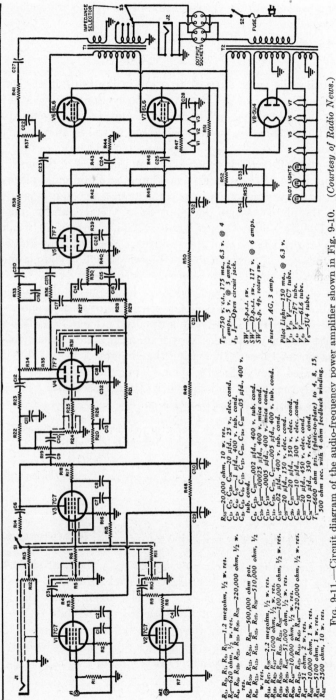

R_1, R_{2}, R_4, R_5, R_7—1.2 megohm, 1/2 w. res.
R_3—620 ohm, 1/2 w. res.
R_{48}, R_{49}, R_{50}, R_{51}, R_{28}, R_{38}, R_{52}—220,000 ohm, 1/2 w. res.
R_6, R_{10}, R_{15}, R_{30}—500,000 ohm pot.
R_9, R_{11}, R_{33}, R_{35}, R_{37}—510,000 ohm, 1/2 w. res.
R_{16}, R_{25}, R_{26}—2.2 megohm, 1/2 w. res.
R_{12}—1000 ohm, 1/2 w. res.
R_{18}, R_{27}, R_{30}, R_{40}, R_{41}—100,000 ohm, 1/2 w. res.
R_{20}, R_{21}—51,000 ohm, 1/2 w. res.
R_{38}, R_{39}—10,000 ohm, 1/2 w. res.
R_{43}, R_{44}, R_{45}, R_{46}, R_{47}—220,000 ohm, 1/2 w. res.
R_{42}—10,000 ohm, 1 w. res.
R_{53}—51 ohm, 2 w. res.
R_{54}—5100 ohm, 1 w. res.
R_{55}—2500 ohm, 10 w. res.

R_{56}—20,000 ohm, 10 w. res.
C_1, C_7, C_{3B}, C_{8B}—20 μfd., 25 v., elec. cond.
C_2, C_4, C_7—.1 μfd., 400 v., tub. cond.
C_3, C_5, C_9, C_{12}, C_{13}, C_{23}, C_{24}, C_{25}—.05 μfd., 400 v. tub. cond.
C_6, C_8, C_{10}—.002 μfd., 400 v. tub. cond.
C_{11}, C_{14}—.00025 μfd., 400 v. mica cond.
C_{15}—.0005 μfd., 400 v. mica cond.
C_{16}, C_{17}—.02 μfd., 400 v. tub. cond.
C_{18}, C_{19}, C_{20}, C_{21}—.005 μfd., 400 v. tub. cond.
C_{27}—20 μfd., 150 v. elec. cond.
C_{28}, C_{31}—20 μfd., 350 v. elec. cond.
C_{29}, C_{32}—10 μfd., 300 v. elec. cond.
C_{33}, C_{34}—20 μfd., 450 v. elec. cond.
T_1—6600 ohm pri. (plate-to-plate) to 4, 8, 15,
    500 ohm sec. with 4 ohm feedback winding.

T_2—750 v. c.t., 175 ma., 6.3 v. @ 4
    amps., 5 v. @ 3 amps.
J_1, J_2—Open circuit jack.

SW₁—S.p.s.t. sw.
SW₂—D.-t. sw., 117 v. @ 6 amps.
SW₃—S.-p. 4p. rotary sw.

Fuse—3 AG, 3 amp.

Pilot Light—150 ma. @ 6.3 v.
V_1, V_2, V_3—7C7 tube.
V_4, V_5—7F7 tube.
V_6, V_7—6L6 tube.
V_8—5U4 tube.

(*Courtesy of Radio News.*)

FIG. 9-11.—Circuit diagram of the audio-frequency power amplifier shown in Fig. 9-10.

the a-c power output for the condition of maximum plate efficiency may
be expressed as

$$P_o = \frac{E_b}{\sqrt{2}} \frac{I_b}{\sqrt{2}} = \frac{E_b I_b}{2} \tag{9-9}$$

Substituting the value of P_o of Eq. (9-9) in Eq. (9-8), it can be seen that
the plate efficiency of a Class A amplifier cannot exceed 50 per cent.
This is the theoretical maximum efficiency and in practical amplifier
circuits the actual efficiency is much lower, as will be seen in the following
examples.

The plate efficiency is dependent upon the ratios of the maximum and
minimum plate voltages and the maximum and minimum plate currents.
These in turn are dependent upon the operating conditions of the tube,
such as the plate voltage, the input signal voltage, and the load impedance.   Using a load resistance whose value is approximately equal to the
tube's plate resistance and increasing the plate voltage and the input
signal voltage will increase the a-c power output.   The plate efficiency
of the amplifier circuit is therefore also increased.

The plate efficiency is generally low in amplifiers designed primarily
for minimum distortion.   The plate efficiency of Class A operated power
tubes as used in radio receivers is usually between 10 and 25 per cent.
The plate efficiency of triodes is lower than the plate efficiency of pentodes
or beam power tubes.   Increasing the amount of permissible distortion
also increases the plate efficiency.   Thus the efficiency of Class A_1
operation is the lowest and the efficiency increases with Class A_2, Class
AB_1, Class AB_2, and Class B operation.

Example 9-8.   What is the plate efficiency of the type 6F6 power output tube of
Examples 9-6 and 9-7 if the average plate voltage is 250 volts?

Given: Find:
P_o = 0.805 watt   Plate efficiency
E_b = 250 volts
I_b = 32 ma

Solution:

$$\text{Plate efficiency} = \frac{P_o}{E_b I_b} \times 100 = \frac{0.805 \times 100}{250 \times 0.032} = 10.06 \text{ per cent}$$

Plate Dissipation and Screen Dissipation.   The heat given off at the
plate of a tube as the result of electron bombardment is called the *plate
dissipation* and its symbol is P_p.   This is a loss in power and is equal to
the difference between the power supplied to the plate of the tube and
the a-c power delivered by the tube to its load impedance.   The heat
given off at the screen grid of a tube as a result of electron bombardment
is called the *screen dissipation*.   In determining the plate efficiency of

pentodes and beam power tubes, the power dissipated in the screen grid must be added to the average d-c power supplied to the plate of the tube in order to obtain the total input to the tube from the B power supply.

Example 9-9.   Determine the plate dissipation of the power amplifier tube as used in Examples 9-6, 9-7, and 9-8?

<table>
<tr><td>Given:</td><td>Find:</td></tr>
<tr><td>$P_o = 0.805$ watt</td><td>$P_p = ?$</td></tr>
<tr><td>$E_b = 250$ volts</td><td></td></tr>
<tr><td>$I_b = 32$ ma</td><td></td></tr>
</table>

Solution:

$$P_i = E_b I_b = 250 \times 0.032 = 8 \text{ watts}$$
$$P_p = P_i - P_o = 8 - 0.805 = 7.195 \text{ watts}$$

The maximum plate or screen dissipation of a power amplifier tube can be obtained by reference to a tube manual.   The maximum plate dissipation listed in the tube manual for a type 6F6 tube, when operated as a triode Class A_1 amplifier, is 10 watts.   This value exceeds the power dissipation as calculated in Example 9-9; therefore, the tube of Example 9-9 is being operated within its rated plate dissipation limit.

Power Sensitivity.   Another term commonly used in the rating of power amplifier tubes is its power sensitivity.   The ratio of the a-c power output to the square of the rms (effective) value of the input signal voltage is referred to as the *power sensitivity*.   The basic unit of power sensitivity is the mho, but, because of the low values of power sensitivity usually obtained, the micromho is more commonly used.

$$\text{Power sensitivity} = \frac{P_o}{E_g{}^2} \times 10^6 \text{ (micromhos)} \qquad (9\text{-}10)$$

Power sensitivity is ordinarily only used in rating amplifier tubes that are operated so that no current flows in the grid circuit.   When this term is used in connection with an amplifier circuit in which the grid circuit consumes power, it refers to the entire amplifier section including the driver tube.   The power sensitivity of pentodes and beam power tubes is considerably greater than for triodes.

The term *power sensitivity* is also used in rating r-f power amplifiers. When used in this manner, it has an entirely different meaning than when used with a-f power amplifiers.   Power sensitivity, as used with r-f power amplifiers, expresses the ratio of the output power to the input power or the power amplification of the circuit.

Example 9-10.   A type 6J5 triode is operated from a 300-volt B power supply and is to produce maximum power output.   The plate resistance of the tube is 8000 ohms and its amplification factor is 20.   The input signal has a maximum value of 4 volts. What is the power sensitivity of the tube?

Given: Find:
  Tube $= 6J5$ Power sensitivity
    $r_p = 8000$ ohms
    $\mu = 20$
    $E_{g \cdot m} = 4$ volts

Solution:

$$P_{o \cdot m} = \frac{(\mu E_{g \cdot m})^2}{8 r_p} = \frac{(20 \times 4)^2}{8 \times 8000} = 0.1 \text{ watt}$$

$$\text{Power sensitivity} = \frac{P_o}{E_g^2} \times 10^6 = \frac{0.1 \times 10^6}{(4 \times 0.707)^2} = 12,500 \ \mu\text{mhos}$$

9-6. Class A_2 Operation. The development of negative feedback amplifier circuits has made it possible to reduce the distortion produced in an amplifier to a minimum. When negative feedback is used it becomes possible to operate a tube as a Class A_2 amplifier without producing excessive distortion.

In a Class A_2 amplifier, the values of the grid bias and the input signal voltage are such that the total instantaneous grid voltage e_c is driven positive during a portion of the input cycle. Grid current will flow during the portion of the cycle in which the grid is positive. Under this condition it is possible to obtain maximum plate current flow, at the positive peaks of the input signal, with a lower value of plate voltage. The plate efficiency and power output is greater with Class A_2 operation than with Class A_1. Plate efficiencies of 30 to 40 per cent are obtainable for power amplifier tubes operated as Class A_2.

The grid bias of a power amplifier tube operated as Class A_2 should be of such a value that rated plate current will flow when the rated plate voltage is applied. The amount that the grid voltage may be driven positive during any portion of the input cycle will then depend upon the amount that the distortion is reduced by the addition of negative feedback.

9-7. Power Diagrams. *Load Line and Power.* It has previously been explained how the load line can be used for determining the dynamic characteristics of a vacuum tube. These characteristics included the operating point, required amount of B supply voltage, maximum and minimum plate voltage, and the maximum and minimum plate current. Many of the other operating characteristics of an amplifier tube can also be determined by use of the load line. These characteristics include the power lost in the load resistor, plate dissipation, power output, distortion, and voltage amplification. Use of the load line in determining these operating characteristics is illustrated in Figs. 9-12 and 9-13. The graphical determination of the power ratings of a 6F6 operated with the same electrode potentials, load resistance, and input signal voltage as used in Examples 9-6, 9-7, 9-8, and 9-9 is illustrated by the power diagram of Fig. 9-12.

Power Output. Referring to the power diagram for the 6F6 (Fig. 9-12), it can be seen that an input signal with a peak value of 20 volts causes the plate voltage to vary from 160 volts to 338 volts, or a total variation of 178 volts. This is referred to as the *peak-to-peak voltage* (from plate to cathode) and also represents the useful signal voltage available to operate the following tube or circuit. The peak-to-peak input signal voltage in Fig. 9-12 is 40 volts. The voltage amplification would then be equal to 178 divided by 40, or 4.45. This checks favorably with the mathematical solution of Example 9-6, in which the voltage amplification was found to be 4.53; hence the graphical method of solution gives results sufficiently accurate to warrant its common use. With this signal input, the plate current varies from a maximum of 50 ma to a minimum of 14 ma, or a total variation of 36 ma.

The a-c power output of the amplifier can be found by the use of the peak-to-peak values of plate voltage and plate current, and the basic power equation $P = EI$. In this equation the voltage and current must be effective values; hence it is necessary to convert the peak-to-peak values of voltage and current to their effective values. This can be done by dividing the peak-to-peak value by a factor of $2\sqrt{2}$. The a-c power output can then be expressed as

$$P_o = \frac{(e_{b \cdot max} - e_{b \cdot min})}{2\sqrt{2}} \times \frac{(i_{b \cdot max} - i_{b \cdot min})}{2\sqrt{2}} \qquad (9\text{-}11)$$

or
$$P_o = \frac{(e_{b \cdot max} - e_{b \cdot min})(i_{b \cdot max} - i_{b \cdot min})}{8} \qquad (9\text{-}11a)$$

Example 9-11. Determine the power output of the 6F6 under the operating conditions indicated on the power diagram of Fig. 9-12.

Given: Find:
    Tube = 6F6 $P_o = ?$
    Power diagram, Fig. 9-12
Solution:

From Fig. 9-12:

$$e_{b \cdot max} = 338 \text{ volts}; \qquad e_{b \cdot min} = 160 \text{ volts}$$
$$i_{b \cdot max} = 50 \text{ ma}; \qquad i_{b \cdot min} = 14 \text{ ma}$$
$$P_o = \frac{(e_{b \cdot max} - e_{b \cdot min})(i_{b \cdot max} - i_{b \cdot min})}{8}$$
$$= \frac{(338 - 160)(0.050 - 0.014)}{8} = 0.801 \text{ watt}$$

The a-c power output is represented on the power diagram by the area of the shaded triangle, QNM. The maximum power output of a Class A amplifier will occur when the area of the shaded triangle is equal to QCH. The output would then be equal to one-half of the plate input, and the plate efficiency would be 50 per cent. In actual practice, it is impossible to obtain this condition since it requires the instantaneous value of plate voltage to reach zero, and the instantaneous plate current to reach its maximum value at full B-supply voltage.

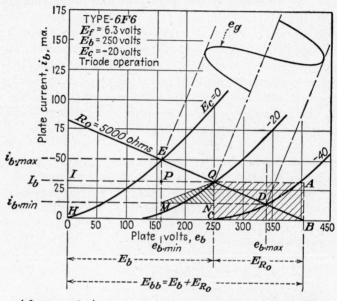

A-C power output_____Area of the triangle *QNM*
Power lost in the output resistor_____Area of the rectangle *QABC*
Plate dissipation_____Area of the rectangle *IQCH*
                        minus the area of the triangle *QNM*
Power supplied by the B power supply____Area of the rectangle *IABH*
Power supplied to the plate of the tube..Area of the rectangle *IQCH*

Fig. 9-12.—Power diagram of a type 6F6 tube connected for triode operation.

Power Losses and Power Ratings. The power consumed by the output resistor is equal to the product of the voltage drop across this resistor and the average plate current. This power is represented by the area of the rectangle, *QABC*. The power taken from the B power supply is equal to the product of the B-power-supply voltage and the average plate current. Thus, the power supplied by the local power supply is represented by the area of the rectangle *IABH*. The input power to the plate circuit of the tube is equal to the product of the average plate voltage and the average plate current. The area of the rectangle *IQCH* therefore represents the input power to the plate of the tube. The plate dissipation of a tube is equal to the difference between the input power to the plate and the output power. This power loss is represented by the area of the rectangle *IQCH* minus the area of the triangle *QNM*.

Example 9-12. Using the power diagram in Fig. 9-12 and the power output as calculated in Example 9-11, determine (*a*) the plate circuit efficiency, (*b*) the plate efficiency, (*c*) the plate dissipation, and (*d*) the power lost in the output resistor.

Given: Find:
    Tube = 6F6   (*a*) Plate circuit efficiency = ?
    Power diagram, Fig. 9-12   (*b*) Plate efficiency = ?
    $P_o = 0.801$ watt   (*c*) $P_p = ?$
                                      (*d*) $P_R = ?$

Solution:

From Fig. 9-12:

$$AB = CQ = 32 \text{ ma or } 0.032 \text{ amp}$$
$$HB = 410 \text{ volts}$$
$$HC = 250 \text{ volts}$$
$$CB = 160 \text{ volts}$$

(*a*) $P_B = HB \times AB = 410 \times 0.032 = 13.12$ watts

    Plate circuit efficiency $= \dfrac{P_o}{P_B} \times 100 = \dfrac{0.801}{13.12} \times 100 = 6.10$ per cent

(*b*) $P_i = HC \times CQ = 250 \times 0.032 = 8$ watts

    Plate efficiency $= \dfrac{P_o}{P_i} \times 100 = \dfrac{0.801}{8} \times 100 = 10.01$ per cent

(*c*) $P_p = P_i - P_o = 8 - 0.801 = 7.199$ watts
(*d*) $P_R = CB \times AB = 160 \times 0.032 = 5.12$ watts

Best Values of Output Resistance and Grid Bias for Maximum Power Output. It has been shown in Eqs. (9-2*b*) to (9-6*a*) that the power output of an amplifier varies as the square of the input signal voltage. Therefore, in order to obtain maximum power output, the maximum input signal voltage must be applied. In order to avoid excessive distortion in Class A amplifiers, the operating voltages and the load resistance should be of such values that when the grid is at its most negative value the instantaneous plate current should not be driven into the region of high distortion (see Fig. 9-13). The curvature of the characteristic lines in this region is quite high. Excessive distortion will therefore be produced if the plate-current variation extends into this region. For a definite value of B supply voltage, maximum undistorted power output will be obtained when the peak value of the input signal voltage is equal to the grid bias and when the load resistance and grid bias are of such values that the varying plate current does not extend into the region of high distortion.

Application of this rule can more easily be understood by analysis of the power diagrams of Figs. 9-12 and 9-13. Under the operating conditions represented by Fig. 9-12, the tube is not producing the maximum amount of undistorted power output that it is capable of delivering. This is due to the fact that although the peak value of the input signal voltage is equal to the grid bias, the distortion is zero as $i_{b \cdot \text{max}} - I_b$ is equal to $I_b - i_{b\cdot min}$. The maximum undistorted power output can be obtained by decreasing the load resistance to a value for which the distortion does not exceed 5 per cent. It can also be shown from Fig. 9-13 that, for a given load resistance and B voltage, the maximum power output is not obtained unless the peak input signal voltage is equal to the grid bias.

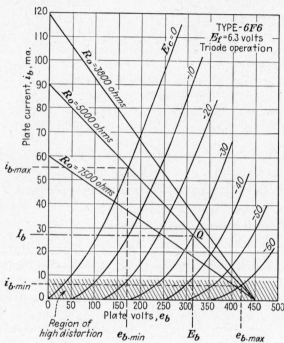

FIG. 9-13.—Distorted output caused by incorrect choice of load line, input signal voltage, or grid bias.

The effect on the power output when incorrect values of grid bias, input signal voltage, or load resistance are used is illustrated by the power diagram of Fig. 9-13 and Example 9-13.

Example 9-13. A 6F6 is being operated as a triode amplifier tube. A load resistance of 5000 ohms, a B supply of 450 volts, and a grid bias of 30 volts are used; the characteristic curves are as shown in Fig. 9-13. (*a*) What is the power output for a signal input voltage whose peak value is 30 volts? (*b*) What is the per cent of second harmonic distortion?

Given:　　　　　　　　　　　Find:
　　Tube = 6F6　　　　　　　　(*a*) P_o = ?
　　Power diagram, Fig. 9-13　　(*b*) Per cent of second harmonic distortion
　　　E_{bb} = 450 volts
　　　E_c = −30 volts
　　　$E_{g\cdot m}$ = 30 volts
　　　R_o = 5000 ohms

Solution:

From Fig. 9-13: $I_b = 27$ ma $E_b = 312$ volts

$i_{b\cdot max} = 55$ ma $e_{b\cdot max} = 420$ volts

$i_{b\cdot min} = 6$ ma $e_{b\cdot min} = 170$ volts

(a) $P_o = \dfrac{(e_{b\cdot max} - e_{b\cdot min})(i_{b\cdot max} - i_{b\cdot min})}{8} = \dfrac{(420 - 170)(55 - 6)}{8} = 1.53$ watts

(b) Per cent of second harmonic distortion $= \dfrac{(i_{b\cdot max} + i_{b\cdot min}) - 2I_b}{2(i_{b\cdot max} - i_{b\cdot min})} \times 100$

$$= \frac{(55 + 6) - 2 \times 27}{2(55 - 6)} \times 100 = 7.14 \text{ per cent}$$

The recommended operating values (Appendix XV) for a 6F6 operated as a Class A triode amplifier are: $E_b = 250$ volts, $E_c = -20$ volts, $E_{g\cdot m} = 20$ volts, $I_b = 31$ ma, and $R_o = 4000$ ohms. Some of the operating values of the 6F6 used in Example 9-13 exceed these recommended values and as a result excessive distortion is produced. If it is desired to operate the tube with the same electrode voltages, the distortion can be reduced by either decreasing the value of the input signal voltage or increasing the value of the load impedance. Decreasing the input signal voltage will decrease the power output considerably, while increasing the value of the load impedance will cause only a comparatively small amount of decrease in the power output. From values obtained from Fig. 9-13, it can be shown that increasing the value of the load resistance to 7500 ohms results in a decrease in the a-c output power to 1.215 watts and reduces the distortion to 6.94 per cent. Although decreasing the value of the load resistance may increase the power output, it may also increase the amount of distortion. Thus, decreasing the value of the load resistance to 3800 ohms increases the a-c power output to 1.71 watts and the distortion to 7.50 per cent.

Higher values of power output and plate efficiency can be obtained by using a higher value of plate voltage than the value usually recommended. When higher plate voltages are used, the grid bias and load resistance should be of such values as to prevent the plate current from exceeding the tube's maximum allowable value. The value of the load resistance used is generally more than twice the value of the plate resistance, and plate efficiencies of 30 to 40 per cent can be obtained. The correct value of grid bias and load resistance for maximum undistorted power output can be obtained either mathematically by use of complex equations, or graphically by the trial-and-error process. The values used should produce the maximum output without exceeding the allowable amount of distortion.

9-8. Class A Power Amplifiers. *Load Lines for Reactive Loads.* It has previously been stated that the load line for a capacitive or inductive load will be an ellipse. This is due to the fact that the voltage across an

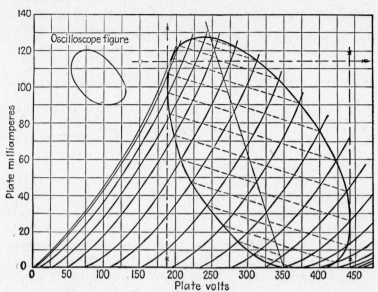

Fig. 9-14.—Graphical construction of load lines for a reactive load. (*From Albert Preisman, Graphical Constructions for Vacuum Tube Circuits.*)

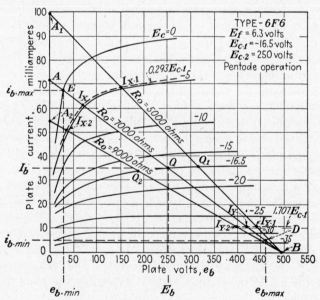

Fig. 9-15.—Load lines for a type 6F6 tube connected for pentode operation.

output reactance is out of phase with the plate current. The output voltage is hence a double-value function of the plate current, and the load line becomes a closed curve (see Fig. 9-14). Increasing the ratio of the output resistance to the output reactance will flatten the ellipse. Thus,

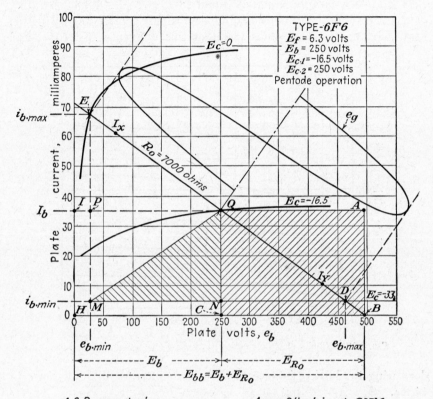

A-C Power output................................Area of the triangle **QNM**
Power lost in the output resistor............Area of the rectangle **QABC**
Plate dissipation................................Area of the rectangle **IQCH**
                                       minus the area of the triangle **QNM**
Power supplied by the B power supply.....Area of the rectangle **IABH**
Power supplied to the plate of the tube.....Area of the rectangle **IQCH**

FIG. 9-16.—Power diagram of a type 6F6 tube connected for pentode operation.

by decreasing the value of the output reactance the ellipse approaches the load line of a resistance and becomes more nearly a straight line.

Load Line for Pentodes and Beam Power Tubes. The load lines for pentodes and beam power tubes are constructed in the same manner as for triodes. Figure 9-15 shows three load lines plotted on the static plate characteristic curves of a 6F6 connected for pentode operation. Recommended values (see Appendix XV) for the 6F6 when operated as a pentode, Class A_1, are: $E_b = 250$ volts, $E_c = -16.5$ volts, $E_{g \cdot m} = 16.5$ volts, $I_b = 34$ ma, and $R_o = 7000$ ohms. The load line for 7000 ohms was plotted on the plate characteristic curves for these operating conditions. For minimum distortion, the load line should be of such a value that $i_{b \cdot max} - I_b$ is approximately equal to $I_b - i_{b \cdot min}$. When operating on the 7000-ohm load line, this difference is only 2 ma. Increasing the load resistance to 9000 ohms increases this difference to 10 ma, and

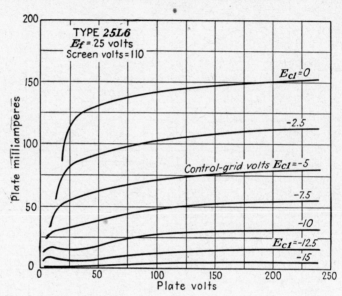

FIG. 9-17.—Family of plate characteristic curves for a beam power tube.

decreasing the load resistance to 5000 ohms increases the difference to 14 ma.

In addition to second harmonic distortion, third harmonic distortion is very pronounced in pentodes and beam power tubes. The reason for this high distortion can be explained by reference to the static plate characteristic curves for these two types of tubes (see Figs. 9-15 and 9-17). It can be seen from these curves that the distance between the grid voltage lines are not uniform. The greatest distance occurs between zero grid bias and the adjacent grid-bias line. The distance between succeeding adjacent grid-bias lines gradually decreases, reaching a minimum between the maximum grid bias and its adjacent grid-bias line. This nonuniform variation between the grid-voltage lines indicates that a change in grid voltage at the higher bias voltages will produce a smaller change in plate current than for the same grid-voltage change at the lower bias voltages. The total distortion produced by pentodes and beam power tubes is therefore higher than the distortion obtained with triodes.

9-9. Effects of Harmonic Distortion. *Calculation of Harmonic Distortion for Pentodes and Beam Power Tubes.* The effects of harmonic distortion on a sinusoidal wave can be observed by reference to the diagrams in Fig. 9-18. A second harmonic tends to change the fundamental wave to a sawtooth wave. This type of distortion is characteristic of all the even harmonics as the addition of the fundamental and all its even harmonics will tend to produce a sawtooth wave. A third harmonic tends to change the fundamental wave to a square wave. This type of distortion is characteristic of all the odd harmonics as the addition of the fundamental and all its odd harmonics will tend to produce a square wave. The distortion produced by both the second and third harmonics results in a wave that is somewhat similar to the distorted saw-tooth wave produced by the second harmonic only. However, the shape of this wave is also dependent upon the ratio of the maximum values of the second and third harmonics. For the resultant wave, shown in Fig. 9-18c, the ratio is 1.

The per cent of harmonic distortion in pentodes and beam power tubes can be calculated by use of Eqs. (9-12), (9-13), and (9-14). As the derivations of these equations are rather complex, they are omitted in this text.

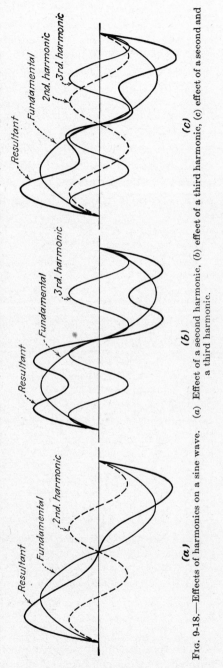

Fig. 9-18.—Effects of harmonics on a sine wave.   (a) Effect of a second harmonic, (b) effect of a third harmonic, (c) effect of a second and a third harmonic.

Per cent of second harmonic distortion

$$= \frac{i_{b\cdot\text{max}} + i_{b\cdot\text{min}} - 2I_b}{i_{b\cdot\text{max}} - i_{b\cdot\text{min}} + 1.41(I_x - I_y)} \times 100 \quad (9\text{-}12)$$

Per cent of third harmonic distortion

$$= \frac{i_{b\cdot\text{max}} - i_{b\cdot\text{min}} - 1.41(I_x - I_y)}{i_{b\cdot\text{max}} - i_{b\cdot\text{min}} + 1.41(I_x - I_y)} \times 100 \quad (9\text{-}13)$$

where I_x = plate current at $0.293E_c$
I_y = plate current at $1.707E_c$

The per cent of the total harmonic distortion (second + third) is equal to the square root of the sum of the per cent of second harmonic distortion squared and the per cent of third harmonic distortion squared.

Per cent of total (second and third) harmonic distortion

$$= \sqrt{\left(\begin{array}{c}\text{Per cent of second}\\\text{harmonic distortion}\end{array}\right)^2 + \left(\begin{array}{c}\text{Per cent of third}\\\text{harmonic distortion}\end{array}\right)^2} \quad (9\text{-}14)$$

Example 9-14. A 6F6, connected as a pentode, is operated along the 7000-ohm load line (Fig. 9-15) with a grid bias of 16.5 volts. If an input signal with a peak value of 16.5 volts is applied, what is the per cent of (*a*) second harmonic distortion? (*b*) Third harmonic distortion? (*c*) Total second and third harmonic distortion?

Given:
Tube = 6F6
E_c = −16.5 volts
$E_{g\cdot m}$ = 16.5 volts
R_o' = 7000 ohms
Load line, Fig. 9-15

Find:
(*a*) Per cent of second harmonic distortion
(*b*) Per cent of third harmonic distortion
(*c*) Per cent of total (second and third) harmonic distortion

Solution:

From Fig. 9-15: $i_{b\cdot\text{max}}$ = 67 ma, $i_{b\cdot\text{min}}$ = 5 ma, I_b = 35 ma, I_x = 61 ma, I_y = 10.5 ma

(*a*) Per cent of second harmonic distortion

$$= \frac{i_{b\cdot\text{max}} + i_{b\cdot\text{min}} - 2I_b}{i_{b\cdot\text{max}} - i_{b\cdot\text{min}} + 1.41(I_x - I_y)} \times 100$$

$$= \frac{67 + 5 - 2 \times 35}{67 - 5 + 1.41(61 - 10.5)} \times 100 = 1.50 \text{ per cent}$$

(*b*) Per cent of third harmonic distortion

$$= \frac{i_{b\cdot\text{max}} - i_{b\cdot\text{min}} - 1.41(I_x - I_y)}{i_{b\cdot\text{max}} - i_{b\cdot\text{min}} + 1.41(I_x - I_y)} \times 100$$

$$= \frac{67 - 5 - 1.41(61 - 10.5)}{67 - 5 + 1.41(61 - 10.5)} \times 100 = 6.91 \text{ per cent}$$

(*c*) Per cent of total harmonic distortion

$$= \sqrt{\left(\begin{array}{c}\text{Per cent of second}\\\text{harmonic distortion}\end{array}\right)^2 + \left(\begin{array}{c}\text{Per cent of third}\\\text{harmonic distortion}\end{array}\right)^2}$$

$$= \sqrt{1.50^2 + 6.91^2} = 7.07 \text{ per cent}$$

The total harmonic distortion of pentodes and beam power tubes for normal operating conditions is usually listed in standard tube manuals.

A total distortion of 8 per cent is listed for the 6F6 when operated under the conditions used in Example 9-14.   The total distortion of 7.07 per cent as calculated in Example 9-14 compares favorably with the value of 8 per cent listed in the tube manual.   From this example it can also be seen that the distortion is above the allowable maximum of 5 per cent and that most of the distortion is caused by the third harmonic.   This is characteristic of pentodes and beam power tubes.   In order to reduce the distortion to the allowable maximum, negative feedback may be applied to the circuits using these types of tubes.   Beam power tubes have a lower percentage of distortion than pentodes and therefore are being used more frequently as power amplifier tubes.

9-10. Power Rating of Pentodes and Beam Power Tubes.   The power diagrams for pentodes and beam power tubes are constructed in a similar manner as for triodes.   Figure 9-16 represents the power diagram for the 6F6 when operated as a pentode.   The same letter notations used in the triode power diagram (Fig. 9-12) are used in the pentode diagram. The power ratings can therefore be found by following the procedure as explained for triodes.   Thus, by using Eq. (9-11a), the power output is found to be 3.375 watts.

Because of the relatively large amount of harmonic distortion in the output of pentodes and beam power tubes, the distortion is generally included in the power output.   The total power output, taking the harmonic power output into consideration, can be calculated by the equation

$$P_o = \frac{[i_{b \cdot \max} - i_{b \cdot \min} + 1.41(I_x - I_y)]^2 R_o'}{32} \qquad (9\text{-}15)$$

Example 9-15.   What is the total power output of the 6F6 pentode used in Example 9-14?

Given: Find:
  Tube $= 6F6$ $P_o = ?$
  $i_{b \cdot \max} = 67$ ma
  $i_{b \cdot \min} = 5$ ma
  $I_x = 61$ ma
  $I_y = 10.5$ ma
  $R_o' = 7000$ ohms

Solution:

$$P_o = \frac{[i_{b \cdot \max} - i_{b \cdot \min} + 1.41(I_x - I_y)]^2 R_o'}{32}$$

$$= \frac{[0.067 - 0.005 + 1.41(0.061 - 0.0105)]^2 \times 7000}{32} = 3.88 \text{ watts}$$

Example 9-16.   The screen grid of the 6F6 used in Example 9-14 is operated at 250 volts and the maximum value of screen-grid current is 10.5 ma.   (*a*) What is the plate dissipation?   (*b*) What is the plate efficiency?   (NOTE: The screen-grid power is considered part of the plate input power.)

Given: Find:
Tube $= 6F6$ (a) $P_p = ?$
$P_o = 3.88$ watts   (b) Plate efficiency $= ?$
$E_b = 250$ volts
$I_b = 35$ ma
$E_{c2} = 250$ volts
$I_{c2} = 10.5$ ma

Solution:
(a) $P_i = E_b I_b = 250 \times 0.035 = 8.75$ watts
     $P_p = P_i - P_o = 8.75 - 3.88 = 4.87$ watts
(b) $P_{c2} = E_{c2} I_{c2} = 250 \times 0.0105 = 2.625$ watts
     $P_{i \cdot T} = P_i + P_{c2} = 8.75 + 2.625 = 11.375$ watts

Plate efficiency $= \dfrac{P_o}{P_{i \cdot T}} \times 100 = \dfrac{3.88}{11.375} \times 100 = 34.1$ per cent

Pentodes and beam power tubes have many advantages over the triodes as a power amplifier. In addition to the higher power output and plate efficiency that is obtainable, less driving voltage is required. This is due to the higher amplification factor of pentodes and beam power tubes.

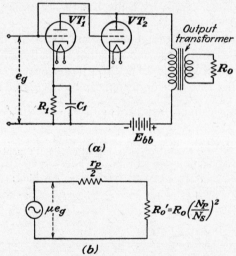

Fig. 9-19.—Two triodes connected for parallel operation. (a) Actual circuit diagram, (b) equivalent electrical circuit.

9-11. Parallel Operation of Power Tubes. If the power output of a single tube is too small to produce a desired amount of volume, two or more power tubes may be connected in parallel in order to obtain the necessary power output. Operating tubes in parallel increases the power output, but the per cent of distortion remains the same as for a single tube. Thus, two identical tubes connected in parallel will provide twice the output of a single tube for the same value of input signal voltage.

The amount of distortion will also be doubled but as the output and the distortion are both doubled, the per cent of distortion remains the same. Figure 9-19a illustrates the manner of connecting two triodes in parallel. The same procedure can be followed for pentodes.

Since the two plates are in parallel, the equivalent plate resistance will be one-half that of a single tube. The voltage generated by each tube will be equal to μe_g. The equivalent electrical circuit for two triodes in parallel can therefore be drawn as shown in Fig. 9-19b.

Example 9-17. A 6L6 beam power pentode is operated so that it produces an output of 6.5 watts. How many of these tubes must be connected in parallel, if it is desired to obtain a 35-db output from the same driving voltage?

Given: Find:
    Tube = 6L6   Number of tubes in parallel = ?
    $P_{o.1}$ = 6.5 watts
    Volume = 35 db
Solution:

$$P_{o.T} = P_R \times \text{antilog} \frac{db}{10} = 0.006 \times \text{antilog} \frac{35}{10} = 18.96 \text{ watts}$$

$$\text{Number of tubes} = \frac{P_{o.T}}{P_{o.1}} = \frac{18.96}{6.5} = 2.92$$

Therefore, use 3 tubes.

9-12. Push-pull Amplifiers. *Push-pull Operation.* Push-pull operation of amplifier tubes is another method of obtaining a greater power output than can be obtained from a single tube. A push-pull amplifier employs two identical tubes operating together as a single stage of amplification. The grids and plates of the two tubes are connected respectively to opposite ends of the secondary of the input transformer and the primary of the output transformer (see Fig. 9-20a). A balanced circuit is obtained by connecting the cathode returns to center taps on the secondary and primary windings of the input and output transformers respectively. As a balanced circuit is necessary for push-pull operation, this system is also referred to as a *balanced amplifier*. A push-pull amplifier circuit may be either resistance-capacitance coupled or transformer coupled.

The varying current in the primary winding of the input transformer, which is actually the output current of the previous stage, induces a corresponding voltage in the secondary. At any instant the two ends of this secondary, 1 and 2 of Fig. 9-20a, are of opposite polarity. Thus the varying input voltages $e_{g.A}$ and $e_{g.B}$ will always be equal and 180 degrees out of phase with each other. Assuming the end of the secondary indicated as 1 to be positive, then the other end indicated as 2 will be negative. The grid of tube A will then become more positive, causing an increase in the plate current flowing through section 3-4 of the primary of the output transformer. The grid of tube B becomes more negative causing the plate current flowing in section 4-5 to decrease. As the two tubes are identical and the changes in their grid voltages are equal, the variation in plate current will also be equal but 180 degrees out of phase with each other. It is apparent that one tube pushes current through one-half of the primary winding of the output transformer while the second tube

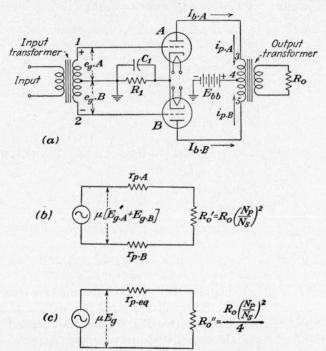

Fig. 9-20.—Push-pull amplifier circuit. (a) Circuit diagram, (b) equivalent electrical circuit, (c) single-tube equivalent electrical circuit.

pulls an equal amount through the other half; hence the name *push-pull*. Push-pull operation is not limited to any particular type of tube; thus triodes, pentodes, or beam power tubes may be operated as balanced amplifiers.

Graphical Analysis of Push-pull Operation. A graphical analysis of push-pull operation for two tubes operating as a Class A₁ amplifier is illustrated in Fig. 9-21. The dynamic characteristics for tube B are plotted inverted with respect to the dynamic characteristics for tube A. The grid of each tube is biased to approximately one-half the cutoff value. With zero signal input, steady plate currents of $I_{b.A}$ and $I_{b.B}$ flow in their respective plate circuits. These two currents are equal and flow in opposite directions in each half of the primary winding of the output transformer.

When an alternating voltage is applied to the two grids, the plate current in one tube increases while the plate current in the other tube decreases. It can be seen that the varying plate current of each tube is badly distorted, as both tubes operate over more than the linear portion

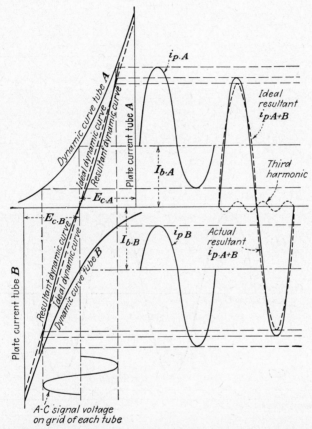

FIG. 9-21.—Graphical analysis of Class A push-pull operation.

of their dynamic curves. The distortion is largely due to the second harmonic since operating over the nonlinear portion of the characteristic curve produces this type of harmonic distortion. The phase relation of the second harmonic produced by each tube is such that they cancel each other in the output transformer. A graphical illustration of how the second harmonic is eliminated is shown in Fig. 9-22. It can also be seen from this figure that the combined output of tubes *A* and *B* is a sine wave devoid of any second harmonic and equal to twice that of either tube.

The net effect of the push-pull action of the varying plate current of each tube flowing through the primary winding of the output transformer is equivalent to an alternating current of twice the value of either plate current flowing through one-half of the primary winding. This effect is

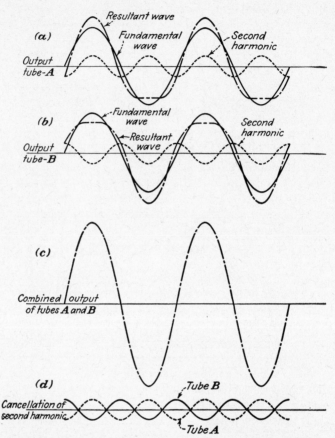

Fig. 9-22.—Input and output waves of a Class A push-pull amplifier.

equivalent to that produced by an input signal voltage equal to the alternating voltage applied to the grid of either tube and operating on a dynamic curve that is the resultant of the dynamic curves of tubes A and B. This ideal dynamic curve is shown as a broken line in Fig. 9-21. The resultant plate current, also shown as a broken line, would be a sine wave. However, the actual resultant dynamic curve is not a straight line as is indicated by the ideal resultant curve, but is slightly curved.

This curvature of the actual resultant dynamic curve produces a third harmonic in the output; with an overload on the tube, a fifth harmonic will also be present.

9-13. Characteristics of Class A_1 Push-pull Amplifiers. Because the second harmonic distortion is balanced out in the output transformer, it is possible to use a load resistance whose value is equal to the plate resistance; thus maximum power output may be obtained. Also, greater values of input signal voltage can be applied to the grid of each tube, as its operation is not limited to the linear portion of its characteristic curve. It is therefore possible to obtain more than twice the power output of a single tube Class A_1 amplifier by operating two similar tubes in push-pull. However, the exciting voltage, measured between the two grids, must be twice that required for one tube.

The average plate currents $I_{b.A}$ and $I_{b.B}$ (Fig. 9-20a) flow in opposite directions in their respective halves of the primary winding of the output transformer. Thus the magnetizing effect of the direct currents on the iron core cancels out. Therefore, there can be no direct current saturation in the core of the output transformer, regardless of how great the average plate currents may be. The incremental inductance will be higher and therefore will improve the low audio-frequency response. Large variable plate currents will produce proportionate changes in the magnetic flux rather than being distorted by the saturation bend in the magnetization curve of the iron.

At any instant, the resultant of the varying plate currents $i_{p.A}$ and $i_{p.B}$ flowing through the B power supply is zero. As there is no current of signal frequency flowing through the source of plate power, there will therefore be no regeneration.

Any alternating voltage that may be present in the plate power supply will also be balanced out in the primary winding of the output transformer. The a-c hum of a push-pull amplifier is therefore greatly reduced.

Because of these many advantages of balanced amplifiers it is more advantageous to use two small tubes in push-pull rather than one large tube capable of producing the same amount of power output.

Although pentodes and beam power tubes may be operated in push-pull, little advantage is gained from the use of these tubes. This is because the third harmonic distortion in pentodes is much higher than in triodes for comparable conditions. The odd harmonics are not balanced out in push-pull operation. In properly designed single-tube class A pentode power amplifiers, the amount of second harmonic distortion is very low.

9-14. Equivalent Electrical Circuit of Push-pull Amplifiers. An equivalent electrical circuit for push-pull operation of two tubes can be drawn as shown in Figs. 9-20b or 9-20c. In the circuit of Fig. 9-20b, the resistance R_o' represents the plate-to-plate load impedance reflected to the full primary winding by the load connected to the secondary of the output transformer. In the circuit of Fig. 9-20c, the two tubes are replaced by an equivalent single tube whose characteristics represent the resultant dynamic curve of Fig. 9-21. The load reflected to this single equivalent tube is designated as R_o'' and is one-fourth the value of R_o' because only one-half of the primary turns are effective with the single equivalent tube. While the operating characteristics of push-pull circuits may be observed from either of the equivalent circuits, the following discussion is based on the equivalent circuit of Fig. 9-20b.

It can be shown from Fig. 9-20b that the effective value of the varying plate current can be expressed as

$$I_p = \frac{\mu(E_{g \cdot A} + E_{g \cdot B})}{r_{p \cdot A} + r_{p \cdot B} + R_o'} \tag{9-16}$$

As $E_{g \cdot A}$ is equal to $E_{g \cdot B}$ and $r_{p \cdot A}$ equals $r_{p \cdot B}$, Eq. (9-16) can be expressed as

$$I_p = \frac{2\mu E_g}{2r_p + R_o'} \tag{9-16a}$$

where $E_g = E_{g \cdot A} = E_{g \cdot B}$
$r_p = r_{p \cdot A} = r_{p \cdot B}$

NOTE: E_g is equal to one-half of the voltage developed across terminals 1 and 2, Fig. 9-20a.

For maximum power output R_o' should be equal to $2r_p$. For this condition, Eq. (9-16a) becomes

$$I_{p \cdot m} = \frac{\mu E_g}{2r_p} \tag{9-17}$$

where $I_{p \cdot m}$ = current at maximum power output.

9-15. Power Output, Load Resistance, and Distortion. From the equivalent electrical circuit shown in Fig. 9-20b, the power output of a push-pull amplifier can be expressed as

$$P_o = \frac{4(\mu E_g)^2 R_o'}{(2r_p + R_o')^2} \tag{9-18}$$

the maximum power output is then equal to

$$P_{o \cdot m} = \frac{(\mu E_{g \cdot m})^2}{4r_p} \tag{9-19}$$

Example 9-18. Two 2A3 tubes are connected to operate as a Class A push-pull amplifier. The operating characteristics of each tube are: $E_b = 250$ volts, $E_c = -45$ volts, and $E_{g \cdot m} = 45$ volts. What is the maximum power output of the two tubes?

Given: Find:
  Tube = 2A3 $P_{o \cdot m}$ = ?
    E_b = 250 volts
    E_c = −45 volts
    $E_{g \cdot m}$ = 45 volts

Solution:

From Appendix XV: r_p = 800 ohms, μ = 4.2

$$P_{o \cdot m} = \frac{(\mu E_{g \cdot m})^2}{4 r_p} = \frac{(4.2 \times 45)^2}{4 \times 800} = 11.16 \text{ watts}$$

The power output may also be determined by means of the tubes' plate characteristic curves and a load line. To plot a load line, the

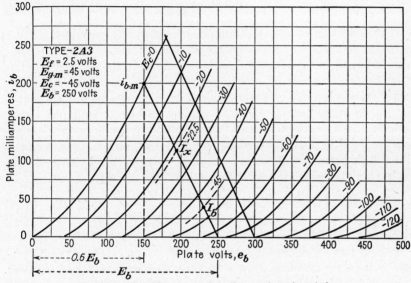

FIG. 9-23.—Load line for push-pull operation of a triode.

desired operating plate voltage must first be known. This value can usually be obtained from the recommended values listed in a tube manual. A vertical line is drawn upward from a point on the abscissa of the plate characteristic curve equal to $0.6 E_b$ (see Fig. 9-23). The point of intersection of this vertical line and the zero grid-voltage curve represents the maximum value of plate current. The load line is drawn from this point of intersection to a point on the abscissa representing the average plate voltage E_b. The maximum power output for two tubes operating Class A push-pull will then be

$$P_{o \cdot m} = \frac{4}{10} \times \frac{E_b}{\sqrt{2}} \times \frac{i_{b \cdot m}}{\sqrt{2}} \qquad (9\text{-}20)$$

or

$$P_{o \cdot m} = \frac{E_b i_{b \cdot m}}{5} \qquad (9\text{-}20a)$$

This simple equation can be used for all triodes operated Class A push-pull. The grid bias and maximum input signal voltage should be approximately equal to those specified for a single-tube Class A operation.

The resistance represented by the load line in Fig. 9-23 is equal to

$$R_o'' = \frac{E_b - 0.6E_b}{i_{b \cdot m}} \tag{9-21}$$

or

$$R_o'' = \frac{0.4E_b}{i_{b \cdot m}} \tag{9-21a}$$

The plate-to-plate load is then equal to

$$R_o' = \frac{1.6E_b}{i_{b \cdot m}} \tag{9-22}$$

The distortion of push-pull amplifiers is generally very low. It can be shown that all even harmonics are eliminated; this is true for the same reason that the second harmonic is balanced out in the primary winding of the output transformer. Although the a-c hum from the plate power supply is balanced out, any hum induced in the input circuit of the amplifier will be amplified in the same manner as any other input signal. Because of the slight curvature of the resultant dynamic curve there will be some third harmonic distortion (see Fig. 9-21) and in some instances also a fifth harmonic distortion. The per cent of third harmonic distortion may be calculated by the equation

$$\text{Per cent of third harmonic distortion} = \frac{i_{b \cdot m} - 2I_x}{2(i_{b \cdot m} + I_x)} \times 100 \tag{9-23}$$

where I_x = plate current at $0.5E_{g \cdot m}$

Example 9-19. Using the plate characteristic curves for a type 2A3 tube (Fig. 9-23) find: (a) the maximum power output, (b) the plate-to-plate load resistance, (c) the per cent of third harmonic distortion for the push-pull circuit of Example 9-18.

Given: Find:

    Tube = 2A3   (a) $P_{o \cdot m}$ = ?

       E_b = 250 volts   (b) R_o' = ?

       E_c = −45 volts   (c) Per of third harmonic distortion

     $E_{g \cdot m}$ = 45 volts

Solution:

From Fig. 9-23: $i_{b \cdot m}$ = 200 ma, I_x = 112 ma

(a) $\quad P_{o \cdot m} = \dfrac{E_b i_{b \cdot m}}{5} = \dfrac{250 \times 0.2}{5} = 10$ watts

(b) $\quad R_o' = \dfrac{1.6E_b}{i_{b \cdot m}} = \dfrac{1.6 \times 250}{0.2} = 2000$ ohms

(c) $\quad$ Per cent of third harmonic distortion $= \dfrac{i_{b \cdot m} - 2I_x}{2(i_{b \cdot m} + I_x)} \times 100$

$$= \frac{0.2 - 2 \times 0.112}{2(0.2 + 0.112)} \times 100 = 3.84 \text{ per cent}$$

The values of power output of the push-pull Class A amplifier using two 2A3 tubes as found in Examples 9-18 and 9-19 compare favorably with each other. From Appendix XV, the maximum undistorted power output obtainable from a single 2A3 tube operated Class A, and with the same electrode potentials and input signal voltage as used in Examples 9-18 and 9-19, is 3.5 watts. The power obtainable from push-pull operation, 10 watts (see Example 9-19), is considerably greater than twice this value. The per cent of distortion is small, being less than the allowable maximum of 5 per cent. It may be noticed that there is a difference in the value of the plate-to-plate resistance used in Example 9-18 and the value calculated in Example 9-19. This difference is due to the fact that in Example 9-18 the plate resistance used is the value obtained for Class A operation at the electrode potentials employed, while in Example 9-19 the plate resistance used is the value obtained from operating on the resultant dynamic curve of the two tubes as indicated on Fig. 9-21.

9-16. Class AB Operation. The distortion caused by operating a tube on the lower bend of its characteristic curve, which is the region of high distortion, is eliminated by the push-pull circuit. It is then possible to increase the bias on the tubes used in a push-pull circuit so that they operate as Class AB. Increasing the grid bias of a tube decreases the value of the plate current with zero signal input. This decrease in the value of the operating plate current permits the use of higher screen-grid and plate voltages, and also increases the plate efficiency of the tube. Because of these factors, a greater power output can be obtained by operating two tubes as Class AB push-pull than by using the same tubes operated as Class A push-pull.

Class AB amplifiers may be operated with or without grid current flowing. As Class AB_1, the grid bias is always greater than the peak value of the input signal voltage applied to each tube. There will be no grid-current flow in either tube as the potential on their grids will not be positive during any part of the input cycle. In Class AB_2, the grid bias is always less than the peak value of the input signal voltage applied to each tube. There will, therefore, be some grid-current flow in each tube during the portion of the input cycle that the grid is positive.

The general operating characteristics of Class AB_1 push-pull amplifiers are similar to those for Class A. The equations given for Class A operation are also applicable for Class AB_1. A higher power output and a higher plate efficiency (with a slight increase in the distortion) can be obtained from Class AB_1 than can be obtained from the same tubes operated Class A.

The grid-current flow in a Class AB_2 amplifier represents a loss of power. This loss plus the power loss in the input transformer represents

the total amount of driving power required by the grid circuit.   In order
to minimize the amount of distortion set up in the grid circuit, the power
of the driving stage is generally made considerably higher than the minimum required amount.   The input transformer of a Class AB_1 push-pull
amplifier is usually a step-down transformer.

Because of the large fluctuations in plate current, a cathode bias
arrangement cannot be used for Class AB operation and the plate power
supply should have good regulation.   The grid bias is usually obtained
from a fixed resistor in the power supply.   In order to obtain satisfactory regulation, the power supply generally used for a Class AB amplifier
employs a choke input filter, a mercury vapor rectifier tube, low-resistance
filter chokes, and a low-resistance power transformer.

9-17. Class B Operation.   The plate current with zero input signal
voltage can be reduced to a minimum by adjusting the grid bias of a tube
to approximately cutoff, which is Class B operation.   Each tube of a
Class B push-pull amplifier is operated in this manner.   Referring to
Fig. 9-20, it can be seen that when the grid of tube A is made more
positive, the grid of tube B will be made more negative.   During this half
of the input cycle the plate current of tube B will be zero.   During the
next half-cycle the grid of tube A becomes more negative and the grid of
tube B more positive.   During this half-cycle the plate current of tube A
will be zero.   Thus, one tube amplifies the positive half-cycles and the
other tube amplifies the negative half-cycles.

The two tubes alternately supply current to the primary winding of
the output transformer.   Each tube delivers power to one-half of the
primary winding for one-half of the cycle.   This is equivalent to one tube
delivering power to one-half of the primary winding of the output transformer for an entire cycle.   Under this condition, the effective load R_o'' is
equal to one-fourth of the value of the impedance, R_o' reflected to the full
primary by the load R_o connected to the secondary of the output transformer.   The equivalent electrical circuit is similar to that for Class A
and Class AB shown in Fig. 9-20.   However, the value of μ and r_p are the
values for Class B operation and are not equal to those values generally
listed in a tube manual which are for Class A operation.   The values of
μ and r_p for Class B operation can be obtained from the plate characteristic curves.   The power output of a Class B amplifier can be obtained by
use of Eqs. (9-18) and (9-19) if the Class B operating values of μ and r_p
are substituted in place of the Class A values.

As the fluctuations in plate current of a Class B amplifier will be higher
than for Class AB, it is important that the power supply used should
have good regulation.   The remarks concerning the power supply used
for Class AB operation therefore also apply to Class B operation.

To avoid the use of large fixed sources of biasing voltage, there are a number of tubes designed especially for Class B operation. These tubes have a high amplification factor and the plate current is small when the grid voltage is zero. These tubes require no bias supply, as they can be operated as Class B at a bias of zero volts. It is also common practice to mount two triode units in one envelope so that only one tube is required for a Class B push-pull stage. The 6N7, 6A6, 6Y7-G, 6Z7-G, and 1G6-G are examples of Class B twin triodes.

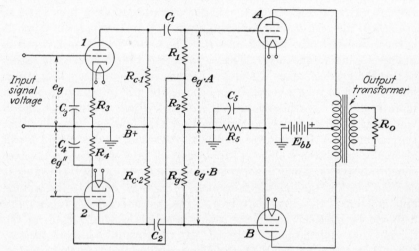

Fig. 9-24.—Use of a phase inverter tube in a resistance-capacitance-coupled push-pull amplifier circuit.

Because the plate current with zero input signal voltage will be practically zero, Class B amplifiers have a high plate efficiency. The grid is usually driven positive and the power output will be unusually high in proportion to the size of the tube. However, because the grids are driven positive and draw considerable power when operated as Class B, a high value of input signal power must be supplied from the driver stage to compensate for this loss of power.

9-18. Phase Inverter. In the analysis of push-pull operation it was shown that in addition to the input signal voltage on the grid of each tube being approximately equal in magnitude to each other at all times, they must also be 180 degrees out of phase with each other. With transformer coupling, the 180-degree phase difference between the two input voltages is obtained by means of an input transformer having a center-tapped secondary (see Fig. 9-20a). With resistance-capacitance coupling, the out-of-phase relationship between the two input voltages is obtained by employing the inverter action of a vacuum tube. A tube used in this manner is called a *phase inverter*.

The circuit diagram for a resistance-capacitance-coupled push-pull amplifier is shown in Fig. 9-24. In this circuit, the driving voltage is obtained from tube 1 and the phase inversion from tube 2. Tubes A and B are the tubes being operated in push-pull; they correspond to tubes A and B of the circuit shown in Fig. 9-20a. When a varying input voltage is applied to the grid of tube 1, the varying output voltage of this tube will be applied to the grid of tube A. By means of the voltage divider resistances R_1 and R_2, a portion of the output voltage of tube 1 is also applied to the grid of tube 2. The output of the phase inverter (tube 2) is then applied to the grid of tube B. The action just described occurs practically instantaneously. Thus a positive output voltage from tube 1 causes the grids of tubes A and 2 to become more positive. The output plate current of tube 2 increases and causes the grid of tube B to become more negative. In this manner, the input voltages at tubes A and B will always be 180 degrees out of phase with each other. In order that the magnitude of the voltages applied to the grids of tubes A and B will always be equal, the voltage e_g'' applied to the grid of the phase inverter should always be equal in magnitude to the input voltage e_g. This is accomplished by making the ratio of $R_1 + R_2$ to R_2 equal to the voltage amplification of the circuit of tube 1. The characteristics of tubes 1 and 2 should be identical and hence a twin triode is generally used for the driving tube and the phase inverter. As the output circuits of the two tubes should also be identical, the plate-coupling resistors $R_{c.1}$ and $R_{c.2}$ are of equal values, and the grid-leak resistor R_g is equal to R_1 plus R_2. The values of the resistors in the voltage divider circuit can be calculated by use of the equations

$$R_2 = \frac{R_g}{VA_1} \qquad (9\text{-}24)$$

$$R_1 = R_g - R_2 \qquad (9\text{-}25)$$

where VA_1 = voltage amplification from tube 1
R_1, R_2, and R_g = resistors as indicated on Fig. 9-24

The values to be used for the plate-coupling and grid-leak resistors will depend upon the tube employed and can be obtained from Appendix XVI.

9-19. Output Transformer Circuit. *Impedance Matching.* In a radio receiver the output of the power tube (or tubes) is used to drive a loudspeaker. The type of loudspeaker most generally used is the dynamic speaker. The output load into which the power tube operates will then be the voice coil of the dynamic speaker. The impedance of the voice coil is generally less than 10 ohms, being mostly resistive with a slight amount of inductance present. For all practical purposes, the impedance of the voice coil may be considered as being only resistance.

Because of the large difference between the resistance of the voice coil and the plate resistance of the power tube, it is obvious that the power tube should not be operated directly into the voice coil. Therefore, an output transformer is used to couple the output of the tube to the voice coil of the loudspeaker. The transformer may be regarded as an impedance changer because the impedance presented to the plate circuit of the tube (impedance of the primary side of the output transformer) is equal to the impedance of the load (impedance of the voice coil connected in the secondary side of the output transformer) multiplied by the square of the ratio of the primary turns to the secondary turns. This relationship can be derived from Eq. (2-76) in Art. 2-29. The value of impedance required for the plate load can therefore be obtained by using a transformer as the coupling device between the plate of the power tube and the voice coil of the dynamic speaker. A transformer used in this manner is called an *output transformer* (see Figs. 9-20a and 9-24).

The Output Transformer. The average radio receiver in the home is usually operated with an audio power output of less than one watt. Three watts of audio power greatly exceeds the amount required to produce sufficient volume for the average person in a normal living room. As output transformers are usually rated from 8 to 20 watts, this transformer is seldom operated at or near its rated output.

A transformer used as an impedance changer will change the magnitude of the impedance without changing the phase relation, assuming it to be an ideal transformer. As the impedance of the voice coil may be considered as being pure resistance, the impedance reflected to the primary winding will also be pure resistance. The turns ratio required of the output transformer is

$$\frac{N_P}{N_S} = \sqrt{\frac{R_o'}{R_o}} \tag{9-26}$$

where N_P = number of turns on the primary winding
N_S = number of turns on the secondary winding
R_o' = required plate load resistance, ohms
R_o = resistance of the voice coil, ohms

Example 9-20. A 7A5 beam power amplifier tube is used in the power output stage of a radio receiver. For the electrode voltages at which the tube is to be operated, it is recommended that the plate-load resistance be 2500 ohms. The resistance of the voice coil of the dynamic speaker is 9.76 ohms. What is the turns ratio required of the output transformer?

Given:
$R_o' = 2400$ ohms
$R_o = 9.76$ ohms

Find:
$\dfrac{N_P}{N_S} = ?$

Solution:

$$\frac{N_P}{N_S} = \sqrt{\frac{R_o'}{R_o}} = \sqrt{\frac{2500}{9.76}} = 16$$

The output transformer used with a push-pull circuit has a center-tapped primary. The core of this type transformer does not have to be as large as for a transformer used with single tube operation. This is

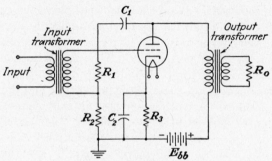

FIG. 9-25.—A voltage-controlled feedback-amplifier circuit as applied to a single-tube power amplifier.

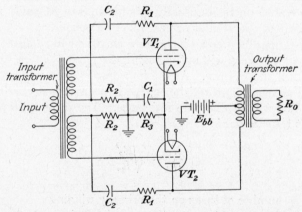

FIG. 9-26.—A push-pull amplifier circuit with voltage-controlled feedback.

due to the fact that the direct currents in the two halves of the primary winding flow in opposite directions and the resultant magnetization of the core is very low.

9-20. Negative Feedback. The distortion developed in the power amplifier circuit can be reduced to a negligible amount by the use of negative feedback. The advantages, operation, limitations, and basic circuit connections for negative feedback as applied to power amplifier circuits are similar to those for the audio amplifier circuits as explained in Arts. 8-14 to 8-17. The equations used in the calculations of feedback in a-f amplifier circuits may, therefore, also be used in the calculation of feedback for power amplifier circuits. As the power output of most radio receivers greatly exceeds the one watt of output power that is usually sufficient for the average home receiver, the loss of power due to negative feedback is of little or no consequence.

Negative feedback as applied to a single stage of power amplification is shown in the circuit diagram of Fig. 9-25. In a push-pull amplifier circuit, negative feedback can be obtained by use of a separate voltage divider network in the plate circuit of each tube as shown in Fig. 9-26.

BIBLIOGRAPHY

ALBERT, A. L., *Fundamental Electronics and Vacuum Tubes*, The Macmillan Company, New York.

EASTMAN, A. V., *Fundamentals of Vacuum Tubes*, McGraw-Hill Book Company, Inc., New York.

GHIRARDI, A. A., Practical Radio Course, *Radio News*, August, September, October, 1943.

HENNEY, K., *Principles of Radio*, John Wiley & Sons, Inc., New York.

PREISMAN, A., *Graphical Constructions for Vacuum Tube Circuits*, McGraw-Hill Book Company, Inc., New York.

REICH, H. J., *Theory and Applications of Electron Tubes*, McGraw-Hill Book Company, Inc., New York.

SMITH, F. L., *The Radiotron Designer's Handbook*, The Wireless Press, Sydney, Australia; distributed in U.S.A. by R.C.A. Manufacturing Company, Inc., Harrison, N. J.

TERMAN, F. E., *Fundamentals of Radio*, McGraw-Hill Book Company, Inc., New York.

QUESTIONS

1. (a) Explain the purpose of power amplifiers. (b) How are power amplifiers classified in terms of operating frequency? (c) How are power amplifiers classified in terms of tube-operating characteristics?

2. Compare voltage amplifiers and power amplifiers in terms of (a) plate circuit impedance, (b) voltage amplification, (c) plate current.

3. (a) Why is it possible to use the static characteristic curves of a tube for analyzing the operation of voltage amplifiers but not for the analysis of power amplifiers? (b) What type of characteristic curves are used in conjunction with power amplifiers?

4. (a) How can the dynamic characteristics of a tube be obtained from the static characteristic curves? (b) What form of load line is obtained when the plate load is resistive? Inductive or capacitive?

5. (a) Why is it desirable to have the dynamic transfer characteristic curves approximately straight lines throughout the signal voltage range? (b) What factors affect the shape and the location of the load line?

6. (a) What is meant by the quiescent point? (b) What determines its location?

7. Explain and establish proof of the phase relation between: (a) e_g and i_p, (b) e_g and e_b, (c) e_g and e_p, (d) e_b and e_p, (e) e_b and i_p.

8. How may a family of dynamic characteristic curves be obtained from the static characteristics?

9. Describe three effects on the dynamic characteristic curves when the value of the plate load resistance is increased.

10. (*a*) What are the two components of the plate current of a tube when an a-c signal is applied to the grid?   (*b*) What does each component contribute to the circuit?

11. (*a*) State the principle of maximum power transfer.   (*b*) Establish proof of this principle.

12. (*a*) What is meant by distortion in an amplifier?   (*b*) What is nonlinear distortion?   (*c*) Why is distortion present in a Class A (single-tube) power amplifier?

13. (*a*) What is meant by the maximum undistorted power output?   (*b*) What per cent of distortion is tolerated in order to obtain maximum power output?   (*c*) What value of load resistance is generally used in order to obtain maximum undistorted power output with a single tube triode power amplifier?

14. (*a*) What is meant by power amplification?   (*b*) What is meant by the driving power?

15. Does a power amplifier generally provide a large or small amount of voltage amplification?   Explain.

16. (*a*) What is the plate circuit efficiency?   (*b*) What is the plate efficiency? (*c*) Which is more commonly used?

17. (*a*) What is the highest possible value of plate efficiency of a single-tube Class A amplifier?   (*b*) Prove the answer given to (*a*).   (*c*) What values of plate efficiency are ordinarily attained in practice?

18. (*a*) What is meant by the plate dissipation of a tube?   (*b*) What is meant by the screen dissipation of a tube?   (*c*) How does the screen dissipation affect the plate efficiency of a tube?

19. (*a*) What is meant by the power sensitivity of a power amplifier tube?   (*b*) When is this term used?

20. (*a*) What is meant by Class A_2 operation of an amplifier?   (*b*) What circuit development has made Class A_2 operation practical?   (*c*) What are the advantages of Class A_2 operation?

21. (*a*) What operating characteristics can be obtained from a power diagram similar to Fig. 9-12?   (*b*) How is each of these characteristics represented on the power diagram?

22. (*a*) In what manner does the output power vary with a change in the value of the input signal voltage?   (*b*) What limits the extent to which the power output may be increased by raising the value of the input signal voltage in Class A amplifiers? Explain.

23. What effect will be produced upon the amount of power output and the second harmonic distortion of a single-tube Class A amplifier by (*a*) increasing the value of the load impedance?   (*b*) Decreasing the value of the load impedance?   (*c*) How can the correct operating value for maximum undistorted power output be determined?

24. (*a*) What is the shape of the load line when the plate load is a reactive load? (*b*) What is the effect on the shape of the load line when resistance is added to the load?

25. With resistive load, what condition is necessary for minimum distortion?

26. (*a*) What harmonic distortion is present in amplifiers employing pentodes and beam power tubes?   (*b*) What causes this distortion?   (*c*) How does this differ from triodes?

27. What effect is produced on a sine wave by (*a*) a second harmonic?   (*b*) A third harmonic?   (*c*) Second and third harmonics?

28. (*a*) How does the distortion in beam power tubes compare with that in pentodes of similar rating? (*b*) Which of these tube types is more commonly used? (*c*) What may be done to reduce the amount of distortion in circuits using these tubes?

29. What does the rated power output of pentodes and beam power tubes represent?

30. What are some of the advantages of pentodes and beam power tubes over triodes?

31. (*a*) What is the purpose of operating two or more tubes in parallel? (*b*) How does parallel operation affect the per cent of distortion?

32. (*a*) What is the purpose of operating two tubes in push-pull? (*b*) How are the grids and the plates of the tubes connected to the transformers? (*c*) Explain why center-tapped transformers are necessary.

33. Explain the importance of the phase relation of the various voltages in push-pull operation.

34. Show how second harmonic distortion is eliminated when two tubes are operated in push-pull.

35. (*a*) What is the cause of third and fifth harmonics in the output of a push-pull amplifier? (*b*) Why does not the push-pull operation reduce the effect of odd harmonics in addition to the even harmonics?

36. (*a*) What are the advantages of push-pull amplifiers? (*b*) Why are triodes generally used in push-pull amplifiers?

37. Explain why the plate-to-plate load impedance should be four times the value of the plate resistance of a single equivalent tube when it is desired to obtain maximum power output from a push-pull amplifier.

38. Work out the derivation of Eq. (9-19) from Eq. (9-18) noting that maximum power output occurs when R_o' is equal to $2r_p$.

39. How does the amount of power output of two tubes operated in push-pull compare with the power output of the same tubes operated in parallel?

40. What are the advantages of Class AB push-pull operation over Class A push-pull?

41. What is the difference between Class AB_1 and Class AB_2 operation of push-pull amplifiers?

42. Why does a Class AB_2 amplifier require a greater amount of driving power than a single-tube Class A amplifier?

43. (*a*) What operating characteristic is required of the power supply for the plate circuit of Class AB power amplifiers? (*b*) Explain why this is necessary.

44. How is cathode bias usually obtained in a Class AB power amplifier?

45. Describe the operation of a Class B push-pull amplifier.

46. What are the operating characteristics of the Class B push-pull amplifier?

47. (*a*) What is a phase inverter? (*b*) What is its purpose? (*c*) When is it used?

48. Explain the operation of a phase inverter as used in conjunction with a push-pull amplifier.

49. (*a*) What important purpose does the output transformer serve? (*b*) Why is the output transformer generally required?

50. (*a*) How much power output is generally required of the average home receiver? (*b*) How does the power rating of power output transformers compare with the amount of power used under average operating conditions?

51. In what manner does the output transformer of a push-pull amplifier differ from one used with a single tube amplifier?

52. (*a*) What advantage is gained by applying negative feedback to a power amplifier? (b) Why is it possible to apply negative feedback to some power amplifier circuits without providing additional gain?

PROBLEMS

1. If an a-c signal whose maximum value is 4 volts is applied to the circuit represented by Figs. 9-2 and 9-4, what is the range of variation of the quantities e_c, e_b, and i_b?

2. If the tube and circuit of Figs. 9-2 and 9-4 are operated with a grid bias of 4 volts and an input signal of 2 volts (peak value), what is the range of variation of the quantities e_c, e_b, and i_b?

3. If the tube and circuit of Figs. 9-2 and 9-4 are operated with a grid bias of 4 volts and an input signal of 4 volts (peak value), what is the range of variation of the quantities e_c, e_b, and i_b?

4. The type 6B4-G is a triode power amplifier tube with characteristics similar to those of the type 2A3 and represented by Fig. 9-23. (a) Replot the static characteristic curves for this tube. (b) Draw the load line for this tube when being operated with a resistive load of 2500 ohms and a B power supply of 400 volts.

5. If the tube and circuit represented by the curves drawn for Prob. 4 are operated with a grid bias of 45 volts and a signal input of 45 volts (peak value), determine (a) the quiescent current, (b) the range of grid voltage variation, (c) the range of plate voltage variation, (d) the range of plate current variation.

6. For the conditions specified for Prob. 5, determine from the curves (a) the maximum amount of plate current variation during the positive half of the input signal, (b) the maximum amount of plate current variation during the negative half of the input signal, (c) the maximum amount of plate voltage variation during the positive half of the input signal, (d) the maximum amount of plate voltage variation during the negative half of the input signal.

7. (a) By use of Eq. (4-8), determine the maximum value of the varying component of the plate current for the circuit of Prob. 5. (NOTE: Use the amplification factor and the plate resistance given in Appendix XV.) (b) By use of Eq. (4-9), determine the maximum value of the varying component of the output signal voltage. (c) Compare the results of (a) and (b) with the answers to Prob. 6 and explain the reason for any variation. (d) What are the effective values of the a-c component of the plate current and of the output signal voltage? (e) Using the values obtained in (d), determine the power output of the amplifier.

8. An amplifier using a type 6B4-G is being operated with a plate voltage of 250 volts and a grid bias of 45 volts. (a) What value of plate-load resistance is required to produce maximum power output? (b) What is the maximum power output obtainable with an input signal voltage of 45 volts peak value?

9. A type 45 triode power amplifier tube being operated with 180 volts at its plate and -31.5 volts at its grid is to be used to amplify a signal with a peak value of 31.5 volts. (a) What value of load resistance is required to produce maximum power output? (b) What is the maximum power output? (c) What is the power output if the value of the load resistor is increased to 2700 ohms and the signal voltage is reduced to 30.6 volts (peak value)?

10. What is the per cent of second harmonic distortion of the amplifier circuit in Prob. 1?

11. What is the per cent of second harmonic distortion of the amplifier circuit in Prob. 5?

12. (a) What value of load resistance is recommended to be used with the amplifier

of Prob. 8 in order to obtain maximum undistorted power output? (b) If it is desired to retain the same zero signal operating point, that is, $E_c = -45$ volts, $E_b = 250$ volts, and $I_b = 60$ ma, what value of B supply voltage is required? (c) What is the power output under this condition if the input signal is 45 volts? [Use Eq. (9-6a).] (d) Add a load line to the curves of Prob. 4 for these conditions and calculate the per cent of second harmonic distortion.

13. (a) What value of load resistance is recommended to be used with the amplifier of Prob. 9 in order to obtain maximum undistorted power output? (b) What is the power output under this condition if the input signal remains 31.5 volts?

14. The amplifier of Prob. 5 produces an output of 4 watts with the following operating values: $R_o = 2500$ ohms, $E_{bb} = 400$ volts, $E_b = 250$ volts, $E_c = -45$ volts, $E_{g \cdot m} = 45$ volts, $I_b = 60$ ma. (a) What is its plate circuit efficiency? (b) What is its plate efficiency?

15. The amplifier of Prob. 12 produces an output of 5 watts with the following operating values: $R_o = 1600$ ohms, $E_{bb} = 346$ volts, $E_b = 250$ volts, $E_c = -45$ volts, $E_{g \cdot m} = 45$ volts, $I_b = 60$ ma. (a) What is its plate circuit efficiency? (b) What is its plate efficiency?

16. What is the plate dissipation of the power tube used in Prob. 14?

17. What is the plate dissipation of the power tube used in Prob. 15?

18. What is the power sensitivity of the tube as operated in Prob. 14?

19. What is the power sensitivity of the tube as operated in Prob. 15?

20. Using the curves of Prob. 4 as the basis of a power diagram, determine the operating characteristics of the circuit with a 2500-ohm load impedance and a peak signal input of 45 volts. (a) What is the power output? (b) What is the plate circuit efficiency? (c) What is the plate efficiency? (d) What is the plate dissipation? (e) What is the power dissipated in the output resistor?

21. Using the curves of Prob. 4 as the basis of a power diagram, determine the operating characteristics of the circuit with a 1600-ohm load impedance and a peak signal input of 45 volts. (a) What is the power output? (b) What is the plate circuit efficiency? (c) What is the plate efficiency? (d) What is the plate dissipation? (e) What is the power dissipated in the output resistor?

22. What is the power output and the per cent of second harmonic distortion for the 6F6 tube, represented by the curves of Fig. 9-13 for triode operation, for a load resistance of 7500 ohms, a B supply of 450 volts, a grid bias of 30 volts, and a signal input with a peak value of 30 volts?

23. What is the power output and the per cent of second harmonic distortion for the 6F6 tube, represented by the curves of Fig. 9-13 for triode operation, for a load resistance of 3800 ohms, a B supply of 450 volts, a grid bias of 30 volts, and a signal input with a peak value of 30 volts?

24. If the 6F6 pentode represented by the curves of Fig. 9-15 is operated with a plate load of 5000 ohms, what are the values of: (a) $i_{b \cdot max}$? (b) $i_{b \cdot min}$? (c) I_b? (d) I_x? (e) I_y? (f) E_b?

25. From the values obtained in Prob. 24, determine (a) the per cent of second harmonic distortion, (b) the per cent of third harmonic distortion, (c) the per cent of total harmonic distortion, (d) the power output, (e) the plate efficiency if the screen grid current is 10.5 ma.

26. If the 6F6 pentode represented by the curves of Fig. 9-15 is operated with a plate load of 9000 ohms, what are the values of (a) $i_{b \cdot max}$? (b) $i_{b \cdot min}$? (c) I_b? (d) I_x? (e) I_y? (f) E_b?

27. From the values obtained in Prob. 26, determine (a) the per cent of second harmonic distortion, (b) the per cent of third harmonic distortion, (c) the per cent of total harmonic distortion, (d) the power output, (e) the plate efficiency if the screen grid current is 10.5 ma.

28. A certain power circuit employs four 6K6-G pentodes operated in parallel. Each tube has an effective plate load of 7600 ohms and is operated with 250 volts at its plate, 250 volts at the screen grid, and -18 volts at the control grid. (a) What is the power output of each tube (Appendix XV)? (b) What is the power output of the circuit? (c) What is the decibel rating of the circuit?

29. How many tubes and what operating values should be used if it is desired to obtain 15 watts of output from a number of type 43 tubes (same as 25A6-GT/G) operated in parallel?

30. (a) What power output will be obtained from five 6F6's operated in parallel as Class A pentode amplifiers if the operating characteristics are: $E_b = 250$ volts, $E_{c.1} = -16.5$ volts, $E_{c.2} = 250$ volts, and $R_o = 7000$ ohms? (b) What is the decibel rating of the circuit?

31. (a) What is the output of the circuit of Prob. 30 if the plate and screen voltages are increased to 285 volts and the grid bias is increased to 20 volts? (b) What is the decibel rating of the circuit?

32. Two 2A3 tubes, represented by Fig. 9-23, are connected to operate as a Class AB_1 push-pull amplifier. The operating characteristics of each tube are $E_b = 300$ volts, $E_c = -60$ volts, and $E_{g.m} = 60$ volts. (a) What are the values of $i_{b.max}$ and I_x? (b) What is the maximum power output of the two tubes? (c) What is the required value of plate-to-plate load resistance? (d) What is the per cent of third harmonic distortion?

33. Two type 6L6 tubes are to be used in a Class A_1 push-pull amplifier. The operating values of the tubes and circuit are $E_b = 250$ volts, $E_{c.1} = -16$ volts, $E_{c.2} = 250$ volts, $r_p = 24,500$ ohms, $g_m = 5500$ micromhos, peak grid-to-grid signal voltage $= 32$ volts, plate-to-plate load resistance $= 5000$ ohms. What is the power output of the amplifier?

34. Two type 6L6 tubes are to be used in a Class AB_1 push-pull amplifier. The operating values of the tubes and circuit are $E_b = 360$ volts, $E_{c.1} = -22.5$ volts, $E_{c.2} = 270$ volts, $r_p = 28,000$ ohms, $g_m = 5000$ micromhos, peak grid-to-grid signal voltage $= 45$ volts, plate-to-plate load resistance $= 4300$ ohms. What is the power output of the amplifier?

35. Two type 6L6 tubes are to be used in a Class AB_2 push-pull amplifier. The operating values of the tubes and circuit are $E_b = 360$ volts, $E_{c.1} = -22.5$ volts, $E_{c.2} = 270$ volts, $r_p = 28,000$ ohms, $g_m = 5000$ micromhos, peak grid-to-grid signal voltage $= 72$ volts, plate-to-plate load resistance $= 3800$ ohms. What is the power output of the amplifier?

36. A 6N7-G twin triode is to be used in a Class B push-pull amplifier. The operating values of the tubes and circuit are $E_b = 300$ volts, $E_c = 0$ volts, $r_p = 13,000$ ohms, $\mu = 35$, peak grid-to-grid signal voltage $= 80$ volts, plate-to-plate load resistance $= 8000$ ohms. What is the power output of the amplifier? Hint: The effective plate-to-plate load resistance is one-quarter of the actual value.

37. A driving tube and a phase inverter, similar to tubes 1 and 2 of Fig. 9-24, are units of a 6N7 twin-triode tube. The plate power supply provides 300 volts, $R_{c.1} = 100,000$ ohms, C_1 and $C_2 = 0.015$ μf, and $R_g = 250,000$ ohms (see Fig. 9-24). (a) What value is recommended for $R_{c.2}$? (b) What voltage amplification is produced by the driver stage (Appendix XVI)? (c) What value is recommended for R_2? (d) What value is recommended for R_1?

38. The output of a 50L6-GT beam power amplifier tube is to be coupled to the voice coil of a loudspeaker by means of an output transformer. (*a*) What turns ratio should the output transformer have if the resistance of the voice coil is 6 ohms and the plate load should be 2000 ohms? (*b*) What current rating (minimum) should the transformer have?

39. A universal output transformer, that is, one with taps brought out from several points on its windings, is designed to provide a 2500-ohm plate load from either a 2-, 4-, 8-, or 500-ohm load. What is the turns ratio if the output load tap used is (*a*) 2? (*b*) 4? (*c*) 8? (*d*) 500?

40. A push-pull amplifier is provided with negative feedback in the manner indicated in Fig. 9-26. What is the per cent of feedback if the value of R_1 is 50,000 ohms and R_2 is 5000 ohms?

41. What values would be required for R_1 and R_2 of Fig. 9-26 if it is desired to produce 10 per cent feedback and the total resistance of the feedback circuit is to be 100,000 ohms?

CHAPTER X

VACUUM-TUBE OSCILLATOR CIRCUITS

The frequency of the varying currents or voltages associated with radio and electronic circuits may vary from a few cycles per second to millions of cycles per second. A vacuum tube, when used in conjunction with the proper combination of circuit elements, may be made to produce an alternating current having almost any value of frequency. The vacuum tube does not create any electrical energy; it merely changes one kind of current to another. The electrical circuit associated with a vacuum tube when used to produce an alternating current is called an *oscillator circuit*. In addition to having a wide frequency range, the frequency and amplitude of the output of vacuum-tube oscillator circuits are comparatively easy to control. The circuits used for oscillators are rather simple to construct and are relatively inexpensive. A vacuum-tube oscillator circuit can be designed so that its output is devoid of any harmonics or so that it is rich in harmonic content. Because of these favorable characteristics, vacuum-tube oscillator circuits form an important part of modern radio and electronic equipment.

10-1. Uses of Vacuum-tube Oscillator Circuits. *Use of Oscillators for Radio Circuits.* The applications of vacuum-tube oscillator circuits are many and varied. The waves sent out by a radio transmitter consist of electromagnetic and electrostatic fields. As these fields are caused by an alternating current, their frequencies are the same as that of the alternating current producing them. The frequency of the alternating currents used in communications ranges from hundreds of thousands of cycles per second to millions of cycles per second. It is physically impossible to construct a generator to rotate at the speed required to produce these high-frequency currents. Hence, radio transmitters depend on vacuum-tube oscillators to produce their high-frequency carrier currents. Vacuum-tube oscillators are as important to a radio transmitting station as the generator is to the power plant.

An oscillator circuit is used in every superheterodyne receiver. This local oscillator is used to generate a stable r-f signal that is heterodyned with the incoming signal to produce an intermediate frequency. The basic local oscillator circuits will be considered in greater detail in a later part of this chapter.

Uses of Oscillators in Test Equipment. The oscillator circuit is also used in radio test equipment such as the signal generator. The r-f signal generator is very useful in aligning the r-f tuned circuits, the oscillator circuit, and the i-f amplifier circuits of a radio receiver. The a-f signal generator is very useful in locating the source of rattles and buzzes in radio equipment.

Use of Oscillators in Electronic and Industrial Equipment. A sweep generator, which is a special form of oscillator circuit, makes it possible to deflect the spot of light across the screen of a cathode-ray tube at a uniform rate. The oscillator circuit is therefore an essential part of practically all types of electronic equipment employing a cathode-ray tube. Among the imposing list of apparatus using the cathode-ray tube are the oscilloscope, television, radar, and numerous types of industrial control equipment.

10-2. Types of Oscillator Circuits. Just as the uses of oscillator circuits are many and varied, so too are the types and kinds of oscillator circuits many and varied. It is beyond the scope of this text to discuss every type of oscillator circuit. However, in order that the reader may have some idea of the large scope of oscillator circuits, a brief outline description of the most important types used in radio and electronics will be given. The general discussion of the principles and the operation of oscillator circuits in this chapter will be limited to those types which are frequently used in the production of a-f and r-f oscillations in radio equipment.

General Classifications of Oscillator Circuits. Vacuum-tube oscillator circuits may be broadly divided into two groups: (1) those circuits used to produce a *nonsinusoidal wave;* (2) those circuits used to produce a *sinusoidal wave.*

Oscillators Producing Nonsinusoidal Waves. Oscillator circuits producing a nonsinusoidal wave are generally used as electronic timing and control circuits in television, radar, oscilloscope, and industrial control equipment. Nonsinusoidal voltages are generally produced by some form of *relaxation oscillator circuit.* In this type of oscillator circuit, one or more voltages or currents change abruptly one or more times during each cycle of oscillation. The types of relaxation oscillator circuits most commonly used are: (1) Van der Pol, (2) multivibrator, (3) glow-tube discharge, (4) arc-tube discharge, (5) saw-tooth wave generators, (6) rectangular or square wave generators.

Oscillators Producing Sinusoidal Waves. An oscillator circuit used to produce a sinusoidal voltage may come under any one of the following classifications: (1) negative resistance, (2) feedback, (3) heterodyne, (4) crystal, (5) magnetostriction, (6) ultra-high frequency.

A circuit element, usually a certain type of electronic tube, is said to possess negative resistance when at some portion of its operating characteristic the current flow through the circuit decreases with an increase in the voltage and vice versa.   Any circuit having a negative resistance characteristic can be used as an oscillator.   Upon first thought, feedback oscillator circuits might be considered as negative resistance oscillators. However, only those circuits having negative a-c resistance, even when not used in connection with an oscillatory circuit, are classified as negative resistance oscillators.   The electric arc and the screen-grid tube possess this characteristic and therefore may be used in this type of circuit. The four types of negative resistance oscillator circuits most commonly used are (1) the *dynatron,* which makes use of the negative screen-grid resistance characteristic of a tetrode; (2) the *transitron,* which makes use of the negative transconductance characteristic of a pentode; (3) the push-pull circuit, which is a variation of the *Eccles-Jordan trigger circuit;* (4) the resistance-capacitance or *resistance-tuned circuit,* in which the frequency of oscillation is dependent upon the resistance and capacitance of the circuit.

The use of positive feedback and a tuned oscillatory circuit is the type of oscillator circuit most commonly used in communications circuits. The principles of operation of the various types of feedback circuits will therefore be considered in greater detail later in this chapter.   As there are numerous circuits that may be used as feedback oscillators, it becomes difficult to name all of them.   However, for the purpose of classification, it is necessary to list only the basic circuits, as all others are merely modifications of these circuits.   The basic feedback oscillator circuits may be considered as follows:

1. Tuned plate
2. Tuned grid
    (a) Inductive feedback
    (b) Capacitive feedback
    (c) Tickler feedback
3. Hartley
4. Colpitts
5. Complex types using more than one tuned circuit
    (a) Tuned-grid tuned-plate
    (b) Meissner
    (c) Tri-tet
    (d) Electron coupled
6. Resistance-capacitance tuned

The heterodyne or beat frequency oscillator consists of two vacuum-tube circuits that are made to oscillate at slightly different radio fre-

quencies.   The output of these two oscillators is simultaneously applied
to a common detector.   By means of an r-f filter, the radio-frequency
currents are removed and the output will be of a frequency equal to the
difference of the two original frequency values.   The heterodyne oscillator circuit is a convenient means of obtaining precise audio frequencies
and is therefore commonly used in radio test equipment operating at
audio frequencies.

Crystal-controlled oscillators are used when the frequency of oscillation must be maintained at a fixed value.   The crystal is not used to
produce oscillations but controls the output frequency of the oscillator
with which it is used.   Crystals and crystal-controlled oscillators are
more fully described later in this chapter.

The magnetostriction oscillator circuit is based on the principle that
a change in magnetization will cause a magnetic material to expand or
contract and, conversely, that a contraction or expansion of a magnetic
material will cause a change in magnetization.   A strong stable oscillation having a frequency of the order of 10,000 to 100,000 cycles per second
can be obtained from this type of oscillator circuit.

The types of oscillator circuits used to generate audio- or radio-frequency currents or voltages cannot be used to produce ultrahigh-frequency currents or voltages.   Various means are employed to obtain
these ultrahigh frequencies, among which are (1) positive grid, (2)
magnetron, (3) velocity modulation, (4) resonant cavities, (5) resonant
lines.   The theory and analysis of ultrahigh-frequency oscillators is
beyond the scope of this text.

10-3. The Amplifier as an Oscillator.   *Amplifier Action of the Oscillator.*   The essential parts of a vacuum-tube oscillator are (1) the oscillatory
or tank circuit, usually a parallel resonant circuit, (2) a vacuum-tube
amplifier, (3) a feedback circuit.   The vacuum-tube oscillator circuit is
so arranged that a portion of the energy developed in the output (or
plate) circuit is returned in the proper phase relationship to the input
(or grid) circuit.   The energy returned is amplified by the tube and a
portion of the energy it develops in the plate circuit is then returned to
the grid circuit.   Each time some energy is taken from the output circuit
it is regenerated in the input circuit.   This cycle of operations is continually repeated.   Because of the amplifying properties of the tube,
the energy in the output circuit will increase with each cycle of operation
until the maximum or saturation value of plate current has been reached
(see Fig. 10-1).   The value of the output plate current will depend upon
the characteristics of the tube and the manner in which it is operated.

As the energy consumed by the input circuit of an amplifier is considerably less than that in its output circuit, it is possible to have an
amplifier supply its own input.   An amplifier operated in this manner

will generate oscillations at a frequency that is determined by the electrical constants of the circuit.   Furthermore, since the tube operates as an amplifier, the oscillator can be made to supply power to an external circuit in addition to supplying the circuit losses required to sustain oscillations.   The tube thus acts as a power converter, changing the direct

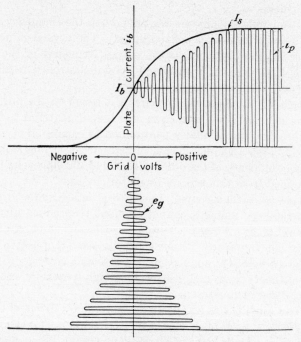

Fig. 10-1.—Illustration of how the oscillations in the tube circuit build up until the saturation value of the plate current is reached.

current power supplied to its plate circuit into alternating-current energy in the amplifier output circuit.   It may thus be seen that a tube cannot produce oscillations by itself and also that the function of the oscillator is not to create energy but to change direct current energy to alternating current energy.   The combination of the vacuum tube and its associated circuits is called a *vacuum-tube oscillator*.

Classification of Tube Operation.   The vacuum-tube oscillator can be considered as an amplifier in which part of the output voltage is returned to the input circuit in such a manner that the tube drives itself.   The tube may be operated as a Class A, B, or C amplifier.   Class A operated oscillators are generally used in high-quality audio-frequency oscillators.   Because of the high efficiency and comparatively low distortion that is obtainable at high frequencies from Class C operation, radio-frequency oscillators are usually operated Class C.

Oscillator Circuits.   A number of circuits may be used to produce the required oscillations, each circuit having its own advantages and disadvantages.   The circuit used will depend upon the frequency and power required and its application.   The oscillatory circuit may be in the grid circuit, the plate circuit, or both.   The manner in which the energy is applied to the input circuit can be by either capacitive or inductive coupling.   Capacitive coupling can be accomplished by use of an external circuit or by use of the interelectrode capacitances within a tube.   Inductive coupling can be accomplished only by means of an external circuit.

10-4. The Oscillatory Circuit.   In the oscillatory circuit of the oscillator, electrical oscillations occur according to the fundamental laws governing capacitor and inductor actions.   The oscillatory or alternating flow of electrons in the parallel resonant or tank circuit is caused by the repeated exchange of energy between the capacitor and inductor.

The operation of the oscillator circuit is explained with the aid of Fig. 10-2.   It is assumed that the capacitor is fully charged (Fig. 10-2a) and just starting to discharge (Fig. 10-2b).   As the capacitor discharges through the inductor, the flow of electrons (as indicated by the arrows on the wires connecting the capacitor and inductor) causes a magnetic field to be built up around the inductor.   Electrons will continue to flow in this direction until the charges on the plates of the capacitor are equal to each other (Fig. 10-2c).   At the instant that the rate of electron flow is zero the magnetic field about the inductor will start to collapse (Fig. 10-2d).   According to Lenz's law, the collapsing of the magnetic field will cause electrons to flow in the same direction as was used to produce the expanding field, thus causing the capacitor to become charged with a polarity opposite to its original charge.   When the field about the inductor has completely collapsed, the energy that had been stored in its magnetic field will be transferred to the electrostatic field of the capacitor (Fig. 10-2e).

Electron flow ordinarily ceases when the charge on the two plates of the capacitor are equal.   However, due to effects of the collapsing magnetic field, electron flow continues past this neutral point.   This action of a parallel resonant circuit is sometimes referred to as the *flywheel effect.*

The capacitor will now discharge and electrons will flow in a direction opposite to that used to charge the capacitor.   This flow of electrons produces an expanding field about the inductor (Fig. 10-2f), until the difference in charge between the two plates is zero (Fig. 10-2g).   As before, the magnetic field collapses, thus causing the electrons to continue to flow in the same direction (Fig. 10-2h).   When the energy stored in the electromagnetic field has been transferred to the electrostatic field, the capacitor becomes fully charged in the opposite polarity. It is thus restored to its original state as in Fig. 10-2a.

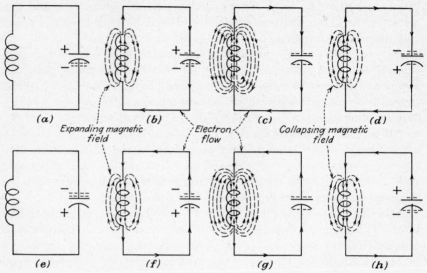

Fig. 10-2.—Oscillatory action of a parallel resonant circuit.

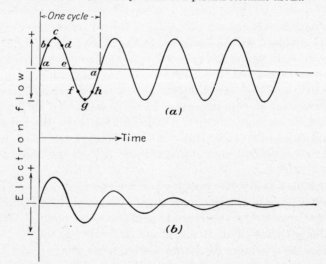

Fig. 10-3.—Flow of electrons in a tank circuit. (a) Theoretical flow, (b) actual flow.

This cycle of operations is repeated at a frequency that is dependent upon the values of the inductance and capacitance in the circuit. This frequency is approximately equal to the frequency of resonance of the parallel circuit as expressed by

$$f_r = \frac{159}{\sqrt{LC}}$$ (2-48)

where f_r = frequency of resonance, kilocycles
L = inductance, microhenries
C = capacitance, microfarads

If the circuit is assumed to have zero resistance, each cycle of electron flow in the tank circuit will be similar to that shown in Fig. 10-3a.   Thus,

theoretically, a sustained alternating-current flow of constant magnitude is produced. As it is impossible to construct a circuit without some amount of resistance, some energy will be lost in the form of heat during each cycle. If no energy is supplied to replace this loss, the magnitude of each oscillation will diminish as shown in Fig. 10-3b. It can thus be seen that a simple tank circuit by itself is not a practical means of producing an alternating current of constant magnitude.

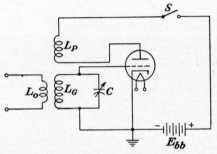

Fig. 10-4.—A fundamental oscillator circuit.

10-5. Fundamental Oscillator Theory. In practical oscillator circuits a vacuum tube and a power supply are used to provide the energy required to overcome the losses caused by the resistance in the circuit, thus producing an alternating current of constant magnitude.

The fundamental oscillator circuit (Fig. 10-4) is capable of producing alternating currents of constant magnitude and constant frequency. The operation of this circuit is similar to most types of feedback oscillators.   In order to simplify the description of the operation of this oscillator circuit, the action in each part will be presented individually.   It must be kept in mind, however, that these actions are not independent of each other but are closely related, all occurring almost instantaneously.

Analysis of the Fundamental Oscillator Circuit. At the instant of closing the switch S (Fig. 10-4), the electrons being emitted from the cathode will be drawn to the plate.   This causes a current to flow from the cathode to the plate, through the plate coil L_P, through the B power supply, and back to the cathode.   As the current through L_P increases, a magnetic field builds up around the plate coil and, by mutual inductance, a voltage of increasing magnitude is induced in the grid coil, L_G.   The grid and plate coils are connected in their respective circuits so that the voltage induced in the grid coil will have a positive potential at the terminal connected to the grid of the tube when the current in L_P is increasing. Two immediate actions result from this positive voltage: (1) the voltage on the grid becomes positive, thereby increasing the amount of plate current flow; (2) the capacitor C in the tank circuit becomes charged. The increasing plate current produces an increase in the strength of the magnetic field about the plate coil, thus causing a greater voltage to be induced in the grid coil. This action makes the grid still more positive,

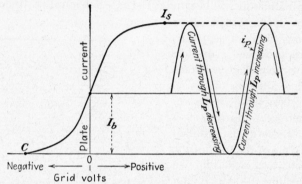

FIG. 10-5.—Variation of plate current in the oscillator circuit of Fig. 10-4.

thereby increasing the plate current still further. This action continues until saturation is reached (Fig. 10-5). The point of saturation will depend on the resistance of the circuit, the plate supply voltage, and the characteristics of the tube. As soon as the plate current ceases to increase, the field about the plate coil ceases to expand and no longer induces a voltage in the grid coil. The tank capacitor C, having been charged to its maximum potential, starts to discharge through the grid coil. This decrease in voltage across the capacitor makes the voltage on the grid less positive thus causing the plate current to decrease, which in turn causes the magnetic field about the plate coil to collapse. A voltage will again be induced in the grid coil but will be opposite in direction to that produced by an expanding field. The voltage on the grid thus becomes negative, thereby decreasing the plate current still further. This action continues until the grid voltage is such that zero plate current flows, point C on Fig. 10-5. During the time in which the plate current has decreased from saturation current to cutoff, the tank capacitor has lost its original charge and has again become charged to its maximum potential, the plates now having a polarity opposite to that of the previous charged condition. As the induced voltage in L_G is zero when cutoff is reached, the capacitor will now start to discharge through the grid coil. This decrease in voltage across the capacitor makes the voltage on the grid less negative, thus causing the plate current to increase and the magnetic field about the grid coil to expand.   The voltage induced in the grid coil will make the grid more positive, thereby increasing the plate current still further until the saturation point is reached in the same manner as explained previously.   This cycle of operations repeats itself continuously as long as energy is supplied to overcome the losses in the circuit.

Output power can be obtained by inductively coupling the output coil L_o to the grid coil L_G (Fig. 10-4).   Oscillating energy from the grid circuit can thus be transferred to the output circuit.   In addition to supplying power to overcome the losses in the circuit, the B power supply must now also supply the power required by the output load.

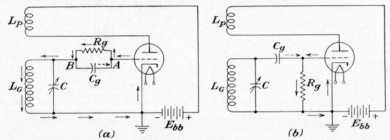

Fig. 10-6.—Two methods of connecting the grid-leak resistor and grid capacitor.

10-6. Grid Bias.   *Need for a Grid-leak Resistor and Grid Capacitor.* During part of each cycle of alternating current in the oscillator the grid is driven positive.   In order to prevent the tube from drawing an excessive amount of plate current during this portion of the cycle, practically all oscillator circuits employ grid-leak bias.   Two methods of connecting the grid resistor are shown in Fig. 10-6.

Operation of Oscillator Circuits with Grid-leak Resistor and Grid Capacitor.   When the oscillator of Fig. 10-6a or 10-6b is started, the initial bias on the grid is zero.   Thus, when positive voltage is applied to the grid, because of the expanding magnetic field about the plate coil, the grid will be driven positive.   The flow of electrons in the grid circuit (caused by the positive grid) produces a voltage drop at the resistor R_g with point A negative and point B positive.   The capacitor C_g will become charged to this polarity.   The grid current flowing through the grid resistor thus causes the voltage on the grid to become negative.   The plate current will then decrease thus causing the magnetic field about the plate coil to collapse.   The cycle then continues as explained for the fundamental oscillator circuit.

Graphical Representation of the Oscillator Circuit Action.   The manner in which the oscillations are produced is illustrated in Fig. 10-7.   In order to simplify the diagram, the dynamic characteristic curve of the oscillator tube, line AC, is assumed to be a straight line. Actually it is slightly curved. At the instant that plate voltage is applied, the plate current will start increasing at a rapid rate. However, the inductive reactance of the plate coil prevents the plate current from becoming maximum instantaneously. The tube is operated as a Class C amplifier with a grid bias whose value is twice the amount required to produce cutoff. The grid bias, being dependent upon the charge (and discharge) of the grid capacitor, will increase to its proper value according to the

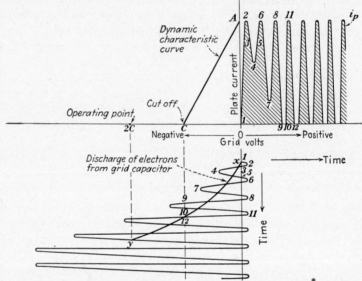

Fig. 10-7.—Use of the dynamic characteristic curve to illustrate the manner in which oscillations are produced.

exponential curve xy, Fig. 10-7. It can be seen from Fig. 10-7 that the grid is driven slightly positive for a small part of each cycle. This is due to the flywheel effect of the tank circuit. During the interval that the grid is positive it acts as a diode plate and thus grid current will flow, thereby charging the grid capacitor. The time required for the grid bias to attain its maximum value is determined by the time constant of the $R_g C_g$ circuit.

Values of C_g and R_g. Any alternating voltage across the grid capacitor will vary the grid excitation voltage. In order to limit this voltage to a minimum, the value of the capacitor should be as large as practical. The maximum value of capacitance is, however, limited by the time constant desired. The time constant should be small enough so that the bias voltage cannot attain a value high enough to stop oscillations, in which case it is said that the tube has become blocked.   The grid-bias requirements for the particular tube used will determine the value of the grid resistor.   Therefore, in order to reduce the time constant, it becomes necessary to use a smaller value of grid capacitance.

Effect of C_g and R_g upon Grid Current.   When the voltage on the grid is positive, current will flow in the grid circuit.   This flow of current produces a power loss in the form of heat.   As this power loss must be supplied from the power supply, the efficiency of the oscillator is decreased. Use of the grid resistor and grid capacitor limits the amount of grid current flow, thus making the oscillator circuit more efficient.

Grid-leak Bias vs. Fixed Bias.   In order to obtain high efficiency, the oscillator tube should be biased beyond the point of cutoff or operated as Class C.   If fixed bias of an amount sufficient to produce cutoff were used, the initial plate current would be zero and thus there would be no power input to the plate coil to start oscillations.   Using a grid-leak resistor and grid capacitor, the initial grid bias will be zero.   The plate current flow will immediately start oscillations and automatically build up the bias to its ultimate operating value.   Thus if the oscillator circuit is to be self-starting, it is essential that grid-leak bias be used.

10-7. Basic Oscillator Circuits.   *The Hartley Oscillator.*   The Hartley oscillator requires very little apparatus and is therefore one of the simplest types of oscillator circuits.   The circuit arrangement for two forms of the Hartley oscillator is shown in Fig. 10-8.   The operation of each of these two forms is identical except for the manner in which the d-c power is supplied to the plate.   As in the fundamental oscillator circuit just described, the amplified energy in the plate circuit is fed back to the grid circuit by means of inductive coupling.   However, in the Hartley oscillator only one coil is used.   A portion L_P of this coil is in the plate circuit, and the remainder L_G is in the grid circuit.   The amount of inductive feedback between these two sections of the common coil will depend on the number of turns in sections L_P and L_G.   Increasing the number of turns in the plate section increases the voltage induced in the grid section, thus increasing the amount of feedback.

The alternating current in the plate section of the coil induces a voltage in the grid section.   This induced voltage is applied to the grid of the tube, is amplified, and again applied to the plate section.   The plate and grid voltages are 180 degrees out of phase with each other as they are taken from opposite ends of the coil with respect to the common lead connected to the cathode.

In the circuit shown in Fig. 10-8a, the plate power supply is connected in series with the plate section and is called a *series-fed circuit*.   The voltages across the tuning capacitor and the inductor (terminals 1 and 3) will be approximately equal to the plate power supply voltage. In order to avoid the danger of high plate voltages appearing across these two circuit elements parallel feed is generally used.

An example of parallel feed is shown in Fig. 10-8*b*. Because the plate circuit is divided into two parallel branches, one to provide a path for the direct current and the other for the alternating current, it is called a *parallel-* or *shunt-fed circuit*. The r-f choke coil keeps the alternating current out of the d-c circuit, and the blocking capacitor C_b keeps the direct current out of the a-c circuit. In order for most of the r-f current to flow through the plate section L_P instead of through the plate power supply, the reactance of the blocking capacitor at the reso-

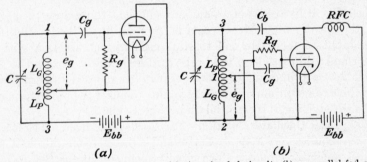

FIG. 10-8.—Hartley oscillator circuits. (*a*) A series-fed circuit, (*b*) a parallel-fed circuit.

nant frequency should be very small in comparison with the reactance of the choke coil at the same frequency.

The frequency of the output of the oscillator is equal to the frequency at which the voltage in the plate circuit is fed back to the grid circuit. In oscillator circuits employing a resonant circuit, the frequency of oscillation is approximately equal to the resonant frequency of the tank circuit. The frequency of oscillation of the circuits shown in Fig. 10-8 is thus equal to the resonant frequency of the parallel circuit formed by the tuning capacitor C and the entire inductor, L_G plus L_P.

Of the various types of self-excited oscillators, the Hartley oscillator is the one most generally used. However, this circuit is seldom used exactly in either of the two forms shown in Fig. 10-8 as many modifications have been made in order to adapt the basic circuit to meet the individual requirements for each of its applications. Two of the modifications are shown in Fig. 10-9. The circuit shown in Fig. 10-9*a* is used in some superheterodyne receivers. Use of mutual inductance coupling is made by employing the circuit shown in Fig. 10-9*b*. The excitation voltage for the grid is obtained by the mutual inductance between the grid and plate coils.

The Colpitts Oscillator.   Another basic type of oscillator circuit is the Colpitts or capacitive feedback oscillator.   In this circuit, the feedback of energy from the plate circuit to the grid circuit is accomplished by means of electrostatic coupling.   The circuit arrangement for the Colpitts oscillator is shown in Fig. 10-10.   Except for the manner in which feedback is obtained, this circuit is similar to the parallel-feed Hartley oscillator.   In the Colpitts oscillator the tank voltage is divided into two parts by tapping the tank capacitor, or rather by connecting two capacitors in series, instead of the inductor.   The grid excitation voltage is

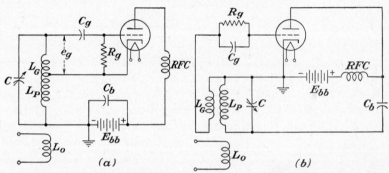

Fig. 10-9.—Two modifications of the basic Hartley oscillator circuit.

obtained from the grid tank capacitor C_G.   The plate and grid voltages are 180 degrees out of phase with each other, since they are taken from opposite ends of the tank circuit with respect to the common lead connected to the cathode.   Although the use of parallel feed is optional (though preferable) in the Hartley circuit, it is obvious that it is necessary in the Colpitts circuit because of the high voltage obtainable at the tank capacitor C_P.

The operation of this circuit is similar to that of the parallel-feed Hartley oscillator.   As plate current starts to flow, the plate blocking capacitor C_b starts to charge, which in turn also causes the plate tank capacitor C_P to charge.   This increase in voltage is transferred to the grid tank capacitor C_G, through the r-f choke, causing the terminal connected to the grid to become more negative.   When the feedback voltage causes the plate current to decrease, less energy will be stored in the plate tank capacitor, thus reversing the direction of the feedback voltage. As this action continues, sustained oscillations will be produced.

It must be remembered that the capacitance of the tank circuit is equal to the resultant capacitance of C_P and C_G in series.   By varying the capacitance of C_P and/or C_G the voltage across the tank circuit may be divided to produce the voltage drop required across C_G for proper grid excitation. Increasing the reactance of the grid tank capacitor will increase the voltage across it.

In order to vary the frequency of oscillation two adjustments, C_P and C_G, are usually made in the Colpitts circuit. It is therefore less conven-

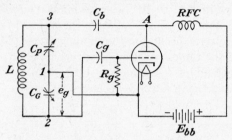

FIG. 10-10.—The Colpitts oscillator circuit.

ient to operate the Colpitts circuit as a variable-frequency oscillator than the Hartley circuit, which requires only a single adjustment. In multiband receivers the Colpitts oscillator has a distinct advantage in that the tank coil has no tap, therefore one less coil circuit needs to be switched each time the receiver is shifted to a different wave band. The Colpitts circuit is also used in the operation of many push-button-tuned receivers.

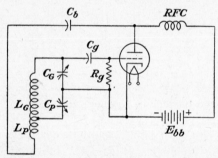

FIG. 10-11.—A modified Colpitts oscillator circuit.

A modified form of the basic Colpitts oscillator is illustrated in Fig. 10-11. This circuit employs both capacitive and inductive feedback. The plate tank capacitor C_P provides the capacitive feedback and the plate section L_P of the inductor provides the inductive feedback. It is possible to obtain fairly uniform output from this oscillator over a wide frequency range by the proper selection of circuit elements.

Tuned-grid Tuned-plate Oscillator. Capacitive feedback is also used in the tuned-grid tuned-plate oscillator, sometimes abbreviated T-G T-P oscillator. The circuit arrangement for this type of oscillator is shown in Fig. 10-12a. Capacitive feedback is obtained by utilizing the grid-plate capacitance C_{gp} of the tube. Usually this capacitance is a nuisance, but this is one of the few circuits in which it is used to advantage. Two parallel resonant circuits are required, one in the grid circuit of the tube and the other in the plate circuit. No inductive coupling should exist between the coils in these two circuits. The frequency of oscillation is

dependent on the resonant frequency of each of the tuned circuits, therefore the name tuned-grid tuned-plate oscillator.

The operation of the tuned-grid tuned-plate oscillator may be more
easily understood by rearranging the schematic diagram into the equivalent circuit form shown in Fig. 10-12b.   The equivalent circuit is simplified by showing the interelectrode capacitance C_{gp} connected across the
resonant circuit instead of across the grid and plate of the tube as shown
in Fig. 10-12a.   This simplification is possible because C_g and C_b, which
act in series with the interelectrode capacitance C_{gp} to form the feedback
circuit, may be neglected, since they are much larger in value than C_{gp}.

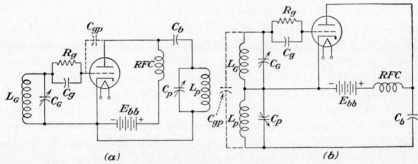

FIG.   10-12.—Tuned-grid   tuned-plate   parallel-feed   oscillator   circuit.   (*a*) Schematic
diagram, (*b*) equivalent circuit.

In order for the system to oscillate, the plate circuit should be tuned
to a slightly lower frequency than the grid circuit.   The resultant inductive reactance of the two tuned circuits will then resonate with the interelectrode capacitive reactance.   The oscillator circuit thus formed is
similar in many respects to the Hartley circuit.   The frequency of the
tuned-grid tuned-plate oscillator is determined by the tuned circuit
having the highest value of Q.

The frequency stability and the voltage amplification of the tuned-grid
tuned-plate oscillator is comparatively high because of the high impedance of the parallel resonant plate load.   Varying the resonant frequency
of either of the tuned circuits will vary the amount of feedback, thus
increasing or decreasing the amplitude of the oscillations.   In practice,
the frequency of oscillation is usually controlled by varying the resonant
frequency of the plate tuned circuit, and the amount of grid excitation is
controlled by varying the resonant frequency of the grid tuned circuit.
The plate circuit is designed to deliver the required power output.   The
properties of the grid tuned circuit are not too important, providing the
desired frequency range can be obtained.   The plate power supply of
the tuned-grid tuned-plate oscillator may be either series fed or parallel

fed.   The tuned-grid tuned-plate circuit is used to some extent in high-frequency oscillators.

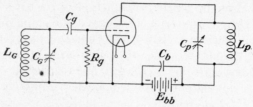

FIG. 10-13.—Tuned-grid tuned-plate series-feed oscillator circuit.

10-8. Circuit Considerations.   *Effect of the Tank Circuit on the Amplitude Stability.*   If the amplitude of the output of an oscillator is unstable the wave form will be distorted thus producing undesirable harmonics. From the previous discussion it can be seen that an oscillator tube generally operates as a Class C amplifier delivering power during less than one-half of the input cycle.   Under this condition, the plate current variation will not produce a sine wave, and a tank circuit (parallel resonant circuit) is added in order to obtain an approximate sine-wave output. In order to have an output of approximately sine-wave form, it is necessary that the tank circuit store energy during the portion of the cycle in which the tube is delivering power and to deliver this stored energy to the load during the portion of the cycle in which no power is being delivered by the tube.

Effect of the Tank Circuit Q on the Wave Shape.   The tank circuit consists of a capacitor and an inductor connected in parallel.   The resistance of the inductor may be considered as a resistance in series with the inductance and the Q of the tank circuit is equal to the ratio of the inductive reactance to the resistance as expressed by Eq. (2-58).   When the tank circuit is supplying power to a load the effect is similar to increasing the series resistance of the tank circuit and consequently reduces the value of Q.   The Q of the circuit when supplying power is referred to as the *effective Q* and is designated as Q_{eff}.   The factor Q_{eff} is also a measure of the ratio of the energy stored during each cycle to the energy dissipated during each cycle [see Eq. (10-16a)].   Thus an increase in the value of Q_{eff} indicates an increase in the amount of energy stored.   Furthermore, the ability to carry each cycle past its neutral point (flywheel effect) can be increased by increasing the effective Q of the tuned circuit.

In order to obtain a satisfactory wave shape at the output of an oscillator (or a Class C amplifier), it is necessary that the amount of energy stored during a portion of each cycle appreciably exceeds the amount of energy dissipated during the remainder of the cycle.   Experience has shown that the value of Q_{eff} should be in the order of 10 to 30.

Under this condition, the amount of energy stored per cycle will be approximately 2 to 5 times the amount of energy dissipated per cycle. When Q_{eff} has a value of 12.5 the harmonic content of the output wave is approximately 3 per cent.   Decreasing the value of Q_{eff} causes an increase in the amount of distortion, while increasing the value of Q_{eff} produces a more nearly sinusoidal output wave.   It should be noted, however, that a high value of Q_{eff} results in a high value of tank circuit current, thereby increasing the losses and reducing the efficiency of the tank circuit.

Efficiency of the Tank Circuit.   The efficiency of the tank circuit may be expressed as the ratio of the power delivered to the load to the power delivered to the tank circuit.   This may be expressed in terms of the circuit Q as

$$\text{Efficiency} = \frac{Q - Q_{eff}}{Q} \times 100 \tag{10-1}$$

where Q = tank circuit Q at no-load
Q_{eff} = tank circuit Q with load

Example 10-1.   The tank circuit of an r-f amplifier, used in conjunction with the oscillator of a radio transmitter, has a circuit Q of 85 at no-load and an effective Q of 12 when load is applied.   What is the efficiency of the tank circuit?

Given: Find:
$Q = 85$ Efficiency
$Q_{eff} = 12$

Solution:

$$\text{Efficiency} = \frac{Q - Q_{eff}}{Q} \times 100 = \frac{85 - 12}{85} \times 100 = 85.8 \text{ per cent}$$

Analysis of the Tank Circuit.   The preceding discussion amply shows the importance of the tank circuit.   There are a number of important considerations in the study of the tank circuit, such as the frequency, impedance, current, power, and energy stored.

The tank circuit should be adjusted so that its resonant frequency corresponds to that of the oscillator.   For the values of Q commonly used with these circuits, the results obtained by use of Eq. (2-48) are sufficiently accurate for general purposes.   Accordingly, Eqs. (2-49) and (2-50) may be used for finding the values of the inductance and capacitance required in the tank circuit.

$$f_r = \frac{159}{\sqrt{LC}} \tag{2-48}$$

$$L = \frac{25,300}{f_r^2 C} \tag{2-49}$$

$$C = \frac{25,300}{f_r^2 L} \tag{2-50}$$

As the resistance of the tank circuit is small compared to the inductive reactance, a sufficiently accurate value of the impedance (at resonance) can be obtained by use of Eq. (2-56).

$$Z_{T \cdot r} = QX_L = \frac{X_L{}^2}{R} \tag{2-56}$$

As $X_L = X_C$ at resonance, then

$$Z_{T \cdot r} = \frac{X^2}{R} = \frac{X_L X_C}{R} = \frac{2\pi f_r L}{2\pi f_r C R} = \frac{L}{CR} \tag{10-2}$$

The voltage at the tank circuit will be approximately equal to the alternating component of the plate voltage E_p. It may also be expressed as

$$E_t = I_p Z_{t \cdot r} \tag{10-3}$$

Correspondingly, the tank circuit current may be expressed as

$$I_{t \cdot r} \cong \frac{E_t}{X_L} \cong \frac{E_p}{X_L} \tag{10-4}$$

An approximate value of the tank circuit current can also be found by use of Eq. (2-57)

$$I_{t \cdot r} = I_L = I_C = QI_p \tag{2-57}$$

At resonance the power delivered to the tank circuit (output load plus tank circuit losses) may be expressed as

$$P_{t \cdot r} = I_p{}^2 QX_L = \frac{E_t{}^2}{QX_L} = \frac{E_p{}^2}{QX_L} \tag{10-5}$$

Example 10-2. The tank circuit of the oscillator in a certain radio receiver has the following circuit values: $L = 80$ μh, $C = {}^{365}\!/_{35}$ $\mu\mu$f, $Q_{\text{eff}} = 20$, $E_t = 10$ volts. Find (a) the value of capacitance when the oscillator is adjusted to a resonant frequency of 1000 kc, (b) the impedance of the tank circuit at resonance, (c) the plate current required to produce the desired voltage at the tank circuit, (d) the current in the tank circuit, (e) the power supplied to the tank circuit.

Given:

$L = 80$ μh
$C = {}^{365}\!/_{35}$ $\mu\mu$f
$Q_{\text{eff}} = 20$
$E_t = 10$ volts
$f_r = 1000$ kc

Find:

(a) $C = ?$
(b) $Z_{t \cdot r} = ?$
(c) $I_p = ?$
(d) $I_t = ?$
(e) $P_t = ?$

Solution:

(a) $C = \dfrac{25,300}{f_r{}^2 L} = \dfrac{25,300}{1000^2 \times 80} = 0.000316$ μf or 316 $\mu\mu$f

(b) $Z_{t \cdot r} = Q_{\text{eff}} X_L = 20 \times 6.28 \times 10^6 \times 80 \times 10^{-6} = 10,048$ ohms

(c) $I_p = \dfrac{E_t}{Z_{t \cdot r}} = \dfrac{10}{10,048} = 0.000995$ amp or 0.995 ma

(d) $I_t = Q_{\text{eff}} I_p = 20 \times 0.995 = 19.9$ ma

(e) $P = E_p I_p = 10 \times 0.000995 = 0.00995$ watt

Energy Stored in the Tank Circuit. An analysis of the tank circuit will show that the amount of energy stored will increase with an increase in the value of either the capacitance or the voltage. The total energy stored in a tank circuit is equal to the sum of the energy stored in the inductor and in the capacitor. From Eqs. (2-3) and (2-18)

$$w_t = \frac{Li_t^2}{2} + \frac{Ce_t^2}{2} \qquad (10\text{-}6)$$

where w_t = total instantaneous energy stored in the tank circuit, watt-
seconds

i_t = instantaneous value of the current flowing in the oscillatory
or tank circuit, amperes

e_t = instantaneous value of the voltage across the tank circuit,
volts

L = inductance of the tank coil, henries

C = capacitance of the tank capacitor, farads

For all practical purposes the voltage across the tank circuit can be considered as being equal to the alternating voltage output of the tube. Then

$$w_t = \frac{Li_t^2}{2} + \frac{Ce_p^2}{2} \qquad (10\text{-}7)$$

When the energy stored in the tank circuit is sufficient to reduce the harmonic distortion to a negligible amount

$$e_p = E_{p \cdot m} \sin \theta \qquad (10\text{-}8)$$

where $\theta = 2\pi ft$

t = time, seconds

As the resistance of a properly designed tank circuit is very small in comparison to either of its reactances, it can generally be ignored in considering the impedance of either branch. The current in the tank inductor lags the applied voltage and can be expressed as

$$i_t = - \frac{E_{p \cdot m}}{2\pi f_r L} \cos \theta \qquad (10\text{-}9)$$

Substituting Eqs. (10-8) and (10-9) in Eq. (10-7)

$$w_t = \frac{LE_{p \cdot m}^2}{2(2\pi f_r L)^2} \cos^2 \theta + \frac{CE_{p \cdot m}^2}{2} \sin^2 \theta \qquad (10\text{-}10)$$

At resonance

$$2\pi f_r L = \frac{1}{2\pi f_r C} \qquad (10\text{-}11)$$

and

$$L = \frac{1}{(2\pi f_r)^2 C} \qquad (10\text{-}12)$$

Substituting this value of L in Eq. (10-10)

$$w_t = \frac{CE_{p\cdot m}{}^2}{2} \cos^2 \theta + \frac{CE_{p\cdot m}{}^2}{2} \sin^2 \theta \qquad (10\text{-}13)$$

or $\qquad\qquad w_t = \dfrac{CE_{p\cdot m}{}^2}{2} (\cos^2 \theta + \sin^2 \theta) \qquad\qquad (10\text{-}13a)$

However, from trigonometry, $\cos^2 \theta + \sin^2 \theta = 1$

and $\qquad\qquad\qquad W_t = \dfrac{CE_{p\cdot m}{}^2}{2} \qquad\qquad\qquad (10\text{-}13b)$

where W_t = energy stored in the tank circuit **per cycle**
Also $E_{p\cdot m} = \sqrt{2}\, E_p$ and $E_{p\cdot m}{}^2 = 2E_p{}^2$
Thus

$$W_t = CE_p{}^2 \qquad (10\text{-}13c)$$

It can be seen from Eq. (10-13c) that the total energy stored in the tank circuit can be increased by using a higher value of capacitance. In order to maintain a fixed value of frequency, an increase in the value of capacitance must be accompanied by a decrease in the value of inductance, thereby reducing the L/C ratio. An increase in the value of the capacitance (and a decrease in the value of the inductance) will result in a lower value of reactance at the fixed value of resonant frequency. From Eq. (10-5) it can be shown that the effective Q of the tank circuit increases with a decrease in the reactance; this is characteristic of a loaded tank circuit and should not be confused with the no-load value of Q, which decreases with a decrease in the reactance. Thus, an increase in the value of capacitance increases the amount of energy stored, decreases the L/C ratio of the tank circuit, and increases the effective Q of the tank circuit.

Increasing the effective Q of the tuned circuit increases its impedance [see Eq. (2-56)], thereby increasing the value of the varying plate voltage output of the oscillator tube. This increase in plate voltage will further increase the total energy stored [Eq. (10-13c)]. However, an increase in the voltage applied to a tuned circuit increases the value of the circulating current, thus increasing the I^2R losses and reducing the overall efficiency of the oscillator circuit. It is therefore good practice to limit the L/C ratio to the value required to produce a satisfactory sinusoidal output.

Relation of Q_{eff} *to the Ratio of Energy Stored to Energy Dissipated.* It has previously been stated that the value of Q_{eff} is also a measure of the ratio of the energy stored during each cycle to the energy dissipated during each cycle. This can now be shown as follows. In the same manner in which Eq. (10-13c) was developed, it can be shown that

$$W_t = LI_t^2 \tag{10-14}$$

The energy dissipated in the tank circuit per cycle may be expressed as

$$W_d = \frac{I_t^2 R_{eq}}{f_r} \tag{10-15}$$

where W_d = energy dissipated in the tank circuit per cycle
   R_{eq} = equivalent series resistance of the tank circuit when loaded.
The ratio of energy stored per cycle to energy dissipated per cycle may
then be expressed as

$$\frac{\text{Energy stored per cycle}}{\text{Energy dissipated per cycle}} = \frac{W_t}{W_d} = \frac{LI_t^2}{\dfrac{I_t^2 R_{eq}}{f_r}} = \frac{f_r L}{R_{eq}} \tag{10-16}$$

Multiplying both the numerator and the denominator by 2π

$$\frac{\text{Energy stored per cycle}}{\text{Energy dissipated per cycle}} = \frac{2\pi f_r L}{2\pi R_{eq}} = \frac{Q_{eff}}{2\pi} \tag{10-16a}$$

Example 10-3. (a) What is the amount of energy stored per cycle in the tank
circuit of Example 10-2? (b) Determine the value of R_{eq} from the values of Q_{eff} and
X_L in Example 10-2. (c) What is the amount of power dissipated by the tank circuit? (d) What is the amount of energy dissipated per cycle? (e) What is the ratio
of the energy stored per cycle to the energy dissipated per cycle? (f) Check the result
of part (e) by use of Eq. (10-16a).

Given:

$$E_t = 10 \text{ volts}$$
$$C = 316 \ \mu\mu\text{f}$$
$$Q_{eff} = 20$$
$$L = 80 \ \mu\text{h}$$
$$f_r = 1000 \text{ kc}$$
$$I_t = 19.9 \text{ ma}$$

Find:

(a) $W_t = ?$
(b) $R_{eq} = ?$
(c) $P_{dis} = ?$
(d) $W_d = ?$
(e) $\dfrac{W_t}{W_d} = ?$
(f) $\dfrac{W_t}{W_d} = ?$

Solution:

(a) $W_t = CE_t^2 = 316 \times 10^{-12} \times 10^2 = 316 \times 10^{-10}$ watt per cycle

(b) $R_{eq} = \dfrac{X_L}{Q_{eff}} = \dfrac{6.28 \times 10^6 \times 80 \times 10^{-6}}{20} = 25.12$ ohms

(c) $P_{dis} = I_t^2 R_{eq} = (19.9 \times 10^{-3})^2 \times 25.12 = 9947 \times 10^{-6}$ watt

(d) $W_d = \dfrac{P_{dis}}{f_r} = \dfrac{9947 \times 10^{-6}}{10^6} = 99.47 \times 10^{-10}$ watt per cycle

(e) $\dfrac{W_t}{W_d} = \dfrac{316 \times 10^{-10}}{99.47 \times 10^{-10}} = 3.17$

(f) $\dfrac{W_t}{W_d} = \dfrac{Q_{eff}}{2\pi} = \dfrac{20}{6.28} = 3.18$

Excitation Voltage. The excitation voltage required to drive the oscillator tube will depend upon the characteristics of the tube, the losses in the circuit, and the power consumed by the load. As the excitation voltage is dependent upon the varying output plate voltage, it will also be affected by changes in the operating potentials of the tube. It can be shown that the varying plate voltage is also dependent upon the effective Q of the tank circuit, and thus any changes in the tuned circuit will also affect the excitation voltage.

If the excitation voltage is too low the tube will not oscillate, and if it is too high it will increase the amount of positive grid. The power consumed by the grid will then be excessive and will decrease the overall efficiency of the oscillator.

Power Output. In radio receivers oscillator tubes operate as voltage amplifiers and the power output and efficiency are not important. Oscillator tubes in radio transmitters operate as Class C power amplifiers. The operating circuit considerations for voltage and power amplifiers previously studied will also apply to oscillators.

The power output of an oscillator is the useful a-c power consumed by the load connected to it. This load may be coupled by means of capacitive, inductive, or electron coupling. The frequency and amplitude stability of an oscillator will be affected by changes in the power taken by the load. In order to maintain a high degree of stability, oscillator circuits are very seldom designed to deliver large amounts of power. When large amounts of power are required the oscillator circuit is used to drive a power amplifier, which in turn produces the desired amount of power output. Most oscillator circuits are therefore used as a frequency controlling device delivering a small amount of power at a comparatively high voltage.

The maximum power output of an oscillator will occur when the effective resistance of the plate load, usually the tuned circuit, is equal to the plate resistance of the tube. However, as oscillator tubes are generally operated as Class C amplifiers, the plate resistance will vary appreciably over the entire cycle. When the plate voltage is high the plate resistance is low, and when the plate voltage is low the plate resistance will be high. The equation for maximum power transfer will therefore be quite complex, thus making it rather difficult to calculate the exact values of the circuit constants required to obtain maximum power transfer.

Efficiency. The plate efficiency of the oscillator tube depends upon its operating characteristics such as the load, plate resistance, excitation voltage, etc. By operating the tube as a Class C amplifier it is possible to increase the plate efficiency of the tube and thus also increase the over-all circuit efficiency.

In Class C operation it is possible to operate a tube with a higher plate voltage and thus a greater power output can be obtained. As the plate voltage is increased the plate current also increases, thus increasing the plate dissipation. However, a higher efficiency and higher power output is obtainable as the power output increases at a greater rate than the plate dissipation. Furthermore, it is possible to limit the plate voltage so that the allowable plate dissipation of the tube is not exceeded and still obtain a higher efficiency and higher power output.

The power lost in the grid will vary, the loss being between 10 and 20 per cent of the output power. As this loss must be supplied by the oscillator's power supply, the overall efficiency will be less than if the tube were being operated as an amplifier.

10-9. Frequency Stability. *Factors Affecting the Frequency Stability.* The ability of an oscillator to maintain a constant frequency in the presence of variable operating conditions is referred to as its *frequency stability.* Because of the small difference in frequency of adjacent radio broadcasting channels, it is evident that the carrier frequency of these stations must be held to a very close tolerance. At present the allowable variation in frequency for broadcasting stations is plus or minus 20 cycles. In a radio receiver, any variation in the output frequency of its local oscillator will vary the beat frequency that is applied to the i-f amplifier. In order to obtain the maximum voltage amplification with a minimum of distortion the beat frequency and the frequency to which the i-f circuit is tuned should be identical. The factors affecting the frequency stability of an oscillator are (1) plate voltage, (2) output load, (3) temperature, (4) mechanical variation of the circuit elements.

Plate Voltage and Output Load. Any variation in the operating voltages applied to the tube will vary the operating characteristics, thus causing a shift in the output frequency of the oscillator. This type of frequency change is referred to as *dynamic instability.* The operating voltages can be stabilized by the use of a regulated power supply.

Any variation in the plate load will affect the frequency of an oscillator in a similar manner as changes in plate voltage. Dynamic instability caused by a variable load can be reduced by the use of (1) electron coupling, (2) a buffer amplifier, (3) a tank circuit having a high effective Q. The electron-coupled oscillator will be taken up later in this chapter. The use of the buffer amplifier applies to transmitters and will be taken up in Chap. XIII. Since the tube and load represent a comparatively low resistance in parallel with the tank circuit, the dynamic instability can be reduced by using a tuned circuit having a high effective Q and a low L/C ratio. Dynamic instability can also be reduced by increasing the effective resistance that the tube reflects to the tank circuit. This can be accomplished by using a higher value of grid-leak resistor, thus increasing the grid bias.

Temperature and Mechanical Variations. The expansion and contraction of the elements in a tube due to temperature changes will cause the interelectrode capacitances to vary accordingly. As these capacitances are part of the tuned circuit, the frequency of oscillation will be affected.

Temperature changes will also slightly affect the values of the tank coil and inductor, causing an additional shift in the resonant frequency. Because the effects of temperature change are comparatively slow in operation, the frequency change is referred to as *drift*. The obvious means of minimizing the amount of drift are by the use of (1) adequate ventilation, (2) a coil wound with large wire, (3) a low direct input voltage. Use of any of these methods will reduce the temperature of the oscillator unit, thus reducing the amount of drift. The variations in the interelectrode capacitances of the tube will have very little effect when they are shunted by a large value of capacitance. It is thus possible to reduce the amount of drift by using a large value of capacitance in the tank circuit thus producing a high C/L ratio.

Mechanical vibration of the circuit elements such as tubes, capacitors, and inductors also causes their values to vary. These changes in the values of inductance and capacitance will cause the resonant frequency to vary with the mechanical vibration. Instability due to mechanical vibration can be minimized by isolating the oscillator from the source of mechanical vibration.

10-10. Crystals. *Uses of Crystals.* The frequency of oscillation of the oscillator circuits previously discussed is controlled by the electrical constants of the circuit. Such oscillators are called *self-controlled oscillators*. Because the values of the circuit elements will be affected by the operating conditions, the frequency of oscillation of all self-controlled oscillators has a tendency to drift. There are a number of applications of oscillator circuits where the frequency of oscillation must be maintained at a fixed frequency or at several definite frequencies. Some of these applications are (1) transmitters, (2) time-signal receivers, (3) police-car radio receivers, (4) military, navigation, and aircraft communication apparatus, (5) test equipment used for calibration purposes. In order to maintain the output frequency of an oscillator at a constant value a crystal may be used to control the frequency of oscillation. This type of oscillator circuit is called a *crystal-controlled oscillator*.

Characteristics of Crystals. When certain crystalline materials are placed under a mechanical strain, such as compression or expansion, an electrical difference of potential will be developed across opposite faces of the crystal. This action is called the *piezoelectric effect.* Conversely, when a voltage is impressed across opposite faces of this type of crystal it will cause the crystal to expand or contract. If the voltage applied is alternating, the crystal will be set into vibration. The frequency of vibration will be equal to the resonant frequency of the crystal as determined by its structural characteristics. When the frequency of the

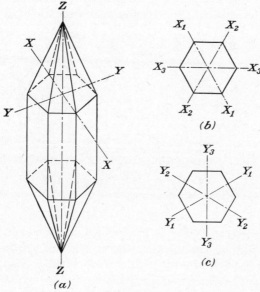

FIG. 10-14.—Quartz-crystal axes. (*a*) Symmetrical quartz crystal, (*b*) electrical axes, (*c*) mechanical axes.

applied voltage is equal to the resonant frequency of the crystal, the amplitude of vibration will be maximum. Because of its piezoelectric effect, a high-quality crystal can maintain the frequency of oscillation so that the variation in frequency will be less than one part in a million.

Piezoelectric effects may be obtained from Rochelle salts, tourmaline, and quartz. Although, theoretically, any one of these crystals can be used, for practical reasons quartz is the one most commonly used. The voltage set up in a Rochelle-salt crystal is much greater than would be set up in a quartz crystal; however, it is much weaker mechanically and is more likely to break. Tourmaline is mechanically stronger than quartz but because it is much less sensitive electrically it is only used for very high-frequency applications where quartz crystals must be ground so thin as to make its use impractical.   Other advantages of quartz are its low cost and the fact that it is available in comparatively large quantities.

Characteristics of Quartz Crystals.   Quartz crystals in their natural state assume the general form of hexagonal prisms with each end surmounted by a hexagonal pyramid (see Fig. 10-14a).   Each crystal has three principal axes: (1) Z or optical axis, (2) X or electrical axis, (3) Y or mechanical axis.   The axis joining the two points at the ends of the crystal is called the Z or *optical axis.*   No piezoelectric effects are produced when electrostatic charges are applied in this direction.   The X axes join opposite points of the hexagonal prism and each axis is parallel to one pair of sides of the hexagon and perpendicular to the optical

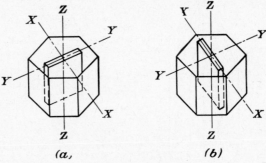

(a,   (b)

Fig. 10-15.—Methods of cutting a quartz crystal.   (a) X-cut, (b) Y-cut.

axis.   The X axes are called the *electrical axes* because the greatest amount of piezoelectric effect is produced along this axis.   The Y axes join opposite sides of the hexagonal prism and are perpendicular to the Z axis and the flat sides that it joins.   Each Y axis is also perpendicular to an X axis.   The Y axis is called the *mechanical axis.*   Each crystal will therefore have one Z axis, three X axes, and three Y axes (see Fig. 10-14).

Crystals used for electronic purposes are cut into thin plates.   When a plate is cut so that the flat surfaces are perpendicular to an X axis (Fig. 10-15a), it is called an *X-cut crystal.*   A plate cut so that its flat surfaces are perpendicular to a Y axis (Fig. 10-15b), is called a *Y-cut crystal.*

Temperature Coefficient.   The resonant frequency of a crystal will vary with temperature changes.   The number of cycles change per million cycles for a one degree centigrade change in temperature is called the *temperature coefficient.*   An X-cut crystal has a negative temperature coefficient and thus an increase in temperature will cause the resonant frequency to decrease.   A Y-cut crystal has a positive temperature coefficient and thus an increase in temperature will cause the resonant frequency to increase.

Two methods are employed to stabilize the resonant frequency of a crystal: (1) enclosing the crystal in a thermostatically controlled container, (2) varying the angle of cut of the crystal in order to obtain a zero temperature coefficient. As an *X*-cut crystal has a negative temperature coefficient and a *Y*-cut crystal a positive temperature coefficient, a crystal having a zero temperature coefficient can be obtained by cutting the crystal at the proper angle between the *X* and *Y* axes. This type of crystal is called an *XY cut*. Because of the inherent irregularities in the natural structure of a crystal, the lengths of all the *X* axes, or *Y* axes, are not equal to each other. In an *XY*-cut crystal it is thus possible to have two resonant frequencies very close to each other. This type of crystal

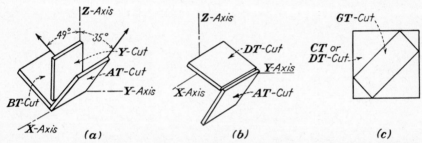

Fig. 10-16.—Crystal cuts having zero temperature coefficient. (*a*) *AT*- and *BT*-cuts (*b*) *DT*-cut, (*c*) *GT*-cut.

is not very practical, as it has the tendency to change its frequency abruptly.

Practical crystals having a zero temperature coefficient have been obtained by rotating the cutting plane about the *X* axis and cutting the crystal at an angle to the *Z* axis. Crystals obtained by cutting at an angle to the *Z* axis are called *AT, BT, CT, DT,* and *GT cuts*. The *AT* cut is obtained by rotating the cutting plane about 35 degrees in a clockwise direction, and the *BT* cut by a rotation of about 49 degrees in a counterclockwise direction (see Fig. 10-16*a*). The *CT* cut is made at approximately right angles to the *BT* cut, and the *DT* cut is made at approximately right angles to the *AT* cut (see Fig. 10-16*b*). These four types of crystal cuts have a zero temperature coefficient at only one temperature. A crystal having a zero temperature coefficient over a wide range of temperature is obtained by rotating the principal axes of a *CT* or *DT* crystal by 45 degrees (Fig. 10-16*c*). This type of crystal is called a *GT* cut.

Frequency—Thickness Ratio. The length and width of a crystal is of relatively minor importance, as crystals are generally cut so that the resonant frequency is determined mainly by its thickness. The frequency of vibration will vary inversely with the thickness as expressed by

$$f = \frac{k}{t} \qquad (10\text{-}17)$$

where f = frequency, kilocycles

t = thickness, inches

k = 112.6 for X-cut

    = 77.0 for Y-cut

    = 66.2 for AT-cut

Example 10-4. What is the thickness of a crystal whose resonant frequency is 1000 kc, when (*a*) X-cut? (*b*) Y-cut? (*c*) AT-cut?

Given:

    f = 1000 kc

Find:

    (*a*) t for X-cut

    (*b*) t for Y-cut

    (*c*) t for AT-cut

Solution:

$$t = \frac{k}{f}$$

(*a*) $t = \dfrac{112.6}{1000} = 0.1126$ inch

(*b*) $t = \dfrac{77.0}{1000} = 0.077$ inch

(*c*) $t = \dfrac{66.2}{1000} = 0.0662$ inch

From Example 10-4, it can be seen that for a given frequency the X-cut crystal is thicker and thus mechanically stronger than either the Y- or AT-cut crystals.

At the very high frequencies, the crystal required becomes too thin for practical use. Crystal control at these frequencies is obtained by the use of harmonic crystals, which will be discussed later in this chapter.

Power Limitations. The amount of current that can safely pass through a crystal ranges from 50 to 200 milliamperes. When the rated current is exceeded, the amplitude of mechanical vibration becomes too great and may crack the crystal. Overloading the crystal affects the frequency of vibration because the power dissipation and crystal temperature will increase with the amount of load current. A small flashlight bulb is sometimes connected in series with the crystal as an indicator of crystal current flow. By choosing a bulb whose current rating is less than that of the crystal, the bulb also serves as a fuse and burns out before a current is reached that will damage the crystal.

10-11. Crystal Oscillator Circuits. *Equivalent Electrical Circuit of a Crystal.* In order to make electrical connections to the crystal it is usually mounted horizontally between two metal plates (Fig. 10-17*a*).

As the crystal must vibrate to produce oscillations, it must be mounted between these two plates in such a manner as to allow for the required amount of mechanical vibration.

As vibration of the crystal will induce electrical charges on the two plates, it is thus possible to consider the crystal and its mountings as an electrical resonant circuit such as shown in Fig. 10-17b.   In this circuit, the capacitor C represents the elasticity of the crystal, the inductor L represents its mass, and the resistor R represents the resistance offered to the vibration by its internal friction.   The capacitor C_M represents the

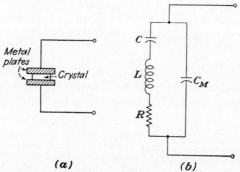

Fig. 10-17.—Crystal characteristics. (a) Crystal and mounting plates, (b) equivalent electrical circuit.

capacitor formed by the two metal plates of the holder separated by the crystal dielectric.

The reactances of L and C will be numerically equal to each other at the resonant frequency of the crystal. Since the crystal forms a series resonant circuit, maximum current will flow through the circuit at its resonant frequency, thus causing the magnitude of the crystal's vibrations to be maximum at this frequency. When the crystal vibrates at its resonant frequency, the voltage that it generates will be maximum and will also be of the same value of frequency.

At some frequency slightly higher than the resonant frequency, the combined effective reactance of L and C is inductive and will be numerically equal to the reactance of the capacitor C_M. At this frequency the crystal circuit acts as a parallel resonant circuit and its impedance is maximum. The circulating current in the circuit $CLRC_M$ is maximum and therefore the crystal vibrations will also be maximum. Thus a parallel resonant tank circuit can be obtained by operating the crystal at the resonant frequency of the parallel tuned circuit formed by $CLRC_M$.

The equivalent inductance of a crystal is very large in comparison with either its equivalent capacitance or its equivalent resistance. Because of this high L/R ratio, the Q of a crystal circuit is many times greater than can be obtained from an electric circuit, as will be shown in Example 10-5. Greater frequency stability and frequency discrimination are obtained because of the high Q and high L/C ratio of the series resonant circuit CLR.

Example 10-5.   A certain X-cut crystal is resonant at 450 kc.   For this frequency, its equivalent inductance is 3.65 henries, its equivalent capacitance is 0.0342 $\mu\mu$f, and its equivalent resistance is 9040 ohms.   What is the Q of the crystal?

Given: Find:
    $L = 3.65$ henries $Q = ?$
    $R = 9040$ ohms
    $f = 450$ kc

Solution:

$$Q = \frac{2\pi f L}{R} = \frac{6.28 \times 450,000 \times 3.65}{9040} = 1141$$

Simple Crystal Circuit.   Since a properly cut quartz crystal has the same characteristics as a high-Q tuned circuit, it can be used in an oscillator circuit to control the frequency of oscillation.   A simple crystal

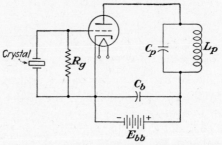

Fig. 10-18.—A simple crystal oscillator circuit.

oscillator circuit is shown in Fig. 10-18.   This circuit is similar to the tuned-grid tuned-plate oscillator except for the substitution of the crystal for the parallel tuned grid circuit.

The voltage returned to the grid circuit, by means of the grid-to-plate capacitance of the tube, is applied to the crystal and causes it to vibrate. The voltage set up by the crystal vibrations is applied to the grid of the tube, thereby controlling the amount of energy that is released in the plate circuit.

The voltage returned to the grid circuit will be maximum when the impedance of the crystal is maximum.   Maximum impedance occurs at the parallel resonant frequency of the crystal circuit.   At this frequency the crystal vibrations will be maximum and thus the voltage generated by the crystal will also be maximum.   The parallel resonant frequency of the crystal circuit thus determines the frequency of oscillation of a crystal-controlled oscillator. As with a tuned-grid tuned-plate oscillator, the resonant frequency of the tuned plate circuit should be slightly greater than the parallel resonant frequency of the crystal circuit.

Pentode Crystal Oscillator Circuit. There are many practical variations of the fundamental crystal-controlled oscillator circuit. Generally, the higher the amplification factor of a tube the smaller will be the amount of driving voltage required to produce the desired output. Crystals used in circuits employing tubes having a high amplification factor require low values of crystal current, and hence the magnitude of the crystal vibrations is also low. As the amplification factor of pentodes and beam power tubes is high, these types of tubes are ideal for use in crystal-controlled

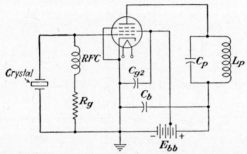

Fig. 10-19.—A crystal oscillator circuit using a pentode.

oscillator circuits. A crystal oscillator circuit using a pentode is illustrated in Fig. 10-19.

10-12. Electron Coupling. *Tetrode Electron-coupled Oscillator.* The tank circuit of an oscillator can be isolated from its plate load by using electron coupling between the oscillator and the load. The impedance of the tank circuit of this type of oscillator will be practically constant, since it will not be affected by changes in plate load. As the frequency of oscillation is dependent upon the impedance of the tank circuit, it will also be practically constant. Thus electron coupling is an effective means of making the frequency of an oscillator independent of variations in load.

Figure 10-20 illustrates two oscillator circuits employing electron coupling. A series-fed Hartley circuit is formed by the cathode, control grid, screen grid, and LC tank circuit. Although the oscillator portion of both of these circuits is of the Hartley type, the Colpitts circuit may be used with equally satisfactory results. In this type of circuit the screen grid serves as a plate and the r-f path to the inductor L in the tank circuit is completed through the screen-grid capacitor $C_{g.2}$. The plate of the tube serves only as an output electrode. Since the screen-grid capacitor blocks the high direct voltage and passes the high-frequency alternating voltage, the screen grid is in effect grounded for the r-f voltages. The plate is thus shielded from the oscillatory section of the tube, thereby preventing the load impedance from reacting on the oscillator.

Since the screen grid is constructed of mesh or fine wire, some of the electrons drawn to it will pass through. As the plate is maintained at a higher potential than the screen grid these electrons will be drawn to the plate. The frequency of the a-c component of the plate current is therefore the same as the oscillator frequency, and thus energy is delivered to the output load through an electron stream. Because the coupling medium is an electron stream, the circuit is called an *electron-coupled oscillator*.

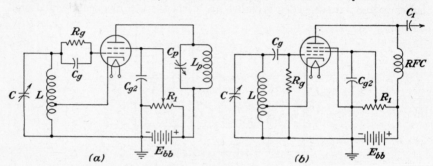

Fig. 10-20.—Electron-coupled oscillator circuits. (a) Tetrode oscillator circuit with a tuned output load, (b) pentode oscillator circuit with an untuned output load.

Pentode Electron-coupled Oscillator. Because of the interelectrode capacitance between the plate and control grid of a tetrode, a small amount of feedback will always be present. The frequency of electron-coupled oscillator circuits using tetrodes is therefore not completely independent of load variations. By substituting a pentode for the tetrode, feedback due to interelectrode capacitance can be eliminated. The frequency stability of electron-coupled oscillator circuits is thereby further improved by using a pentode.

An electron-coupled oscillator using a pentode is illustrated in Fig. 10-20b. The connections and circuit actions are the same as for the tetrode electron-coupled oscillator except for the suppressor grid. This grid may be connected to either the cathode or to ground potential. It thus acts as an electrostatic screen, thereby shielding the plate from the screen grid and the control grid. For all practical purposes, the capacitances existing between the tube elements are thereby eliminated. Since the electron stream flows in only one direction and the interelectrode capacitances are eliminated, the variations in load will have no effect on the frequency of oscillation.

Plate Voltage Supply. Increasing the plate voltage of an electron-coupled oscillator will cause the frequency of oscillation to change.

Increasing the screen-grid voltage of an electron-coupled oscillator will also cause the frequency of oscillation to change but in an opposite direction to that caused by a plate voltage increase.   If the voltage on the screen grid is obtained from a variable voltage divider, as shown in Fig. 10-20, the screen-grid voltage can be adjusted so that these two actions balance each other.   The frequency of oscillation will then be practically independent of variations in the supply voltages.

10-13. Frequency Multiplication. *Harmonic Generation.* It has previously been shown that the thickness of a crystal varies inversely as its frequency.   For very high frequencies the crystal would have to be very thin and might easily be broken.   The frequency at which a crystal becomes too thin to be practical or durable will vary with the crystal material and the type of cut that is used.   The practical limit for quartz crystals is approximately 11 megacycles; however, it is possible to grind a quartz plate to operate as high as 20 megacycles.   In order to obtain crystal control of an oscillator at the high frequencies, frequency multiplication is employed.   This is accomplished by using a crystal-controlled oscillator of a comparatively low resonant frequency and using a harmonic of the oscillator output to drive a power amplifier.

The output current of a highly biased Class C operated tube is not a sine wave but is a wave made up of a fundamental and a number of its harmonics.   Increasing the bias on the tube will increase the intensity of the higher order of harmonics.   Knowing the frequency of a crystal, the harmonic components of the output of the tube can be used as a frequency standard over a wide frequency range.   Harmonics of a high order can be obtained from such a circuit and it is possible that as high as a fiftieth harmonic may be used as a means of checking and calibrating high frequencies.   Thus, if the fundamental frequency of an oscillator is 1000 kc the twentieth harmonic is 20,000 kc or 20 mc, and the fiftieth harmonic is 50,000 kc or 50 mc.   The crystal used to control these circuits would be required to have a resonant frequency of only 1000 kc.

A frequency doubler is commonly used in connection with crystal oscillators to obtain a frequency higher than that for which the crystal is ground.   Frequency multipliers are also used in radio transmitters designed to operate at two or more frequencies that are multiples of one another.

A crystal-controlled oscillator circuit which possesses good frequency stability is practical at only relatively low radio frequencies.   In order to obtain good frequency stability at the very high and ultrahigh radio frequencies it is necessary to obtain the frequency by multiplication or harmonic generation.   An oscillator circuit that gives a harmonic output is called a *frequency multiplier.*

Tri-tet Oscillator. The frequency-load stability of electron-coupled oscillators is excellent; however, the output wave form contains many harmonics. These harmonics may be advantageous, since they can be used to produce frequencies that are multiples of either the tank circuit frequency or the crystal frequency. The oscillator circuit illustrated in Fig. 10-21 uses a single tube as both a triode and tetrode, hence the name *tri-tet oscillator.* This circuit is a combination of a triode crystal oscillator and an electron-coupled oscillator. The oscillator circuit is electron

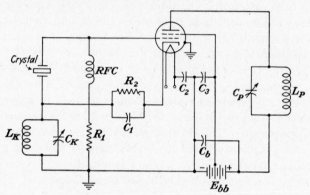

FIG. 10-21.—A tri-tet oscillator circuit.

coupled to the output circuit $L_P C_P$ and is thus electrostatically shielded from the output by the screen grid. A pentode-type tube can also be used if the connection to the suppressor grid can be made externally. The suppressor grid should be connected either directly to ground or may be operated at approximately 50 volts positive. Operating the suppressor grid slightly positive produces a higher power output.

The tank circuit $L_K C_K$ in the cathode circuit is always tuned to a frequency somewhat higher than that of the crystal. The tank circuit $L_P C_P$ in the output circuit is tuned to either the fundamental crystal frequency or one of its multiples.

The two outstanding features of the tri-tet oscillator are (1) its ability to operate as a frequency multiplier, (2) the buffer action between the oscillator and output circuits, that is, isolating the output circuit from the crystal oscillator circuit.

BIBLIOGRAPHY

EASTMAN, A. V., *Fundamentals of Vacuum Tubes*, McGraw-Hill Book Company, Inc., New York.

GHIRARDI, A. A., Practical Radio Course, *Radio News*, March, April, May, June, 1945.

HENNEY, K., *Principles of Radio*, John Wiley & Sons, Inc., New York.

NILSON, A. R., and HORNUNG, J. L., *Practical Radio Communication*, McGraw-Hill Book Company, Inc., New York.

Post, M. D., Oscillations Simplified, *Radio News*, May, 1944.

Reich, H. J., *Theory and Applications of Electron Tubes*, McGraw-Hill Book Company, Inc., New York.

Rider, J. F., *The Oscillator at Work*, John F. Rider, Publisher, Inc., New York.

Terman, F. E., *Fundamentals of Radio*, McGraw-Hill Book Company, Inc., New York.

QUESTIONS

1. (*a*) Define the oscillator circuit.   (*b*) What is the function of a vacuum tube in an oscillator circuit?

2. (*a*) Why are vacuum-tube oscillators necessary in radio equipment?   (*b*) What is their purpose in transmitters?   (*c*) What is their purpose in receivers?

3. Name some applications of vacuum-tube oscillators other than radio transmitters and receivers.

4. (*a*) Into what two classifications may vacuum-tube oscillator circuits be divided?   (*b*) Give a further subdivision of each of these general classifications.

5. What is meant by (*a*) negative resistance?   (*b*) Dynatron?   (*c*) Transitron?

6. How may feedback oscillator circuits be classified?

7. (*a*) What is the principle of the heterodyne oscillator?   (*b*) What are its uses?

8. (*a*) When are crystal-controlled oscillators used?   (*b*) What purpose does the crystal serve?

9. (*a*) What is the principle of the magnetostriction oscillator?   (*b*) What are its uses?

10. Can any oscillator circuit be used to produce ultrahigh-frequency currents? Explain.

11. Explain the amplifier action of an oscillator circuit.

12. (*a*) What are the essential parts of a vacuum-tube oscillator?   (*b*) What is the purpose of each part?

13. Why are radio-frequency oscillator tubes generally operated as Class C?

14. Explain the oscillatory action that takes place in the tank circuit of an oscillator.

15. What is the relation of the factors that affect the frequency of oscillations in a tank circuit?

16. (*a*) What is the wave form of the current in a tank circuit if no energy is supplied to the circuit to compensate for the I^2R loss?   (*b*) What wave form will be obtained if sufficient energy is supplied to the circuit to overcome its losses?

17. Describe the operation of the fundamental oscillator circuit.

18. How may energy from the oscillator circuit be applied to the load?

19. Explain the purpose and operation of the grid-leak resistor and grid capacitor in an oscillator circuit.

20. (*a*) What determines the value of the time constant recommended for the grid bias circuit of an oscillator?   (*b*) How are the values of R_g and C_g determined?

21. What is the objection to using a fixed bias with an oscillator whose tube is being operated Class C?

22. (*a*) What are the characteristics of the Hartley circuit?   (*b*) Describe the operation of the Hartley circuit.   (*c*) What determines its frequency?

23. Compare the characteristics of series feed and parallel feed for the Hartley oscillator.

24. (*a*) What are the characteristics of the Colpitts circuit?   (*b*) Describe the operation of the Colpitts circuit.   (*c*) What determines its frequency?

25. Why is parallel feed necessary with the Colpitts oscillator?

26. What are the applications of (*a*) the Hartley oscillator?   (*b*) The Colpitts oscillator?

27. (*a*) What are the characteristics of the tuned-grid tuned-plate oscillator? (*b*) Describe its operation.   (*c*) What determines its frequency?

28. (*a*) What is meant by amplitude stability?   (*b*) What factors affect the amplitude stability?

29. How does the tank circuit Q affect the wave shape of the oscillator output?

30. What factors affect the amount of energy stored in the tank circuit?

31. (*a*) What factors affect the value of excitation voltage required to drive the oscillator tube?   (*b*) What is the effect of too high an excitation voltage?   (*c*) What is the effect of too low an excitation voltage?

32. (*a*) Why are oscillator circuits seldom required to deliver large amounts of power?   (*b*) How is a large power output generally obtained?

33. What factors affect the plate efficiency of an oscillator tube?

34. (*a*) What is meant by frequency stability?   (*b*) What factors affect the frequency stability?

35. (*a*) What is meant by dynamic instability?   (*b*) What is its cause?

36. (*a*) What is meant by frequency drift?   (*b*) What is its cause?

37. (*a*) What is meant by a crystal-controlled oscillator?   (*b*) What are some applications of the crystal-controlled oscillator?

38. (*a*) Describe the piezoelectric effect of the crystal.   (*b*) What materials can be used for crystals and what is the advantage or disadvantage of each?

39. (*a*) What are the three axes of a quartz crystal?   (*b*) Describe the electrical axes.

40. (*a*) What is meant by the temperature coefficient of a crystal?   (*b*) What is its importance?

41. Describe and give the temperature characteristics of the following types of crystal cuts: (*a*) *X* cut, (*b*) *Y* cut, (*c*) *XY* cut, (*d*) *CT* cut, (*e*) *DT* cut, (*f*) *GT* cut.

42. (*a*) What is the range of current rating of the average crystal?   (*b*) What is the possible effect of overloading a crystal?   (*c*) What protection is recommended?

43. Describe the equivalent electrical circuit of a crystal.

44. Compare the crystal-controlled oscillator circuit with the tuned-grid tuned-plate oscillator.

45. Explain the operation of a simple crystal-controlled oscillator.

46. (*a*) Explain the principle of electron coupling.   (*b*) What are the advantages of electron-coupled oscillators?

47. (*a*) Explain the principle of frequency multiplication.   (*b*) When is frequency multiplication used in oscillator circuits?

48. (*a*) Explain the principle of the tri-tet oscillator.   (*b*) What are its advantages?

PROBLEMS

1. The tank section of an oscillator circuit used in a superheterodyne receiver contains an inductance of 90 μh shunted by a variable capacitor of $^{365}\!\!/_{35}$ $\mu\mu$f.   What is the frequency range of the oscillator circuit if the distributed capacitance of the coil and wiring is disregarded?

2. What is the frequency range of the oscillator circuit of Prob. 1 if the distributed capacitance of the coil and wiring is known to be 15 $\mu\mu$f?

3. What is the frequency range of the oscillator circuit of Prob. 1 if a padding capacitor of 0.001 μf is connected in series with the tuning capacitor?   The distributed capacitance of the coil and wiring is 15 $\mu\mu$f.

4. If the oscillator of Prob. 3 produces a frequency 465 kc higher than the frequency of the r-f circuit throughout its working range, what is the tuning range of the receiver?

5. The oscillator section of a certain radio receiver obtains its grid bias by use of a 50,000-ohm grid-leak resistor and a 50-$\mu\mu$f grid capacitor. (*a*) What is the time constant of the circuit? (*b*) What is the time required to complete one-half of an output cycle if the frequency of the oscillator is 2200 kc? (*c*) Is the time constant of the $R_g C_g$ combination long or short compared to the time of one-half of a cycle of the oscillator output?

6. The oscillator section of a certain radio receiver uses a type 6SA7 tube. A grid bias of 10 volts is to be obtained by means of a grid-leak resistor. (*a*) What value of resistance is required if the grid current is 0.5 ma? (*b*) What value of grid capacitor should be used if the time constant of the $R_g C_g$ combination should be approximately one microsecond?

7. A parallel-fed Hartley oscillator circuit similar to Fig. 10-8*b* uses an r-f choke of 2.5 mh and a blocking capacitor of 0.005 μf. (*a*) What is the reactance of the choke and of the capacitor at 2200 kc? (*b*) What is the ratio of X_L to X_C at this frequency? (*c*) What is the reactance of the choke and of the capacitor at 1000 kc? (*d*) What is the ratio of X_L to X_C at this frequency?

8. What is the frequency of a Hartley oscillator circuit similar to Fig. 10-8*a* if the total inductance of L_P and L_G is 80 μh and the total capacitance of the tuning circuit is 180 $\mu\mu$f?

9. What is the frequency of a Colpitts oscillator circuit similar to Fig. 10-10 if the value of the inductor L is 140 μh, C_P is 200 $\mu\mu$f, and C_G is 300 $\mu\mu$f?

10. The inductor of a certain tank circuit has an inductance of 100 μh and a resistance of 10 ohms at 1600 kc. What is the efficiency of the tank circuit at 1600 kc if the Q of the circuit when loaded is 15?

11. The efficiency of a tank circuit is 90 per cent and its no-load value of Q is 150. What is the effective Q of the circuit when loaded?

12. The effective Q of a certain tank circuit is 12.5. What is the no-load value of Q if the efficiency of the circuit is 92 per cent?

13. The oscillator section of a radio receiver that is using a 6A8 tube has a 100-μh inductor and a $^{35}\!/_{40}$-$\mu\mu$f tuning capacitor for its tank circuit. The Q of the circuit when loaded is 30 and the alternating voltage across the tank circuit is 15 volts (rms). Find (*a*) the value of capacitance when the oscillator is adjusted to a resonant frequency of 1500 kc, (*b*) the current in the tank circuit, (*c*) the power supplied to the tank circuit, (*d*) the amount of energy stored in the tank circuit during each cycle, (*e*) the ratio of energy stored per cycle to the energy dissipated per cycle.

14. An r-f Class C power amplifier is to supply 60 watts at a frequency of 2 megacycles. The value of E_p (and E_t) is 1000 volts and in order to obtain satisfactory wave form the effective Q of the plate tank circuit should not be less than 15. (*a*) What value of inductance should be used in the tank circuit? (*b*) What value of capacitance should be used? (*c*) What is the current in the tank circuit? (*d*) What is the plate circuit current?

15. The tank circuit of a certain Class C power amplifier is operated at a frequency of 5 megacycles. The power supplied to the tank circuit is 500 watts and the value of the alternating component of the plate voltage (also E_t) is 1500 volts. It is desired that the effective Q of the tank circuit be 12.5. Find (*a*) the value of inductance required, (*b*) the value of capacitance required, (*c*) the current in the tank circuit, (*d*) the current supplied to the tank circuit, (*e*) the amount of energy stored in the tank circuit per cycle.

16. Repeat Prob. 15 for a value of Q equal to 50.

17. A Hartley oscillator, similar to Fig. 10-9a, is to be operated so that the tube will deliver 2.5 watts of power to the tank circuit (plate section) at a resonant frequency of 1500 kc. The alternating component of the plate voltage is to be 140 volts and the voltage at L_G is to be 20 volts. In order to obtain the desired wave form at the output, the effective Q of the tank circuit (plate section L_P) is to have a value of approximately 20. Find (a) the inductance required for section L_P of the tank circuit, (b) the inductance required for section L_G assuming 100 per cent coupling between L_P and L_G, (c) the value of capacitance required for the tank circuit, (d) the amount of energy stored in the tank circuit per cycle.

18. A Colpitts oscillator, similar to Fig. 10-10, is to be operated so that the tube will deliver 2.5 watts of power to the tank circuit (plate section) at a resonant frequency of 1500 kc. The alternating component of the plate voltage is to be 140 volts and the voltage at C_G is to be 20 volts. In order to obtain the desired wave form at the output, the effective Q of the tank circuit (plate section C_P) is to have a value of approximately 20. Find (a) the capacitance required for the capacitor C_P, (b) the capacitance for the capacitor C_G, (c) the value of inductance required for the tank circuit.

Hint: For solution of part (a) use Eq. (10-15), substituting X_C in place of X_L.

19. A certain X-cut quartz crystal has a resonant frequency of 3 mc at 20°C. The crystal has a negative temperature coefficient of 25 cycles per megacycle per degree centigrade. How much will the frequency vary if the temperature changes to (a) 30°C? (b) 15°C? (c) 10°C?

20. A certain Y-cut quartz crystal has a resonant frequency of 3 mc at 20°C. The crystal has a positive temperature coefficient of 80 cycles per megacycle per degree centigrade. How much will the frequency change if the temperature changes to (a) 30°C? (b) 15°C? (c) 10°C?

21. A certain crystal whose resonant frequency is 450 kc has an inductance of 3 henries and its effective series resistance is 2000 ohms. What is the value of Q for this crystal?

22. If the crystal of Prob. 21 is represented by the equivalent circuit of Fig. 10-17b, what is the equivalent capacitance C?

23. What is the thickness of an X-cut crystal whose resonant frequency is (a) 250 kc? (b) 2500 kc? (c) 10,000 kc?

24. What is the thickness of a Y-cut crystal whose resonant frequency is (a) 200 kc? (b) 2000 kc? (c) 8000 kc?

25. What is the resonant frequency of an AT-cut crystal if its thickness is (a) 0.1655 inch? (b) 0.0301 inch? (c) 0.01655 inch?

CHAPTER XI

POWER SUPPLY CIRCUITS

In the previous chapters the use of vacuum tubes and their associated circuits as detectors, amplifiers, and oscillators has been presented. In order to obtain the desired performance of these circuits it is necessary that the voltages applied to the tubes' electrodes be of the proper values. The unit used to supply these voltages is called the *power supply*.

The power supply unit is an essential part of every type of radio and electronic equipment, since it supplies the proper voltages and currents to the filaments (or heaters), plates, and grids of the various tubes used. The general requirements of a power supply are: (1) the output voltages should be of the correct values for the apparatus used; (2) the variation in the output voltage between no-load and full-load conditions should be as small as is economically practical; (3) the output voltage should be an unvarying voltage or as nearly constant in value as is economically practical.

The equipment used to supply power to radio and electronic apparatus may be divided into three classes: (1) batteries, (2) electromechanical systems, (3) commercial power lines.

11-1. Sources of Power Supply. *Batteries.* In the early stages of radio development batteries were used to supply the power for practically all equipment. The use of batteries is generally divided into three classifications: (1) A power supply, used to supply power to the heaters or filaments; (2) B power supply, used to supply power to the plate and screen-grid circuits; (3) C power supply, used to supply voltage for the grid bias. Some types of radio equipment still operate on power supplied by batteries. Dry-cell batteries and air-cell batteries are used to supply the power required to operate portable receivers and transceivers (transmitter and receiver in one unit). The power required to operate radio equipment in automobiles and aircraft is usually obtained from storage batteries.

The current flow from a battery is smooth, as it is devoid of any ripple or other variation. This uniform flow of power is one of the desirable characteristics of batteries. However, batteries have a limited amount of energy and must be either recharged or replaced periodically. As the available energy decreases, the voltage delivered also decreases and eventually causes unsatisfactory operation of the equipment. Other disadvantages of batteries are their weight, bulk, and cost. Battery power is more expensive and not nearly so convenient as power that can be obtained from the ordinary lighting circuit. For a detailed description of the principle of operation, characteristics, construction, and care of batteries, the reader is referred to Chap. III of the authors' text on *Electrical Essentials of Radio*.

Electromechanical Systems. The power required to operate certain types of radio transmitters, radio receivers, and electronic equipment is obtained from electromechanical systems. This type of power equipment may be in either of two forms: (1) generator systems, (2) vibrator systems.

Generator systems appear in various forms such as electric-motor-driven generators, gasoline-engine-driven generators, hand-driven generators, dynamotors, and converters. The type of mechanical equipment used will depend upon the kind and amount of energy available as a prime mover. The output of the d-c generator is not a continuous current but is a pulsating current. The pulsations are caused by the commutator and are generally referred to as *commutator ripple* (see Chap. VII of the authors' *Electrical Essentials of Radio*). As one of the requirements of power supplies is to provide a current with a minimum amount of pulsations, it is necessary to use filter circuits with this type of equipment in order to smooth out the commutator ripple.

The type of power supply most commonly used for automobile and aircraft radio equipment is a six-volt storage battery used in conjunction with a vibrator unit. Power for the filaments (or heaters) is obtained directly from the battery. The high voltage required for the plates and screen grids is obtained by means of a vibrator unit, which is described in detail later in this chapter.

Power Lines. Power obtained from an a-c or d-c power line is the least expensive and the most convenient source of power. Because of this, it is desirable whenever practical to use power lines to supply all the voltages required by electronic devices such as radio receivers and transmitters. As the high operating voltages required for the plates and screen grids of electronic tubes cannot be taken directly from the power lines, it is necessary to employ suitable equipment to change the input voltage to the desired values of voltage. Since a-c power is almost universally used for lighting circuits, it is also the source of power for most stationary types of electronic equipment.

The power supply unit used in radio equipment to convert alternating current to direct current consists of four parts: (1) the power transformer, (2) the rectifier, (3) the filter, (4) the voltage divider. The power transformer increases the line voltage to a value high enough to obtain the high voltage required at the output of the power supply unit. The rectifier allows current to flow in only one direction and therefore converts the alternating current to a pulsating unidirectional current. The filter removes the ripples from the pulsating current so that the output of the power supply is practically a continuous current. The voltage divider, as its name implies, divides the output voltage of the filter into the several values of voltage required by the plates and grids of the tubes.

Types of Power Supplies. Power supply units as used in radio receivers operated from a-c power lines may be divided into four basic types: (1) the half-wave rectifier, (2) the full-wave rectifier, (3) the bridge-type rectifier, (4) the voltage-doubler-type rectifier. Each of these types of power supply has different operating characteristics. The choice of power supply will depend upon the operating voltages and currents desired. The operating characteristics of a power supply will also be affected by the type of filter circuit used and the values of the circuit elements. The output requirements of a power supply will therefore determine the type of rectifier and filter circuit to be used. In analyzing the requirements of the power supply, the operating characteristics to be taken into consideration are (1) the required output voltage, (2) the required output current, (3) the allowable peak voltage, (4) the ripple voltage, (5) the voltage regulation.

11-2. The Power Transformer. *Requirements of the Power Transformer.* The main purpose of the power transformer is to increase the line voltage so that the power supply unit will be able to furnish the high operating voltages required by the plates and screen grids of the vacuum tubes in the equipment being supplied. The power transformer may also be required to furnish the low voltages for the filaments or heaters of the tubes. In this case, one or more low-voltage secondary windings are provided on the power transformer.

For a high power rectifier, such as used in a transmitter or where a comparatively high voltage is required by the plate circuits, it is necessary that the filaments be operated from a separate transformer. A transformer used to supply only the plate power requires a primary winding and only a single secondary winding (see Fig. 11-1a). A transformer of this type is used in a half-wave rectifier circuit. In a full-wave rectifier circuit the secondary is usually center-tapped, as shown in Fig. 11-1b.

When the output of the power supply is comparatively low, such as those used in radio receivers, it is common practice to combine the plate and filament transformers into one unit, as shown in Figs. 11-1c and 11-1d. In this type of power transformer, the line voltage will also have to be decreased to the value, or values, required by the heaters of the tubes to be supplied. As it is sometimes necessary to provide separate filament voltage sources for the rectifier tube, the r-f tubes, and the a-f tubes, the number of filament windings on the power transformer will be determined by the requirements of the particular radio receiver.   It can be seen from Fig. 11-1 that all the filament windings of a power transformer are secondary windings and, together with the secondary for the plate supply, operate from a common primary winding.

Ratings of Power Transformers.   Power transformers are usually rated in secondary volts at full load and milliamperes output (d-c) at full load.   The secondary volts is measured across the full high-voltage

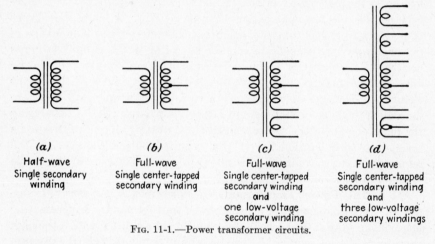

(a)	(b)	(c)	(d)
Half-wave	Full-wave	Full-wave	Full-wave
Single secondary	Single center-tapped	Single center-tapped	Single center-tapped
winding	secondary winding	secondary winding	secondary winding
		and	and
		one low-voltage	three low-voltage
		secondary winding	secondary windings

Fig. 11-1.—Power transformer circuits.

winding, or from plate-to-plate of the rectifier tube.   This should be the voltage at full load and hence should be measured with the rated current being drawn from the rectifier.   Thus a transformer rated 350-0-350 secondary volts and 120 ma output current should indicate 700 volts across the two ends of the high-voltage secondary winding and 350 volts from either end to the center tap when 120 ma is being drawn from the rectifier.

The rms value of the high voltage output of the power transformer should be slightly higher than the sum of the required output voltage and the voltage drops at the filter chokes and the rectifier tube.   Transformers used with full-wave center-tapped rectifiers should produce this amount of voltage from the center tap to each side of the secondary winding.   The output current rating should be approximately 10 per cent greater than the sum of the currents taken by the various tubes and the bleeder resistor.

In a full-wave center-tapped rectifier circuit, the load is alternately transferred electronically from one-half of the secondary winding to the other, and thus only one-half of the secondary winding is used at a time. Each half of the secondary should therefore be capable of delivering the required voltage and current.

In some instances, manufacturers also rate power transformers according to the voltage that will be obtained at the output of a two-section filter. This rating also takes into account the voltage drop through the rectifier tube.

Voltage Regulation. The voltage delivered to the secondary winding of a power transformer will decrease in value as the current taken by the

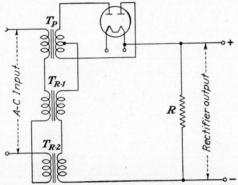

Fig. 11-2.—Circuit showing the connections of a voltage-regulating transformer.

load is increased. Power transformers used in radio receivers are designed to operate continuously under full-load condition with excellent regulation. The variation in output voltage from no-load to full-load for this type of transformer is comparatively small and usually can be ignored.

In some types of electronic equipment it is necessary that a constant voltage be maintained at the secondary terminals regardless of the value of the load. In this type of equipment a voltage regulating transformer, whose circuit is similar to that shown in Fig. 11-2, is used in the power supply unit. An increase in the load current will decrease the output voltage but will also increase the flux in the cores of the regulating transformers $T_{R \cdot 1}$ and $T_{R \cdot 2}$ toward saturation. The impedance of the primary windings of these transformers is thus decreased, thereby increasing the voltage across the primary of the power transformer T_P and also increasing the voltage across the output. A decrease in load current will cause these actions to take place in an opposite direction to those taking place with an increase in current. As these actions take place almost instantaneously, the output voltage can be maintained practically constant.

Because the secondaries of the regulating transformers are connected in series with the output of the rectifier tube, it is necessary that the output of these transformers be eliminated. This is accomplished by connecting the transformers in series opposition. It is important that the regulating transformers be perfectly balanced; otherwise an alternating current ripple will be produced in the output of the power supply.

11-3. Rectifiers of Alternating-current Power. *Purpose of the Rectifier.* The purpose of the rectifier is to change the alternating-current output of the power transformer to a unidirectional current. The action of a rectifier that permits current to flow through it more easily in one direction than the other makes possible its use as a device for changing alternating current to direct current.

The Diode Rectifier. The principle of operation of a rectifier may be either mechanical, thermal, chemical, or electronic. Of these, the elec-

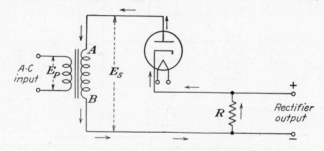

→ *Electron flow when* **A** *is positive*

Fig. 11-3.—A single-diode rectifier circuit.

tronic principle, as applies to a diode, is the one most generally used in the rectifier of d-c power supplies associated with electronic equipment.

Current will flow in the plate-cathode circuit of a tube only when the plate is positive with respect to the cathode. If an alternating current is applied between the plate and cathode of a diode as in Fig. 11-3, plate current will flow only during that portion of the cycle when the plate is positive. During the half-cycle in which the plate is negative, no plate current will flow. The diode rectifier is thus alternately a conductor and an insulator.

The rectifier tube may be either of the high vacuum type or the gaseous type. The high vacuum tube is generally used for high-voltage and low-current outputs. The gaseous-type rectifier tube is generally used for high-current outputs.

Tube Voltage Drop. During the portion of the cycle in which the tube is conducting, voltage drops will be produced at the tube and the secondary winding of the transformer. Since these voltage drops reduce the voltage available across the output load they should be kept as low as is practical.

The internal voltage drop of a high-vacuum-type rectifier tube will vary in almost direct proportion to its load current (see Fig. 11-4). A varying load current will cause the voltage drop across the tube to vary, thus also causing a variation in the voltage across the output load. The voltage regulation of high-vacuum-type rectifier tubes is therefore very poor. The internal voltage drop of directly heated (filament-type) high vacuum rectifier tubes is comparatively high. This can be seen by an

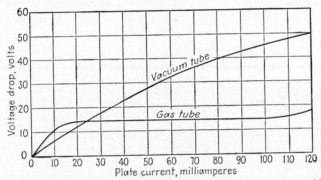

FIG. 11-4.—Internal voltage drop between cathode and plate for comparable gas and vacuum tubes.

examination of the internal voltage drop at rated operating values for rectifier tubes of this type. From a tube manual, the voltage drop for the 5T4 is 45 volts and for the 5Y4-G it is 60 volts.

As one of the factors affecting the internal voltage drop in a tube is its space charge, the voltage drop can be decreased by reducing the effect of the space charge. The space charge is reduced in some high-vacuum-type rectifier tubes by decreasing the spacing between the cathode and plate. This method is used in rectifier-type tubes having a heater cathode such as the 35Z5-G and the 117Z6-G. The internal voltage drop of these two tubes at rated operating values is 21 volts for the 35Z5-G and 15.5 volts for the 117Z6-G.

The space charge in a tube can also be reduced by ionization. This method is used in the mercury-vapor type of rectifier tube such as the 83 and also in the ionic-heated cathode type of rectifier tube such as the 0Z4. The internal voltage drop of mercury-vapor tubes is very low, being approximately 15 volts. The voltage regulation of mercury-vapor tubes is very good as the internal voltage drop is practically independent of the load current (see Fig. 11-4).

The cathode of the ionic-heated type of rectifier tube is heated by the bombardment of the cathode by the ions from within the tube. As no external current is required to heat the cathode, it is also referred to as a *cold-cathode* type of rectifier tube. As energy is taken from the ionization discharge to heat the cathode, the internal voltage drop of this type tube is slightly higher than the hot-cathode mercury-vapor rectifier tube. The internal voltage drop of the 0Z4 at rated operating conditions is 24 volts.

Ratings of Rectifier Tubes. Rectifier tubes are generally rated according to (1) the alternating voltage per plate, (2) the peak inverse voltage, (3) the peak plate current, (4) the load current. These ratings are not fixed values but vary with the rectifier tube and filter circuits with which the tube is associated. This can be observed from the operating characteristics of the 5T4 as listed in Table XI-I.

TABLE XI-I

Filter circuit	Alternating voltage per plate (rms)	Peak inverse voltage	Peak plate current (per plate)	Load current (d-c)
Capacitor input to filter........	450 volts	1270 volts	675 ma	225 ma
Choke input to filter..........	550 volts	1550 volts	675 ma	225 ma

The *alternating voltage per plate* is the highest rms value of voltage that can safely be applied between the plate and cathode of the tube. In a half-wave rectifier circuit the open circuit voltage across the secondary winding of the power transformer should not exceed this value. In a full-wave rectifier circuit the open circuit voltage between either end of the secondary winding of the power transformer and its center tap should not exceed this value.

The *peak inverse voltage* rating is the maximum value of voltage that a rectifier tube can safely withstand between its plate and cathode when the tube is not conducting. During the portion of the a-c input cycle when the plate is negative with respect to the cathode, no voltage drops will exist in the rectifier circuit and hence the full secondary voltage will be impressed between the plate and cathode. For normal operating conditions this voltage is equal to the peak value of the transformer secondary voltage. For transient conditions this peak value of voltage may be greatly exceeded.

The *peak plate current* represents the maximum amount of electron emission that the cathode can supply. It is the maximum instantaneous value of current that can safely flow through the rectifier tube.

The *load current* is the maximum safe value of direct current that the tube can deliver. Since current flows through a plate circuit of a rectifier tube during only half of the input cycle, the average value of its direct current output will be less than one-half of its peak plate current.

The Contact Rectifier. A metal disk or plate that is held in contact, under pressure, with another substance is also used as a rectifier of alternating current. This type of unit is called a *dry disk* or *contact rectifier.* The resistance to electron flow from the metal to the substance with which it is in contact is very low. The resistance to electron flow in the reverse direction is very high. Because of this characteristic the contact rectifier can be used to rectify alternating current.

Three types of contact rectifiers are available, namely, the copper oxide, copper sulphide, and selenium rectifiers. The copper-oxide rectifier consists of a copper disk that is oxidized on one of its sides and a soft lead washer. The washer is used to provide electrical contact with the oxidized surface. This type of unit is generally used in power supplies associated with instruments. In the copper-sulphide rectifier one of the surfaces of the copper disk is coated with copper sulphide and the electrical contact is made with this surface by means of a magnesium washer. This type of unit is generally used in battery chargers. The selenium rectifier consists of an aluminum plate or disk that has one of its surfaces coated with selenium. Electrical contact with the selenium-coated surface is made directly with the uncoated surface of the adjacent plate or disk. This type of unit can be used in place of most rectifier tubes and hence has many applications in radio and electronic circuits.

11-4. Fundamental Rectifier Circuits. *Half-wave Rectifier Circuit.* In a half-wave rectifier circuit a single diode vacuum or gas tube is used and is connected to the power transformer as shown in Fig. 11-5a. When the tube is conducting, electrons flow from the cathode to the plate, through the secondary of the power transformer, through the output circuit, and back to the cathode, as indicated by the arrows on this illustration. When the plate is positive with respect to the cathode, the tube acts as a conductor and current flows in the output circuit. When the plate is negative with respect to the cathode, the tube acts as an insulator and no current flows in the output circuit. The relation between the input voltage and the output current for the single diode rectifier is shown in Fig. 11-5. From this figure it can be seen that the output current flows during only one-half of the input cycle. Because of this, the single diode tube is also referred to as a *half-wave rectifier.*

The output of a half-wave rectifier is a pulsating unidirectional current. Because the output current flows in only one direction through the secondary winding, the iron core of the power transformer will tend to become saturated thus distorting the output wave. The simple half-wave rectifier circuit as shown in Fig. 11-5 is a comparatively poor type of rectifier and therefore is seldom used.

The inverse peak voltage is equal to the maximum voltage of the transformer secondary. For a sine-wave input this peak value is equal to 1.41 times the rms value of the secondary output voltage, or 1.41 times E_s.

Full-wave Rectifier Circuit Using a Center-tapped Transformer. The operating characteristics of a rectifier will be improved if current can be made to flow in the output circuit for the entire period of the input cycle. This may be accomplished by using two single diode tubes or a duplex diode (two single diodes in one envelope) in conjunction with a center-

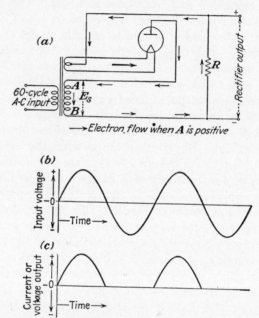

Fig. 11-5.—A half-wave diode rectifier. (a) The circuit, (b) wave form of the input voltage, (c) wave form of the output current or voltage.

tapped power transformer, as shown in Fig. 11-6. Because the two plates of the rectifier tube are connected to opposite ends of the secondary winding, their polarity with respect to their common cathode connection will always be opposite to each other. Thus during one-half of the input cycle one plate will be conducting and the other will not be conducting, and during the second half-cycle the second plate will be conducting and the first will not be conducting. Under this condition, current will flow in the output circuit during both halves of the input cycle. It can be seen from Fig. 11-6 that both halves of the input cycle have been rectified and hence the name *full-wave rectifier*. Since each rectifier section supplies energy for one-half of the cycle, the plates of a full-wave rectifier will have to carry only one-half the amount of plate current required by a half-wave rectifier for equal amounts of load current.

The action of this type of full-wave rectifier circuit may be explained in the following manner. During one-half of the input cycle plate 1 will be positive and plate 2 negative. During this period electrons will flow from cathode to plate 1, through one-half of the secondary winding (terminal 1 to the center tap), to the output circuit, and back to the cathode. The wave form of the output current for this half-cycle is

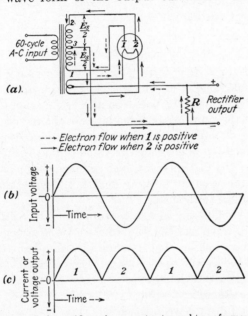

FIG. 11-6.—A full-wave diode rectifier using a center-tapped transformer. (*a*) The circuit, (*b*) wave form of the input voltage, (*c*) wave form of the output current or voltage.

indicated by the sections labeled 1 on Fig. 11-6*c*. During the other half of the input cycle plate 2 becomes positive and plate 1 negative. Electrons will now flow from the cathode to plate 2, through the other half of the secondary winding (terminal 2 to the center tap), to the output circuit, and back to the cathode. The wave form of the output current for this half-cycle is indicated by the sections labeled 2 on Fig. 11-6*c*.

The full-wave center-tapped-transformer rectifier circuit is the one most generally used in transformer type power supplies. While one section of the rectifier is conducting, the peak inverse voltage across the other section will be equal to 1.41 times the rms value of the full secondary voltage, or 1.41 times E_S.

Output Voltage. The output voltage of a power supply unit whose rectifier output is applied directly to a resistance load will be a pulsating unidirectional voltage as represented by Figs. 11-5c and 11-6c. The output voltage as recorded with a d-c voltmeter would be the average value of the pulsations. For sine-wave input voltages and resistance loads, the output voltage for full-wave rectification will be

$$E_o = \frac{0.637}{0.707} E_{a\text{-}c} = 0.9E_{a\text{-}c} \tag{11-1}$$

For sine-wave input voltages and resistance loads, the output voltage for half-wave rectification will be

$$E_o = \frac{0.637}{2 \times 0.707} E_{a\text{-}c} = 0.45E_{a\text{-}c} \tag{11-2}$$

where $E_{a\text{-}c}$ = rms value of alternating voltage per plate

These two equations are based on the assumption that there is no voltage drop at the transformer secondaries or the rectifier tubes. With the same value of alternating volts per plate, the output voltage with half-wave rectification is one-half the value of that with full-wave rectification, because the half-wave rectifier supplies current and voltage for only one-half the amount of time that a full-wave rectifier supplies current and voltage to the load.

When filter circuits are used in conjunction with rectifiers, it will be found that a full-wave rectifier will require a transformer with twice the value of secondary voltage that is required with a half-wave rectifier in order to obtain the same output voltage. The action of the filter circuit is presented later in this chapter.

11-5. Bridge Rectifier Circuits. *Full-wave Bridge Rectifier Circuits.* The bridge type full-wave rectifier circuit (Fig. 11-7) is another method of obtaining a continuous flow of rectified current in the output circuit of a rectifier. The operation of this circuit is explained in the following manner. During the portion of the input cycle that terminal A of the secondary winding is positive, electrons will flow from the cathode to the plate of tube 2, through the secondary winding, from the cathode to the plate of tube 4, through the output circuit, and back to the cathode of tube 2. The flow of electrons during this half-cycle is indicated by the solid line arrows in Fig. 11-7a. The wave form of the output current for this half-cycle is indicated by the sections labeled 2 and 4 on Fig. 11-7c. During the other half of the input cycle, terminal A of the secondary winding becomes negative and terminal B becomes positive. During this half-cycle electrons will flow through tube 3, the secondary winding, tube 1, the output circuit, and back to the cathode of tube 3. The flow of electrons for this half-cycle is indicated by the broken line arrows in

Fig. 11-7*a*. The wave form of the output current for this half-cycle is indicated by the sections labeled 1 and 3 on Fig. 11-7*c*.

60-cycle
A-C input
A
B
E_S
1
2
3
4
R
Rectifier output
(a)
→Electron flow when A is positive
--→Electron flow when B is positive
(b)
Input voltage
Time→
(c)
Current or voltage output
2 and 4
1 and 3
2 and 4
1 and 3
Time→

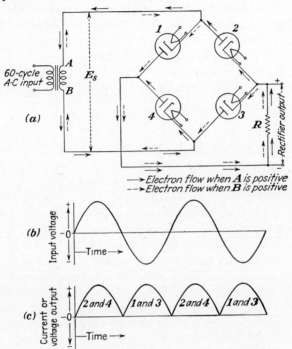

FIG. 11-7.—A full-wave rectifier using four diodes. (*a*) Diagram of a simple bridge-type rectifier circuit, (*b*) wave form of the input voltage, (*c*) wave form of the output current or voltage.

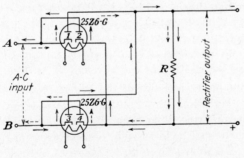

25Z6-G
A
B
A-C
input
R
Rectifier output
→ Electron flow when A is positive
--→ Electron flow when B is positive

FIG. 11-8.—A full-wave duplex-diode bridge-type rectifier circuit.

The transformer used with a bridge-type rectifier does not require a center-tapped secondary winding for its plate circuit supply. As this secondary supplies plate voltage for two tubes in series, its voltage may be made equal to twice the plate voltage required for each tube. This circuit utilizes the complete secondary winding for the entire period of each cycle. The output voltage for the bridge-type rectifier circuit will thus be twice that obtainable from a full-wave center-tapped circuit using a similar transformer. The inverse peak voltage is equal to the maximum transformer voltage, or 1.41 times E_S.

Another form of bridge-type rectifier is shown in Fig. 11-8. This circuit operates directly from the power source without a transformer and

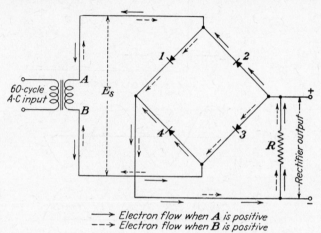

→ Electron flow when **A** is positive
--→ Electron flow when **B** is positive

Fig. 11-9.—A full-wave contact-type rectifier bridge circuit.

uses two duplex diodes of the heater-type cathode. Contact rectifiers may be used in bridge circuits instead of vacuum tubes and four rectifier units are required as shown in Fig. 11-9. It can be seen that the basic circuit of Figs. 11-7, 11-8, and 11-9 are all the same. The operation and the output wave form of the duplex-diode bridge rectifier circuit and the contact rectifier circuit will therefore be the same as for the circuit using four single diodes.

The important characteristics of the bridge-type rectifier circuit are its low plate voltage, low power output, compactness, and economy. Because of these features, it is generally used for supplying power to radio test equipment such as test oscillators and vacuum-tube voltmeters.

11-6. Other Rectifier Circuits. *Full-wave Voltage Doubler.* The voltage multiplier type of rectifier circuit makes it possible to obtain a d-c output whose voltage is equal to some multiple of the alternating voltage applied to the plates of the rectifier tube. The most common type of voltage multiplier circuit is the voltage doubler. This circuit is used to obtain an output voltage equal to approximately twice the alternating input voltage.

Figure 11-10 illustrates the circuit connections for a full-wave voltage doubler circuit. The operation of this circuit is explained in the following manner. During a portion of the half-cycle that terminal A is positive, electrons will flow through tube 1 and the secondary winding to charge capacitor C_1 as indicated. During a portion of the next half-cycle terminal B becomes positive and electrons will flow through tube 2 and the secondary winding to charge capacitor C_2 as indicated. It will be noted that the terminals of the capacitors that are joined are of opposite

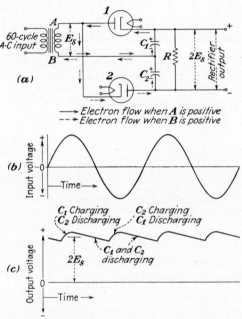

FIG. 11-10.—A full-wave voltage doubler circuit. (a) The circuit, (b) wave form of the input voltage, (c) wave form of the output voltage.

polarity. If neither capacitor discharged through the output circuit, the voltage across the two capacitors in series would be equal to twice the peak plate voltage less the voltage drops in the tubes. Hence the name *voltage doubler*. However, the capacitors do discharge through the output circuit, capacitor C_1 discharging while capacitor C_2 is charging and vice versa. If a comparatively large time constant is provided, these capacitors will lose only a small portion of their charge in the short interval required for the line voltage to reverse its polarity. Therefore, during the half-cycle that one tube is conducting, the capacitor in its output circuit will not start charging until the instantaneous value of the line voltage (less the tube drop) exceeds the capacitor terminal voltage.

The wave form of the output voltage illustrating the charge and discharge actions of the two capacitors is shown in Fig. 11-10c.

Because of the high values of capacitance used at C_1 and C_2, the output of a full-wave voltage doubler circuit is nearly uniform. For best results, these capacitors should be of equal value and not less than 16 μf. The voltage regulation of the voltage doubler circuit is inherently poor and may be improved by using higher values of capacitance for C_1 and

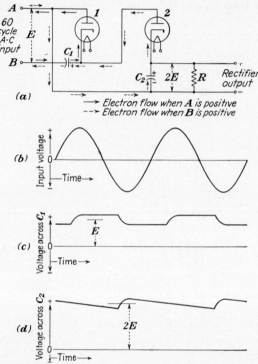

Fig. 11-11.—A half-wave voltage doubler circuit. (a) The circuit, (b) wave form of the input voltage, (c) wave form of the voltage across C_1, (d) wave form of the voltage across C_2 or the output voltage.

C_2. As increasing the capacitance of C_1 and C_2 will increase the peak plate current of the rectifier tubes, the maximum values of these capacitors will be limited by the peak current rating of the tubes. Each capacitor is charged by a separate diode and thus the voltage across either capacitor will never be greater than the peak value of the plate voltage. Because the size of the capacitors required would make the cost prohibitive, this circuit is not practical for rectifying large amounts of current.

Half-wave Voltage Doubler. Another form of voltage doubler circuit that is used is the half-wave voltage doubler. The connections for this circuit are shown in Fig. 11-11.   This rectifier operates in a somewhat different manner from the full-wave voltage doubler and its operation is explained in the following manner.   During the half-cycle that the plate of tube 1 is positive, electrons will flow through the tube charging capacitor C_1 to the peak line voltage (less the drop in tube 1), and with the polarity as indicated.   During the next half-cycle, the voltage across C_1

will be added to the line voltage and tube 2 will conduct.   The electron flow will charge capacitor C_2 to a voltage equal to the peak line voltage plus the voltage across C_1 (less the drop in tube 2).   However, capacitor C_2 would only attain this full charge when no load is being drawn from the power supply unit. When the unit is supplying power to a load, capacitor C_2 will charge and partially discharge during alternate halves of the input cycle.   Capacitor C_1, likewise, will charge and discharge during alternate halves of the input cycle, but during opposite times that C_2 is charging and discharging.   Thus capacitor C_2 will be charging when tube 2 is conducting, the energy being obtained from capacitor C_1, which is then discharging to C_2 and the load.   When tube 2 is not conducting, capacitor C_2 is discharging through the load.   Tube 1 is then conducting and capacitor C_1, which acts as a reservoir for C_2, is being recharged, so that the cycle

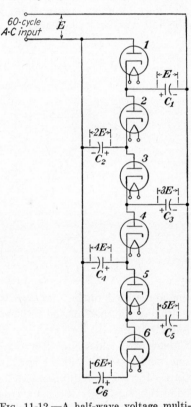

Fig. 11-12.—A half-wave voltage multiplier circuit.

repeats itself continually.   The wave form of the voltages across capacitors C_1 and C_2, shown in Figs. 11-11c and 11-11d respectively, illustrates the charging and discharging periods of these two capacitors.

The voltage regulation of the half-wave voltage doubler circuit is not so good as that of the full-wave voltage doubler circuit.   Another disadvantage is that the voltage rating of capacitor C_2 must be twice as high as that of the capacitors in a full-wave circuit of the same rating.

An advantage of the circuit of Fig. 11-11a is that one side of the power line and the negative terminal of the output capacitor C_2 may be con-

nected to a common terminal, usually the chassis.   This makes it possible
to use a series connected heater circuit arranged so that the heaters of the
high gain r-f tubes will be at practically ground potential.   Thus, by
keeping the voltage difference between the heater and cathode of the
high gain tubes at a low value, the possibility of cathode-to-heater
leakage and its resulting hum is reduced.

Other Types of Voltage Multiplier Circuits.   The principles involved in
the half-wave voltage doubler circuit of Fig. 11-11a are utilized in obtain-

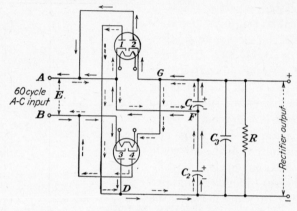

→ *Electron flow when **A** is positive*
--→ *Electron flow when **B** is positive*

Fig. 11-13.—A full-wave voltage tripler circuit.

ing a rectified output voltage that may be any multiple of the input
voltage.   In the voltage multiplier circuit of Fig. 11-12, capacitors C_1
and C_2 operate in the same manner as capacitors C_1 and C_2 of Fig. 11-11.
Capacitor C_2 then adds its voltage (now double the line voltage) to the
line voltage when tubes 1 and 3 are conducting.   This action then continues for the remaining capacitors and tubes.   After steady operating
condition has been obtained, current will flow from the individual rectifiers for only that portion of the cycle necessary to replace the amount of
charge lost by the capacitors in the previous half cycles.   Thus, after the
steady state operating condition has been reached, capacitor C_1 will be
charged to approximately the peak line voltage, capacitor C_2 to approximately twice the peak line voltage, capacitor C_3 to approximately three
times the peak line voltage, etc.

The principles involved in the full-wave voltage doubler circuit of Fig.
11-10 may also be utilized in obtaining a rectified output voltage that may
be any multiple of the input voltage.   A full-wave voltage tripler circuit
is shown in Fig. 11-13, and the same principles can be applied to produce
voltages of $4E$, $5E$, etc.

The voltage multiplier circuit is very useful for obtaining high output voltages. However, the voltage regulation of the voltage multiplier circuit is poor. Furthermore, unless adequate provisions are made, the difference in voltage between the cathode and heater of the tube (or tubes) at the high voltage terminal of a series heater string may greatly exceed the maximum voltage rating of the tube and thus cause it to break down.

Multiphase Rectifier Circuits. In the preceding discussion, only single-phase rectifier circuits have been presented. When large amounts

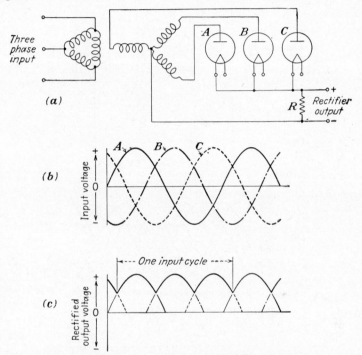

FIG. 11-14.—A three-phase half-wave rectifier. (*a*) The circuit, (*b*) wave form of the input voltage, (*c*) wave form of the rectified output voltage.

of power are to be rectified, such as one kilowatt or more, multiphase circuits are generally used. Although multiphase circuits may employ any number of phases (some use 100 or more phases), the three-phase circuit is most generally used for radio transmitters. The rectifier circuits may be connected for either half-wave or full-wave rectification. The principle of operation of multiphase rectifier circuits is the same as for single-phase circuits. The connections of a three-phase half-wave rectifier circuit are shown in Fig. 11-14. The connections for a three-phase full-wave rectifier circuit are shown in Fig. 11-15. From these two figures it can be seen that because the voltages of phase *A*, *B*, and *C* are

120 degrees out of phase with each other, the rectified output approaches a steady direct current more closely than the output of a single-phase rectifier circuit. Because of this, multiphase rectifier circuits require less filtering than single-phase rectifiers. Another advantage of the multiphase rectifier is that a higher output voltage is obtained for a given peak input voltage than is obtained from a single-phase rectifier circuit.

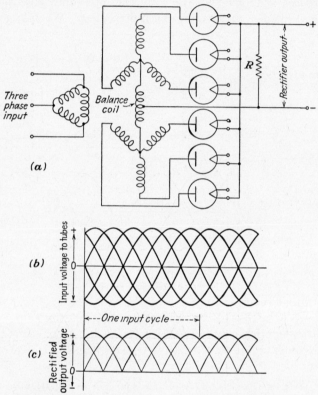

Fig. 11-15.—A three-phase full-wave rectifier. (*a*) The circuit, (*b*) wave-form of the input voltage to tubes, (*c*) wave form of the rectified output voltage.

Parallel Operation of Rectifiers. Another method of obtaining a higher output current from a rectifier is to connect two or more single-phase rectifier units in parallel. The circuit connections for parallel operation of four vacuum tubes to produce full-wave rectification is shown in Fig. 11-16. From this figure it can be seen that two plates are connected together and two cathodes are connected together so that the circuit operates similar to the single-tube full-wave rectifier circuit of Fig. 11-6.

When gas tubes are operated in parallel, a slight difference in the operating characteristics of the tubes may cause one tube to ionize at a lower voltage than the other. The tube ionizing first will carry the entire load, since the voltage drop in this tube will decrease the input voltage to the second tube, thus preventing it from becoming ionized. In order to

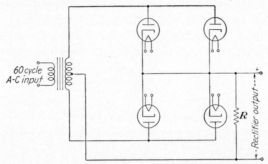

60 cycle A-C input

R

Rectifier output

FIG. 11-16.—Parallel operation of two full-wave rectifiers.

correct this condition, a resistor is connected in series with the plate of each tube. Then, if one tube ionizes before the other, the voltage at the second tube will still remain high enough to cause it to ionize, thus ensuring successful parallel operation of the two tubes.

Selenium Rectifier Circuits. Before the development of the selenium rectifier, the amount of current flow at the junction point in contact rectifiers was limited to a comparatively low value, as the operating temperature at the junction had to be very low. The breakdown voltage at the junction point of the contact rectifiers was also very low, being approximately 11 volts peak for the copper-oxide type of rectifier. Because of these current and voltage characteristics, the use of the contact-type rectifiers was limited to low current and voltage applications. In some applications of

FIG. 11-17.—A five-plate selenium rectifier unit. (*Courtesy of Federal Telephone and Radio Corporation.*)

these rectifiers, increased current and voltage ratings are obtained by connecting a number of single units in series or parallel combinations.

The operating current and voltage characteristics of the selenium-type rectifier shown in Fig. 11-17 are such that it is possible to use this type of unit in place of most rectifier tubes. Selenium units are available in a number of sizes with output current ratings from 75 ma to 200 ma and with a maximum rms voltage rating of 130 volts. Their maximum inverse peak voltage rating is 380 volts. Units can be obtained that are capable of withstanding a maximum peak current of 2000 ma and a maximum rms current of 550 ma. Compared with the vacuum-tube rectifier, the selenium rectifier has many advantages, among which are (1) smaller size (approximately $1\frac{1}{4}$ by $1\frac{1}{4}$ by $\frac{3}{4}$ inch), (2) durability and cooler operation, (3) less fragility, (4) longer life, (5) only two required connections therefore easier to install, (6) lower voltage drop at the

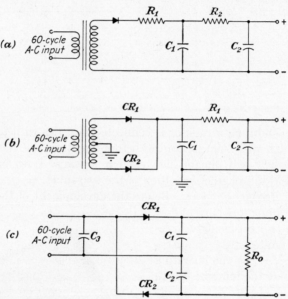

Fig. 11-18.—Several applications of contact rectifiers to rectifier circuits.   (a) Half-wave rectifier, (b) full-wave rectifier, (c) voltage doubler.

rectifier (approximately 5 volts), (7) better voltage regulation, (8) lower cost of rectifier unit since no tube socket or special mounting is required.

A selenium rectifier has two terminals, one positive and the other negative. These two terminals correspond to the plate and cathode of a vacuum tube. The positive side is usually indicated by a red dot or a + sign. The negative side is indicated by a yellow dot or a − sign, or it may be left blank. Rectifier circuits employing selenium rectifier units as a half-wave rectifier, a full-wave rectifier, and a voltage doubler circuit are shown in Fig. 11-18.

11-7. Filters. *Purpose of the Filter.* Although the output of a rectifier circuit is unidirectional, this output is not steady but is pulsating. Because of the variations in magnitude of the output current of a rectifier circuit, the current cannot be used in this form for radio applications.

A filter must be used in conjunction with a rectifier to smooth out these variations in current in order that the output of the power supply unit will become practically a steady direct current.

Ripple Voltage. The unidirectional output voltage of a power supply unit may be considered as a steady voltage having an alternating voltage superimposed upon it. The alternating component of the output voltage is referred to as the *ripple voltage.* The frequency of the ripple voltage will depend upon the frequency of the input voltage and the type of rectifier. Since the ripple voltage does not vary in the same manner as a perfect sine-wave voltage, it may be considered as consisting of a fundamental and a series of harmonics. In general, the relative effect of the harmonics is negligible as compared to the fundamental and the harmonics can usually be ignored. The fundamental frequency of the ripple voltage is equal to the input frequency for half-wave rectifiers and twice the input frequency for full-wave rectifiers.

The effectiveness of a filter is measured by the ratio of the effective (rms) value of the fundamental component of the ripple voltage to the output voltage. This ratio is called the *ripple factor.*

$$k_r = \frac{E_r}{E_{d-c}} \tag{11-3}$$

where k_r = ripple factor
   E_r = rms value of the fundamental component of the ripple voltage
   E_{d-c} = average value of the output voltage

The ripple voltage is often expressed in terms of its percentage of the output voltage, as

$$\text{Per cent } E_r = \frac{E_r}{E_{d-c}} \times 100 \tag{11-4}$$

The type of service for which a power supply is to be used determines its allowable value of ripple voltage. For the plate supply voltages of the average radio receiver, a ripple voltage of 0.25 per cent or less is required in order to reduce the hum to a negligible amount. The ripple voltage for the microphone circuit in a radio transmitter should be less than 0.003 per cent. In cathode-ray oscilloscopes, a ripple voltage as high as 1 per cent is sometimes permitted.

Example 11-1. The output voltage of a power supply unit is 300 volts and the rms value of the ripple voltage is 0.6 volt. What is the per cent of ripple voltage?

Given: Find:
   E_{d-c} = 300 volts   Per cent E_r = ?
   E_r = 0.6 volt

Solution:

$$\text{Per cent } E_r = \frac{E_r}{E_{d-c}} \times 100 = \frac{0.6}{300} \times 100 = 0.2 \text{ per cent}$$

Operation of the Filter Circuit. Filter circuits associated with rectifier units use the energy-storing properties of capacitors and inductors to smooth out the ripple in the rectified output. The function of the capacitor is to smooth out the voltage variations and also increase the value of the output voltage. The function of the inductor is to smooth out the variations in current. The capacitor will store electrons during a portion of each cycle that the voltage increases, indicated as 1 to 2. 3 to 4, and 5

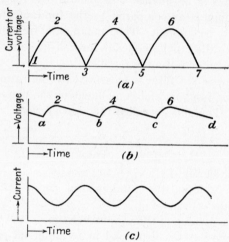

Fig. 11-19.—Filter action of a capacitor and an inductor. (a) Current or voltage output of a full-wave rectifier, (b) output from a capacitor, (c) output from an inductor.

to 6 on Fig. 11-19a. During the portion of the cycle that the voltage decreases (2 to 3, 4 to 5, and 6 to 7 on Fig. 11-19a), the capacitor will slowly discharge some of its stored electrons. The voltage across the capacitor is thus made more uniform as indicated by Fig. 11-19b. Because electrolytic capacitors provide high voltage and high capacitance ratings in comparatively small-size units, they are generally used in power supply filter circuits associated with radio receivers. The capacitance of electrolytic capacitors used for this purpose generally ranges from 4 μf to 50 μf and the d-c voltage rating may be as high as 800 volts. When a higher voltage rating is required, oil-impregnated paper dielectric capacitors are used.

A characteristic of inductors is that they oppose any change in the amount of current that flows through them. Thus, when the output current of a rectifier flows through an inductor, the variations in current strength (both increases and decreases) will be opposed by the action of the inductor.   The output will thus be more uniform as indicated in Fig. 11-19c.   The inductors used in power supply filter circuits are called *filter chokes* and are wound on a soft-iron core.   In order to maintain a high value of inductance for a wide variation in current flow, the iron core of some chokes is made with a small air gap to prevent saturation.   The inductance of the filter chokes used in the average radio receiver ranges from 10 to 30 henries.

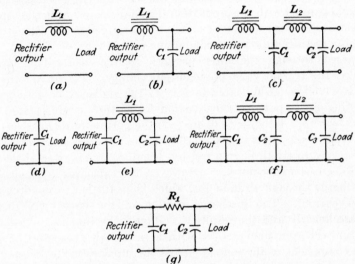

Fig. 11-20.—Types of filter circuits used with rectifiers.

Resistors may be used with a capacitor to form a resistance-capacitance filter circuit.   The time constant of resistance-capacitance filters must be large compared to the time of one cycle of the lowest frequency to be attenuated.   Because of this, the d-c resistance of this type filter is comparatively high and thus the voltage drop, voltage regulation, and heat dissipation are great.   The development of low-cost electrolytic capacitors having a high capacitance has made possible the use of lower values of resistance with this type of circuit.   Resistance-capacitance filters are used when the requirements of low cost and compactness outweigh the desirability of a high degree of filtering.

Types of Filter Circuits.   Power supply filter circuits are of the low-pass type, using one or more series inductors and one or more shunt capacitors.   These filter circuits are usually referred to as being *choke input* or *capacitor input* filters depending upon whether an inductor or a capacitor is the first element in the filter network.   A number of different types of filter circuits are shown in Fig. 11-20, the choke-input filters being represented by (a), (b), and (c), and the capacitor-input filters by (d), (e), (f), and (g). These filter circuits may be further classified as single-section filters represented by (a), (b) and (d); two-section filters as in (c), (e) and (g); and three-section filters as in (f). The number of sections of filtering that is required will depend upon the rectifier, the type of filter circuit, and the allowable ripple factor.

11-8. Capacitor-input Filter. *Theory of Operation.* A capacitor-input filter is a filter circuit in which the first element is a capacitor connected in parallel with the input from the rectifier. During the time that the rectifier tube is conducting energy will be stored in the capacitor, and when the rectifier tube is not conducting part of the stored energy will be discharged through the filter network to the load. The capacitor increases the average value of the output voltage. The wave form of the capacitor voltage is indicated in Fig. 11-19b and may be considered as consisting of two parts: (1) the portion during the charging period represented by a to 2, b to 4, c to 6, etc.; (2) the portion during the discharge period represented by 2 to b, 4 to c, 6 to d, etc. If the capacitor were to be discharged directly through a resistor, the discharge portion of the curve would decrease exponentially. However, the capacitor is usually made to discharge through an inductor, which helps further to smooth out the output current. The discharge portion of the curve will therefore decrease linearly and the resultant voltage wave that is applied to the inductor will approach a wave with a saw-tooth characteristic. The ripple component of the voltage across the input capacitor is prevented from reaching the output circuit by the combined actions of the inductor (or inductors) and capacitor (or capacitors) that follow the input capacitor in the filter circuit. The mathematical analysis of this type of wave is quite complex and is beyond the scope of this text.

Ripple Voltage. The per cent of ripple voltage that is developed across the input capacitor will vary inversely with the frequency of the rectified output, the effective load resistance, and the capacitance of the input capacitor. Thus, increasing any of these three factors in a filter circuit will decrease the per cent of ripple voltage. The effect of a variation in any of these factors on the d-c output can be seen by observation of Fig. 11-19b. Increasing the frequency of the rectified output decreases the time that the input capacitor is permitted to discharge. The capacitor will lose less of its charge, thus maintaining the voltage across it more nearly uniform. The extent to which the voltage across the input capacitor drops off is also affected by the time constant of the RC circuit, consisting of the input capacitor C_1 and the effective load resistance R_o. Increasing either of these two values will increase the time constant of the R_oC_1 circuit, thereby decreasing the rate of discharge.   The voltage across the input capacitor will thus be maintained more nearly uniform.

Although it is difficult to obtain accurate calculations of the per cent of ripple voltage, the following equations will provide reasonable results for ripple voltages of 10 per cent or less; beyond this amount the accuracy decreases.   The per cent of ripple voltage at the output of a single-section capacitor-input filter as shown in Fig. 11-20d, is

$$\text{Per cent } E_{r\cdot 1} \cong \frac{10^8 \sqrt{2}}{2\pi f_r R_o C_1} \cong \frac{2245 \times 10^4}{f_r R_o C_1} \tag{11-5}$$

where f_r = frequency of the ripple voltage, cycles per second

R_o = resistance of the load, ohms

C_1 = capacitance of the input filter capacitor, microfarads

This equation can also be used to calculate the per cent of ripple voltage at the output of the first section (per cent of ripple voltage at C_1) for any multisection capacitor-input filter, examples of which are shown as (e), (f), and (g) of Fig. 11-20.

Example 11-2.   A power supply unit has a 60-cycle input to its rectifier, uses a single-section capacitor-input filter (Fig. 11-20d), and delivers 40 ma direct current at 320 volts to the load.   Determine the per cent of ripple voltage for (a) half-wave rectification and an 8-μf filter capacitor, (b) full-wave rectification and an 8-μf filter capacitor, (c) half-wave rectification and a 16-μf filter capacitor, (d) full-wave rectification and a 16-μf filter capacitor.

Given:

$E_{d\text{-}c} = 320$ volts

$I_{d\text{-}c} = 40$ ma

$C_1 = 8$ μf (a), (b)

$C_1 = 16$ μf (c), (d)

$f_r = 60$ (a), (c)

$f_r = 120$ (b), (d)

Find:

(a) Per cent $E_{r\cdot 1}$, half-wave

(b) Per cent $E_{r\cdot 1}$, full-wave

(c) Per cent $E_{r\cdot 1}$, half-wave

(d) Per cent $E_{r\cdot 1}$, full-wave

Solution:

$$R_o = \frac{E_{d\text{-}c}}{I_{d\text{-}c}} = \frac{320}{40 \times 10^{-3}} = 8000 \text{ ohms}$$

(a)   Per cent $E_{r\cdot 1} \cong \dfrac{2245 \times 10^4}{f_r R_o C_1} = \dfrac{2245 \times 10^4}{60 \times 8000 \times 8} = 5.84$ per cent

(b)   Per cent $E_{r\cdot 1} \cong \dfrac{2245 \times 10^4}{f_r R_o C_1} = \dfrac{2245 \times 10^4}{120 \times 8000 \times 8} = 2.92$ per cent

(c)   Per cent $E_{r\cdot 1} \cong \dfrac{2245 \times 10^4}{f_r R_o C_1} = \dfrac{2245 \times 10^4}{60 \times 8000 \times 16} = 2.92$ per cent

(d)   Per cent $E_{r\cdot 1} \cong \dfrac{2245 \times 10^4}{f_r R_o C_1} = \dfrac{2245 \times 10^4}{120 \times 8000 \times 16} = 1.46$ per cent

The results of Example 11-2 show that the per cent of ripple voltage for a single-section filter is considerably higher than is usually acceptable for radio applications.   The additional filtering necessary to reduce the ripple voltage to an acceptable value can be obtained by providing additional filter sections, as indicated by Figs. 11-20e, 11-20f, and 11-20g. The per cent of ripple voltage at the output of a two-section capacitor-input filter similar to that of Fig. 11-20e can be found by use of Eq. (11-6). The results obtained with this equation are not extremely accurate but provide reasonable accuracy for low percentages of ripple voltage.

$$\text{Per cent } E_{r.2} \cong \frac{\text{Per cent } E_{r.1}}{[10^{-6}(2\pi f_r)^2 L_1 C_2] - 1} \tag{11-6}$$

where $E_{r.2}$ = ripple voltage at capacitor C_2 (Fig. 11-20e)
per cent $E_{r.1}$ = obtained by use of Eq. (11-5), which is the ripple at
　　　　　　capacitor C_1 (Fig. 11-20e)
　　f_r = frequency of the ripple voltage, cycles per second
　　L_1 = inductance of L_1 (Fig. 11-20e), henries
　　C_2 = capacitance of C_2 (Fig. 11-20e), microfarads

Example 11-3. A power supply unit using a full-wave rectifier and a filter circuit similar to Fig. 11-20e has a 60-cycle input and delivers 40 ma direct current at 320 volts to the load. Capacitors C_1 and C_2 are each 16 µf, and the inductance of L_1 is 15 henries. What is the per cent of ripple voltage at (a) C_1? (b) C_2?

Given:　　　　　　　　　　　　　　Find:
　　　f_r = 120 cycles　　　　　　　　(a) Per cent E_r at C_1
　　　L_1 = 15 henries　　　　　　　　(b) Per cent E_r at C_2
　　C_1, C_2 = 16 µf
Solution:

(a)　Per cent $E_{r.1} \cong 1.46$ per cent　　[Same as Example 11-2 (d).]

(b)　Per cent $E_{r.2} \cong \dfrac{\text{Per cent } E_{r.1}}{[10^{-6}(2\pi f_r)^2 L_1 C_2] - 1} = \dfrac{1.46}{[(2 \times 3.14 \times 120)^2 15 \times 16 \times 10^{-6}] - 1}$

　　　　　　　　= 0.010 per cent

An approximate value of the per cent of ripple voltage $E_{r.3}$ at the output of a three-section capacitor-input filter similar to that of Fig. 11-20f can be found by using a variation of Eq. (11-6). In this case Eq. (11-6) becomes

$$\text{Per cent } E_{r.3} \cong \frac{\text{Per cent } E_{r.2}}{[10^{-6}(2\pi f_r)^2 L_2 C_3] - 1} \tag{11-6a}$$

In a similar manner, Eq. (11-6) can be modified to determine the per cent of ripple voltage at the output of any number of succeeding sections of a multisection capacitor-input filter of this type.

For a two-section resistance-capacitance filter similar to that of Fig. 11-20g, an approximate value of the per cent of ripple voltage at the output can be found in the same manner as Example 11-3 by use of Eqs. (11-5) and (11-7). Equation (11-7) can also be modified in the same

manner as described above for Eq. (11-6) to determine the per cent of
ripple voltage at the output of succeeding sections of multisection resistance-capacitance filters.

$$\text{Per cent } E_{r\cdot2} \cong \frac{\text{Per cent } E_{r\cdot1} \times 10^6}{2\pi f_r C_2 R_1} \qquad (11\text{-}7)$$

where C_2 = capacitance, microfarads

R_1 = resistance, ohms

The results obtained with this equation are not extremely accurate but
provide reasonable accuracy when the product of $C_2 R_1$ is 10,000 or more.

Output Voltage. The output voltage of a capacitor-input filter
circuit will vary with the capacitance and with changes in the effective
load resistance. At no-load, or with a comparatively light load, the
effective load resistance is comparatively high. The time constant of
the $R_o C_1$ circuit will therefore also be comparatively high and the output
voltage will approach the peak value (also referred to as the *crest value*)
of the alternating voltage being rectified. As the load current increases,
the effective load resistance will decrease, thus also decreasing the time
constant of the circuit. The resulting increase in the rate of discharge of
the input capacitor will lower the average value of the voltage across this
capacitor. When the output current is high, the effective load resistance
is low, thus causing a considerable decrease in the output voltage. For
average applications of capacitor-input filters, the output voltage at
full-load will be approximately equal to the effective value of the alternating voltage being rectified.

The variation in output voltage with changes in current is called the
voltage regulation of the circuit and is usually expressed as a percentage.

$$\text{Voltage regulation} = \frac{E_{NL} - E_L}{E_L} \times 100 \qquad (11\text{-}8)$$

where E_{NL} = no-load voltage

E_L = full-load voltage

Since variations in the load current of a capacitor-input filter circuit
result in a wide range of output voltage, the voltage regulation of this
type of circuit is very poor.

Example 11-4. It is desired to have a power supply unit that will provide 300 volts
at the output terminals when supplying its rated full load current. What is the per
cent of regulation if (a) the unit employs a full-wave rectifier and a capacitor-input
filter, and the voltage with no load rises to 426 volts? (b) The unit employs a half-
wave rectifier and a capacitor-input filter, and the voltage with no load rises to 480
volts?

Given:

E_L = 300 volts

E_{NL} = 426 volts

E_{NL} = 480 volts

Find:

(a) Per cent of regulation

(b) Per cent of regulation

Solution:

(a) Per cent of regulation $= \dfrac{E_{NL} - E_L}{E_L} \times 100 = \dfrac{426 - 300}{300} \times 100 = 42$ per cent

(b) Per cent of regulation $= \dfrac{E_{NL} - E_L}{E_L} \times 100 = \dfrac{480 - 300}{300} \times 100 = 60$ per cent

Characteristics of the Capacitor-input Filter.   Compared to the choke-input filter, the capacitor-input filter will deliver a higher voltage at light loads, has a slightly better filtering characteristic, but has poorer voltage regulation.   The current in the rectifier associated with a capacitor-input filter circuit does not flow uniformly but flows in pulses, hence the ratio of peak rectifier current to average current will be higher than in the choke-input system.   The d-c voltage rating of the input capacitor should never be less than the peak transformer voltage, since at light loads the output voltage approaches this value.   In order to provide a safety factor, it is usually desirable to use a capacitor whose working voltage rating is somewhat higher than this value.   Capacitor-input filter circuits are generally used in power supply units that are required to deliver only small amounts of power, such as radio receivers, public-address systems, and testing apparatus.

11-9. Choke-input Filter. *Theory of Operation.* A choke-input filter is a filter circuit in which the first element is an inductor connected in series with the input from the rectifier.   The filtering action of the series input inductor of the choke-input filter circuit (Fig. 11-20) can be explained in the following manner.   During the portion of the rectified output cycle in which the current increases, the strength of the magnetic field about the inductor will increase and energy will be stored in the field. The inductor also opposes the increase in current.   During the portion of the rectified output cycle in which the current decreases, the magnetic field about the inductor collapses, returning part of its stored energy to the circuit, and also opposes the decrease in current.   These actions of an inductor thus tend to smooth out the ripple in the rectified output, as shown in Fig. 11-19c.   From this figure, it can be seen that the current through the inductor is made up of an a-c component and a d-c component.   The capacitor following the input inductor will tend to short-circuit the a-c component, thus producing a practically smooth voltage at its output terminals.

If the ripple voltage from a single-section filter circuit exceeds the allowable percentage, it can be reduced by using additional filter sections as shown in Fig. 11-20c.   The first inductor is usually called the *input choke* and the second inductor is called the *smoothing choke.*

Ripple Voltage. The per cent of ripple voltage that is developed across the first capacitor C_1 (Fig. 11-20b and 11-20c) will vary inversely with the capacitance of C_1 and the inductance of the input choke.   There are no simple equations for determining the exact value of the per cent of ripple voltage; however, for most practical purposes an approximate value of the per cent of ripple voltage for a single-section filter can be obtained by use of the following equation.

$$\text{Per cent } E_{r.1} \cong \frac{144 \times 10^4}{f_r{}^2 L_1 C_1} \qquad (11\text{-}9)$$

where f_r = ripple frequency, cycles
   L_1 = inductance of the input choke, henries
   C_1 = capacitance of the first capacitor, microfarads
This equation may be further simplified for determining the approximate per cent of ripple voltage of a single-section filter whose ripple frequency is 120 cycles, as is the case when the input to the filter is obtained from a full-wave rectifier operated from a 60-cycle power source.   Equation (11-9) may then be simplified to

$$\text{Per cent } E_{r.1} \cong \frac{100}{L_1 C_1} \qquad (11\text{-}9a)$$

Example 11-5.   Determine the approximate per cent of ripple voltage at the output of a single-section choke-input filter circuit using a 15-henry choke and a 4-μf capacitor.   The input to the filter is obtained from a full-wave rectifier operated from a 60-cycle power source.

Given: Find:
   $L_1 = 15$ h   Per cent $E_{r.1}$
   $C_1 = 4$ μf
Solution:

$$\text{Per cent } E_{r.1} \cong \frac{100}{L_1 C_1} = \frac{100}{15 \times 4} = 1.66 \text{ per cent}$$

An approximate value of the per cent of ripple voltage at the output of a two-section choke-input filter circuit can be obtained by use of the equation

$$\text{Per cent } E_{r.2} \cong \frac{1350 \times 10^8}{f_r{}^4 L_1 L_2 (C_1 + C_2)^2} \qquad (11\text{-}10)$$

where L_2 = inductance of the smoothing choke, henries
   C_2 = capacitance of the second capacitor, microfarads
This equation may be further simplified for determining the approximate per cent of ripple voltage of a two-section filter whose ripple frequency is 120 cycles, as is the case when the input to the filter is obtained from a full-wave rectifier operated from a 60-cycle power source.   Equation (11-10) may then be simplified to

$$\text{Per cent } E_{r.2} \cong \frac{650}{L_1 L_2 (C_1 + C_2)^2} \qquad (11\text{-}10a)$$

Example 11-6.   Determine the approximate per cent of ripple voltage at the output of a two-section choke-input filter circuit using two 15-henry chokes and two 4-μf capacitors.   The input to the filter circuit is obtained from a full-wave rectifier operated from a 60-cycle power source.

Given: Find:
$$L_1 = L_2 = 15 \text{ h}$$ Per cent $E_{r \cdot 2}$
$$C_1 = C_2 = 4 \ \mu f$$

Solution:

$$\text{Per cent } E_{r \cdot 2} \cong \frac{650}{L_1 L_2 (C_1 + C_2)^2} = \frac{650}{15 \times 15 (4 + 4)^2} = 0.0451 \text{ per cent}$$

Example 11-7.   Determine the approximate per cent of ripple voltage at the output of the single-section choke-input filter circuit used in Example 11-5, if the input is obtained from a full-wave rectifier circuit having a 25-cycle input.

Given: Find:
$$L_1 = 15 \text{ h}$$ Per cent $E_{r \cdot 1}$
$$C_1 = 4 \ \mu f$$
$$f_{\text{in.}} = 25 \text{ cycles}$$

Solution:

$$f_r = 2 f_{\text{in.}} = 2 \times 25 = 50 \text{ cycles}$$
$$\text{Per cent } E_{r \cdot 1} \cong \frac{144 \times 10^4}{f_r^2 L_1 C_1} = \frac{144 \times 10^4}{50 \times 50 \times 15 \times 4} = 9.6 \text{ per cent}$$

The Input Choke.   The input choke of a filter circuit serves two functions: (1) to maintain a continuous flow of current from the rectifier, (2) to prevent the output voltage from increasing above the average value of the alternating voltage applied to the rectifier.   The output voltage and the peak plate current of the rectifier are both dependent upon the inductance of the input choke and the d-c resistance of the load.   The minimum value of inductance required to maintain the output voltage at the average value of the alternating voltage being rectified is called the *critical inductance*.   For a rectified output having a 120-cycle ripple frequency, an approximate value of the critical inductance may be obtained by use of the following equation.

$$L_c = \frac{R_o}{1000} \tag{11-11}$$

where L_c = critical value of inductance, henries
      R_o = output load resistance, ohms
If the inductance of the input choke is less than its critical value, its impedance to the a-c component of the rectified output will be so small that the filter circuit will tend to operate as a capacitor-input filter. Increasing the inductance of the input choke to more than its critical value will further decrease the ratio of peak to average plate current, thus maintaining a more nearly uniform flow of current through the inductor. Increasing the value of the inductance beyond twice the critical value

does not correspondingly improve the operating characteristics of the filter.   The *optimum* value of inductance is thus equal to twice the critical value of inductance.

Example 11-8.   Determine the optimum value of inductance for the input choke of a filter circuit having a d-c load resistance of 4000 ohms.   The frequency of the rectified input is 120 cycles.

Given: Find:
R_o = 4000 ohms L_o = ?
f_r = 120 cycles

Solution:

$$L_c = \frac{R_o}{1000} = \frac{4000}{1000} = 4 \text{ henries}$$
$$L_o = 2L_c = 2 \times 4 = 8 \text{ henries}$$

Swinging Choke.   It can be seen from Eq. (11-11) that the value of the inductance required for the input choke will vary directly with the effective load resistance and inversely with the load current.   Thus, if the load current varies over a wide range, some means must be provided for preventing the ratio of peak to average plate current from becoming excessive.   The inductance of the choke coil will vary inversely with the value of the direct current flowing through it.   A choke coil having an inductance of 10 henries with 100 ma flowing through it may have an inductance of 15 henries when the current flow is reduced to practically zero.   A choke designed to have a critical value of inductance at full-load and an optimum value of inductance at no-load is called a *swinging choke.*

Output Voltage.   The average value of the output voltage at full-load of a choke-input filter is in the order of 65 to 75 per cent of the rms volts per plate at the rectifier.   It should be observed that the output voltage with a choke-input filter is lower than that with a capacitor-input filter supplied with the same value of rms volts per plate.   The decrease in output voltage is due to the effect of the inductance being introduced into the circuit and to the voltage drop at the choke due to its d-c resistance.   In order to reduce the drop in voltage at the filter chokes, their d-c resistance should be kept as low as possible.

Characteristics of the Choke-input Filter.   Although the choke-input filter circuit delivers a lower output voltage than the capacitor-input filter circuit, its voltage regulation is much better.   Another advantage of the choke-input filter is that the input choke prevents high instantaneous peak currents, thus protecting the rectifier tube from being damaged.

The input inductor and the first capacitor of a choke-input filter form a series resonant circuit.   If the values of these two circuit elements make the circuit resonant to the ripple frequency, high values of ripple voltage will be produced. It is therefore important that the values of inductance and capacitance used do not form a series resonant circuit that is tuned to the ripple frequency.

Choke-input filter circuits are generally used where the output current is large or where the voltage regulation must be fairly good. Because choke-input filters operate best when the current flow is sustained over the complete cycle, they are usually used only with full-wave rectifiers. Filter circuits used with multiphase rectifiers are generally of the choke-input type.

11-10. The Voltage Divider. *Bleeder Resistor.* Removing the external load from a power supply unit causes a high voltage to be

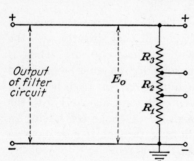

developed across the filter capacitors. If the voltage becomes too high, it will cause a breakdown of the insulation in these capacitors. The voltage developed across the terminals of the filter capacitors when the external load is zero can be reduced to a safe value by connecting a fixed resistor across the output terminals of the filter circuit. This resistor is called a *bleeder resistor*. The amount of bleeder current varies with the requirements of the individual power supply unit and generally ranges from 10 to 25 per cent of the total current drawn from the rectifier.

Fig. 11-21.—Connection of a voltage divider used in a power supply unit.

As a capacitor will retain its charge for a considerable length of time, the bleeder resistor also provides a path through which the filter capacitors will discharge when the power is turned off. This eliminates the danger of a high voltage shock when occasion arises to repair the power supply unit.

Since the bleeder resistor draws a fixed amount of current continuously from the power supply unit, it reduces the value of the output voltage at no-load. The bleeder resistor thus also serves to improve the voltage regulation of the power supply unit by reducing the difference in voltage between that obtained at no load and that obtained at full load.

The Voltage Divider. Because the elements of various types of electronic tubes operate with different amounts of voltage, the power supply unit is generally required to deliver more than one value of voltage. The various voltages may be obtained by connecting a tapped resistor across the output terminals of the filter circuit (see Fig. 11-21). A resistor connected in this manner is called a *voltage divider*. The voltage and current requirements of the power supply unit will determine the number of taps and the value of resistance between each pair of taps. The voltage divider also serves as a bleeder resistor.

In addition to supplying the high operating voltages required by the plates and screen grids of electronic tubes, the power supply unit may also be required to supply the necessary grid bias voltages. This is accomplished by connecting the voltage divider as shown in Fig. 11-22.

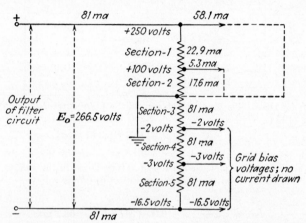

FIG. 11-22.—A voltage divider circuit used for providing plate and grid-bias voltages

Calculation of a Voltage Divider Circuit. The calculation of the correct resistance values and the power rating of the voltage divider may be accomplished by use of Ohm's law. The following procedure should be followed.

1. Determine the voltage required at each tap and the current to be drawn from it.

2. Determine the amount of bleeder current desired. This is the difference between the total current required by the tubes and the current necessary to operate the power supply at approximately 90 per cent of its rated value.

3. Determine the current flow in each section of the voltage divider.

4. Calculate the resistance of one section at a time.

5. Determine the power rating of the voltage divider.

Example 11-9.   Determine the resistance values of a voltage divider for a small superheterodyne receiver that employs a 6A8 oscillator-mixer tube, a 6SK7 i-f amplifier tube, a 6SQ7 detector-amplifier tube, and a 6F6 power output tube.   The operating voltages and currents are to be similar to those listed in Appendix XV for plate voltages of 250 volts.   A power transformer rated at 90 ma is to be operated at 90 per cent of its rated value.

Given:

    Tubes—6A8, 6SK7, 6SQ7, 6F6

    $I_T = 90$ ma

    $I_S = 0.9I_T$

Find:

    R of each section

Solution:

From Appendix XV:

TABLE XI-II

Tube	6A8	6SK7	6SQ7	6F6
E_b — volts	250	250	250	250
$E_{c.2}$ — volts	100	100	...	250
$E_{c.1}$ — volts	−3	−3	−2	−16.5
I_b — ma	7.5	9.2	0.9	34
$I_{c.2}$ — ma	2.7	2.6	...	6.5

NOTE: I_b for the 6A8 is equal to the sum of the plate current (3.5 ma) and anode grid current (4 ma).

Using the values of voltage and current as listed in Table XI-II, the voltage and current at each tap of the voltage divider will be as shown in Fig. 11-22. The total voltage required from the power supply unit will be equal to the sum of the highest amount of plate voltage and the highest amount of grid-bias voltage.

$$E_o = 250 + 16.5 = 266.5 \text{ volts}$$
$$I_{250} = 7.5 + 9.2 + 0.9 + 34 + 6.5 = 58.1 \text{ ma}$$
$$I_{100} = 2.7 + 2.6 = 5.3 \text{ ma}$$
$$I_o = I_{250} + I_{100} = 58.1 + 5.3 = 63.4 \text{ ma}$$
$$I_{\text{Bleeder}} = (0.9I_T) - I_o = (0.9 \times 90) - 63.4 = 17.6 \text{ ma}$$
$$R_{\text{Sec.1}} = \frac{e_1}{i_1} = \frac{250 - 100}{22.9 \times 10^{-3}} = 6550 \text{ ohms}$$
$$R_{\text{Sec.2}} = \frac{e_2}{i_2} = \frac{100 - 0}{17.6 \times 10^{-3}} = 5681 \text{ ohms}$$
$$R_{\text{Sec.3}} = \frac{e_3}{i_3} = \frac{2 - 0}{81 \times 10^{-3}} = 24.7 \text{ ohms}$$
$$R_{\text{Sec.4}} = \frac{e_4}{i_4} = \frac{3 - 2}{81 \times 10^{-3}} = 12.3 \text{ ohms}$$
$$R_{\text{Sec.5}} = \frac{e_5}{i_5} = \frac{16.5 - 3}{81 \times 10^{-3}} = 166 \text{ ohms}$$

Power Rating of the Voltage Divider. Assuming that a single resistor of uniform wire size is to be used, the voltage divider will have a uniform power rating. For this type of voltage divider, the highest current flowing through any part of the voltage divider must be used in determining the power rating. However, a separate resistor can be used for each section of the voltage divider, in which case the power rating of each section or resistor is determined by its own current and resistance ratings.

As the voltage divider is usually mounted under the chassis of the radio receiver and therefore does not have much ventilation, it is recommended that its power rating be approximately double that of the load it is to carry.

Example 11-10.   Determine the power rating of the voltage divider used in Example 11-9 for (*a*) a single resistor having four taps, (*b*) five separate resistors.

Given: Find:
   Resistance and current values   (*a*) P_R—single resistor
   determined in Example 11-9   (*b*) P_R—separate resistors

Solution:

(*a*) $R_T = R_{Sec \cdot 1} + R_{Sec \cdot 2} + E_{Sec \cdot 3} + R_{Sec \cdot 4} + R_{Sec \cdot 5}$
      $= 6550 + 5681 + 24.7 + 12.3 + 166 = 12{,}434$ ohms
    $P_R = 2I_{max}{}^2 R_T = 2 \times (81 \times 10^{-3})^2 \times 12{,}434 = 162$ watts
(*b*) $P_{R \cdot Sec \cdot 1} = 2i_1{}^2 R_1 = 2 \times (22.9 \times 10^{-3})^2 \times 6550 = 6.87$ watts
    $P_{R \cdot Sec \cdot 2} = 2i_2{}^2 R_2 = 2 \times (17.6 \times 10^{-3})^2 \times 5681 = 3.52$ watts
    $P_{R \cdot Sec \cdot 3} = 2i_3{}^2 R_3 = 2 \times (81 \times 10^{-3})^2 \times 24.7 = 0.324$ watt
    $P_{R \cdot Sec \cdot 4} = 2i_4{}^2 R_4 = 2 \times (81 \times 10^{-3})^2 \times 12.3 = 0.162$ watt
    $P_{R \cdot Sec \cdot 5} = 2i_5{}^2 R_5 = 2 \times (81 \times 10^{-3})^2 \times 166 = 2.18$ watts

Thus, if a single resistor having four taps is to be used, the approximate power rating of the voltage divider of Example 11-9 would be 162 watts. Using five separate resistors, each designed to carry the amount of current actually flowing through it, the total power rating of the five resistors would be approximately 13 watts. As the five-section voltage divider has a much lower power rating, it is less expensive and also more practical.

If one or more sections of a voltage divider breaks down, it is not necessary to replace the entire divider. Resistors of the correct values may be substituted in place of the defective sections after they have been disconnected from the circuit.

11-11. The Power Supply Unit. *Components of the Power Supply Unit.* In the preceding discussion, the four components of the power supply unit, namely, the transformer, rectifier, filter, and voltage divider, have been considered as separate units. These four units are closely associated with each other and may be connected to one another to form the complete power supply unit as shown in Fig. 11-23. The rating of the transformer and the type of rectifier tube to be used will be determined by the values of output current and voltage required. The per cent of allowable ripple voltage will determine the type of filter circuit, the number of sections required, and the values of its components. The position of the taps on the voltage divider will be determined by the value of the plate and screen-grid voltages of the tubes to be supplied. In some receivers, the speaker field is substituted for the smoothing choke L_2 of Fig. 11-23; thus one less part is required.

Output Voltage.   Because of the resistance of the tube and the filter chokes, there will be a drop in voltage at each of these circuit elements. These voltage drops must be added to the output voltage in order to

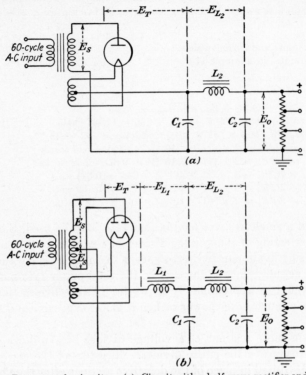

FIG. 11-23.—Power supply circuits.   (*a*) Circuit with a half-wave rectifier and a capacitor-input filter, (*b*) circuit with a full-wave rectifier and a choke-input filter.

determine the rms value of the voltage required at the secondary of the power transformer.   The output voltage at normal load for the full-wave-rectifier choke-input-filter power supply unit of Fig. 11-23*b* can be expressed as

$$E_o = 0.9E_S - E_T - E_{L.1} - E_{L.2} \qquad (11\text{-}12)$$

For the half-wave-rectifier capacitor-input-filter power supply unit of Fig. 11-23*a*

$$E_o = E_S - E_T - E_{L.2} \qquad (11\text{-}13)$$

where E_o = output voltage of the power supply unit

   E_S = rms volts per plate at the rectifier

   E_T = voltage drop at the rectifier tube

   $E_{L.1}$ = voltage drop at the input choke

   $E_{L.2}$ = voltage drop at the smoothing choke

Example 11-11.   A choke-input filter circuit similar to that shown in Fig. 11-23*b* is to be used in the power supply unit of the superheterodyne receiver of Example 11-9. The d-c resistance of the input or swinging choke is 80 ohms.   A speaker field having a d-c resistance of 900 ohms is used as the smoothing choke.   Determine the alternating voltage at the plates of the rectifier when using a full-wave rectifier tube whose internal voltage drop is 30 volts at full load.

Given: Find:
$$E_o = 266.5 \text{ volts}$$ $$E_S = ?$$
$$E_T = 30 \text{ volts}$$
$$R_{L \cdot 1} = 80 \text{ ohms}$$
$$R_{L \cdot 2} = 900 \text{ ohms}$$
$$I_S = 81 \text{ ma}$$

Solution:

$$E_{L \cdot 1} = I_S R_{L \cdot 1} = 81 \times 10^{-3} \times 80 = 6.48 \text{ volts}$$
$$E_{L \cdot 2} = I_S R_{L \cdot 2} = 81 \times 10^{-3} \times 900 = 72.9 \text{ volts}$$
$$E_S = \frac{E_o + E_T + E_{L \cdot 1} + E_{L \cdot 2}}{0.9} = \frac{266.5 + 30 + 6.48 + 72.9}{0.9} = 417 \text{ volts}$$

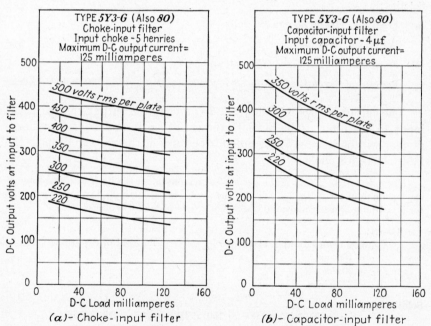

FIG. 11-24.—Operating characteristics of a power supply unit.   (*a*) With a choke-input filter, (*b*) with a capacitor-input filter.

Voltage Regulation.   The results of Example 11-4 indicate that the regulation of a power supply unit that does not use a bleeder resistor is very poor.   When a bleeder resistor (which may also be serving as a voltage divider) is used, disconnecting the external load does not cause the no-load current to drop to zero milliamperes.   Instead, the no-load current now has an appreciable value that may be determined by Ohm's law. Under this condition, the no-load voltage will be considerably lower than if the current had dropped to zero. From Eq. (11-8), it can be seen that a reduction in the no-load voltage will result in a smaller variation between the no-load and full-load voltages, thus improving the regulation of the power supply unit. The curves of Figs. 11-24 and 11-25 illustrate the operating characteristics of several power supply systems.

Example 11-12. A power supply unit represented by the curves of Fig. 11-24 is to supply 300 volts at the input to the filter at 100 ma and its no-load current is 20 ma. What is the per cent of regulation for (*a*) the capacitor-input filter circuit? (*b*) the choke-input filter circuit?

Given:
$$E_L = 300 \text{ volts}$$
$$I_L = 100 \text{ ma}$$
$$I_{NL} = 20 \text{ ma}$$

Find:
(*a*) Per cent of regulation
(*b*) Per cent of regulation

Solution:

(*a*) From Fig. 11-24*b*, $E_{NL} = 380$ volts

$$\text{Per cent of regulation} = \frac{E_{NL} - E_L}{E_L} \times 100 = \frac{380 - 300}{300} \times 100 = 26.6 \text{ per cent}$$

(*b*) From Fig. 11-24*a*, $E_{NL} = 330$ volts

$$\text{Per cent of regulation} = \frac{E_{NL} - E_L}{E_L} \times 100 = \frac{330 - 300}{300} \times 100 = 10 \text{ per cent}$$

The curves of Figs. 11-24 and 11-25 indicate the output voltage at the input to the filter. The output voltage at the terminals of the voltage divider will be less than this amount because of the voltage drop at the filter choke (or chokes).

Example 11-13. What is the per cent of regulation on the basis of the voltage at the terminals of the voltage divider for the conditions of Example 11-12 with a capacitor-input filter whose smoothing choke has a resistance of 335 ohms?

Given:
Voltages from Example 11-12*a*
$$I_L = 100 \text{ ma}$$
$$I_{NL} = 20 \text{ ma}$$
$$R_L = 335 \text{ ohms}$$

Find:
Per cent of regulation

Solution:
$$E_{o \cdot L} = E - IR_L = 300 - 100 \times 10^{-3} \times 335 = 266.5 \text{ volts}$$
$$E_{o \cdot NL} = E - IR_L = 380 - 20 \times 10^{-3} \times 335 = 373.3 \text{ volts}$$
$$\text{Per cent of regulation} = \frac{E_{NL} - E_L}{E_L} \times 100 = \frac{373.3 - 266.5}{266.5} \times 100 = 40 \text{ per cent}$$

11-12. Transformerless Power Supply Units. *A-C/D-C Power Supplies.*

The voltage from an a-c power source may be rectified by applying this voltage directly to the plate-cathode circuit as in Fig. 11-26. The output voltage of this power supply unit will be approximately equal to the alternating voltage input to the rectifier. If a higher output voltage is required, a voltage multiplier rectifier circuit is used (see Fig. 11-27 and Art. 11-6). Since a transformer is no longer required to step

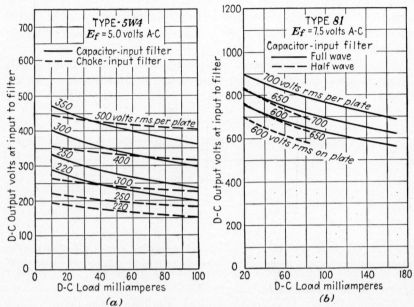

Fig. 11-25.—Operating characteristics of power supply units. (*a*) Characteristics with capacitor-input and choke-input filters for circuits using a type 5W4 tube, (*b*) half-wave and full-wave characteristics with capacitor-input filter for circuits using type 81 tubes.

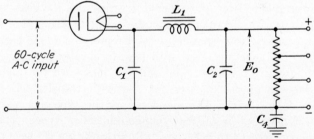

Fig. 11-26.—A transformerless power supply unit employing a half-wave rectifier operated directly from the power line.

up the line voltage, this type of power supply unit can be operated directly from either an a-c or a d-c power line.

Another advantage of the line rectifier type of power supply is its compactness, which has made it possible to manufacture the small a-c/d-c radio receivers. In addition to radio receiver applications, the transformerless power supply is also used in test equipment and electronic apparatus where a limited amount of space is available.

A resistor can be substituted for the smoothing choke as shown in Fig. 11-27, thus making the power supply unit still more compact by eliminating the choke coil. The cost of this type of power supply unit is comparatively low, as both the power transformer and the filter choke are eliminated.

In some types of electronic equipment, the magnetic fields set up about the power transformer and filter chokes are undesirable. The line

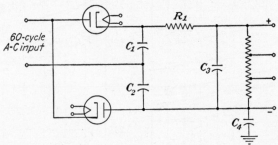

Fig. 11-27.—A transformerless power supply unit employing a voltage doubler rectifier.

rectifier type of power supply has an advantage in this kind of application since both units can be eliminated.

Rectifier Tubes. In order to eliminate the filament transformer, the heater of a line voltage rectifier is connected in series with the heaters of the other tubes in the receiver (or other electronic device) and the power line. If the sum of the heater voltages of all the tubes is less than the line voltage, a suitable resistor is connected in series with the heaters and the power line to provide the required voltage drop (see Art. 4-3). Since the energy consumed by the dropping resistor represents a loss, high-voltage heater tubes are generally used with transformerless power supplies in order to minimize or totally eliminate this loss. All the high-voltage heater tubes designed expressly for use with transformerless power supplies are of small size. Rectifier tubes for this type of service may be half-wave, full-wave, or of the voltage-multiplier type. The heater voltages range from 12 to 117 volts. Representative of these tubes are the types 12Z3, 25Z5, 35Z5-GT, 45Z5-GT, and the 117Z6-GT. The output current of line rectifier tubes is lower than for tubes designed for transformer operation.

Some line rectifier tubes are combined in a common envelope with a beam power amplifier. Examples of this type of tube are the 70L7-GT and the 117L/M7-GT. Because of the high voltage on the heater, these tubes draw a comparatively low amount of current; the heater current of the 117L/M7-GT is only 90 milliamperes. Combining the rectifier and power amplifier in a single envelope physically eliminates a tube and socket. This feature is desirable where space is limited or where the cost is a deciding factor.

Characteristics of the Transformerless Power Supply Unit. From a study of the principle of operation of the line voltage rectifier, it can be seen that a capacitor-input filter circuit should be used with this type of rectifier. The voltage regulation is comparatively poor and is dependent upon the capacitance values of the filter capacitors. The higher the capacitance, the better will be the voltage regulation. Filter capacitors used with transformerless power supplies may range from 16 μf to 40 μf.

Because of the comparatively low output current of the rectifier tube, the output current of the power supply unit is also low. As the heaters of these tubes radiate a considerable amount of heat, the filter capacitors should not be placed near the rectifier tube or the capacitor may become damaged.

In the transformerless power supply units of Figs. 11-11 and 11-12 one side of the power line is connected directly to the negative terminal of the output of the power supply unit, generally referred to as B−. Essentially the same condition exists in the case of the circuit of Fig. 11-13, since the B− terminal is connected to one side of the power line through capacitor C_2. The high value of capacitance normally used at C_2 results in a low impedance and hence the line may be considered as being conductively connected to the B− terminal. If this negative terminal is connected directly to the chassis, as is commonly done with transformer-type power supply units, it introduces two possible sources of danger, namely, electric shock and fire hazard. This danger is present when one side of the power line is grounded at the service entrance, as is done in most communities. Since either side of the power line may be connected to the chassis, depending upon the direction in which the attachment plug is inserted in the power outlet, it will be possible to connect either the grounded or the ungrounded side of the power line to the chassis. When the ungrounded side is connected to the chassis, touching any metal part of the receiver may result in an electric shock. Also, an accidental short circuit of the B power leads or a breakdown of a capacitor will cause a virtual short circuit of the power lines with its attendent fire hazard. Grounding the radio receiver to a radiator, water pipe, etc., whether intentionally or not, will also be a possible source of danger.

The danger of electric shock, and the danger caused by grounding the chassis to water pipes, etc., can be eliminated by using a bus bar or conductor that is insulated from the chassis as the B− line. Under this condition, the chassis is usually connected to the B− line through a capacitor of about 0.1 μf or less. This capacitor, C_4 in Figs. 11-26 and 11-27, provides a low impedance path for r-f grounding yet presents a high enough impedance at 60 cycles to practically eliminate the afore-mentioned dangers. The danger of fire hazard is generally reduced by enclosing in metal containers those parts connected in the circuit in such a manner that a breakdown may present fire hazards.

11-13. Vibrator Power Supply Units. *Types of Vibrators.* When a radio receiver or other type of electronic equipment is to be operated from a low voltage d-c power supply such as a storage battery, the con-ventional power transformer and rectifier tube circuit cannot be used for obtaining the high operating voltages required for the plate and screen-grid circuits. The direct current power from the battery can be changed to alternating current by use of an electromagnetic device that reverses the direction of current flow in the power transformer during each vibration of its vibrating armature. This device is called a *vibrator*. It is used extensively in the power supplies of battery-operated electronic equipment to convert the low direct voltage of the battery to an alternat-ing voltage that can be increased to any desired value by means of a transformer.

Basically, there are two types of vibrators: (1) the *synchronous* vibrator, (2) the *nonsynchronous* vibrator. The nonsynchronous vibra-tor interrupts the d-c circuit at a frequency that is unrelated to the other circuit constants. Since the high alternating voltage output of the power transformer is then normally rectified by means of a rectifier tube, this type of vibrator may also be called a *tube-type* vibrator. A synchronous vibrator, in addition to changing the low direct voltage to an alternating voltage, simultaneously rectifies the high alternating voltage output at the secondary of the power transformer. Rectification is accomplished by employing an additional set of contacts, thereby eliminating the need of a rectifier tube.

Nonsynchronous Vibrator Power Supply Unit. A circuit diagram of a nonsynchronous vibrator power supply unit is shown in Fig. 11-28. At the instant that the switch S_1 is closed, current will flow from the battery through coil L_1, section 1-2 of the primary winding of the transformer, coil L_2, and back to the battery. Coil L_2 is wound on a soft-iron core, which becomes magnetized when current flows through the coil. The vibrating reed R is so constructed that when a current flows through L_2, the reed is attracted toward the magnet. As the reed approaches the magnet it makes contact with point A, thus short-circuiting the coil L_2. Since the iron core is then no longer magnetized, the vibrating reed is released and tends to return to its normal position. However, because of the force present when it is released, the reed moves past its normal position and makes contact with point B and then returns to its normal position. At the instant that contact is being made at point B, current will flow through section 1-3 of the primary winding of the transformer. Current will flow in this circuit for only a very short period of time because contact is made at point B only instantaneously during the forward swing of the vibrating reed after it is released from point A. When the reed returns to its normal position, current will again flow through coil L_2 and the cycle of operations will be repeated. These operations occur

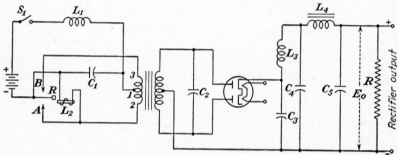

Fig. 11-28.—Circuit diagram of a power supply unit using a nonsynchronous vibrator.

very rapidly and the complete cycle of operations is repeated many times per second.

It can be seen that for each cycle of operations the current is caused to flow in opposite directions through each half of the primary winding of the transformer. Since this flow of current is essentially the same as an alternating current, the voltage at the secondary terminals can now be increased to any desired value by increasing the ratio of secondary to primary turns of the transformer. The output of the secondary winding is then rectified by a tube and filtered in the usual manner.

Synchronous Vibrator Power Supply Unit. The output from the secondary of the power transformer can be rectified by adding another set of points to the vibrator, thereby eliminating the need of a rectifier tube. These points are connected to opposite ends of the secondary winding of the transformer as shown in Fig. 11-29. In this circuit, when the vibrating reed makes contact with point A it also makes contact with point C, thus grounding terminal 2 of the primary winding and terminal 4 of the secondary winding of the transformer. In a similar manner, when the reed makes contact with point B it also makes contact with point D, thus grounding terminals 3 and 5 of the transformer. Terminal 6, which is one terminal of the output circuit, is thus always positive and terminals 4 and 5 are alternately connected to ground during opposite halves of the cycle. It can thus be seen that the output of the transformer is rectified since current flows in opposite directions in each half of the secondary winding during alternate halves of the cycle.

Filters. A surge of current will occur each time the primary winding is connected to or disconnected from the d-c power source. Connecting a capacitor across the primary winding will absorb this surge of current, thus preventing the contact points or rectifier tube from being damaged. The amount of capacitance required to absorb this surge will decrease with an increase in the applied voltage. It is thus more economical to connect a capacitor across the secondary winding of the power transformer (C_2 in Figs. 11-28 and 11-29) because the higher voltage at the secondary winding makes it possible to use a lower value of capacitance. This capacitor is called a *buffer capacitor.* As the capacitance reflected

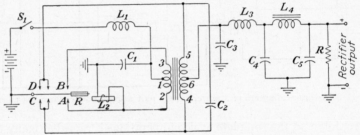

Fig. 11-29.—Circuit diagram of a power supply unit using a synchronous or self-rectifying vibrator.

to the primary from the secondary increases as the square of the secondary to primary turns ratio [see Eq. (2-82)], it produces substantially the same result as connecting a high value of capacitance in the primary circuit.

Each time the contacts are opened, sparking will take place at the contacts. This sparking produces radio-frequency transients, thus causing interference if the power supply is used with a radio receiver. This interference is commonly referred to as *hash* and may be minimized by use of filter circuits and by shielding the entire vibrator unit. A hash filter circuit is usually connected in the battery circuit and consists of an r-f choke coil and a 0.5-μf to 1-μf capacitor as represented by L_1 and C_1 in Figs. 11-28 and 11-29. Another hash filter circuit is connected in the output circuit and consists of an r-f choke coil and a 0.01-μf to 0.1-μf capacitor as represented by L_3 and C_3 in Figs. 11-28 and 11-29.

Characteristics of the Vibrator Power Supply Unit. The vibrator power supply unit represents an inexpensive compact means of obtaining the high operating voltage for the plate and screen-grid circuits from a low-voltage battery. It can thus be very effectively used in all types of portable electronic equipment that is to be operated from low-voltage batteries.   However, the vibrator has a limited life, and its associated circuits require a complex filtering and shielding system.

The type of vibrator to be used will depend upon the power supply requirements.   In addition to the choice of either the synchronous or nonsynchronous type of vibrator, the current output and the type of interrupter and rectifier circuits must also be considered.   Figure 11-30 shows the construction of an eight-contact vibrator.   This unit may be connected to operate simply as an interrupter or as a self-rectifier.   In

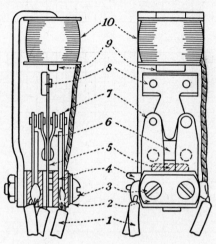

1. Stranded leads and   6. Reed contact arms
   soft rubber tubing   7. Outer contact arms
2. Spring washer-plate   8. Reed and armature
3. Stack clamping screws   9. Pole-piece integral
4. Stops and solder lugs   with frame
5. Reed slot for starting   10. Coil

FIG. 11-30.—Construction of a vibrator unit employing four sets of contactors.   (*Courtesy of P. R. Mallory & Company, Inc.*)

either circuit, the vibrator is capable of carrying the current required to produce 30 watts of output power.

11-14. Voltage Regulation. *Gaseous Regulator Tubes.*   It has been shown that because of various circuit conditions the output voltage will vary inversely with the output load.   Variations in the voltage of the a-c input to the power supply will also cause the output voltage to vary. There are a number of power supply applications where the voltage applied to the load must be maintained practically constant regardless of the voltage regulation of the power supply unit.   For low current applications, a cold-cathode gaseous diode having a practically constant internal voltage drop can be used as a voltage regulator.   Typical voltage regulator tubes are the 0B3/VR90, 0C3/VR105, and the 0D3/VR150.

The voltage regulating characteristics of these three tubes are illustrated by the curves of Fig. 11-31. From these curves it can be seen that the variation in operating voltage from no-load to full-load for these tubes is approximately only five volts.

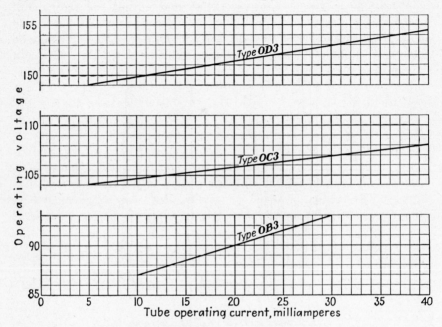

Fig. 11-31.—Operating characteristics of typical voltage-regulating tubes.

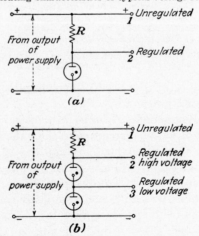

Fig. 11-32.—Voltage-regulating circuits using gaseous regulator tubes. (a) Circuit providing one value of regulated voltage, (b) circuit providing two values of regulated voltage.

A voltage slightly higher than the operating voltage must be used to ionize the gas inside the tube in order to have it start operating. Once the tube is started, it will continue to operate at some value of voltage within its operating range.

Voltage Regulator Tube Circuits. The voltage regulator tube is connected to the output of the power supply as shown in Fig. 11-32. In order to limit the current flowing through the regulator tube to a safe value, a resistor should always be connected in series with the tube and the power supply unit. The value of this resistor will depend upon the output voltage of the power supply and the operating voltage of the regulator tube. When it is required to provide a regulated voltage that is higher than that obtained from one tube, two or more similar voltage regulator tubes may be connected in series, as shown in Fig. 11-32b. The voltage at terminal 1 of either Fig. 11-32a or 11-32b will be approximately equal to the output voltage of the power supply unit. This voltage is unregulated and its variation will be dependent upon load conditions. The voltage obtained at terminal 2 or 3 is regulated and its value will be dependent upon the voltage rating of the tube or tubes used.

BIBLIOGRAPHY

ALBERT, A. L., *Fundamental Electronics and Vacuum Tubes*, The Macmillan Company, New York.

EASTMAN, A. V., *Fundamentals of Vacuum Tubes*, McGraw-Hill Book Company, Inc., New York.

HENNEY, K., *Principles of Radio*, John Wiley & Sons, Inc., New York.

MYE Technical Manual, P. R. Mallory & Co., Inc., Indianapolis, Ind.

NILSON, A. R., and HORNUNG, J. L., *Practical Radio Communication*, McGraw-Hill Book Company, Inc., New York.

REICH, H. J., *Theory and Applications of Electron Tubes*, McGraw-Hill Book Company, Inc., New York.

SMITH, F. L., *The Radiotron Designer's Handbook*, The Wireless Press, Sydney, Australia; distributed in U.S.A. by RCA Manufacturing Company, Inc., Harrison, N. J.

TERMAN, F. E., *Fundamentals of Radio*, McGraw-Hill Book Company, Inc., New York.

The Radio Amateur's Handbook, The American Radio Relay League, Inc., West Hartford, Conn.

QUESTIONS

1. (a) What is the purpose of the power supply? (b) What are the general requirements of a power supply? (c) How may power supplies be classified?

2. What is the purpose of (a) the A power supply? (b) The B power supply? (c) The C power supply?

3. (a) What are the advantages of battery power supplies? (b) What are the disadvantages of battery power supplies?

4. (a) What method is commonly used to obtain d-c power at high voltages from a low-voltage battery? (b) Where is this method generally used?

5. (a) Why is the power line the most desirable source of power for stationary electronic equipment? (*b*) Explain why the voltages required to operate electronic tubes cannot be taken directly from the power line.

6. (*a*) Name the four parts of a power supply unit used to convert alternating current to direct current. (*b*) Explain the function of each of these parts.

7. (*a*) Name the four basic types of power supplies used in radio receivers that operate from a-c power lines. (*b*) What factors determine the type of power supply to be used? (*c*) What factors must be taken into consideration when determining the requirements of a power supply?

8. (*a*) What is the main purpose of the power transformer? (*b*) For what additional purpose is it sometimes used?

9. (*a*) How are power transformers usually rated? (*b*) What additional rating is sometimes used?

10. Explain the principle of operation of a voltage regulating transformer.

11. Explain how alternating current may be rectified by use of a diode.

12. (*a*) For what type of service are high-vacuum-type tubes used? (*b*) For what type of service are gaseous-type tubes used?

13. How are the following types of rectifier tubes classified in terms of their voltage regulation: (*a*) high-vacuum-type rectifier tubes? (*b*) Mercury-vapor rectifier tubes? (*c*) Ionic-heated cathode rectifier tubes?

14. (*a*) What four factors are generally used in rating rectifier tubes? (*b*) Are these ratings fixed values? (*c*) Explain your answer to part (*b*).

15. Define: (*a*) Alternating voltage per plate, (*b*) peak inverse voltage, (*c*) peak plate current, (*d*) load current.

16. (*a*) Describe the construction of the contact-type rectifier. (*b*) Explain the principle of operation of the contact-type rectifier.

17. What are the applications of (*a*) copper-oxide rectifiers? (*b*) Copper-sulphide rectifiers? (*c*) Selenium rectifiers?

18. (*a*) Explain the principle of operation of a half-wave rectifier circuit using a single diode. (*b*) What are the output current and inverse peak voltage characteristics of this type circuit?

19. (*a*) Explain the principle of operation of a full-wave rectifier circuit using two diodes and a power transformer having a center-tapped secondary. (*b*) What are the output current and inverse peak voltage characteristics of this type circuit?

20. Compare the output voltage of a half-wave and a full-wave rectifier for a sine-wave input. Assume that the output is applied directly to a resistive load and that the voltage drops at the transformer secondaries and the rectifier tube are negligible.

21. (*a*) Explain the principle of operation of a full-wave bridge rectifier circuit. (*b*) What are the output current and inverse peak voltage characteristics of this type of circuit?

22. (*a*) What are the important characteristics of bridge-type rectifier circuits? (*b*) Where is this type of circuit generally used?

23. Explain the principle of operation of a full-wave voltage doubler circuit.

24. (*a*) How may the voltage regulation of the voltage doubler circuit be improved? (*b*) What is the limiting factor that must be taken into consideration when using this method?

25. (*a*) Explain the principle of operation of a half-wave voltage doubler circuit. (*b*) What are the advantages and disadvantages of this type of circuit?

26. Explain the principle of operation of a half-wave voltage multiplier circuit.

27. Explain the principle of operation of a full-wave voltage multiplier circuit.

28. What provisions should be made in voltage multiplier circuits to prevent the rectifier tubes from being damaged?

29. (*a*) How does the principle of operation of multiphase rectifier circuits compare with single-phase rectifier circuits? (*b*) What are the advantages of multiphase rectifier circuits? (*c*) For what type of service are multiphase rectifier circuits generally used?

30. (*a*) What is the purpose of parallel operation of rectifier tubes? (*b*) What safety provisions should be made when operating gas tubes in parallel?

31. What were some of the objections to the use of contact type rectifiers before the development of the selenium rectifier?

32. What are some of the advantages of the selenium type contact rectifier over the vacuum tube rectifier?

33. Define: (*a*) ripple voltage, (*b*) ripple factor, (*c*) per cent of ripple voltage.

34. What is the function of (*a*) the filter circuit? (*b*) The filter capacitor? (*c*) The filter choke?

35. Explain the filtering action of (*a*) the filter capacitor, (*b*) the filter choke.

36. (*a*) What are the operating requirements and characteristics of a resistance-capacitance filter circuit? (*b*) Where is this type of filter circuit used?

37. What is meant by (*a*) a low-pass filter? (*b*) A choke-input filter? (*c*) A capacitor-input filter? (*d*) A single-section filter? (*e*) A multisection filter?

38. Explain the principle of operation of a single-section capacitor-input filter circuit.

39. Explain how the per cent of ripple voltage is affected by changes in (*a*) the frequency of the rectified output, (*b*) the effective load resistance, (*c*) the capacitance of the input capacitor.

40. Why does a capacitor-input filter circuit have poor voltage regulation?

41. How do the operating characteristics of a capacitor-input filter circuit compare with those of a choke-input filter circuit?

42. For what type of service are capacitor-input filter circuits generally used?

43. What is the purpose of connecting a low value of resistance directly in the rectifier tube circuit of a power supply unit employing a capacitor-input filter?

44. Explain the principle of operation of a single-section choke-input filter circuit.

45. Explain how the per cent of ripple voltage of a choke-input filter circuit is affected by (*a*) the input choke, (*b*) the first capacitor, (*c*) the smoothing choke, (*d*) the second capacitor.

46. Give two functions of the input choke.

47. What is meant by (*a*) the critical value of inductance? (*b*) The optimum value of inductance?

48. How does the value of inductance of the input choke affect the operation of the filter circuit?

49. (*a*) What is meant by a swinging choke? (*b*) What is its function?

50. What are the characteristics of a choke-input filter circuit?

51. For what type of service are choke-input filter circuits generally used?

52. What are the functions of the bleeder resistor?

53. What are the functions of the voltage divider?

54. What are the advantages of using a separate resistor for each section of a voltage divider rather than a single resistor having the necessary taps?

55. Explain how the use of a bleeder resistor improves the voltage regulation of a power supply unit.

56. Describe four advantages of the transformerless type of power supply.

57. Why do the rectifier tubes used in transformerless power supplies have high-voltage heaters?

58. Why are capacitor-input filter circuits used with transformerless power supply units?

59. What are the characteristics of transformerless power supplies?

60. (*a*) Explain how the negative terminal of a transformerless power supply unit introduces two possible sources of danger. (*b*) Describe a few of the methods that can be used to eliminate these sources of danger.

61. (*a*) What is a vibrator type of power supply unit? (*b*) What is the purpose of the vibrator? (*c*) Where are vibrator power supplies used?

62. What is meant by (*a*) a synchronous vibrator? (*b*) A nonsynchronous vibrator?

63. Describe the principle of operation of a nonsynchronous vibrator power supply circuit.

64. Describe the principle of operation of a synchronous vibrator power supply circuit.

65. (*a*) What is the purpose of the buffer capacitor? (*b*) How is the buffer capacitor connected in the circuit?

66. (*a*) What is meant by hash? (*b*) How is hash eliminated?

67. What are the advantages and disadvantages of vibrator power supply units?

68. For what types of service are gaseous voltage regulator tubes used?

69. (*a*) How are voltage regulator tubes connected in the power supply circuit? (*b*) Why should a resistor always be connected in series with the regulator tube and the power supply?

70. Explain how it is possible to obtain voltage regulation in a power supply circuit whose regulated output voltage is higher than the voltage rating of the standard regulating tubes?

PROBLEMS

1. A certain power supply unit using a single diode has its output connected directly to a resistance load. The voltage at the secondary terminals of the power transformer is 300 volts. (*a*) What is the output voltage of the power supply unit if the voltage drops at the tube and the transformer secondary are neglected? (*b*) Draw a sketch of the wave form of the output voltage. (*c*) What is the output voltage if the drop at the tube is 30 volts and the drop at the transformer secondary is 15 volts? (*d*) What is the peak inverse voltage?

2. A power supply unit using a duo-diode as a full-wave rectifier has its output connected directly to a resistance load. The secondary of the power transformer is center-tapped and has a voltage of 300 volts from each side to the center tap. (*a*) What is the output voltage of the power supply unit if the voltage drops at the tube and the transformer secondary are neglected? (*b*) Draw a sketch of the wave form of the output voltage. (*c*) What is the output voltage if the drop from each plate to cathode is 25 volts and the drop from the center tap to the outside terminals of the transformer secondary is 15 volts? (*d*) What is the peak inverse voltage?

3. A power supply unit using four diodes in a full-wave bridge rectifier circuit has its output connected directly to a resistance load. The voltage across the secondary terminals of the power transformer is 450 volts. (*a*) What is the output voltage of the power supply unit if the voltage drops at the tubes and the transformer secondary are neglected? (*b*) Draw a sketch of the wave form of the output voltage. (*c*) What is the output voltage if the drop at each tube is 30 volts and the drop from the center tap to the outside terminals of the transformer secondary is 15 volts? (*d*) What is the peak inverse voltage?

4. A full-wave voltage doubler power supply circuit similar to Fig. 11-10*a* is being supplied with a secondary voltage of 300 volts. What is the output voltage if the capacitors used are capable of maintaining an average value of voltage equal to (a) the rms value of the voltage at the secondary terminals? (b) 90 per cent of the rms voltage at the secondary terminals? (c) 80 per cent of the rms voltage at the secondary terminals?

5. A half-wave voltage doubler circuit similar to Fig. 11-11 is being operated from a 120-volt a-c power line. (a) What is the peak voltage possible at capacitor C_1? (b) What is the peak voltage possible at capacitor C_2? (c) What is the peak inverse voltage at tube 1? (d) What is the peak inverse voltage at tube 2?

6. A half-wave voltage multiplier circuit similar to Fig. 11-12 is being operated from a 120-volt a-c power line. (a) What is the peak voltage possible at each capacitor? (b) What is the peak inverse voltage at each tube?

7. (a) Draw a diagram of a half-wave voltage multiplier circuit using three tubes and three capacitors to provide an output voltage of approximately 350 volts when operated from a 117-volt a-c power line. (b) What is the minimum standard voltage rating recommended for each capacitor? (c) What standard voltage rating capacitors would you recommend if it is desired to allow for a reasonable safety factor? (d) What is the peak inverse voltage at each tube?

8. (a) Draw a diagram of a half-wave voltage multiplier circuit using four tubes and four capacitors to provide an output voltage of approximately 450 volts when operated from a 115-volt a-c power line. (b) What is the minimum standard voltage rating recommended for each capacitor? (c) What standard voltage rating capacitors would you recommend if it is desired to allow for a reasonable safety factor? (d) What is the peak inverse voltage at each tube?

9. If the rectifier circuit of Fig. 11-16 employs four 35Z4-GT tubes, what is the maximum load current that the circuit can supply? (Obtain current rating of the tubes from Appendix XV.)

10. A power supply circuit similar to Fig. 11-16 employs four 5T4 duo-diodes with their plates connected in parallel so that each tube acts as a diode. The maximum d-c output of a tube connected in this manner is 225 ma. What is the maximum load current that the circuit can supply?

11. A certain half-wave power supply unit is being operated with 260 volts and 60 cycles at the input. It is being operated without a filter circuit, hence the output is fed directly to its resistance load. The rms value of the fundamental component of the ripple voltage is 130 volts. (a) What is the average value of the output voltage? (b) What is the per cent of ripple voltage? (c) What is the frequency of the ripple voltage?

12. A certain full-wave power supply unit is being operated with 300 volts at 60 cycles applied between the center tap and each side of the secondary of its power transformer. It is being operated without a filter circuit, hence the output of the rectifier is fed directly to its resistance load. The rms value of the fundamental component of the ripple voltage is 127 volts. (a) What is the average value of the output voltage? (b) What is the per cent of ripple voltage? (c) What is the frequency of the ripple voltage?

13. A three-phase half-wave rectifier circuit is being operated from a 60-cycle power line and without a filter circuit. The output voltage is 300 volts and the ripple voltage is 17.7 per cent. (a) What is the rms value of the ripple voltage? (b) What is the ripple frequency (see Fig. 11-14c)?

14. A three-phase full-wave rectifier circuit is being operated from a 60-cycle power line and without a filter circuit. The output voltage is 300 volts and the ripple voltage is 4 per cent. (a) What is the rms value of the ripple voltage? (b) What is the ripple frequency (see Fig. 11-15c)?

15. The plate circuit of a certain a-f amplifier is to be operated at 180 volts and the per cent of ripple is not to exceed 0.05 per cent for operation without noticeable hum. What is the highest rms value of ripple voltage permitted?

16. The amplifier of Prob. 15, if operated from a power supply with a ripple voltage of 1 per cent, will produce a slight amount of hum in the output, which may not be objectionable for some applications. What is the highest rms value of ripple voltage permitted under this condition?

17. A simple power supply unit using a single half-wave rectifier tube is to be operated from a 60-cycle power line. What is the approximate per cent of ripple voltage at the first capacitor of its capacitor-input filter circuit if the effective load resistance is 5000 ohms and the value of capacitance is 20 μf?

18. A simple power supply unit using a full-wave rectifier tube is to be operated from a 60-cycle power line. (a) What is the approximate per cent of ripple voltage at the first capacitor of its capacitor-input filter circuit if the effective load resistance is 3000 ohms and the value of capacitance is 15 μf? (b) What is the magnitude of the ripple voltage if the output is 250 volts?

19. It is desired to determine whether it would be practical to use a 35Z5 rectifier tube and a single-unit filter, consisting of a single capacitor, to provide a 60-ma load at 90 volts with a maximum ripple of 0.25 per cent. The peak plate current of the 35Z5 is 600 ma. (a) What is the effective load resistance? (b) What value of capacitance is required? (c) What is the capacitive reactance of the required capacitor to 60-cycle current? (d) If the peak value of the 60-cycle input voltage to the rectifier is 165 volts, what is the magnitude of the rectifier current during the first cycle after the power is applied? (e) What effect will the current during this first cycle have upon the tube? (f) Is this circuit design practical?

20. A power supply unit being operated from a 60-cycle power line is supplying a load with 100 ma at 250 volts. A full-wave rectifier is used and the filter circuit is similar to that of Fig. 11-20e. The values of C_1 and C_2 are 10 μf each and L_1 is 20 henries. What is the per cent of ripple voltage at (a) C_1? (b) C_2?

21. A power supply unit being operated from a 60-cycle power line is supplying a load with 120 ma at 300 volts. A half-wave rectifier is used and the filter circuit is similar to that of Fig. 11-20e. The values of C_1 and C_2 are 15 μf each and L_1 is 20 henries. What is the per cent of ripple voltage at (a) C_1? (b) C_2?

22. A power supply unit being operated from a 60-cycle power line is supplying a load with 120 ma at 360 volts. A full-wave rectifier is used and the filter circuit is similar to that of Fig. 11-20f. The values of C_1, C_2, and C_3 are 10 μf each; L_1 is 20 henries and L_2 is 15 henries. What is the per cent of ripple voltage at (a) C_1? (b) C_2? (c) C_3?

23. A power supply unit being operated from a 60-cycle power line is supplying a load with 120 ma at 360 volts. A half-wave rectifier is used and the filter circuit is similar to that of Fig. 11-20f. The values of C_1, C_2, and C_3 are 10 μf each; L_1 is 20 henries and L_2 is 15 henries. What is the per cent of ripple voltage at (a) C_1? (b) C_2? (c) C_3?

24. A power supply unit being operated from a 60-cycle power line is supplying a load with 50 ma at 100 volts. A half-wave rectifier is used and the filter circuit is similar to that of Fig. 11-20g. The values of C_1 and C_2 are 40 μf each and R_1 is 1000 ohms. What is the per cent of ripple voltage at (a) C_1? (b) C_2?

25. A power supply unit being operated from a 60-cycle power line is supplying a load with 50 ma at 80 volts. A half-wave rectifier is used and the filter circuit is similar to that of Fig. 11-20g. The value of C_1 is 30 μf, C_2 is 50 μf, and R_1 is 800 ohms. What is the per cent of ripple voltage at (a) C_1? (b) C_2?

26. A power supply unit being operated from a 60-cycle power line is supplying a load with 14 ma at 80 volts. A half-wave rectifier is used and the filter circuit is similar to that of Fig. 11-20g. The current for the power tube is taken off at capacitor C_1, and hence this current does not flow through resistor R_1. The value of C_1 is 40 μf, C_2 is 20 μf, and R_1 is 1200 ohms. What is the per cent of ripple voltage at (a) C_1? (b) C_2?

27. What is the per cent of regulation of the power supply unit of Prob. 20 if its output voltage is 250 volts at full-load and 350 volts at no-load?

28. What is the per cent of regulation of the power supply unit of Prob. 21 if its output voltage is 300 volts at full-load and 450 volts at no-load?

29. What is the per cent of regulation of the power supply unit of Prob. 25 if the output voltage is 80 volts at full-load and 150 volts at no-load?

30. If it is desired to limit the regulation of the power supply unit of Prob. 25 to 20 per cent by adding a bleeder resistor to the unit, to what value of no-load voltage must the circuit be limited?

31. A power supply unit being operated from a 60-cycle power line is supplying a load with 125 ma at 300 volts. A full-wave rectifier is used and the filter circuit is similar to that of Fig. 11-20b. The value of L_1 is 10 henries and C_1 is 4 μf. What is the per cent of ripple voltage at the output?

32. A power supply unit being operated from a 60-cycle power line is supplying a load with 150 ma at 450 volts. A full-wave rectifier is used and the filter circuit is similar to that of Fig. 11-20b. The value of L_1 is 10 henries and C_1 is 16 μf. What is the per cent of ripple voltage at the output?

33. A power supply unit being operated from a 60-cycle power line is supplying a load with 170 ma at 425 volts. A full-wave rectifier is used and the filter circuit is similar to that of Fig. 11-20c. The values of L_1 and L_2 are 20 henries each, and C_1 and C_2 are 4 μf each. What is the per cent of ripple voltage at (a) C_1? (b) C_2?

34. A power supply unit being operated from a 60-cycle power line is supplying a load with 200 ma at 450 volts. A full-wave rectifier is used and the filter circuit is similar to that of Fig. 11-20c. The value of L_1 is 20 henries, L_2 is 15 henries, C_1 is 2 μf, and C_2 is 4 μf. What is the per cent of ripple voltage at (a) C_1? (b) C_2?

35. Determine the per cent of ripple voltage at the output of the power supply unit of Prob. 31 if it is to be operated from a 25-cycle power line.

36. Determine the per cent of ripple voltage at the output of the power supply unit of Prob. 32 if it is to be operated from a 40-cycle power line.

37. Determine the per cent of ripple voltage at the output of the power supply unit of Prob. 33 if it is to be operated from a 50-cycle power line.

38. Determine the optimum value of inductance for the input choke of the power supply unit in Prob. 31.

39. Determine the optimum value of inductance for the input choke of the power supply unit in Prob. 32.

40. Determine the resistance values of a voltage divider for a superheterodyne receiver that employs a 6SA7 converter, a 6SG7 i-f amplifier tube, a 6SQ7 detector-amplifier tube, and a 6K6-GT/G power output tube. The operating voltages and currents are to be similar to those listed in Appendix XV for plate voltages of 250 volts. (The screen grid of the 6SG7 is to be operated at 150 volts.) The voltage divider should have taps to supply all plate, screen-grid, and grid-bias voltages. Its power transformer, rated at 90 ma, is to be operated at 90 per cent of its rated current.

41. Determine the power rating of the voltage divider of Prob. 40 for (a) a single resistor having five taps, (b) six separate resistors.

42. Determine the resistance values of a voltage divider for a superheterodyne receiver that employs a 7B8 converter, a 7A7 i-f amplifier tube, a 7B6 detector-amplifier tube, and a 7B5 power output tube. The operating voltages and currents are to be similar to those listed in Appendix XV for plate voltages of 250 volts. All control-grid bias voltages are to be obtained by separate cathode bias resistors, and hence these voltages are not to be provided by the voltage divider. Its power transformer, rated at 90 ma, is to be operated at 90 per cent of its rated current.

43. Determine the power rating of the voltage divider of Prob. 42 for (a) a single-tapped resistor, (b) two separate resistors.

44. In the modern receiver circuit shown in Fig. 14-13, the voltage divider is replaced by the voltage dropping resistors R_6 and R_9. (a) What purpose does R_6 serve? (b) What purpose does R_9 serve? (c) What is the voltage at the second grid of VT_2 if 4 ma flows through R_6 (a 30,000-ohm, 1-watt resistor) and the voltage of the B+ line is 300 volts? (d) How much power is dissipated by this resistor, R_6? (e) What voltage is applied to the screen grids of VT_1, VT_2, and VT_3 if 6.5 ma flows through R_9 (a 30,000-ohm 1-watt resistor) and the voltage of the B+ line is 300 volts? (f) How much power is dissipated by this resistor, R_9?

45. What rms value of alternating voltage must be supplied by the power source to the plate of the rectifier tube of Prob. 21 if the resistance of L_1 is 150 ohms and the internal tube drop is 25 volts? Assume that the average value of the rectifier output voltage is equal to the rms value of the applied voltage when the tube drop is neglected.

46. What rms value of alternating voltage must be supplied by the power source to the plate of the rectifier tube of Prob. 22 if the resistance of L_1 is 150 ohms, L_2 is 100 ohms, and the internal drop of the tube is 30 volts? Assume that the average value of the rectifier output voltage is equal to the rms value of the applied voltage when the tube drop is neglected.

47. What rms value of alternating voltage must be supplied by the power source to the plate of the rectifier tube of Prob. 26 if the internal drop of the tube is 20 volts? Assume that the average value of the rectifier output voltage is equal to the rms value of the applied voltage when the tube drop is neglected.

CHAPTER XII

AUDIO UNITS

Radio is a one way form of communication in which no wires are used to connect the sending and receiving stations. The sound waves produced at a sending station may be reproduced practically instantaneously at numerous receiving stations situated at either short or great distances from the transmitter. Sound waves are capable of traveling only comparatively short distances and travel at a speed of approximately 1130 feet per second. The instantaneous reproduction of sound waves over large distances therefore cannot be accomplished by the direct transmission of the sound waves, but requires the transmission of electrical waves whose frequencies are a faithful reproduction of the frequencies of the sound waves to be reproduced. For complete radio communication it is therefore necessary that some device for changing the sound waves to electrical waves be situated at the sending station and another device for changing the electrical waves back to sound waves be situated at the receiving station. The audio unit used at the sending station for converting sound waves to electrical waves is called a *microphone*. At the receiving station, an audio unit called the *loudspeaker*, commonly referred to as simply the *speaker*, is used to convert the electrical waves back to sound waves.

Two other audio units used in radio communication are (1) a device called a *phonograph pickup*, which is used for converting sound on records to electric waves, (2) a device called a *magnetic reproducer*, which is used for converting sound on wire to electric waves.

12-1. Microphones. *Air-pressure-type Microphones.* The most commonly used type of microphone is the one that converts the mechanical variations in air pressure caused by the human voice or a musical instrument to an equivalent electrical wave of similar frequency. In the early stages of radio this type of microphone was generally mounted on a floor stand. With the many new fields of application for radio communication, and also because of the constant incentive for improvement, numerous types of microphones have been developed. Maximum performance can only be obtained if the correct type of microphone is used for the specific application.

The general-purpose microphone, shown in Fig. 12-1a and 12-1b, can be mounted on either a floor stand or a desk stand. This type of microphone is usually arranged so that it may be tilted through an angle of 90 degrees. For hanging-microphone applications, such as are required in stage work, this type of unit may be obtained with provisions that permit it to be suspended from a wire or cable.

Freedom of movement of the operator is obtained by use of the *lapel-type microphone* shown in Fig. 12-1c. This type of microphone has found favor in applications such as on-the-spot broadcasts, etc. A variation of the lapel microphone is one in which the microphone is mounted on a rigid support shaped in the form of a gooseneck. The microphone is kept in its correct position at all times by mounting the support on the speaker's shoulder. This type of microphone is very useful for applica-

(a) (b) (c)

Fig. 12-1.—Sound-wave-type microphones. (a) Floor model, (b) desk-stand type, (c) lapel type. (*Courtesy of Shure Brothers, Inc.*)

tions where, in addition to freedom of movement, both hands must be kept free.

Contact-type Microphones. An instrument used to convert the mechanical vibrations of a medium other than air into electrical waves is called a *contact microphone*. This type of microphone is fastened in direct contact with that part of an object or person's body whose vibration it is designed to pick up. Contact microphones have a number of fields of application and hence are made in a variety of forms, each to suit a particular need (see Fig. 12-2).

Contact-type microphones can be used to pick up the mechanical vibrations of wind, string, or percussion-type musical instruments. Such a unit is small and compact and is provided with a spring mounting clamp that permits it to be fastened with comparative ease to various types of musical instruments.

The contact microphone is also used for industrial purposes. An analysis of the vibration of a machine or any of its parts can easily be obtained by mounting a contact microphone directly to that part of the machine to be studied.

Contact microphones are very useful for applications where the surrounding noise level is very high.   Two types of units used in this field of application are the *throat microphone* and the *lip microphone*.   These microphones are strapped to the throat or lip and react directly to the vibration of these organs rather than to the sound waves they produce. The extraneous noises in the vicinity of the microphone produce only variations in air pressure and thus are not picked up.

(a)   (b)   (c)

Fig. 12-2.—Contact-type microphones.   (a) For musical instruments, (b) throat microphone, (c) lip microphone.

12-2. Requirements of the Microphone.   *Frequency Response.*   The

sounds produced by the loudspeaker of a radio receiver should be essentially the same as those produced by the artists in the studio of the transmitting station.   The frequency elimination and intensity characteristics of audible sounds as presented in Art. 8-1 for the audio amplifier will therefore also apply to the microphone.   Since the fidelity of reception can only approach but never equal the fidelity of transmission, the microphone should have a more uniform response over a wider range than the audio-frequency components in the radio receivers.   The frequency range of microphones used at a transmitter usually is from 30 to 10,000 cycles as compared to a range of 50 to 5000 cycles for the average home receiver.

Sensitivity.   Sound waves are the mechanical vibration of air in space at audio-frequency rates.   These vibrations cause the air pressure to vary above and below its normal pressure.   The variations in air pressure on the eardrum produce the sensation of sound in the brain.   A sound that is just barely audible increases the normal air pressure by only about one-millionth of 1 per cent. A sound that is so loud that it causes pain increases the normal air pressure by only about one-tenth of 1 per cent. For perfect fidelity, a microphone should be sensitive to these small variations in air pressure for the entire range of hearing.

Since the intensity of a sound wave decreases as the distance from its source increases, so, too, the sensitivity of a microphone will decrease as

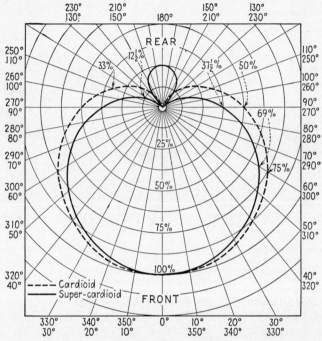

Fig. 12-3.—Range of pickup for cardioid- and supercardioid-type microphones. (*Courtesy of Shure Brothers, Inc.*)

the distance between the microphone and the source of the sound wave is increased. Maximum response is thus obtained when the distance between the microphone and the source of the sound is at a minimum.

Range of Pickup. The maximum response from any type of microphone will be obtained from those sound waves which are produced directly in front of the microphone. The response will decrease as the angle between the front of the microphone and the direction of the sound waves is increased. The sound waves entering the back of a microphone are usually produced by an audience or by background reflections. The sound waves from the loudspeakers of public-address systems may also enter the back of a microphone either directly or by reflection from walls, ceiling, or the floor and thus produce feedback. It can therefore be seen that for most applications it is desirable to reduce to a minimum the response of those sound waves entering the back of a microphone.

For most applications, it is desirable that the response characteristics of the microphone be unidirectional and that its range of pickup be approximately 180 degrees. The response characteristics of two types of unidirectional microphones, the cardioid and the supercardioid, are shown in Fig. 12-3. The ratio of front to rear pickup of random sound energy is 7 to 1 for the cardioid and 14 to 1 for the supercardioid.

In many microphone applications the sound waves do not always originate directly in the front or rear of a microphone. Because of this, it is desirable for a unidirectional microphone to reproduce with as nearly equal response as is practicable all sound waves produced in an imaginary hemisphere in front of the microphone. By the same reasoning, the response for all sound waves produced in an imaginary hemisphere in back of a microphone should be reduced to a minimum. From Fig. 12-3 it can be seen that the cardioid type of microphone has a wide range of pickup. At a 60-degree angle, the response for the cardioid and super-cardioid microphones is respectively 75 and 69 per cent of their maximum response.

12-3. Microphone Ratings. *Pressure Rating.* As the output of a microphone varies with the pressure of the sound waves, it is necessary to rate the output of a microphone for some definite unit of pressure. The unit of pressure most generally used is the *bar*. The term *bar* actually means a unit of atmospheric pressure, which is equal to a pressure of approximately one million dynes per square centimeter. However, in the rating of microphones many manufacturers consider the bar as the cgs (centimeter-gram-second) absolute unit of pressure which is equal to a pressure of one dyne per square centimeter. The ASA (American Standards Association) recommends the use of the phrase *dynes per square centimeter* as the unit of sound pressure.

Impedance Classification. Microphones may be classified according to their impedance as being either low-impedance or high-impedance microphones. The low-impedance group includes the carbon, velocity, and dynamic types of microphones. The high-impedance group includes the crystal and capacitor types. The velocity and dynamic microphones can be obtained with a self-contained high-impedance transformer that enables these two types of microphones to be used as high-impedance instruments.

Low-impedance Microphone Ratings. One of the important factors in the choice of low-impedance microphones is their power output. Low-impedance microphones are therefore rated on the basis of the decibels below a zero power level for a zero reference pressure level. These microphones are usually rated with a zero power reference level of six milliwatts, although a one-milliwatt zero reference level is also used. The zero reference pressure level is generally one bar, although a ten-bar zero reference level is also used. Because of the lack of consistent use of a single reference level, it is very important to express and interpret carefully the manner in which a microphone is rated.

The power in a microphone circuit can readily be determined from its decibel rating by the methods presented in Art. 8-3. However, before determining the power output of a microphone from its decibel rating, it is necessary that the decibel be expressed in terms of its reference pressure level. The effect of variations in pressure upon the decibel rating is expressed by the equation

$$db = 20 \log \frac{F}{F_R} \tag{12-1}$$

where db = output rating at the higher pressure
F = higher pressure, bars
F_R = reference pressure level, bars

The following example illustrates the interpretation of low-impedance microphone ratings.

Example 12-1. A certain low-impedance microphone is rated at 62.8 db below 6 milliwatts per 10-bar signal. What is the power output for (*a*) a 10-bar signal? (*b*) A 300-bar signal?

Given:
$P_R = 6$ mw
$db = -62.8$
$F_R = 10$ bars

Find:
(*a*) P_o @ 10 bars
(*b*) P_o @ 300 bars

Solution:

(*a*) $db = 10 \log \dfrac{P_R}{P_o}$

$P_o = \dfrac{P_R}{\text{antilog} \dfrac{db}{10}} = \dfrac{0.006}{\text{antilog} \dfrac{62.8}{10}} = \dfrac{0.006}{1.906 \times 10^6}$

$= 0.0031 \times 10^{-6}$ watt, or 0.0031 μw

(*b*) Output rating $= 20 \log \dfrac{F}{F_R} = 20 \log \dfrac{300}{10} = 20 \times 1.4771 = 29.54$ db

Output $= -62.8 + 29.54 = -33.26$ db

$P_o = \dfrac{P_R}{\text{antilog} \dfrac{db}{10}} = \dfrac{0.006}{\text{antilog} \dfrac{33.26}{10}} = \dfrac{0.006}{2.12 \times 10^3} = 2.83 \times 10^{-6}$ watts, or 2.83 μw

High-impedance Microphone Ratings. One of the important factors in the choice of high-impedance microphones is their voltage output. High-impedance microphones are therefore rated in decibels below one volt per bar. This means that an alternating sound pressure of one dyne per square centimeter rms will produce an output voltage, across an open circuit grid, of the rated decibels below one volt.

Example 12-2. A certain high-impedance microphone is rated at 55 db below one volt per bar. What is the voltage output for (*a*) a signal of one bar? (*b*) A 300-bar signal?

Given:

 $db = -55$

 $F_R = $ one bar

Find:

 (*a*) e_o @ one bar

 (*b*) e_o @ 300 bars

Solution:

(*a*) $db = 20 \log \dfrac{e_R}{e_o}$

 $e_o = \dfrac{e_R}{\text{antilog } \dfrac{db}{20}} = \dfrac{1}{\text{antilog } \dfrac{55}{20}} = \dfrac{1}{562.3} = 0.00177$ volt

(*b*) Output rating $= 20 \log \dfrac{F}{F_R} = 20 \times \log \dfrac{300}{1} = 20 \times 2.4771 = 49.54$ db

 Output $= -55 + 49.54 = -5.46$ db

 $e_o = \dfrac{e_R}{\text{antilog } \dfrac{db}{20}} = \dfrac{1}{\text{antilog } \dfrac{5.46}{20}} = \dfrac{1}{1.875} = 0.533$ volt

Impedance Matching. In order to obtain maximum power transfer it is necessary to match the microphone impedance with its load. Thus, a low-impedance microphone should feed into a low load impedance, and a high-impedance microphone should feed into a high load impedance.

Transformers are generally used to couple low-impedance microphones to their amplifier circuits. The turns ratio of the microphone transformer should be of such a value that the load reflected to the primary circuit by the loaded secondary will be equal to the impedance of the microphone. From Eq. (2-73), the turns ratio may be expressed as

$$N = \sqrt{\frac{Z_o}{Z_M}} \tag{12-2}$$

where $N = $ turns ratio (secondary to primary)

 $Z_o = $ output impedance, ohms

 $Z_M = $ microphone impedance, ohms

Example 12-3. A certain low-impedance microphone has a resistance of 50 ohms. The secondary of the microphone transformer feeds into a 450-ohm line. Determine the transformer turns ratio.

Given:

 $Z_M = 50$ ohms

 $Z_o = 450$ ohms

Find:

 $N = ?$

Solution:

$$N = \sqrt{\frac{Z_o}{Z_M}} = \sqrt{\frac{450}{50}} = 3$$

Resistance-capacitance coupling is generally used to couple high-impedance microphones to their amplifier circuits.   Maximum power transfer is obtained by using the proper value of plate resistor.

Effect of the Microphone Connecting Line.   The distributed capacitance of the line connecting the microphone to its amplifier may be considered as a capacitor of equivalent value connected across the load.   The impedance of this capacitor is dependent upon the frequency of the a-f signal and the length of the connecting line.   In a low-impedance microphone circuit the lowest impedance of this capacitor, which occurs at the highest audio frequency, will be many times greater than the microphone impedance.   The shunting effect of this capacitance is thus very small and can usually be ignored.   Increasing the length of the connecting line increases its distributed capacitance, which decreases its impedance and thereby increases the shunting effect of the line.   However, the shunting effect of even long lines may still be ignored when used with low-impedance microphones.

If the connecting line used with a high-impedance microphone is too long, the microphone impedance may be many times greater than the highest value of shunting impedance owing to the distributed capacitance of the line.   Under this condition, the distributed capacitance of the line will have considerable effect on both the frequency response and the energy output of a high-impedance microphone circuit and therefore the length of the connecting line is an important factor.   The ratings of high-impedance microphones are usually listed by the manufacturers for definite lengths of connecting lines.

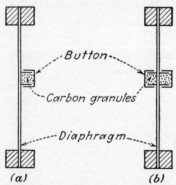

12-4. Carbon Microphones. *Operation of Carbon Microphones.*   The operation of the carbon microphone is based upon the principle that the resistance of a pile of carbon granules will vary as the pressure exerted upon it is varied.   The basic construction of a carbon microphone is illustrated in Fig. 12-4.   The carbon granules are loosely piled in an insulated cup called the *button*.   This button is mounted so that it is always in direct contact with the dia-

Fig. 12-4.—Basic construction of a carbon microphone. (a) Single-button type, (b) double-button type.

phragm.   Any movement of the diaphragm will vary the amount of pressure exerted on the carbon granules and will vary the resistance of the carbon pile.

The manner in which the variations in the resistance of the pile of carbon granules is utilized to convert sound waves to electrical waves can be seen by studying the operation of the single-button carbon microphone circuit shown in Fig. 12-5a.   The microphone button is connected in series with a battery and the primary winding of the microphone transformer.   With no movement of the diaphragm the resistance of the carbon pile remains constant and a steady amount of direct current will flow through the circuit.   When sound waves strike the diaphragm they cause it to vibrate.   Vibrations of the diaphragm will cause variations in the amount of pressure being exerted on the pile of carbon granules.

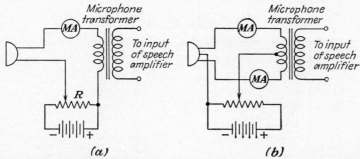

Fig. 12-5.—Carbon microphone circuits.   (a) Single-button type, (b) double-button type.

Increasing the pressure packs the carbon granules more closely, thus decreasing the amount of contact resistance between granules and thereby decreasing the resistance of the entire carbon pile.   Just as the variations in pressure on the diaphragm are controlled by the intensity and frequency of the sound waves that strike it, so, too, the variations in resistance of the carbon pile will also be dependent on the intensity and frequency of the sound waves.   The variations in resistance of the carbon pile will cause the current flowing in this circuit to vary with the intensity and frequency of the sound waves.   The output at the secondary of the microphone transformer will therefore be an alternating voltage of magnitude and frequency corresponding to the sound waves.

Any distortion that may be caused by the nonlinear response of the carbon microphone can be reduced by use of the double-button microphone circuit shown in Fig. 12-5b.   The two buttons in conjunction with the center-tapped primary form a push-pull arrangement that tends to cancel out all the even-order harmonics.   Otherwise, the operation of the double-button microphone circuit is similar to the single-button microphone circuit.

Characteristics of Carbon Microphones.   One of the disadvantages of the carbon microphone is that the random changes in contact resistance between the carbon granules produces a steady hiss in the output circuit.

The push-pull arrangement of the double-button microphone circuit helps to balance out this hiss to some extent. However, the hiss cannot be entirely eliminated and the amplitude of the weakest note that can be applied to the microphone and be faithfully reproduced is limited by the magnitude of the hiss.

Another disadvantage of the carbon microphone is that an excessive amount of pressure or current may cause the carbon granules to stick to each other and become packed. In order to prevent the packing of the carbon granules by the flow of too much current, the potentiometer R (Fig. 12-5) should be adjusted so that the current flow in the microphone

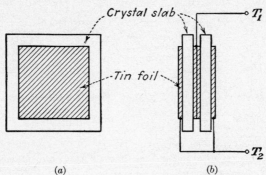

(a)   (b)

FIG. 12-6.—Basic construction of a crystal sound cell. (a) Single crystal, (b) bimorph cell.

circuit does not exceed its rated value. The rated button current varies with the type of microphone and the manufacturer and may range from 5 to 100 milliamperes.

The response of the carbon microphone is practically independent of frequency up to the mechanical resonant frequency of the diaphragm. The response decreases rapidly for those sound waves having a frequency above this value. In order to obtain a uniform response over the entire audio-frequency range it becomes necessary to increase the mechanical resonant frequency of the diaphragm. This is accomplished by stretching the diaphragm close to its elastic limit. Since stretching the diaphragm also decreases the sensitivity of the microphone, a compromise is usually made as to which is the more important factor, the sensitivity or the frequency response.

Despite these disadvantages, the carbon microphone has certain advantages that make it important in its field. It is the only microphone that is also an amplifier in that its electrical energy output is greater than the energy required to produce the vibrations of the diaphragm. Other advantages are its light weight, low initial cost, rugged construction, and the fact that it is portable. It is therefore used where high sensitivity is an important factor or where voice reproduction rather than musical entertainment is the primary object.   Carbon microphones are used for amateur, police, and military work and also in some contact microphones.

12-5. Crystal Microphones.   *Operation of Crystal Microphones.*   The crystal microphone makes use of the piezoelectric characteristics of certain crystalline materials (see Art. 10-10).   Because the voltage output of a Rochelle-salt crystal is much greater than for other crystalline materials it is the one most generally used for microphone applications.   The basic crystal sound cell, sometimes called a *bimorph cell,* is made by clamping two thin crystal slabs together, as is shown in Fig. 12-6.   Electrical contact is made with each crystal by cementing a sheet of tin foil on both of its faces.   The microphone can be constructed so that the movement of the crystal is actuated directly by the sound waves.   However, this method is not very effective and in the more sensitive types of microphones the crystal is fastened directly to the diaphragm.   Vibration of the diaphragm by sound waves will cause the crystal to vibrate and because of its piezoelectric action an alternating voltage having a frequency and intensity corresponding to the sound waves will be produced at the terminals of the crystal.   Because the output voltage of a single cell is very small, several cells are usually connected in series in order to obtain a higher voltage.   The crystal microphone requires no separate source of current or voltage and hence its output is applied directly to the input circuit of a speech amplifier.

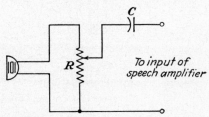

Fig. 12-7.—A crystal microphone circuit.

Because of the comparatively low voltage output of the crystal microphone several stages of high-gain speech amplification are required. Since transformer coupling may pick up an excessive amount of hum, the coupling between stages should be of the resistance-capacitance type. For the same reasons as given for the carbon microphones, the diaphragm of a crystal microphone must be stretched in order to increase the mechanical resonant frequency.

Characteristics of Crystal Microphones.   Crystal microphones are purely pressure operated and do not possess any cutoff effect at the low audio frequencies.   Its frequency response is comparatively flat over the entire a-f range.   It is also entirely nondirectional and therefore may be used at any angle.   Other advantages of the crystal microphone are its light weight, comparative ruggedness, ease of maintenance, and the fact that no external power source is required.

Crystal microphones are used in high-quality public-address systems, broadcasting stations, and recording equipment.   Because exposure to high temperatures (above 125° Fahrenheit) may permanently damage a crystal, precautions should be taken when using crystal microphones to keep the crystal from being exposed to high temperatures such as rays from the sun, radiators, etc. If the seal on a crystal microphone is broken the crystal will absorb moisture from the air and become useless. Another precaution that should be taken when using crystal microphones is to make sure that no voltage is applied to it. The battery voltage of an ohmmeter can destroy a crystal microphone.

12-6. Capacitor Microphones. *Operation of Capacitor Microphones.* The capacitor type of microphone is essentially a two-plate variable capacitor. The flexible metal diaphragm forms the movable plate and is

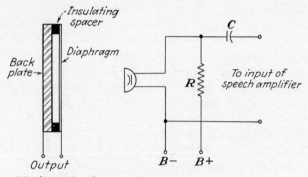

(*a*)-Basic construction   (*b*)-Microphone circuit

Fig. 12-8.—A capacitor microphone and its circuit.

separated from the back plate, which is fixed in position, by an insulating ring, as is shown in Fig. 12-8*a*. Sound waves will cause the diaphragm to vibrate, thus also causing the capacitance of this capacitor to change owing to the variations in the air gap, which is equivalent to varying the thickness of the dielectric. A potential of several hundred volts is applied between the capacitor plates. The changes in capacitance cause a small charging current to flow through the high resistance R that is connected in parallel with the capacitor (see Fig. 12-8*b*). A corresponding voltage drop is produced across this resistor and this voltage is fed to the input of the speech amplifier through the coupling capacitor C. An electrical equivalent of the sound waves is thus obtained, since these voltage drops will vary in accordance with the sound waves. The diaphragm of this type of microphone is usually stretched to the elastic limit in order to obtain a resonant mechanical frequency that is higher than the highest audio frequency to be reproduced.

Characteristics of Capacitor Microphones. The capacitor-type microphone has a high impedance and thus its output and frequency response is seriously affected by the capacitance of the cable connecting the microphone to the first stage of amplification.   Because of the losses in the connecting cable the capacitor microphone usually has at least one stage of preamplification built into the microphone head or physically close to it; this is one of its disadvantages.   Another disadvantage is that its sensitivity is very low; it is only a small fraction as sensitive as the carbon microphone.   The response of a capacitor microphone is reasonably uniform over a wide range of frequencies.   It is used principally for making sound measurements and is seldom used for radio or public-address applications.

12-7. Dynamic Microphones.   *Operation of Dynamic Microphones.* The dynamic microphone makes use of a nonrigid unstretched diaphragm.

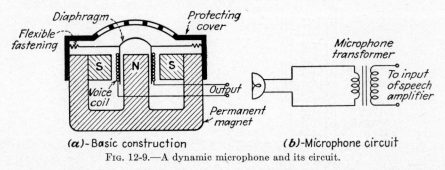

(*a*)-Basic construction   (*b*)-Microphone circuit
Fig. 12-9.—A dynamic microphone and its circuit.

A coil of wire that is rigidly attached to the back of the diaphragm is so arranged that it is free to move back and forth in the strong magnetic field produced by a permanent magnet (see Fig. 12-9).   When sound waves strike the diaphragm the coil will move back and forth in a radial magnetic field, thus inducing in the coil a voltage that is a faithful electrical reproduction of the sound waves.   A number of flexible circular corrugations on the diaphragm permit it to have a large amount of displacement.   The response of a dynamic microphone at the very low audio frequencies is therefore very good.   If the microphone is designed so that the voltage induced in the moving coil is exactly proportional to the pressure of the sound waves striking the diaphragm, the response of the dynamic microphone can be made practically independent of the frequency over a range of 40 to 10,000 cycles.   Because the coil of a dynamic microphone moves with the diaphragm it is also called a *moving-coil microphone.*

Characteristics of Dynamic Microphones.   The sensitivity of the moving-coil microphone is higher than other types of nonamplifying microphones.   It is light in weight, small in size, and requires no external source of power.   It is unusually rugged as it is practically immune to the effects of moisture, temperature, and mechanical vibration.   It can therefore be used outdoors even in a strong wind. The impedance of the dynamic microphone is normally very low, thus making it possible to use long connecting lines between the microphone and the first stage of amplification. However, it is also possible to obtain a dynamic microphone having a high impedance. This high-impedance microphone may be used in conjunction with a crystal microphone amplifier circuit or any other amplifier having an input impedance of 100,000 ohms or more. The dynamic-type microphone is used widely where high-quality reproduction is required, such as public-address systems, broadcasting studios, and recording equipment.

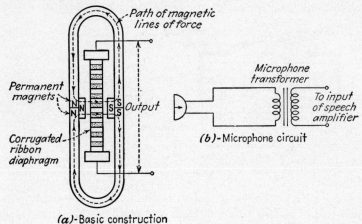

(a)-Basic construction

Fig. 12-10.—A velocity microphone and its circuit.

12-8. Velocity Microphones. *Operation of Velocity Microphones.* The velocity microphone is a variation of the moving-coil microphone. In place of the moving coil, a strip of metal is caused to vibrate in a magnetic field. As only a single conductor cuts the magnetic lines of force, the velocity microphone is not so sensitive as the dynamic microphone. The basic construction of this type of microphone is shown in Fig. 12-10. A thin, lightweight, flexible corrugated metal strip (usually aluminum or duralumin) is suspended between the poles of a permanent magnet. Because this metal strip resembles a ribbon this type of microphone is called a *ribbon microphone*. The ribbon will vibrate in accordance with the sound waves that strike it. As the conductor cuts the magnetic lines of force a voltage proportional to the frequency and pressure of the sound waves will be induced in the ribbon. The force exerted on the ribbon by a sound wave is equal to the difference between the pressures on the front and back of the ribbon. The resulting force is proportional to the velocity of the particles of air set in motion by the sound wave and hence the name *velocity microphone*.

Characteristics of Velocity Microphones. The velocity microphone
has an extremely good frequency response. It is comparatively rugged
and requires no external source of power. Its response is very directional
and thus it will only reproduce those sound waves made directly in front
of the microphone. However, the ribbon is very delicate and must be
protected from strong drafts or winds.

12-9. Magnetic Loudspeakers. *Horn-type Loudspeakers.* In the
simple radio receiver presented in Chap. III, a set of earphones is used to
convert the variations in electrical energy to sound waves. In order that

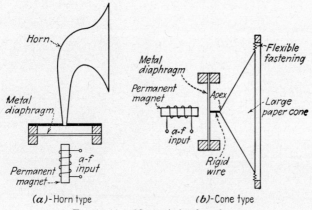

(*a*)- Horn type   (*b*)- Cone type

Fig. 12-11.—Magnetic loudspeakers.

more than one person may listen to the radio and at the same time enjoy
the comforts of the home, it is necessary to use a loudspeaker.

The principle of operation of the early type of loudspeaker is the same
as that of the earphone (see Art. 3-9). A strong magnet was used and
the coil was wound with a large number of turns. In order to obtain
increased volume, a horn was mechanically coupled to the audio unit to
concentrate and direct the sound waves (see Fig. 12-11*a*). For practical
reasons, the diaphragm of this type of loudspeaker cannot be very large
and the amount of air that it can displace is comparatively small. The
loudness of the sound that the horn-type magnetic loudspeaker can produce is therefore limited.

Cone-type Loudspeakers. A more practical form of the magnetic type
of loudspeaker is one using a paper cone in place of the horn (see Fig.
12-11*b*). One end of a rigid wire is mechanically fastened to the center of
the vertical diaphragm and the other end is fastened to the apex of a
paper cone. The vibrating diaphragm moves the wire, which in turn
moves the cone. Because of the large surface area of the paper cone, a
large quantity of air is set into motion, thus creating a loud sound.

Freedom of movement of the paper cone is obtained by the use of a flexible fastening between the large end of the cone and the surface to which it is attached.

Characteristics of Magnetic Loudspeakers. One of the faults of the magnetic loudspeaker is that it cannot be used to reproduce high values of audio-frequency currents. If the current flowing through the coil on the permanent magnet is too high, the diaphragm will strike the iron core and thus produce a rattle in the loudspeaker. The distance between the

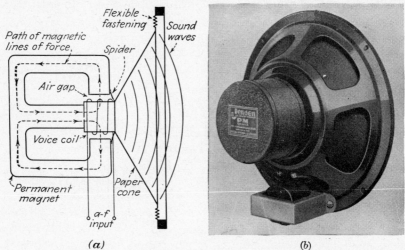

(a)　　　　　　　　　　　　　　　　(b)

Fig. 12-12.—A permanent-magnet dynamic loudspeaker. (a) Basic construction, (b) a commercial loudspeaker. (*Photograph courtesy of Jensen Radio Manufacturing Company.*)

core and the diaphragm is determined by the lowest value of the a-f current to be reproduced. For practical reasons, this distance cannot be made too large. Magnetic loudspeakers are not generally used with modern radio receivers because these receivers usually have a high current output.

12-10. Dynamic Loudspeakers. *Principle of the Dynamic Loudspeaker.* The ability to reproduce signals having high values of a-f current was made possible by the development of the dynamic loudspeaker (see Figs. 12-12 and 12-13). In this type of loudspeaker the a-f current flows through a coil that is mechanically coupled to a paper cone. Since only a-f currents flow through this coil it is generally referred to as the *voice coil*. The interaction between the varying magnetic field set up about the voice coil by the varying a-f current and the constant magnetic field of the stationary magnet causes the voice coil to move back and forth in the constant magnetic field. The paper cone being mechanically coupled to the voice coil will move back and forth at a frequency and intensity that are determined by the frequency and intensity of the a-f current. The motion of the paper cone will thus set up sound waves corresponding to the a-f currents in the voice coil. Freedom of movement of the paper cone is obtained in the same manner as in the cone-type magnetic loudspeaker. Because of the movement of the voice coil this type of loudspeaker is also called a *moving-coil loudspeaker*. The constant stationary magnetic field may be produced either by a permanent magnet, as in the case of the permanent-magnet dynamic loudspeaker, or by an electromagnet, as in the case of the electrodynamic loudspeaker. The dynamic loudspeaker is the type of loudspeaker most commonly used in modern receivers. The response of the dynamic loudspeaker is fairly uniform over a frequency range that is adequate for the ordinary radio receiver, namely, up to 5000 cycles. For high-fidelity reproduction, a high-quality dynamic loudspeaker can be obtained with fairly uniform response up to 10,000 cycles.

Permanent-magnet Dynamic Loudspeaker. The basic construction of a permanent-magnet dynamic loudspeaker, commonly referred to as a *pm dynamic loudspeaker*, is shown in Fig. 12-12. The fixed magnetic field is produced by a permanent magnet. The voice coil is wound on a thin bakelite tube that is mounted in a manner which permits it to move back and forth along the core of the permanent magnet. The voice coil is centered between the poles of the permanent magnet by means of a thin springy sheet of bakelite or metal called a *spider*. The spider permits the coil to move down along the core, and because of its spring action it also forces the coil to move back when the pull on the coil is reduced or eliminated.

The movement of the coil and the cone to which it is attached is directly dependent upon the strength of both the fixed and the varying magnetic fields. Thus the greater the strength of the fixed magnetic field, the greater will be the movement of the paper cone. Also, the greater the current flowing through the voice coil, the greater will be the movement of the cone. The strength of the fixed magnetic field is limited by the size and the material of which the permanent magnet is made and it is therefore not practical to use this type of loudspeaker for public-address systems or other applications that require very loud sounds. Because the strength of a permanent magnet becomes weaker in time, the volume output of the loudspeaker will also become weaker in time. Advantages of the pm dynamic loudspeaker are its light weight, compactness, low cost, and the fact that it requires no external source of power. Because of these advantages this type of loudspeaker is used extensively in portable, small-size, and low-price radio receivers.

Permanent-magnet dynamic loudspeakers are usually rated as to their power output, impedance of the voice coil, and the outside diameter of the cone.   The power output of this type of loudspeaker ranges from one to ten watts.   The impedance of its voice coil has a range of approximately three to eight ohms.   The outside diameter of the cone may be as small as two inches or as large as twelve inches.

In order to obtain the maximum transfer of energy from the a-f signal in a high-impedance plate circuit of an output stage to the low-impedance voice coil, it is necessary to use an output transformer, as described in Art.

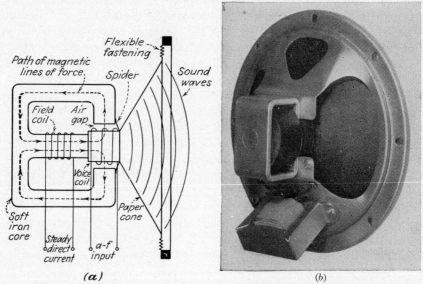

(a)   *(b)*

Fig. 12-13.—An electrodynamic loudpseaker.   (*a*) Basic construction, (*b*) commercial loudspeaker.   (*Photograph courtesy of Jensen Radio Manufacturing Company.*)

9-19.   It is not at all uncommon to find the output transformer mounted on the framework of the loudspeaker.

Electrodynamic Loudspeaker.   In order to obtain a stronger magnetic field and one whose strength does not decrease in time, an electromagnet may be substituted for the permanent magnet.   A loudspeaker that employs an electromagnet for its fixed magnetic field is called an *electrodynamic loudspeaker*.   The basic construction of such a loudspeaker is shown in Fig. 12-13.   The coil of the electromagnet is wound with a large number of turns and is usually called the *field coil*.   Because of the large number of turns on the field coil a strong magnetic field is set up about this coil when a steady direct current is flowing through it.   In all other respects the construction and the operation of the electrodynamic loudspeaker is similar to the pm dynamic loudspeaker.

There are several methods of obtaining the direct current required for the field winding. One method commonly used in the average radio receiver is to use the loudspeaker field winding (and its core) as a filter choke in the power supply unit. In addition to supplying current for the loudspeaker field, this method also provides additional filtering of the rectifier output without the use of an extra filter choke. In automobile radio receivers, the storage battery may be used to supply the direct current for the field winding of the electrodynamic loudspeaker. Loudspeakers designed for use in public-address systems require a larger amount of power to operate the field winding, and hence a separate power supply (rectifier and filter) is generally used for this purpose.

Electrodynamic loudspeakers are rated in the same manner as pm dynamic loudspeakers, except for the additional rating of the resistance and power consumption of the field coil. The outside diameter of the paper cone ranges from 3 to 18 inches, and the power output ranges from 2 to 50 watts. As with the pm dynamic loudspeaker, the impedance of the voice coil is very low and is generally less than 10 ohms. Because the fixed magnetic field will always remain constant in strength, and also because of its wide range of power output the electrodynamic loudspeaker is the most practical form of loudspeaker and hence is used extensively.

12-11. Horns. Because of the poor coupling between the air and the vibrating cone (also called a *direct radiator*), the efficiency of cone-type loudspeakers in transforming electrical energy to sound energy is very low. The efficiency of the average loudspeaker is less than 5 per cent. Because the average radio receiver has a much greater power output than the relatively small amount required by the loudspeaker, the poor efficiency of transformation is of little consequence and is usually ignored. Where a large amount of power output is required, such as in public-address systems, the efficiency of transformation becomes an important factor.

A higher efficiency of transformation can be obtained by mechanically coupling a dynamic loudspeaker, called the *driver unit*, to a horn, as shown in Fig. 12-14. The small end of the horn is called the *throat*, and the large end is called the *mouth*. The purpose of the horn is to transform sound energy having a high pressure and low velocity to sound energy having a low pressure and high velocity. A horn may be considered as a matching device for coupling the heavy vibrating surface at the throat of the horn to a relatively light medium, which is the air, at the mouth of the horn. The shape of the horn will depend upon the rate of increase of the cross-sectional area as shown in Fig. 12-15. The function of the horn contour is to produce a smooth and continuous increase in the cross-sectional area. The efficiency of transmission along the length of the horn is controlled by the rate of increase in cross-sectional area, also called the *taper*.   High audio frequencies are transmitted quite well by all horns.   At the low audio frequencies, the efficiency decreases for both the conical and the parabolic tapers, is fairly uniform for the exponential taper, and is comparatively uniform for the hypex.   In order to make the horn more compact it is generally folded upon itself one or more times, as shown in Fig. 12-16.

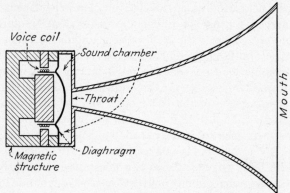

Fig. 12-14.—Basic structure of horn and driver unit.   (*Courtesy of Jensen Radio Manufacturing Company.*)

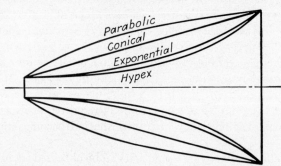

Fig. 12-15.—Comparative shapes of different types of horns with the same throat and mouth diameters.   (*Courtesy of Jensen Radio Manufacturing Company.*)

12-12. Recording and Reproduction of Sound Records.   *Recorders and Reproducers of Sound Records.*   A permanent record of any audible program or event can be made with the aid of modern recording apparatus.   It is also possible to reproduce readily and faithfully the audible sounds from this record with the aid of modern reproducing apparatus. It thus becomes possible for a broadcasting station to record a program at any convenient time and to broadcast this program at the most advantageous time for that station.   If proper equipment is employed, it is almost impossible for the average listener to detect whether a program is originating directly from the studio or from a recording.   Because of this flexibility in broadcasting, practically all broadcasting stations have apparatus capable of accurately recording and reproducing such program transcriptions.

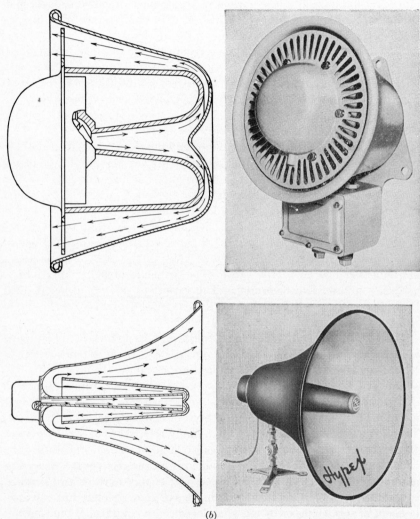

(b)

FIG. 12-16.—Horn-type reproducers. (a) Single-fold horn reproducer for speech reproduction, (b) two-fold horn reproducer for general reproduction of speech and music. (*Courtesy of Jensen Radio Manufacturing Company.*)

Entertainment to suit the mood or occasion can be obtained by the average person with the aid of a record player. This unit may be obtained separately or in combination with a radio receiver. The introduction of low-cost home recording equipment has made it possible to obtain a permanent record of important or festive occasions within the home. Many radio manufacturers have introduced combination units that in addition to the normal radio receiver provide one or more of the following features: (1) record player, (2) automatic record changing mechanism, (3) recording apparatus.

The various methods of making a record of sound are (1) mechanical, (2) magnetic, (3) tape, (4) light. In the mechanical method a thin disk made of wax, aluminum, or acetate-coated cardboard, glass, or metal may be used. A continuous groove is cut in the disk, starting near the outside and ending near the center. Two methods of cutting the groove, the lateral cut and the vertical cut, are employed. In the *lateral-cut* method, the depth of the groove is kept constant and the sides are undulated according to the variations in frequency and amplitude of the program being recorded. In the *vertical-cut* method, the sides of the groove are kept uniform and the depth of the cut is varied. The lateral cut is the one most commonly used. In the magnetic method sound is recorded on a thin wire by magnetizing the wire according to the variations in frequency and amplitude. A paper tape may be used to record code messages by punching a series of holes in the tape or by inking a dot-and-dash line along the tape. The principle of light variations is used in sound on film recording. The variations in light are controlled by a photoelectric cell that changes the electrical equivalent of the sound waves to light waves.

12-13. Mechanical Sound Recorders and Reproducers. *Principles of Mechanical Sound Recorders and Reproducers.* The mechanical method is used extensively in radio broadcasting stations. It is also used in home recording and reproduction apparatus. In recording apparatus the variations in electrical energy are transformed to an equivalent mechanical energy by cutting a groove in a disk, also called a *record*. The unit used for this purpose is commonly referred to as a *cutting head*. In reproduction apparatus a unit called a *pickup head* transforms the variations in mechanical energy obtained from the grooves in a record to an equivalent electrical energy. Electrical energy may be transformed to mechanical energy, or vice versa, in the cutting or pickup heads by use of magnetic principles or by use of a piezoelectric crystal. By means of a suitable switching apparatus a single amplifier circuit can be used for both recording and reproducing. When the unit is recording, sound energy is transformed to an equivalent electrical energy by a microphone and then strengthened by a speech amplifier. The output of the amplifier is fed into the cutting head and thus controls the manner in which the groove is cut. When the unit is reproducing, the vibration of the needle caused by the undulations in the groove of the record is changed to an equivalent electrical energy by the pickup head. This electrical energy is strengthened by the speech amplifier, whose output is then fed into a loudspeaker.

A sharp point, called a *stylus*, is used for cutting the groove in a record. Points used for this purpose are made of hard steel, a sapphire, or a diamond. For reproducing the audible sounds from a record a needle with a hard steel or sapphire point is used.

Magnetic Pickup and Magnetic Recording Heads. The basic circuit of a magnetic pickup or cutting head is shown in Fig .12-17. The needle used in conjunction with a phonograph pickup, when traveling in the groove of a record, is caused to move from side to side because of the lateral-cut groove. An iron core is mounted in the center of the coil and also on a pivot so that it is free to move between two poles of a permanent magnet. A needle is mechanically coupled to this armature. In its normal position the needle is at point A and the top of the armature is at A'. When the needle moves to point B the top of the armature moves to B', and when the needle moves to C the top of the armature moves to C'. It can be seen that as the armature moves back and

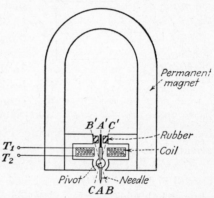

FIG. 12-17.—Magnetic pickup or recording head

forth the magnetic lines of force linking the coil are varied, thus causing an a-f voltage to be induced in the coil. The output from this coil is taken from terminals T_1 and T_2 and is fed into a speech amplifier.

When the magnetic unit is used in conjunction with a cutting head the a-f current from a speech amplifier is fed into the coil through terminals T_1 and T_2. The varying current flowing in the coil sets up a varying magnetic field that causes the armature to move from side to side. This movement of the armature also moves the cutting stylus, thus causing a lateral-cut groove to be made in the record. The undulations in the sides of the groove will thus be made in accordance with the frequency and amplitude variations of the a-f current.

The basic magnetic unit as described has a number of disadvantages. In order to provide the necessary damping, the top of the armature is embedded in a cushion of soft rubber. As rubber loses its resiliency in a comparatively short time, it must be replaced at frequent intervals.

The aging of the rubber also affects the frequency response and thus the response of a magnetic unit employing this type of construction will vary with its age. Because of its disadvantages, the basic magnetic unit is seldom used in the average pickup or recording head.

Three variations of the basic magnetic unit are the Cobra Tone Arm, Pickering pickup, and the Caltron pickup. These units are used for high-quality reproduction. In order to maintain the needle tangent to the record groove over the entire record, the mounting arm of the Cobra unit is designed with a special curve, while the Pickering unit uses an offset head. The mechanical construction of these units is such as to reduce the losses due to the impedance of the moving elements to a low value. In the Cobra unit this is accomplished by coupling the stylus to a nonmagnetic resistive vane by means of a compliant wire. In the Pickering unit a sapphire stylus is held in an aluminum mounting that is spun inside of a very light, rigid cylinder. The cylinder is suspended between the magnetic poles of the unit by means of a cantilever spring. In the Caltron unit a vibrating reed armature is used to reduce the mechanical losses.

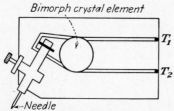

Fig. 12-18.—Crystal pickup or recording head.

Crystal Pickup and Crystal Recording Heads. The basic circuit of a crystal pickup or cutting head is shown in Fig. 12-18. When used as a phonograph pickup, the vibration of the needle in the record groove distorts the crystal element. Because of the piezoelectric effect, a voltage will be generated across the faces of the crystal. This voltage will vary with the amplitude and frequency at which the crystal is distorted. The a-f output of this unit is obtained from terminals T_1 and T_2 and is fed to a speech amplifier. When used in conjunction with a cutting head, the operation is reversed. The a-f output of a speech amplifier is applied across the faces of the crystal, thus causing the crystal to be distorted because of piezoelectric action. These distortions will then cause the stylus, to which it is mechanically coupled to cut a groove whose undulations conform to the variations in the amplitude and frequency of the a-f current. A Rochelle-salt crystal is generally used for this purpose.

Because the operation of a crystal unit depends on the piezoelectric effect of a crystal, its output is independent of the effects of mechanical inertia. Because of this feature the fidelity of a crystal unit is very high. The frequency response is quite uniform over a range of from 50 to 10,000 cycles. Another advantage of the crystal unit is that because of its light weight (approximately one ounce), record wear and background noise are almost eliminated. Because of these advantages the crystal unit is used extensively.

Scratch Filter. Surface noise or needle scratch is produced when the needle passes over the minute irregularities in the surface of the record groove. This surface noise can be reduced by use of a scratch filter. Where maximum fidelity is not important the level of the audible needle scratch can be practically eliminated by use of the scratch filter circuit shown in Fig. 12-19. The circuit is essentially a series resonant circuit with the values of L and C adjusted to resonate at the frequency of the scratch, which is approximately 5000 cycles. The degree of attenuation can be controlled by varying the rheostat R, which is connected in series with the resonant circuit.

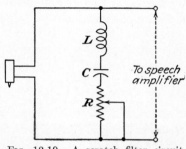

Fig. 12-19.—A scratch filter circuit.

12-14. Magnetic Sound Recorders and Reproducers. *Principles of the Magnetic Sound Recorder and Reproducer.* The magnetic wire recorder, commonly called a *sound-on-wire recorder,* is a comparatively new method of recording sound. The principle of operation of this method of recording is illustrated in Fig. 12-20. A single unit can be used as a recorder and also as a reproducer. To record, the sound impulse is changed to an electrical impulse by the microphone. This electrical impulse is strengthened by an amplifier and fed into a recording head, which consists of a coil wound on a soft-iron core that has a small air gap. The varying electrical impulse produces a pulsating magnetic field in the recording head. A thin unmagnetized wire is passed over the air gap. As the magnetic lines of force pass through the section of the recording wire that is over the air gap, a magnetic pattern of the sound fed into the microphone is induced in the wire (see Fig. 12-20a). When used as a reproducer, the above operations are reversed. As the magnetized wire passes over the air gap, a pulsating magnetic field is produced in the recording head. The pulsating lines of force cut the coil and thus induce electrical impulses in the coil. The electrical impulses are then strengthened by the amplifier and transformed into sound waves by a loudspeaker.

The wire used for this type of recorder is usually made of a medium carbon steel and is generally about four mils in diameter. The wire is wound on a spool about $3\frac{3}{4}$ inches in diameter and $1\frac{1}{4}$ inches wide. The spool holds approximately 11,000 feet of wire and provides about one hour of continuous recording.

Characteristics of the Magnetic Sound Recorder and Reproducer. As there is no wear on the wire in either the recording or the playback operation, it can be used almost indefinitely. If the wire should break the two ends can be knotted together and still be able to pass through the recording head. If the recording is no longer needed, the sounds impressed on the wire can be removed by passing it through a demagnetizing unit.

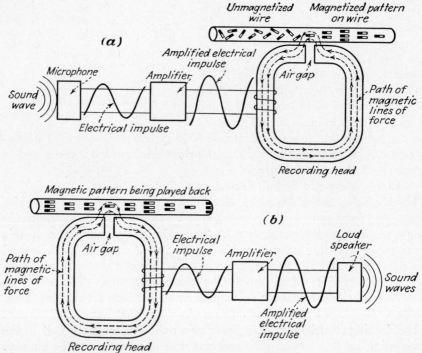

Fig. 12-20.—Schematic diagram of the operation of a magnetic sound recorder and reproducer. (a) Recording, (b) playback.

The wire can thus be reused many times. If it is so desired, portions of a recording can be removed and new recordings inserted.

Other important advantages of the magnetic wire recorder and reproducer are: (1) excellent fidelity can be obtained without elaborate precautions; (2) longer recording times; (3) it plays records in any position; (4) the practically indestructible and compact record simplifies storage and handling; (5) it provides instantaneous playback without processing; (6) it has a minimum of background noise; (7) it is affected very little by external vibrations and severe shock; (8) it is completely portable.

12-15. Sound Amplifiers. *Requirements of the Sound Amplifier.* Sound amplifiers are used to increase the voltage and current output of a

microphone, phonograph pickup, or radio receiver.   Since this amplifier
is used to increase the voltage and power of the a-f signals, the explanation
of the principles, operation, and characteristics of the a-f voltage and
power amplifiers described in Chaps. VIII and IX will also apply to sound
amplifiers.   Because of the number of different applications of the sound
amplifier, it is referred to by various names such as the microphone
amplifier, preamplifier, speech amplifier, phonograph amplifier, public-
address amplifier, etc.   The power output, frequency response, and distortion of a sound amplifier will depend upon its use.

Fig. 12-21.—A magnetic wire-recorder and playback unit.   (*Courtesy of General Electric
Company.*)

The purpose of the voltage amplifier is to increase the input voltage
to an amount high enough to operate a power amplifier that will produce
the desired amount of power output.   The power output of sound amplifiers used in public-address systems ranges from only a few watts to
several hundred watts.   The amount of power needed will depend upon
the area to be covered and whether it is to be used indoors or outdoors.
The driver voltage requirements of the power amplifier stage will determine the number of stages of voltage amplification that must be used.
The overall voltage amplification is equal to the product of the amplifications of each stage of voltage amplification used.   In order to reproduce
speech with a fair degree of fidelity, the variation in the overall gain of the
amplifier over a range of 100 to 4000 cycles should not exceed one decibel.

Because of the much wider frequency range required for the reproduction of music, the frequency response of an amplifier used for this purpose should be fairly uniform over a range of 50 to 8000 cycles.

Public-address Systems. A public-address unit is usually entirely self-contained. The complete unit consists of a power supply, voltage amplifier, power amplifier, microphone, and loudspeaker. As some public-address applications require that more than one microphone be used simultaneously, the input circuit of a public-address system is

Fig. 12-22.—A commercial 15-watt amplifier. (*Courtesy of Thordarson Electric Manufacturing Division Maguire Industries, Inc.*)

usually provided with more than one channel. Thus the input circuit may have one or more high-impedance channels for crystal, dynamic, or velocity microphones, and one or more high-impedance phonograph channels for crystal or magnetic pickups. Provision is also usually made for operating more than one pm dynamic or electrodynamic loudspeakers from the output circuit. In order to facilitate impedance matching to the voice coil, the output transformer is usually tapped at various voice-coil impedances such as 2, 4, 8, etc., ohms.

A public-address unit of a comparatively low power output is illustrated in Fig. 12-22 and its circuit diagram is shown in Fig. 12-23. The unit is entirely self-contained and operates from a 115-volt 60-cycle line. Full-wave rectification is obtained in the power supply by use of a duo-diode and a transformer having a center-tapped secondary. Three high-gain resistance-capacitance-coupled voltage amplifier stages are used to provide sufficient voltage to drive the grids of the power amplifier tubes. The power amplifier uses two beam power tubes operated as a Class A_1 push-pull amplifier. Inverse feedback is obtained by use of a separate

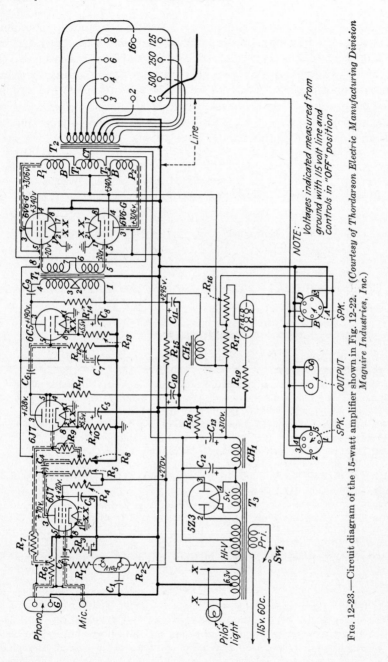

FIG. 12-23.—Circuit diagram of the 15-watt amplifier shown in Fig. 12-22. (Courtesy of Thordarson Electric Manufacturing Division Maguire Industries, Inc.)

NOTE:
Voltages indicated measured from ground with 115 volt line and controls in "OFF" position

winding on the output transformer. A high-impedance microphone channel and a high-impedance phonograph channel are provided with separate controls for each channel. A terminal board is provided with the necessary jumpers so that either two pm dynamic or two electro-dynamic loudspeakers may be used. The distortion of this amplifier when operating at full output is comparatively low, it being less than 5 per cent of the total output. This unit may be used as a voice amplifier in a small hall or for other similar applications.

Example 12-4. A microphone whose output is 60 db below 6 mw is feeding an amplifier that delivers 15 watts of undistorted output power. What is the overall gain from the microphone to the loudspeaker?

Given:　　　　　　　　　　　　　　　　Find:
　　Input = 60 db below 6 mw　　　　　　　Overall gain
　　P_o = 15 watts
Solution:

$$\text{db output} = 10 \log \frac{P_o}{P_r} = 10 \log \frac{15}{0.006} = 10 \log 2500 = 10 \times 3.3979 \cong 34 \text{ db}$$

Overall gain = db output − db input = 34 − (−60) = 94 db

BIBLIOGRAPHY

ALBERT, A. L., *Electrical Fundamentals of Communication*, McGraw-Hill Book Company, Inc., New York.

BUTLER, F. E., Techniques of Sound Recording, *Radio News*, November, 1943.

GOODELL, J. D., The Reproduction of Disc Recordings, *Radio News* (Radio-Electronic Engineering Edition), October, 1946.

HICKS, H. J., *Principles and Practice of Radio Servicing*, McGraw-Hill Book Company, Inc., New York.

Jensen Technical Monographs, Jensen Radio Manufacturing Company, Chicago, Ill.

MOODY, W., Microphones—How To Use Them, *Radio News*, January, 1943.

NILSON, A. R., and HORNUNG, J. L., *Practical Radio Communication*, McGraw-Hill Book Company, Inc., New York.

SEITZ, H. J., Meet the Microphone, *Radio News*, August, 1946.

SMITH, F. L., *The Radiotron Designer's Handbook*, The Wireless Press, Sydney, Australia; distributed in U.S.A. by RCA Manufacturing Company, Inc., Harrison, N. J.

TERMAN, F. E., *Fundamentals of Radio*, McGraw-Hill Book Company, Inc., New York.

QUESTIONS

1. What is the purpose of each of the following audio units: (*a*) the microphone? (*b*) The loudspeaker?   (*c*) The phonograph pickup?   (*d*) The magnetic reproducer?

2. Define (*a*) air-pressure-type microphone, (*b*) contact-type microphone.

3. Name and describe the applications of two types of air-pressure microphones.

4. Name and describe the applications of three types of contact microphones.

5. What are some of the advantages of contact-type microphones?

6. Which type of audio unit normally has a wider frequency response characteristic, a microphone as used at a transmitter or a loudspeaker as used with an average home receiver? Explain the reason for your answer.

7. What is meant by the sensitivity of a microphone?

8. (*a*) What is meant when it is stated that a microphone has a unidirectional frequency response characteristic? (*b*) Why is this type characteristic desirable in most types of microphone applications?

9. (*a*) What is meant by a cardioid or supercardioid type microphone? (*b*) What is the main advantage of this type of microphone?

10. (*a*) Why is it necessary to rate a microphone for some definite unit of pressure? (*b*) What is the unit of pressure most generally used?

11. (*a*) What does the term *bar* actually mean? (*b*) In rating microphones, what do many manufacturers consider the term *bar* to represent?

12. (*a*) What is meant by a low-impedance microphone? (*b*) Name three types of low-impedance microphones.

13. (*a*) What is meant by a high-impedance microphone? (*b*) Name two types of high-impedance microphones.

14. Is it possible to use a low-impedance microphone in a high-impedance speech amplifier circuit? Explain.

15. (*a*) How are low-impedance microphones usually rated? (*b*) Why is this type of rating used?

16. (*a*) What zero power reference level is usually used in the rating of low imped-ance microphones? (*b*) What zero reference pressure level is usually used?

17. (*a*) How are high-impedance microphones usually rated? (*b*) Explain the meaning of this rating. (*c*) Why is this type of rating used?

18. What method is used to couple the amplifier circuit to (*a*) a low-impedance microphone? (*b*) A high-impedance microphone?

19. How is maximum power transfer obtained between the microphone and ampli-fier circuit (*a*) with a low-impedance microphone? (*b*) With a high-impedance microphone?

20. Explain why the length of the line connecting the microphone to its amplifier circuit can be of any length with a low-impedance microphone but must be com-paratively short with high-impedance microphones?

21. Explain the principle of operation of a single button carbon microphone circuit.

22. Explain the principle of operation of a double-button carbon microphone circuit.

23. What are the advantages and disadvantages of the carbon microphone?

24. For what types of service are carbon microphones generally used?

25. Describe the construction and operation of a bimorph cell.

26. What material is generally used for constructing bimorph cells associated with microphones? Explain why this material is used.

27. What type of interstage coupling is used in amplifier circuits associated with crystal microphones? Explain.

28. (*a*) What are the advantages of crystal microphones? (*b*) For what types of service are crystal microphones generally used? (*c*) What precautions must be taken when using crystal microphones?

29. Describe the construction and principle of operation of the capacitor micro-phone.

30. (*a*) What are the disadvantages of the capacitor-type microphone? (*b*) For what type of service is the capacitor microphone generally used?

31. Describe the construction and principle of operation of the dynamic or mov-ing-coil type of microphone.

32. (*a*) What are the advantages of the dynamic-type microphone? (*b*) For what types of service are dynamic microphones generally used?

33. Describe the construction and principle of operation of the velocity- or ribbon-type microphone.

34. What are the advantages of the velocity-type microphone?

35. (*a*) Describe the construction and principle of operation of the horn-type magnetic loudspeaker. (*b*) Explain the limitation in output of this type of loudspeaker.

36. (*a*) Describe the construction and principle of operation of the cone-type magnetic loudspeaker. (*b*) Explain the main advantage of this type of loudspeaker.

37. Explain why it is not practical to use a magnetic loudspeaker for reproducing high values of audio-frequency currents.

38. (*a*) Describe the construction and principle of operation of the permanent-magnet dynamic loudspeaker. (*b*) Explain why it is not practical to use the pm dynamic loudspeakers for reproducing high values of audio-frequency currents.

39. Describe the construction and principle of operation of the electrodynamic loudspeaker.

40. (*a*) What are the advantages of the pm dynamic loudspeakers? (*b*) For what types of service are pm dynamic loudspeakers generally used? (*c*) How are pm dynamic loudspeakers usually rated?

41. Explain why it is necessary to use an output transformer to couple the power output stage of a radio receiver to a dynamic-type loudspeaker.

42. Explain three methods used to obtain the direct current required for the field windings of electrodynamic loudspeakers.

43. (*a*) What are the advantages of the electrodynamic-type loudspeaker? (*b*) How are electrodynamic loudspeakers usually rated? (*c*) For what types of service are electrodynamic loudspeakers generally used?

44. (*a*) What is the purpose of a horn as associated with loudspeakers? (*b*) How does the horn accomplish this purpose?

45. In horn-type loudspeakers what is meant by (*a*) the driver unit? (*b*) The throat? (*c*) The mouth?

46. How does the efficiency of transmission for the audio-frequency range of sounds vary for a horn with (*a*) a conical taper? (*b*) A parabolic taper? (*c*) An exponential taper? (*d*) A hyperbolic taper?

47. (*a*) How is sound recorded mechanically on disks? (*b*) What materials are used for making disks?

48. (*a*) What is meant by a vertical-cut record? (*b*) What is meant by a lateral-cut record? (*c*) Which of these two methods is most commonly used?

49. (*a*) What is the purpose of the stylus? (*b*) What materials are used in making a stylus?

50. Describe the construction and principle of operation of the basic magnetic pickup or recording head.

51. (*a*) What disadvantage is present in the basic magnetic unit? (*b*) Describe three variations of the basic magnetic unit that have been developed for high-quality reproduction.

52. (*a*) Describe the construction and principle of operation of a crystal pickup or recording head. (*b*) What are some of the advantages of the crystal unit?

53. (*a*) What is meant by surface noise? (*b*) Explain the action of the circuit used to minimize surface noise.

54. (*a*) Explain the principle of operation of a magnetic sound recorder and reproducer. (*b*) What are the advantages of the magnetic recorder and reproducer?

55. What are the requirements of a sound amplifier?

56. What basic units are required for a complete public-address system?

57. Why is it desirable for the input circuit of a public-address unit to have more than one channel?

58. What provision must be made when operating more than one loudspeaker from the output circuit of a sound amplifier system?

PROBLEMS

1. A certain single-button carbon microphone has an output power rating of 12 db below 6 mw for a 100-bar signal. What is the power output with an input signal of (*a*) 100 bars? (*b*) 10 bars? (*c*) 10 dynes per square centimeter? (*d*) 200 bars?

2. What is the power output of a carbon microphone with an input signal of 100 dynes per square centimeter if the output level rating of the microphone is 27 db below 6 mw for 10 dynes per square centimeter pressure?

3. If the microphone of Prob. 2 has a voltage rating of 50 db below 1 volt per bar, what is the output voltage with a pressure of 100 dynes per square centimeter?

4. What is the power output of a double-button carbon microphone whose output level rating is 55 db below 6 mw for a 10-bar speech signal when the input signal is (*a*) 10 bars? (*b*) 100 bars?

5. What is the power output of a low-impedance (250 ohms) dynamic-type microphone whose output level rating is 63.8 db below 6 mw, when feeding into a 250-ohm impedance, for a 10-bar signal when the input signal is (*a*) 10 bars? (*b*) 50 bars?

6. A certain dynamic-type microphone has a self-contained transformer, which increases its output impedance to 35,000 ohms. If its output level rating is 55 db below 1 volt per bar what is the output voltage for (*a*) a 10-bar signal? (*b*) A 100-bar signal?

7. (*a*) A certain low-impedance (50 ohms) dynamic-type microphone has a voltage output level rating of 86 db below 1 volt per bar. What is the output voltage for a 1-bar signal? (*b*) When the same microphone is equipped with a transformer that raises the impedance at its output terminals to 38,000 ohms, the voltage output level is 54 db below 1 volt per bar. What is the output voltage for a 1-bar signal?

8. What is the output voltage of a velocity-type microphone equipped with a transformer that produces an output impedance of 35,000 ohms and then has a voltage output level rating of 65 db below 1 volt per bar, for an input signal of (*a*) 1 bar? (*b*) 10 bars?

9. What is the voltage output of a crystal-type microphone that has a voltage output level rating of 48 db below 1 volt per bar for an input signal of (*a*) 1 bar? (*b*) 10 bars?

10. A certain crystal-type microphone has a voltage output level rating of 58 db below 1 volt per bar at the microphone terminals and 61.5 db below 1 volt per bar at the end of a 25-foot cable. For an input signal of 10 bars, find (*a*) the output voltage at the microphone terminals, (*b*) the output voltage at the end of the 25-foot cable, (*c*) the voltage drop in the cable, (*d*) the per cent of voltage loss in the cable.

11. The output level (in decibels below 1 volt per bar) at the terminals of the cable for a certain crystal microphone is given for various lengths of cable in the following table. Prepare a table showing the output voltage and the per cent of voltage available for the various cable lengths listed, using the output with a 7-foot cable as 100 per cent.

Cable Length, Feet	Output Level, Decibels
7	−53
25	−55
50	−58
75	−60
100	−61.5
150	−64
200	−66

12. The output level (in decibels below 1 volt per bar open circuit) at the terminals of the cable for a certain dynamic microphone with an impedance of 50 ohms is given for various lengths of cable in the following table. Prepare a table showing the output voltage and the per cent of voltage available for the various cable lengths listed, using the output with a 25-foot cable as 100 per cent.

Cable Length, Feet	Output Level, Decibels
25	−83
250	−83.5
500	−84
1000	−85
2000	−86.5

13. What turns ratio is required of a transformer used to couple a single-button carbon microphone whose impedance is 100 ohms to a grid circuit whose input impedance should be 60,000 ohms?

14. A certain transformer designed for coupling the output of a dynamic microphone to the grid circuit of a tube provides a choice of 7.5 ohms or 30 ohms primary impedance and 50,000 ohms secondary impedance. What is the turns ratio for (*a*) the 7.5/50,000-ohm connection? (*b*) The 30/50,000-ohm connection?

15. A microphone transformer used for matching the output of a crystal microphone to its connecting cable has a number of secondary terminals so that it can be operated with lines of various values of impedance. The rated primary impedance is 100,000 ohms and the secondary is rated at 50, 200, and 500 ohms. What is the turns ratio for (*a*) the 100,000/50-ohm connection? (*b*) The 100,000/200-ohm connection? (*c*) The 100,000/500-ohm connection?

16. The microphone transformer used to couple a certain velocity-type microphone to its line has an impedance ratio of 0.2/500 ohms. What is its turns ratio?

17. A general-purpose transformer designed for matching low-impedance sources to a grid circuit has an impedance ratio of 200/50 ohms primary to 500,000 ohms secondary. What is the turns ratio for (*a*) 200/500,000 ohms? (*b*) 50/500,000 ohms?

18. A general-purpose output transformer that can be used to match the output of the average output tube of a small radio receiver to a line or to a voice coil of the loudspeaker has a primary impedance of 5000 ohms and by choice of terminals secondary impedance values of 500, 200, 50, 15, 8, 5, 3, and 1.5 ohms can be obtained. What is the turns ratio for each of these impedance ratios?

19. (*a*) If the scratch filter circuit of Fig. 12-19 uses a 160-mh choke, what value of capacitance should be used to make the filter most effective for 5000-cycle currents? (*b*) What is the impedance of the filter circuit to 5000-cycle currents if the value of the resistance is 100 ohms? (*c*) What is the impedance to 3000-cycle currents for the same circuit values as in (*b*)?   (*d*) What is the impedance to 7000-cycle currents for the same circuit values as in (*b*)?

20. (*a*) If the scratch filter circuit of Fig. 12-19 uses a 220-mh choke, what value of capacitance should be used to make the filter most effective for 5000-cycle currents? (*b*) What is the impedance of the filter circuit to 5000-cycle currents if the value of the resistance is 100 ohms?   (*c*) What is the impedance to 3000-cycle currents for the same circuit values as in (*b*)?   (*d*) What is the impedance to 7000-cycle currents for the same circuit values as in (*b*)?

21. A public-address sound system that is capable of delivering 35 watts of undistorted output power is being used with a microphone whose power output level rating is 72 db below 6 mw.   What is the overall decibel gain from the microphone to the loudspeaker when the system is delivering its rated output of 35 watts?

22. A 20-watt public-address sound system is being used with a microphone rated at 65 db below 6 mw.   What is the minimum overall gain that the system should be capable of delivering?

23. A certain public-address sound system is rated to produce an output of 15 watts.   The gain of the system for the microphone input channel is 113 db and for the phono input channel it is 72 db.   (*a*) What is the minimum output that the microphone may supply in order to produce the rated output?   (*b*) What is the minimum output that the phonograph pickup unit must supply in order to produce the rated output?

CHAPTER XIII

TRANSMITTING CIRCUITS

The purpose of a radio transmitter is to produce and send out into space radio-frequency energy. Any of the oscillator circuits described in Chap. X may be used to generate a steady high-frequency current. This steady current is commonly called the *carrier wave* or simply the *carrier*. The steady r-f current does not contain any signal and hence the information to be transmitted must be added to it. The process of adding the signal to the carrier wave is referred to as *modulation*. The modulation or control of a carrier wave can be accomplished by mechanical means, as in a radio telegraph transmitter, by means of sound, as in a radio telephone, or by visual images as in television.

An antenna is used to send out the modulated r-f energy over large distances. This is accomplished by feeding the energy to be transmitted into the antenna circuit. The high-frequency current flowing in the antenna circuit sets up magnetic and electric fields about it. Because alternating current is used, these two fields are constantly being pushed away from the antenna, thus causing the energy to be radiated into space.

The essential parts of a simple transmitting circuit are (1) an oscillator to produce the carrier wave, (2) a modulating device to control the output signal, (3) an antenna to radiate the output signal into space.

13-1. Types of Broadcasting Systems. *Need of a Carrier Wave.* Theoretically, electromagnetic fields can be produced and radiated into space by feeding an a-f signal current directly into the antenna. There are, however, two considerations that make this impractical. First, the amount of energy required for transmission over any reasonable distance would be prohibitive. This may be seen from the statement that the energy radiated for a given amount of power input varies directly as some power of the frequency. As the power rating of broadcast transmitters operating at frequencies around one million cycles (1000 kc) generally is from $\frac{1}{4}$ to 50 kilowatts, it becomes evident that in order to radiate an equal amount of energy at a frequency of 100 cycles a tremendous amount of power would be required. Second, if sufficient power was available to transmit at the audio frequencies, all broadcasting stations' signals would interfere with each other therefore only one station could be operated at a time. The use of high-frequency carrier waves eliminates both of these handicaps.

Types of Waves. The following definitions are from the IRE Standards. The term *signal* is defined as the form or variation with time of a wave whereby the information, message, or effect is conveyed in communication. A *signal wave* is a wave the form of which conveys a signal. A *carrier wave* is the unmodulated component of a signal wave. A *modulated wave* is a wave of which either the amplitude, frequency, or phase is varied in accordance with a signal. A *side band* is a band of frequencies on either side of the carrier frequency, produced by the process of modulation.

Modulation. The carrier wave of a radio transmitting system is a wave of constant value of frequency and amplitude. The carrier wave by itself will not produce any sound at the loudspeaker of the ordinary broadcast receiver. The transmission of intelligence occurs when the carrier wave is modulated by a signal. The IRE definition of modulation states that *modulation* is the process by which some characteristic of a periodic wave is varied with time in accordance with a signal. Modulation is generally accomplished by combining a signal and a carrier wave. The signal is also referred to as a *modulating wave* and the resultant wave is called the *modulated wave* (see Figs. 13-1, 13-2, 13-4, and 13-5).

Although many methods of modulation can be devised, the only ones of practical value at present are amplitude modulation, frequency modulation, and phase modulation. Of these, only amplitude modulation and frequency modulation are used in radio broadcast transmission.

Mathematically, a carrier wave may be considered as

$$e = E_m \sin (2\pi ft + \theta) \qquad (13\text{-}1)$$

From Eq. (13-1) it can be seen that the wave form can be varied by three factors, namely, E_m, f, and θ. *Amplitude modulation* occurs when modulation is obtained by varying only the voltage E_m. *Frequency modulation* occurs when modulation is obtained by varying only the frequency f. *Phase modulation*, which is very similar to frequency modulation, occurs when modulation is obtained by varying only the phase relationship represented by θ. The types of broadcasting systems in present use are thus classified as either amplitude modulated, abbreviated a-m, or frequency modulated, abbreviated f-m.

13-2. Amplitude Modulation. *Amplitude-modulated Wave.* An amplitude-modulated wave is defined by the IRE standards as one whose envelope contains a component similar to the wave form of the signal to be transmitted. In amplitude modulation the amplitude of the carrier wave is varied by the strength of the signal, which is the modulating quantity. The effect of amplitude modulation can be seen from a study of Fig. 13-1. Figure 13-1a represents a high-frequency carrier wave of constant amplitude and frequency.   The wave of Fig. 13-1*b* represents an audio-frequency signal of sine-wave form; the sine-wave form is used here to show the effect of modulation more clearly.   (The effect of voice modulation is illustrated in Fig. 13-2.)   Figure 13-1*c* shows the result obtained by modulating the carrier wave (*a*) with the modulating wave

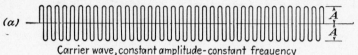

(a)

Carrier wave, constant amplitude-constant frequency

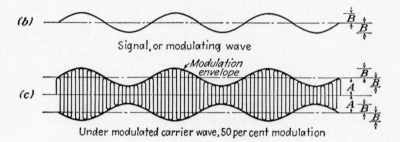

(b)

Signal, or modulating wave

(c)

Under modulated carrier wave, 50 per cent modulation

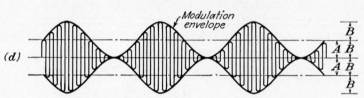

(d)

Fully modulated carrier wave, 100 per cent modulation

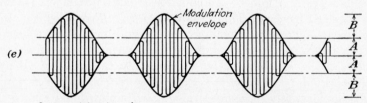

(e)

Over modulated carrier wave, modulation exceeding 100 per cent

Fig. 13-1.—Wave shapes of a carrier wave that is amplitude-modulated by a sine-wave signal.

(*b*).   Further examination of Fig. 13-1*c* will show that the outline of the modulated carrier-wave is similar in form to the modulating wave; accordingly, this outline is commonly called the *modulation envelope*.

Per Cent of Modulation.   In amplitude modulation it is common practice to refer to the per cent of modulation, usually designated as *M*. Actually this is a means of expressing the degree to which the signal

modulates the carrier wave.   The per cent of modulation is proportional
to the ratio of the maximum values of the signal and carrier waves, or

$$M = \frac{\text{maximum value of signal}}{\text{maximum value of carrier}} \times 100 \qquad (13\text{-}2)$$

This may be expressed in terms of Fig. 13-1 as

$$M = \frac{B}{A} \times 100 \qquad (13\text{-}3)$$

where M = per cent of modulation
   B = maximum value of the modulating wave, volts
   A = maximum value of the carrier wave, volts
The effect of different amounts of modulation upon the carrier wave is
shown by the various illustrations in Fig. 13-1.   As the maximum undis-

(a)
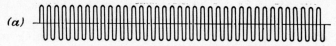

Carrier wave, constant amplitude-constant frequency

(b)
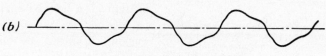

Voice signal, or modulating wave

(c)
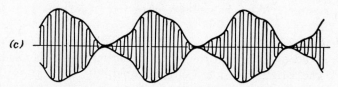

Modulated carrier wave, 100 per cent modulation at signal peaks

FIG. 13-2.—Wave shapes of a carrier wave that is amplitude-modulated by a voice signal.

torted power output of a transmitter is obtained with 100 per cent
modulation, it is generally desirable to operate with such a fully modulated carrier wave.   If the modulation is less than 100 per cent, the power
output is reduced, even though the power of the carrier wave has not been
reduced.   If the modulation exceeds 100 per cent, the output of the
transmitter will be a distorted version of the original modulating wave.

   Side Bands.   During the process of modulation a heterodyne action
(see Art. 5-7) takes place and as a result two additional frequencies

appear. These new frequencies are the result of the heterodyning action and are beat frequencies whose values are equal to the sum and difference of the carrier frequency and the modulating frequency. The value of frequency equal to the sum of the carrier and modulating frequencies is called the *upper side frequency*, and the value equal to the difference of the carrier and modulating frequencies is called the *lower side frequency*.

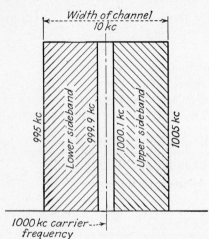

FIG. 13-3.—Illustration of the side bands and the channel width for a 1000-kc carrier wave that is being amplitude-modulated by audio frequencies ranging from 100 to 5000 cycles.

In radio broadcasting the modulating frequency varies continually and over a considerable range. Accordingly, the single value of upper side frequency referred to above is replaced by a band of frequencies, called the *upper side band*, whose width is equal to the difference between the maximum and minimum values of the modulating frequencies. Likewise, the single value of lower side frequency will be replaced by a *lower side band*. For example, if a 1000-kc carrier wave is modulated by audio signals varying between 100 and 5000 cycles, the maximum upper side frequency is 1005 kc and the minimum lower side frequency is 995 kc. Under this condition, the transmitter requires a 10-kc channel extending from 995 to 1005 kc (see Fig. 13-3).

The mathematical explanation of side-band frequencies can be derived from the fundamental equations of the carrier wave and the modulating signal. The carrier wave may be represented by

$$e_c = E_{c \cdot m} \sin 2\pi f_c t \tag{13-4}$$

and the signal may be represented by

$$e_s = m E_{c \cdot m} \sin 2\pi f_s t \tag{13-5}$$

When the carrier wave is being modulated by a sine-wave signal of constant frequency and f_c is large compared to f_s, the modulation envelope may be represented by

$$e_{m \cdot e} = E_{c \cdot m}(1 + m \sin 2\pi f_s t) \sin 2\pi f_c t \tag{13-6}$$

where $e_{m \cdot e}$ = instantaneous value of the modulation envelope

$E_{c \cdot m}$ = maximum value of the carrier wave

m = modulation factor = $\dfrac{M}{100}$

f_s = frequency of the modulating signal

f_c = frequency of the carrier wave

Expanding Eq. (13-6) produces

$$e_{m \cdot e} = E_{c \cdot m} \sin 2\pi f_c t + m E_{c \cdot m} \sin 2\pi f_c t \sin 2\pi f_s t \qquad (13\text{-}6a)$$

From trigonometry

$$\sin 2\pi f_c t \sin 2\pi f_s t = \tfrac{1}{2} \cos (2\pi f_c t - 2\pi f_s t) - \tfrac{1}{2} \cos (2\pi f_c t + 2\pi f_s t) \qquad (13\text{-}7)$$

Substituting Eq. (13-7) in (13-6a) and rearranging terms

$$e_{m \cdot e} = E_{c \cdot m} \sin 2\pi f_c t + \frac{m E_{c \cdot m}}{2} \cos 2\pi (f_c - f_s)t - \frac{m E_{c \cdot m}}{2}$$
$$\cos 2\pi (f_c + f_s)t \qquad (13\text{-}8)$$

Equations (13-8) indicates the existence of three distinct frequencies, namely, the carrier frequency f_c, the lower side band $(f_c - f_s)$, and the upper side band $(f_c + f_s)$. This leads to the conclusion that amplitude

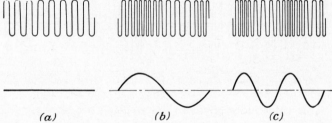

(a)   (b)   (c)

Fig. 13-4.—Wave shapes of a carrier wave that is frequency-modulated by a sine-wave signal. (a) No modulating signal, (b) 500-cycle modulating signal, (c) 1000-cycle modulating signal.

modulation adds side-band frequencies above and below the carrier frequency. However, for convenience of illustration it is common practice to show the combined wave form of the carrier and its side bands as indicated by Figs. 13-1c, d, e, and 13-2c.

13-3. Frequency Modulation. *Frequency-modulated Wave.* In frequency modulation, the amplitude of the modulated wave is maintained at a constant strength, namely, the same value as the unmodulated carrier wave. The frequency of the modulated wave is varied in proportion to the amplitude of the modulating signal, and at a rate determined by the frequency of the modulating signal. This is illustrated by Figs. 13-4 and 13-5. From Fig. 13-4 it can be seen that the frequency of the modulated wave increases as the signal voltage increases and that it decreases as the signal voltage decreases. Comparison of Figs. 13-4*b* and 13-4*c* shows that the variation in frequency is determined only by the amplitude of the signal and that the rate of variations in frequency is determined by the frequency of the signal. Figure 13-5 is another method of illustrating the effect of the amplitude of the signal upon the frequency of the modulated wave.

Frequency Deviation. The frequency of an f-m transmitter without any signal input is referred to as the *resting frequency* or the *center fre-*

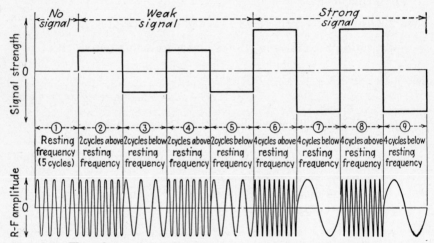

FIG. 13-5.—Wave shapes of a carrier wave that is frequency-modulated by square-wave signal voltages. (*From N. M. Cooke and J. Markus, Electronics Dictionary.*)

quency. This value corresponds to the assigned frequency of the transmitter. When a signal is applied, the variation in frequency either above or below the resting frequency is called the *frequency deviation*, and the total variation in frequency is called the *carrier swing*. For example, in Fig. 13-5 the resting frequency is 5 cycles, the deviation for the weak signal is 2 cycles, and the carrier swing is 4 cycles. With the strong signal, the deviation is 4 cycles and the carrier swing is 8 cycles. It should be realized that the values of frequency used in Fig. 13-5 are not practical values; they have been made of very low values for convenience of illustration. Actually, f-m broadcast transmitters operate at higher frequencies than a-m broadcast transmitters. They were originally assigned frequencies of from 42 to 50 mc, but have since been changed to frequencies of from 88 to 106 mc.

Modulation. In a-m systems the per cent of modulation expresses the degree to which the amplitude of the signal modulates the carrier.

With f-m systems, the amplitude of the carrier remains constant, hence some other means must be used to express the degree of modulation. Because the amplitude of the signal produces a variation in the frequency of the modulated carrier, the degree of modulation is expressed in terms of the frequency deviation. A frequency deviation of 75 kc is now considered equivalent to 100 per cent modulation in the a-m system. Under this condition, the total carrier swing will be 150 kc. To avoid possible interference between stations on adjacent channels, the assigned frequencies are at least 200 kc apart, thereby allowing an ample safety zone.

The frequency deviation is sometimes expressed in terms of the ratio of maximum frequency deviation to the maximum audio frequency being transmitted; this is commonly referred to as the *deviation ratio*. For example, if an f-m transmitter operates with a maximum frequency deviation of 75 kc and reproduces audio signals up to 15 kc, its deviation ratio is 5.

Side Bands. Side bands are also present in f-m transmission. From the foregoing discussion it can be seen that the side-band frequencies are determined by the amplitude of the modulating signal. While the sideband frequencies are apparently unlimited, present f-m transmission is based on a 75-kc frequency deviation. For example, with a given signal frequency the frequency deviation, and hence the number of side bands, is dependent upon the amplitude of the signal. If the value of the deviation ratio is approximately 5, the side bands above the

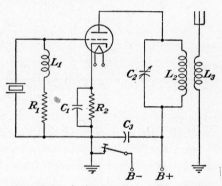

FIG. 13-6.—A simple transmitting circuit.

maximum frequency are so small that they may be ignored. Under this condition, the channel width for f-m transmission should be approximately double the value of the maximum frequency deviation. On this basis, it can be seen that a 150-kc carrier swing can reproduce a-f signals up to 15,000 cycles.

13-4. Transmitter Requirements. *The Oscillator as a Transmitter.* A simple transmitter can be made by coupling the output of an oscillator circuit directly to the antenna. The output of this simple transmitter can be controlled by connecting a key in the B power supply circuit as shown in Fig. 13-6. As the plate supply voltage is interrupted when the key is open, the circuit will oscillate only as long as the key is kept closed. Thus by the proper operation of the key, it is possible to control the continuous wave output in accordance with a prearranged code. This circuit can be used for radio telegraphy. In this method of communication the key reduces the c-w output to zero when its contacts are open, and permits the full power output to reach the antenna when the contacts are closed.

In the transmitter circuit shown in Fig. 13-6 the plate power supply is interrupted and hence this method of control is called *plate-supply keying*. The method of keying shown in Fig. 13-6 is seldom used because of the high voltage at the key and its potential danger to the operator. Two

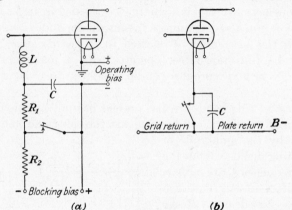

(a) (b)

Fig. 13-7.—Methods of obtaining low-voltage keying. (a) Blocked-grid keying, (b) cathode keying.

systems of keying generally used are the *blocked-grid* and the *cathode* methods. In each of these methods a comparatively low value of voltage is interrupted. Grid-blocked keying is accomplished by applying a suitable amount of negative voltage to the control grid when the key is opened (see Fig. 13-7a). This voltage is called the *blocking bias* and should be high enough to cut off completely the plate current flow. Closing the key disconnects the blocking bias from the circuit, leaving only the operating bias in the grid circuit. Cathode keying is accomplished by connecting the key in the cathode circuit so that both the grid and plate circuits are opened at the same time (see Fig. 13-7b).

The Oscillator as a Frequency Controlling Device. Because a crystal is capable of handling only a small amount of current the simple crystal-controlled-oscillator transmitter can be used for delivering only a relatively small amount of power output. A larger power output can be obtained by using a self-controlled oscillator. However, this method is also unsatisfactory, as very little power can be taken directly from the oscillator without producing instability of the frequency and amplitude of its output curreut. A more satisfactory method is to feed the low power output from the oscillator to the input circuit of an r-f amplifier. The output of the amplifier may then be fed directly to the antenna or to the input circuit of an additional r-f amplifier. In this type of transmitter the oscillator is used only as a frequency controlling element, the desired power output being obtained from the r-f amplifiers. A number of amplifier stages can be used and thus with this method of producing r-f power it is possible to obtain outputs of thousands of watts. The combination of the oscillator and its successive r-f amplifiers is usually referred to as the *master oscillator power amplifier* and is generally abbreviated as MOPA or mopa.

Dynamic instability caused by variations in the antenna load is greatly reduced by use of the master oscillator power amplifier. Since the antenna is coupled directly to the r-f power amplifier, any change in capacitance between the antenna and ground will only affect the resonance conditions between these two circuits. The effects of this difference in resonance is very small and can usually be ignored. The r-f amplifier, in addition to increasing the r-f power output, also serves to isolate the oscillator circuit from the output load of the transmitter. Because of this action it is called a *buffer amplifier*. In a transmitter circuit employing more than one stage of r-f amplification the only stage called a buffer amplifier is the one that is coupled directly to the oscillator. This stage of amplification is usually a voltage amplifier and serves to isolate the oscillator from the effects of any variations in the succeeding r-f power amplifiers.

The frequency stability requirement of transmitters is very high, hence it has become common practice to use a crystal-controlled oscillator as the master frequency control. However, a crystal-controlled oscillator can be used only for producing medium radio frequencies because of the physical limitations of the crystal. In order to produce r-f outputs above 10 mc it is desirable to use frequency multiplication (see Art. 10-13).

Block Diagram of an Amplitude-modulated Transmitter. A transmitter may be considered as an assembly of such components that will produce a modulated output of the desired frequency and power. The type and number of components that are required will depend upon the desired frequency and power output. This can be seen by a study of the block diagrams of the radio transmitters shown in Fig. 13-8. Transmitters with a low power output and medium radio frequencies require only a few components of comparatively small size. The r-f portion of such a transmitter consists of a crystal-controlled oscillator, a buffer amplifier, and a power amplifier. The crystal-controlled oscillator produces an alternating current of the required carrier frequency value.

The power output of the oscillator is increased by the buffer amplifier to the value required to drive the power amplifier. The r-f amplifier produces the desired power output. The a-f portion of the transmitter consists of a microphone, a speech amplifier, and a modulator. The low voltage output of the microphone is increased by the speech amplifier to a value that is high enough to drive the modulator. The modulator is the last stage of the a-f amplifier and produces the a-f output required to obtain 100 per cent modulation. The output of the modulator is fed into

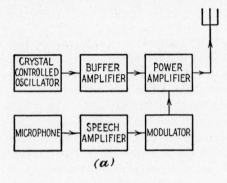

(a)

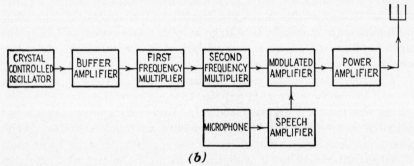

(b)

Fig. 13-8.—Block diagrams of an amplitude-modulated transmitter. (a) Radiotelephone transmitter for medium frequencies, (b) radiotelephone transmitter for high frequencies.

the r-f power amplifier, which also serves as a modulating amplifier. The *modulating amplifier* is a linear r-f amplifier of the carrier frequency and is the stage in which the modulation actually occurs.

In order to produce a radio frequency output greater than 10 mc, one or more stages of frequency multiplication are generally used. In addition to producing a multiple of its input frequency the frequency multiplier also serves as an r-f amplifier.

In order to produce a high power output a push-pull r-f amplifier or several stages of single-tube amplification may be used. The r-f amplifier section that precedes the power amplifier is usually referred to as the *exciter*.

The number and also the operating characteristics of the amplifier units in the exciter are determined by the power required to drive the power amplifier tube. The calculation of the amount of power required to drive a power amplifier tube efficiently is a rather complex procedure. For practical purposes the driving power is generally assumed to be approximately 10 per cent of the required amplifier tube power output.

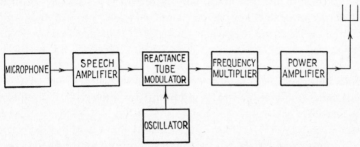

Fig. 13-9.—Block diagram of a frequency-modulated transmitter.

Block Diagram of a Frequency-modulated Transmitter. The type and number of components used in an f-m transmitter depends upon the system of modulation employed, the power output required, and the method used to stabilize the carrier or resting frequency. A block diagram of an f-m transmitter using the reactance tube system of modulation is shown in Fig. 13-9. The reactance tube modulator combines the outputs of the oscillator and speech amplifier to produce a frequency-modulated output. The modulator operates at a fraction of the transmitter frequency, hence a frequency multiplier is used to obtain the desired operating frequency. The output of the frequency multiplier drives the power amplifier, which in turn produces the desired power output.

Transmitter Components. It can be seen from the description of the block diagrams of the a-m and f-m transmitters that most of the components are some form of either oscillator or amplifier circuits. A power supply, although not shown on the block diagrams, is also required to provide the necessary operating voltages for the tubes. The characteristics and operating principles of all the components with the exception of the r-f power amplifier (see Art. 13-5) have been presented in detail in the previous chapters of this text.

13-5. Radio-frequency Power Amplifier Circuits. *Class C Operation.* Because of the relatively large amount of power required by a radio transmitter it is desirable that the overall efficiency of the unit be as high as it is practicable to obtain. A Class C amplifier operates with a grid bias that is greater than the value required to produce cutoff (see Fig.

7-1). The plate current flows for appreciably less than one-half of each input cycle and is zero for the remainder of the cycle. The efficiency for Class C operation of amplifiers is therefore higher than for either Class A or Class B operation. It is possible to design a Class C amplifier having an efficiency of 75 per cent as compared to approximately 25 per cent for Class A operation. Because of this high efficiency, r-f power amplifiers as used with transmitters are generally operated Class C. In order to obtain maximum efficiency the relation between the grid bias and the peak value of the input signal should be such that positive plate current saturation will occur during a portion of each positive half of the input cycle. An approximate value of the grid bias required to produce maximum efficiency can be obtained by adding 25 to 50 per cent of the peak value of the input voltage to the minimum value of grid bias required to produce cutoff.

Class C Amplifier Circuits. Since current flows in the plate circuit of a Class C amplifier for only a portion of each input cycle, and also because the grid of a Class C amplifier tube used for r-f power amplification in a transmitter is driven positive during a portion of each input cycle, the output current for this type of amplification will be distorted. In transmitting circuits the r-f amplifier operates at a fixed frequency with a tuned circuit as the plate circuit load (see Figs. 13-10 to 13-14). When the plate circuit is tuned to the frequency of the input signal applied to the grid circuit of the tube, the amplifier may be operated as Class C without producing distortion. Because of the properties of parallel resonant circuits (see Art. 10-8), the r-f circulating current in the plate tank circuit will have an undistorted wave form.

Since the tank circuit is tuned to the same frequency as the input signal applied to the grid, the plate load will be resistive and thus the plate current will be maximum when the plate voltage is at a minimum. The plate dissipation of the tube will also be low which is another reason for the high efficiency of Class C amplifiers.

Radio-frequency Amplifier Tubes. The low power output vacuum tube designed for radio receiver application can also be operated as a Class C r-f power amplifier when the output required is only a few watts. When larger amounts of power are required vacuum tubes having a larger power output must be used. The amount of power that a tube can deliver is determined by (1) the electron emission of the cathode, (2) the amount of voltage that can safely be applied to the plate, (3) the amount of power that can be dissipated within the tube without overheating. In order to obtain the large amount of electron emission required for r-f power tubes, a correspondingly larger cathode is used. Ample insulation must be provided between the tube's electrodes so that a high plate voltage can be applied.   To provide for ample power dissipation of air-cooled vacuum tubes, the size of the glass envelope and the plate electrodes are increased correspondingly.   When the power output required is very large, vacuum tubes are constructed to permit the circulation of water around the plate during operation of the tube.   Transmitting tubes can be obtained in various sizes capable of delivering an output power of one watt to hundreds of watts.

13-6. Methods of Producing Amplitude Modulation. *Types of Modulation.*   The process of modulation, that is, changing the wave form of the carrier by adding the signal to it, is accomplished by means of vacuum-tube circuits.   There are several methods of using a vacuum tube and its associated circuits to produce amplitude modulation.   In the method most generally used the modulating signal is applied to the plate circuit of an r-f amplifier tube; this method is called *plate modulation*. Another method is to apply the modulating signal to the control grid circuit of an r-f amplifier tube; this method is called *grid modulation*.   In still another method the modulating signal is applied simultaneously to both the control grid and plate circuits of an r-f amplifier tube, thereby varying the cathode current; this method is called *cathode modulation.*

Low-and High-level Modulation.   Modulation may be accomplished in any stage of the r-f amplifier system.   The methods of modulation may therefore be further classified according to the level of the modulating signal used, namely, *low-level* and *high-level* modulation.

In low-level modulation the modulating signal is added to the carrier wave in one of the low-power r-f amplifier stages.   The main advantage of this system of modulation is that very little a-f power is required.   The a-f amplifier may therefore consist of only a few stages of low-level amplification.   A disadvantage of this system of modulation is that in order to avoid distortion of the modulated signal all stages of amplification following the modulating amplifier must be linear.   As high efficiencies are usually not obtained from linear amplifiers, the efficiency of a transmitter using low-level modulation is comparatively low.

In high-level modulation the modulating signal is added to the carrier wave in the final r-f amplifier stage.   The main advantage of this system of modulation is that the r-f amplifiers preceding the modulating amplifier do not have to be linear.   Since high-gain amplifiers can be used in each r-f stage of amplification in this system of modulation, the efficiency of a transmitter using high-level modulation is comparatively high.   A disadvantage of this system of modulation is that high a-f power is required and a number of stages of a-f amplification must be used.

Grid Modulation.   In this method of modulation the output of an a-f amplifier is used to vary the grid bias of an r-f Class C amplifier, thus causing the r-f output to be modulated in accordance with the a-f signal. Because modulation is accomplished by varying the grid bias of a tube, this method is also called *grid-bias modulation*.

A circuit for producing grid modulation is shown in Fig. 13-10. The r-f excitation voltage is coupled to the grid of the modulated amplifier tube VT_1 by means of the transformer T_1. The a-f signal output from the modulator tube VT_2 is coupled to the grid of VT_1, in series with the operating bias of the C battery, by means of transformer T_3. Capacitor

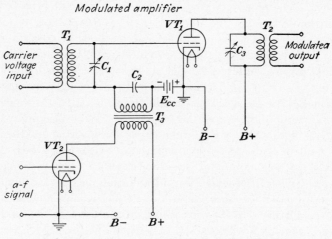

Fig. 13-10.—Basic circuit for obtaining grid modulation.

C_2 is used to keep the r-f excitation voltage out of the a-f circuit. The modulated output is coupled to the next amplifier stage or to the antenna by means of transformer T_2.

An advantage of grid modulation is that only a small amount of power is required to modulate the carrier wave of a transmitter having a comparatively high power output.

Plate Modulation. In this method of modulation the output of an a-f amplifier is applied to the plate of an r-f amplifier tube, thus causing the r-f output to be modulated in accordance with the a-f signal. Because modulation is accomplished by varying the plate voltage of a tube this method is called *plate modulation*.

There are various methods of obtaining plate modulation. One method commonly used is the Heising system. The basic circuit diagram for this system of modulation is shown in Fig. 13-11. The r-f carrier signal is applied to grid of the modulated amplifier tube VT_1, and the a-f output from the modulator tube VT_2 is coupled to the plate of VT_1 by means of the a-f choke coil L_4. The blocking capacitor C_1 is used to prevent the plate supply from being short-circuited.   The r-f choke L_1 isolates the r-f signal from the plate supply.   Resistor R_1 serves as a voltage-dropping resistor so that the modulated amplifier tube will operate at a lower plate voltage than the modulator tube.   Capacitor C_3, which is shunted across the plate voltage-dropping resistor, provides a path for the a-f variations in current.   Without this capacitor a large portion of the a-f signal voltage would be absorbed by the plate voltage-dropping resistor, thus producing distortion.   Capacitor C_2 and the

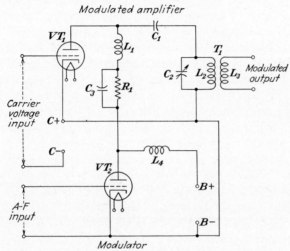

FIG. 13-11.—Basic circuit for obtaining plate modulation.

primary winding L_2 of the output transformer T_1 form the tank circuit, which is tuned to the carrier frequency.

The operation of this circuit is explained in the following manner. Both the modulator and the r-f amplifier tubes receive their plate supply voltage from a common source of power.   With zero a-f signal, the r-f voltage applied to the grid of VT_1 causes an r-f current to circulate in the plate tank circuit C_2L_2.   When an a-f signal is applied to the grid of VT_2 the plate current of this tube will increase and decrease in accordance with the input signal.   However, the high inductance of the a-f choke coil L_4 opposes any change in the amount of the current flowing through it and hence tends to keep the amount of current drawn from the B power supply at a constant value.   Because of the action of the a-f choke coil this system of modulation is also referred to as the *constant current system*. Since the plates of both tubes are supplied from a common source of power, whose current remains practically constant, the plate current output of VT_2 can only vary if the plate current of VT_1 is also varied.

Hence when the a-f input cycle swings negative the plate current of VT_2 decreases, causing the plate current of VT_1 to increase, and when the a-f input cycle is positive the plate current of VT_2 will increase, causing the plate current of VT_1 to decrease. It can thus be seen that when a signal is applied to the input circuit of the modulator tube the plate current of the modulated amplifier tube and the r-f current in the tank circuit C_2L_2 will then be modulated in accordance with the frequency and amplitude of the a-f signal applied to the modulator tube.

In order to reduce the distortion to a minimum the modulator tube should be operated as a Class A audio amplifier. The modulated amplifier tube should be operated as Class C with a grid bias equal to approximately twice the value required to produce cutoff. A high percentage of modulation is obtained by operating the modulated amplifier tube at a lower plate voltage than the modulator tube. For proper operation of the modulated amplifier the circuit should be adjusted so that the r-f current in the plate tank circuit varies directly with changes in its plate voltage. Thus if the plate voltage is increased to twice its normal value the tank current should double, and if the plate voltage is decreased to one-half its normal value the tank current should decrease to one-half its normal value. With 100 per cent modulation the peak value of the modulating voltage and the plate voltage of the modulated amplifier tube (with zero modulation) are equal. For 100 per cent modulation the modulating power will be equal to one-half the power supplied by the plate voltage source. The power that the modulator is required to deliver becomes exceedingly high for high-power-output r-f amplifiers, which is one of the disadvantages of plate modulation. However, because of the high overall efficiency obtainable with plate modulation it is the method most generally used.

13-7. Interstage Coupling. *Types of Coupling.* The transfer of energy from one vacuum-tube stage to another is accomplished by means of *interstage coupling.* For maximum efficiency, the transfer of energy should be accomplished with a minimum amount of loss, a minimum amount of loading of the driver stage, and a minimum amount of extraneous interaction between stages. By proper impedance matching, the energy loss and the loading of the driver stage can be reduced to a minimum. The extraneous interaction between stages can be reduced by minimizing the amount of stray electrostatic coupling. In a transmitter, the transfer of energy from one vacuum-tube stage to another may be accomplished by capacitive, impedance, or link coupling.

Capacitive Coupling. With capacitive coupling the voltage developed across a capacitor is used to drive the grid of the following stage. An example of the use of this type of coupling is shown in Fig. 13-12. In this circuit, the voltage developed across the tank circuit will divide across the capacitors C_1 and C_2 in proportion to their reactances. The voltage developed across C_2 drives the grid of VT_2 and thus the amount of grid excitation voltage for VT_2 can be increased by decreasing the capacitance of C_2. Any change in the capacitance of only C_2 will cause a change in the resonant frequency of the tank circuit, hence for any decrease in the capacitance of C_2 a corresponding increase must also be made in the

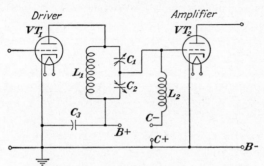

FIG. 13-12.—An example of capacitive coupling.

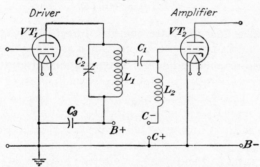

FIG. 13-13.—An example of impedance coupling.

capacitance of C_1. An advantage of this method of coupling is that with the proper adjustment of these two capacitors it is possible to provide a continuous variation in load. Furthermore, the variable adjustment of the grid excitation voltage is also an advantage of this method of coupling.

Impedance Coupling. An example of impedance coupling is shown in Fig. 13-13. In this circuit, the plate voltage of the driver tube is isolated from the grid of the amplifier tube by means of the blocking capacitor C_1. The amount of grid excitation can be adjusted by moving the tap on the plate tank coil L_1. Moving the tap on this coil can also be used as a means to provide for proper impedance matching. Because of its simplicity, this method of coupling is used extensively in transmitter circuits. However, because of the extraneous capacitance of the circuit elements a practical *LC* ratio of the tank circuit cannot be used at high frequencies.

Link Coupling. A method commonly used to couple vacuum-tube stages at the higher frequencies is called *link coupling.* An example of this method of coupling is illustrated in Fig. 13-14. Link coupling requires the use of two tuned circuits, one in the plate circuit of the driver tube and the other in the grid circuit of the amplifier tube. A low-impedance line having a coil with one or two turns at each of its

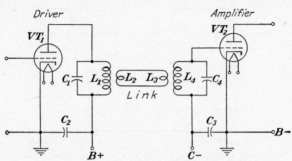

Fig. 13-14.—An example of link coupling.

ends is used to couple the plate and grid tuned circuits. This type of coupling has many advantages, among which are: (1) there is no need of tapping the grid or plate inductors, as the amount of grid excitation can be adjusted by varying the coupling between L_1 and L_2 or L_3 and L_4; (2) because of the low-impedance line connecting coils L_2 and L_3 the two stages may be separated from each other by an appreciable distance; (3) separate parts of the transmitter may be constructed as individual units without having to use long leads at high r-f voltages; (4) series feed may be used in both the grid and plate circuits; (5) interaction between stages is reduced considerably; (6) the effects of the tube capacitances on the *LC* ratio can be reduced to a minimum.

13-8. Amplitude-modulated Transmitter. A portable a-m transmitter that can be operated from either a 6-volt battery or a 115-volt a-c line is illustrated in Fig. 13-15. The circuit diagram for this transmitter is shown in Fig. 13-16. The vibrator-type power transformer T_1 may be used with either 6 volts d-c or 115 volts a-c. The heater voltage is obtained from the battery with d-c operation, and from a secondary winding of the transformer T_1 with a-c operation. When the transmitter is operated from a battery switch S_1 controls the heater circuit and switch S_2 controls the vibrator circuit. When the transmitter is operated from an a-c power line, switch S_1 is closed and the complete power supply is then controlled by switch S_2. Full-wave rectification is obtained by

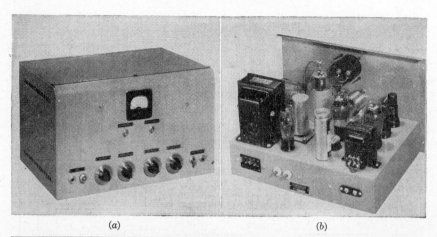

(a)   (b)

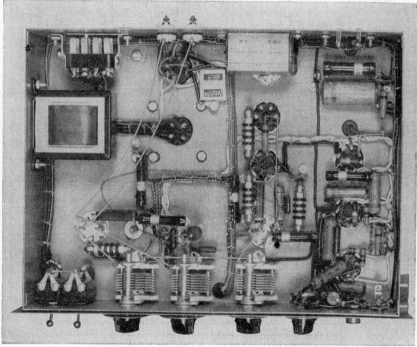

(c)

FIG. 13-15.—Three views of a 12-watt universal amplitude-modulated transmitter. (a) Panel view, (b) chassis view, (c) bottom view.   (*Courtesy of Thordarson Electric Manufacturing Division, Maguire Industries, Inc.*)

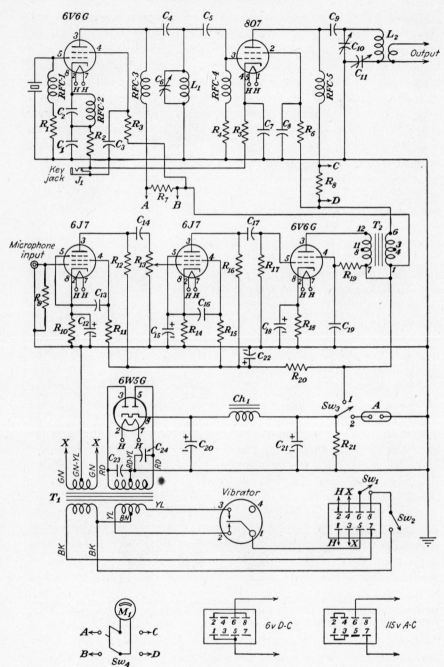

Fig. 13-16.—Circuit diagram of the transmitter illustrated in Fig. 13-15. (*Courtesy of Thordarson Electric Manufacturing Division, Maguire Industries, Inc.*)

means of the center-tapped secondary of the power transformer T_1 and the 6W5-G rectifier tube. Filtering of the B power supply is accomplished by use of the capacitor-input pi-type filter circuit. A source of high direct voltage is made available at the terminal board A by means of the spdt switch S_3. For transmitter operation this switch should be in position 1. When this switch is in position 2, the plate voltage is removed from the transmitter tubes and is made available at the terminal board A. Between transmissions, currents up to 100 ma may be drawn from the power source to supply the high voltage for operating a receiver or other auxiliary equipment.

A regenerative-type crystal-controlled oscillator circuit employing a 6V6-G tube is used to produce the carrier wave. The r-f power amplifier is plate modulated and uses an 807 tube. In the a-f section, two stages of amplification using resistance-capacitance coupling and 6J7 tubes are used to increase the microphone output sufficiently to drive the Class A operated 6V6-G modulator tube. The final tank circuit is connected in the plate circuit of the r-f power amplifier and consists of the two capacitors, C_{10} and C_{11}, and the coil L_2. The degree of loading, as determined by the antenna used, can be adjusted by varying the capacitors C_{10} and C_{11}. Decreasing the capacitance of capacitor C_{11} increases the load. The milliammeter and the dpdt switch S_4 provide a means of reading the plate current of either the oscillator or the r-f power amplifier tubes.

13-9. Methods of Producing Frequency Modulation. *Types of Modulation.* In frequency modulation the a-f signal is applied to the transmitter circuit in such a manner that it causes the frequency of the output wave to vary in proportion to the amplitude of the a-f signal and at a rate corresponding to the frequency of the a-f signal. There are two methods of producing frequency modulation in general use, namely, the *Crosby system* and the *Armstrong system*. The characteristics of the output wave are the same for both methods of modulation.

The Crosby system employs the *reactance-control* or *reactance-tube modulator* method of frequency modulation, in which the frequency-modulated wave is produced directly by connecting the modulator tube in the oscillator circuit. As the frequency of the oscillator is varied by the amplitude of the input signal, a crystal-controlled oscillator cannot be used at this stage. It is therefore necessary to employ some indirect means of maintaining the center or resting frequency at a constant value.

The Armstrong system employs the *balanced modulator* method of frequency modulation in which the frequency-modulated wave is produced indirectly by means of phase modulation. This method actually uses phase modulation to ultimately achieve frequency modulation.

The operation of this system is based upon the principle that any shift in phase will be accompanied by a momentary change in frequency. In the Armstrong system the oscillator supplies a standard frequency, which is fed to the modulator where it is modulated by the a-f signal. Side bands are produced, which are then shifted in phase with respect to the carrier wave. The side bands and the carrier are then combined to produce the frequency-modulated wave. The carrier frequency is obtained directly from a crystal-controlled oscillator, and hence it is not necessary to employ any indirect means for its stabilization.

Reactance-tube Modulator. The purpose of a reactance modulator is to vary the r-f output of the oscillator circuit in accordance with the

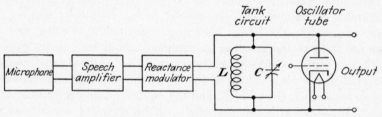

Fig. 13-17.—Principle of the reactance modulator.

amplitude and frequency changes of the a-f input signal. This is accomplished by connecting a variable-reactance circuit, called a *reactance modulator*, in parallel with the tank circuit of the oscillator as shown in Figs. 13-17 and 13-18. The a-f voltage applied to the reactance modulator will cause the resonant frequency of the tank circuit to vary in accordance with the instantaneous variations of the a-f signal. As the impedance of a circuit having a reactive component will vary with the applied frequency, there are many types of reactance modulator circuits. The type most generally used is the reactance-tube modulator circuit.

The circuit diagram of a reactance-tube modulator is shown in Fig. 13-18. The oscillator circuit consists of the vacuum tube VT_1, the tank circuit L_1C_3, the grid-leak resistor R_2, and the grid capacitor C_5. The modulator tube VT_2 is connected across resistor R_1 and capacitor C_2. The series circuit R_1C_2 is thus connected in parallel with the internal resistance (plate-to-cathode) of VT_2 to form a simple phase shifting circuit, which is connected across the oscillator tank circuit. Capacitor C_4 provides a path for the a-f current and also serves to block the d-c plate voltage.

In order for the current in the R_1C_2 circuit to be in phase with the voltage across the tank circuit, the resistance of R_1 is made much higher than the reactance of C_2. The voltage across C_2 will thus lag the current in this circuit by 90 degrees. This voltage is applied to the input circuit of the modulator tube by means of capacitor C_1. Since the output current of a tube is always in phase with its input voltage, the current through the modulator tube lags the voltage across the tank circuit by 90 degrees. Vacuum tube VT_2 thus acts in the same manner as an inductor.   Since the tube VT_2 and the inductor L_1 are connected in parallel their effective

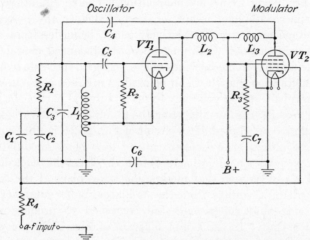

Fig. 13-18.—Circuit diagram of a reactance-tube modulator.

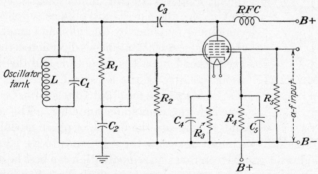

Fig. 13-19.—A reactance-tube modulator circuit using a type 6L7 tube.

inductance will always be less than the value of the smallest inductance. Although the inductance of L_1 is relatively constant, the effective inductance of VT_2 will vary as the voltage on the grid of the tube is varied. When an a-f voltage is applied to the grid of VT_2 the frequency of the oscillator circuit will thus be modulated in accordance with the amplitude and frequency variations of the a-f voltage.

Frequency modulation may also be obtained by having the tube act as a capacitor. This can be accomplished by making the capacitive reactance of C_2 much higher than the resistance of R_1. The voltage across R_1 is then applied to the grid of VT_2. A single tube such as the 6L7 may be used in place of both the oscillator tube VT_1 and the modulator tube VT_2, as is shown in Fig. 13-19.

The reactance-tube modulator is a comparatively simple and effective means of producing frequency modulation. Unlike amplitude modulation, the speech amplifier is not required to deliver any power and its output voltage need only be relatively small, being less than 20 volts.

Balanced Modulator. The purpose of the balanced modulator is to convert the amplitude modulations of the a-f signal into side bands of the oscillator voltage so that they can be used to produce phase modulation. A 90-degree phase shifter generally forms an integral part of the balanced modulator circuit. Before analyzing the functions of the various components of the balanced modulator circuit of Fig. 13-21, it will be of advantage first to obtain an overall picture of how phase modulation (and ultimately frequency modulation) is obtained. From the block diagram of Fig. 13-23 it can be seen that modulation takes place at the combining amplifier, where a voltage from the oscillator, buffer amplifier and the 90-degree side-band components are combined to produce a phase-modulated output. In the vector diagram of Fig. 13-20 the vector E_o

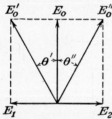

FIG. 13-20.—Vector diagram illustrating the manner in which phase modulation is obtained.

is a constant-amplitude voltage supplied to the combining amplifier by the buffer stage. Vectors E_1 and E_2 are the side-band voltages supplied to the combining amplifier by the side-band amplifier; the magnitude and instantaneous direction of these voltages depend upon the amplitude and the instantaneous polarity of the a-f signal. Vectors $E_o{}'$ and $E_o{}''$ represent the resultant voltage after being combined in the combining amplifier. The angles θ' and θ'' indicate the degree of phase modulation as a result of adding the side bands to E_o. From this vector diagram it can be seen that phase modulation can best be obtained by combining voltages with a 90-degree phase displacement and that when E_o is constant the amount of phase modulation is dependent upon the magnitude of the modulating voltages E_1 and E_2.

The circuit diagram of a balanced modulator is shown in Fig. 13-21. Tubes VT_1 and VT_2 should have identical characteristics and are operated with the same values of operating voltages. The two control grids are connected in parallel and are excited by the oscillator signal. The screen grids of these two tubes are connected in push-pull and are excited by the a-f modulating signal. The plates are connected so that the plate currents of the two tubes will flow through the two halves of the primary winding of the transformer T_2 in opposite directions. With zero a-f signal, the currents in L_1 and L_2 will be equal and as they flow in opposite directions in the two halves of the primary winding of T_2 the circuit will thus be balanced and the net induced voltage at the terminals of the secondary L_3 will be zero.   When an a-f signal is applied, the screen-grid voltage on one tube increases and that on the other decreases by an amount proportional to the a-f signal.   Since the voltages on the screen grids are no longer equal, the currents in the two plate circuits will no longer be equal and a voltage will now be present at the terminals of L_3.

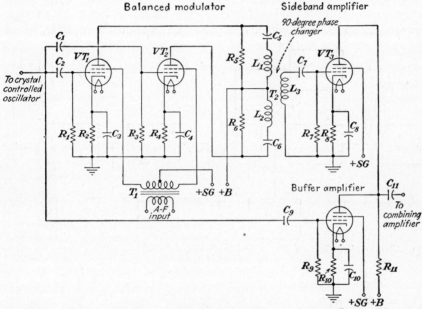

Fig. 13-21.—Balanced modulator, 90-degree phase-shifting network, buffer amplifier, and side-band amplifier.

As the side-band voltage must be 90 degrees out of phase with the oscillator voltage in order to readily produce phase modulation, a 90-degree phase shift is introduced at the transformer T_2. The 90-degree phase shift is accomplished at T_2 by adding capacitors C_5 and C_6, thus making the transformer winding sections L_1 and L_2 part of a tuned circuit.   With the L_1C_5 and L_2C_6 circuits resonant to the oscillator frequency, the currents in L_1 and L_2 will be in phase with the oscillator voltage.   As the induced voltage at the secondary of a transformer is 90 degrees out of phase with the primary (magnetizing) current, the voltage at the terminals of L_3 will be 90 degrees out of phase with the oscillator voltage. It should now be evident that the balanced modulator circuit of Fig. 13-21 will produce 90-degree side-band components (similar to E_1 and E_2 of Fig. 13-20) that will vary in magnitude in accordance with the a-f modulating signal and at a rate corresponding to the frequency of the a-f signal. It should be observed here that the 90-degree phase shift could have been introduced at a number of other points in the circuit, hence this is only one of the various types of phase shifting methods.

13-10. Frequency-modulated Transmitters. *Crosby System.* The fundamental principles of operation of an f-m transmitter employing the Crosby system can be seen from a study of the block diagram of Fig. 13-22. With zero a-f signal, oscillator 1 provides an r-f signal whose frequency is only a fraction of the final output frequency value. When an a-f signal is introduced at the microphone it is passed on to a speech amplifier, where

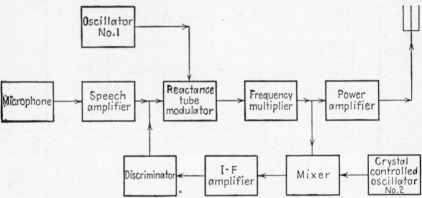

Fig. 13-22.—Block diagram of a frequency-modulated transmitter employing the reactance tube method of modulation.

the a-f signal is increased in strength. After being amplified, the signal is fed into the reactance-tube modulator circuit, where it is used to modulate the frequency of oscillator 1. In order to obtain a high quality of modulation it is considered good practice to limit the frequency deviation produced at the point of modulation to approximately 10 kc. Consequently, in order to obtain the ultimate desired 75-kc frequency deviation it is necessary to feed the output of the reactance modulator circuit into a frequency multiplier stage. For example, in order to obtain a 75-kc frequency deviation at the output when the deviation produced at the point of modulation is 7.5 kc, a frequency multiplication of 10 is required. With a multiplication factor of 10 it is apparent that in order to obtain a final center frequency value of 100 mc, the frequency of oscillator 1 must be 10 mc. The output of the frequency multiplier is passed on to the r-f power amplifier, where the modulated signal is brought up to the desired strength before applying it to the antenna to be broadcast.

Because the output of oscillator 1 is frequency modulated and hence cannot be crystal controlled, it is necessary to add a frequency stabilizing circuit to prevent excessive drift of the center frequency value. The stabilizing circuit consists of oscillator 2, the mixer, i-f amplifier, and the discriminator. The operation of this circuit is as follows. A portion of the output of the frequency multiplier is combined by heterodyne action in the mixer stage (see Art. 14-7) with the crystal-controlled output of oscillator 2 to produce a comparatively low intermediate frequency. This signal is then amplified and fed into the discriminator (see Art. 14-17), which converts the frequency-modulated signal into an a-f signal. The a-f output of the discriminator is then fed into the reactance-tube modulator in series with the output from the speech amplifier in such a manner as to correct the tendency of any frequency drift of the center frequency value of oscillator 1.

Armstrong System. The fundamental principles of operation of an f-m transmitter employing the Armstrong system can be seen from a study of the block diagram of Fig. 13-23. Oscillator 1 supplies a comparatively low value of frequency to a buffer amplifier and its output is crystal controlled. A low value of frequency must be used because the frequency deviation produced by the phase-modulation method is very small. In the block diagram illustrated, the value of the oscillator frequency is 200 kc and the maximum original frequency deviation is 10 cycles. The buffer amplifier supplies voltage to both the combining amplifier and the balanced modulator. When an a-f signal is introduced at the microphone it is passed on to an audio amplifier and a correcting network. The audio amplifier increases the strength of the signal and the correction network, which merely consists of one or more resistors and capacitors, is used to make the amplitude of the a-f signal vary inversely with the signal frequency before applying the a-f signal to the modulator. The ultimate purpose of the correction network is to change phase modulation to frequency modulation. By applying the corrected a-f signal to the balanced modulator and 90-degree phase shifter the sideband components are produced. The side-band amplifier increases the amplitude of the side-band components to the value required to produce the proper amount of phase modulation, usually not to exceed 30 degrees. The output of the combining amplifier will be a frequency-modulated signal whose center frequency is 200 kc and whose frequency deviation is 10 cycles. In order to increase the original frequency deviation of 10 cycles to the ultimate desired value of 75 kc requires a frequency multiplication of 7500. Therefore the output of the combining amplifier must be fed through one or more stages of frequency multiplication. However, if the same amount of multiplication is applied to the center frequency its value will be increased to 1500 mc, which is much higher than the 88-106 mc band assigned to f-m broadcast transmitters. This condition is corrected by placing a frequency converter between two multiplier stages. At the first multiplier stage the center frequency and the frequency deviation are increased 100 times, hence at the output of this stage the center frequency will be 20 mc and the deviation will be 1000 cycles. The signal is then fed into a frequency converter (see Art. 14-7), where it is heterodyned with the 18.7-mc output of the crystal-controlled oscillator 2. The frequency converter reduces the center frequency but does not

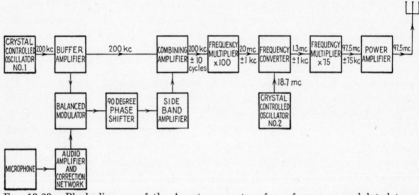

Fig. 13-23.—Block diagram of the Armstrong system for a frequency-modulated transmitter.

affect the deviation. Thus the output of the frequency converter will have a center frequency value of 1.3 mc and a frequency deviation of 1 kc. This signal is then fed into a multiplier stage, which produces a multiplication factor of 75 times. At the output of this stage the center frequency will have a value of 97.5 mc and a frequency deviation of 75 kc. The output of this stage is passed on to the r-f power amplifier, where the modulated signal is brought up to the desired strength before applying it to the antenna to be broadcast.

13-11. Antennas. *Requirements of the Antenna.* A single conductor, or system of two or more conductors, used for radiating or receiving radio waves is called an *antenna*. At a transmitting station the antenna is used to radiate radio waves while at a receiving station it is used to receive radio waves. Antennas possess the same electrical characteristics as a tuned circuit and thus will resonate at a definite frequency. As an antenna is used to couple either a transmitter or a receiver to space, the most effective transmission or reception is obtained when the antenna is designed to resonate at the signal frequency. The efficiency, frequency, and directional characteristics of an antenna will be the same whether it is used for radiating or receiving radio waves. An antenna

used with a transmitter to radiate a signal at a definite frequency will
operate equally well as a receiving antenna for a signal of the same frequency.   As a transmitter should send out the greatest possible amount
of energy, it is important that the antenna used with the transmitter
be designed to couple the greatest amount of energy into its circuit.
Because of the high sensitivity of modern broadcast receivers, the antenna
used with receivers is usually not given much attention.

Principle of the Antenna.   An alternating current flowing through a
conductor produces an alternating magnetic field in the space surrounding

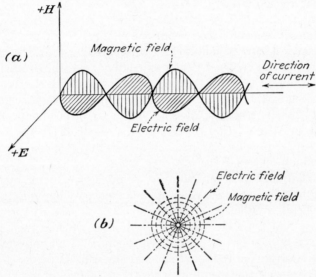

FIG. 13-24.—Illustration of the relations among the electric field, magnetic field, and the
direction of current.   (a) Viewed along the conductor, (b) end view.

the conductor.   If a second conductor is placed in this space, the magnetic lines of force will cut it and a voltage will be induced in the second
conductor.   The value of the induced voltage will be dependent upon the
strength of the magnetic field and the frequency with which the magnetic
lines of force cut the conductor.   Because the strength of the magnetic
field about the second conductor is less than that around the first conductor, a difference of potential will exist between the two conductors.
Because of this difference of potential an electric field is also set up
between the two conductors.   Electric and magnetic fields in motion are
always associated with one another and the two fields combined are
called an *electromagnetic field.*   Both fields contain equal amounts of
energy, are at right angles to each other, and also at right angles to the
flow of current.   The relation between the magnetic field, the electric
field, and the current flow is shown in Fig. 13-24.

If the first conductor is replaced by a transmitting antenna and the second conductor by a receiving antenna, the two antennas may be considered in the same manner as the primary and secondary windings of an r-f transformer. Because of the large distance between the two antennas, the coupling between them is very low, and in order to have any appreciable amount of voltage induced in the receiving antenna a high current must flow in the transmitting antenna. The r-f energy in the transmitting antenna produces radio waves consisting of electric and magnetic fields in the same manner that the alternating current produces these fields about a conductor.

Radiation. The flow of alternating current in an antenna causes the electromagnetic field produced about the antenna to alternately expand and contract. As a certain finite time is required for the electromagnetic field to expand and contract, a new expanding field will be produced by the second half cycle of alternating current before the electromagnetic field produced by the first half cycle has had time to collapse completely. Thus part of the original field does not return to the conductor but is left suspended in space. The portion of the electromagnetic field that remains in space is called the *radiation field* and that portion that returns to the conductor is called the *induction field.*

The radiation field is pushed away from the conductor by the new expanding field because each new field has a polarity opposite that of its preceding field. With each succeeding cycle of alternating current more sections are added to the radiation field, thus causing each previous section to be pushed farther away from the antenna and out into space. The ratio between the radiation and induction fields increases directly with the frequency and thus the higher the frequency of the alternating current the greater will be the ratio between these two fields. For most effective transmission, it is desirable that this ratio be as high as it is practicable to obtain, hence the current fed into the antenna should be of a high radio frequency.

Radiation Resistance. In order to effectively radiate radio waves into space it is necessary to use a circuit that does not confine the radiation field to the immediate vicinity of the antenna. It has been found that a large portion of the energy fed into an antenna will be radiated when an open oscillatory circuit having its inductance and capacitance distributed over a large area is used. This principle can be shown by the following experiment.

A simple oscillator circuit is used as a transmitter to produce a 5-mc (60-meter) output that is coupled to two wires approximately 15 meters long and 1 foot apart (see Fig. 13-25). Capacitor C_3 is adjusted so that the current in the antenna circuit as indicated by the ammeter A is at its maximum value.   This maximum value of antenna current should be simultaneously adjusted to a small fraction of the rated current of the oscillator by means of the potentiometer R_1.   A receiver is placed near the transmitter and the strength of the output signal of the receiver is noted.   The ends of the two conductors are then moved from positions A_1 and B_1 to positions A_2 and B_2.   Moving the two conductors changes their inductance and capacitance and it is therefore necessary to readjust capacitor C_3 in order to obtain the maximum current in the antenna

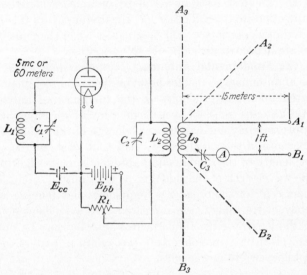

Fig. 13-25.—Circuit for demonstrating the effect of radiation resistance.

circuit.   It will be noted that this maximum value of current is less than that obtained when the ends of the two conductors were at positions A_1 and B_1.   This current should now be increased to its original value by adjusting potentiometer R_1, which increases the power output of the oscillator.   It will now be noted that when the current in the antenna circuit is adjusted to its original maximum value the strength of the signal picked up by the receiver has increased.   Reduce the strength of the output signal of the receiver to its original value by changing the position of the receiver but not varying its volume control.   It will be noted that in order to reduce the strength of this signal to the original value, the receiver must be moved farther away from the transmitter.   Moving the ends of the two conductors from positions A_2 and B_2 to positions A_3 and B_3 will further decrease the maximum value of the current flowing in the antenna circuit and the potentiometer R_1 must be readjusted to have the oscillator supply additional power.   It will also be noted that in order for the strength of the signal picked up by the receiver to be the same as the original value, the receiver must be moved still farther away from the antenna.

The conclusions that may be drawn from this experiment are: (1) when the ends of the two conductors are moved farther apart, more power must be supplied by the oscillator in order to maintain the current in the antenna circuit at a constant maximum value, hence the resistance of the antenna circuit increases as the ends of the two conductors are moved apart; (2) the greatest resistance will be obtained when the ends are diametrically opposite to each other; (3) the useful part of this resistance, called the *radiation resistance*, will be greatest when the ends of the two conductors are diametrically opposite to each other.

13-12. The Fundamental Antenna. *Characteristics.* The operation of all types of antennas, no matter how simple or complex their construction, is based upon the principles of the fundamental antenna. The fundamental antenna consists of a single wire whose physical length is equal to approximately one-half the wavelength of the signal to be transmitted. Because of the capacitance effect that exists at the ends of an antenna the length of the fundamental antenna is made slightly less than one-half the wavelength of the signal to be transmitted. This difference is about 4 per cent for the broadcast frequencies and increases slightly as the frequency of transmission is increased. A convenient equation for computing the length of the fundamental antenna may be obtained by dividing Eq. (1-2) by two, converting the length in meters to feet, and converting kilocycles to megacycles.

$$l = \frac{492 \times k}{f} \tag{13-9}$$

where l = length of the antenna, feet
   k = correction factor
   f = frequency, megacycles

   for frequencies less than 3 mc . . . . $k = 0.96$
   for frequencies of 3 mc to 30 mc . . . . $k = 0.95$
   for frequencies above 30 mc . . . . $k = 0.94$

Any conductor has distributed throughout its length the fundamental characteristics of inductance, capacitance, and resistance. Thus for every length of wire there is a resonant frequency at which the reactances are equal and the current flow (circulating current) is at a maximum. An antenna being a conductor is subject to these same characteristics (see Art. 3-3 and Figs. 3-6 and 3-7). An antenna is thus an open oscillatory circuit and functions in accordance with the principles of parallel resonance in the same manner as a coil and capacitor.

Standing Waves. The energy radiated by an antenna is dependent upon the amount of current in the antenna conductor and hence will be greatest when the antenna current is the highest. In a properly designed antenna, the current at one or more points along the length of the conductor is increased beyond the amount produced by the transmitter by setting up standing waves of current. The manner in which standing waves are produced is presented in the study of transmission lines (Art. 13-14).

Voltage and Current Distribution along the Fundamental Antenna. Standing waves of current and voltage will be produced on the fundamental or half-wave antenna in such a manner as to cause the current to be maximum at the center of the antenna and practically zero at the two ends. The voltage distribution will be just opposite, being practically zero at the center and maximum at both ends. Figure 13-26 shows the voltage and current distri-

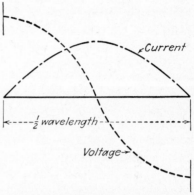

FIG. 13-26.—Distribution of the current and voltage along a fundamental or half-wave antenna.

bution along a half-wave antenna. The points at which the current and voltage are at their minimum are called *nodes* and the points where the current and voltage are at their maximum are called *loops* or *antinodes*.

Because the inductance, capacitance, and resistance of an antenna are distributed over its entire length, rather than being concentrated at any one point, the fundamental antenna will also resonate at frequencies that are integral multiples of the fundamental frequency. The fundamental antenna can therefore be operated at harmonics of its fundamental frequency. The current and voltage distribution for harmonic operation of the fundamental antenna is illustrated in Fig. 13-27. From this figure it can be seen that there are two standing waves for second harmonic operation and three standing waves for third harmonic operation. It can also be noted that the number of points where the current is at a maximum also corresponds to the order of the harmonic. The fundamental antenna thus operates as a full-wave antenna for the second harmonic and as a three-half-wave antenna for its third harmonic.

Impedance of the Antenna. The impedance of the antenna is determined by the values of the standing waves of voltage and current and is equal to the ratio of the voltage to the current. Referring to Figs. 13-26 and 13-27, it can be seen that the impedance along the length of an antenna is not a constant value but varies along its length. In the case of the fundamental antenna the impedance is at its maximum at both ends and is at a minimum in the center. Because the nodes of the standing waves never actually reach zero, the impedance at the center of the fundamental antenna never has the theoretical zero value at its center. Actually the impedance at the center of the fundamental antenna is approximately 72 ohms and has this value regardless of the length as determined by its resonant frequency. Since the antenna operates at its

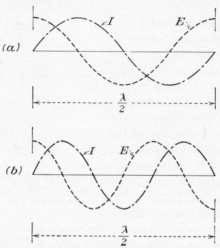

Fig. 13-27.—Distribution of the current and voltage along an antenna operated on harmonics of its fundamental frequency. (*a*) Second harmonic operation, (*b*) third harmonic operation.

fundamental frequency this impedance is pure resistance. Practically all this resistance is radiation resistance, as the ohmic resistance of the conductor is relatively small. The higher the frequency of transmission the shorter will be the required length of the antenna and hence also the lower its ohmic resistance. Since the impedance at the center of the fundamental antenna is practically constant regardless of its length, the efficiency of transmission at the higher frequencies is greater than at the lower frequencies.

Radiation resistance is the term generally used in conjunction with the antenna current to determine the power radiated by the antenna. The power is equal to the product of the square of the antenna current and the radiation resistance.

$$P_r = I_a{}^2 R_r \qquad\qquad (13\text{-}10)$$

where P_r = radiated power, watts

I_a = antenna current, amperes

R_r = radiation resistance, ohms

13-13. Types of Antennas. Antennas may be divided into two groups, namely, (1) the ungrounded or *Hertz antenna*, (2) the grounded or *Marconi antenna*. The Hertz antenna operates in the same manner as the fundamental antenna and is also referred to as a *doublet*, a *dipole*, or a *half-wave antenna*. The Marconi antenna is also referred to as a *quarter-wave antenna*. The operation of both types of antennas is based upon the principles of operation of the fundamental antenna.

Hertz Antenna. The basic Hertz antenna consists of a single wire whose length is equal to approximately one-half the wavelength of the signal to be transmitted. This definition is the same as that for the fundamental antenna and hence its theory of operation will also be the same.

The Hertz antenna may be erected horizontally or vertically. The manner in which the antenna is to be erected will be determined by the direction in which it is desired that the transmitted waves be polarized. The direction of the electrostatic lines of flux is called the direction of *polarization* of the wave. A vertical antenna will transmit waves that are polarized vertically and a horizontal antenna will transmit waves that are polarized horizontally. The angle at which the radiation from the antenna is at a maximum is determined by the direction in which it is polarized. Maximum radiation of the ground wave (see Art. 13-15) is obtained with vertical polarization.

One of the disadvantages of the Hertz antenna is that its length for the low radio frequencies becomes excessive. One of its main advantages is that it requires no ground and can be mounted high above the earth or other absorbent bodies.

Marconi Antenna. The basic Marconi antenna consists of a single wire whose length is equal to approximately one-fourth the wavelength of the signal to be transmitted. One end of this wire is connected to the ground and the other end is left suspended in space. This type of antenna may be erected either vertically or partly vertical and partly horizontal as shown in Fig. 13-28. Because of the capacitive effect of the antenna, the wavelength at which the Marconi antenna resonates is approximately 4.2 times the length from its free end to ground.

When an antenna consists of a vertical wire having one end connected to ground, the electromagnetic field will spread out and extend through the ground in the same manner as if a wire similar to the one extending above the ground was substituted for the ground. The ground acts as a mirror reflecting an image of the electromagnetic field above it. The electric field about the antenna and its reflection by the ground is shown in Fig. 13-29. Although the magnetic field is not shown, it is also present but has been omitted for convenience and simplicity of drawing. A quarter-wave antenna having one end connected to ground will therefore have another quarter-wave added to it by its ground image. The Marconi antenna thus acts in the same manner as the fundamental antenna; its voltage and current distribution are shown in Fig. 13-30.

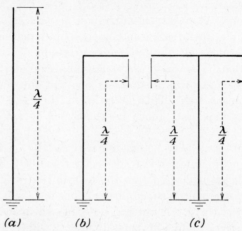

(a)   (b)   (c)

Fig. 13-28.—Three methods of erecting the Marconi antenna.   (a) Vertical, (b) inverted-L (c) T-antenna.

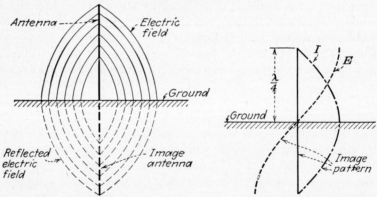

Fig. 13-29.—Electric field about a grounded antenna.

Fig. 13-30.—Distribution of the current and voltage along a grounded quarter-wave antenna.

The grounded end of the antenna is at minimum voltage because this point is at ground potential. A high value of current will flow into ground as the current is maximum at the grounded end of the antenna. It is therefore desirable that the resistance of the ground connection be kept at a minimum. When the soil is moist, a good ground can be obtained by using a water pipe, a metal rod driven into the earth, or a metal plate buried several feet underground. If the surrounding soil is dry and sandy, or if no ground connection can be made, a counterpoise can be substituted for the ground. A *counterpoise* consists of one or more conductors stretched below the antenna and may be mounted just above the ground or buried below its surface. Radio installations in vehicles generally use a counterpoise. The end of the antenna that is usually connected to ground is connected to the body of the vehicle, the circuit being completed by the capacitance that exists between the body of the vehicle and the ground.

(a)   (b)

FIG. 13-31.—Modern transmitting antennas. (a) Half-wave vertical radiator antenna developed by the Bell Telephone Laboratories and Western Electric Company, (b) cloverleaf f-m antenna developed by the Bell Telephone Laboratories and Western Electric Company. (*Courtesy of American Telephone and Telegraph Company.*)

One of the advantages of the Marconi antenna is that its length is only one-half that of the Hertz antenna. The Marconi antenna is therefore more practical to use for the transmission of the lower radio frequencies and also for portable equipment. One of its disadvantages is that because one end must be grounded its height above the ground is limited. The Marconi antenna can be effectively fed from a low-impedance source, as the impedance at its grounded end is only 37 ohms.

Loading an Antenna. It is sometimes inconvenient or impractical to construct an antenna of the length required for the frequency at which it is to be operated. If the antenna is not of the proper physical length to resonate at the desired frequency, resonace may be obtained by loading the circuit with either inductance or capacitance, depending upon whether it is too long or too short. For example, an automobile antenna is usually shorter than the length required for resonance and to compensate for this condition the antenna is loaded by connecting an inductance in series with the antenna. If an antenna is too long to tune the desired wavelength, a capacitor may be connected in series with the antenna to make it resonant at the desired frequency. While loading an antenna will make it resonate at the desired frequency, it introduces additional losses and hence reduces the efficiency of the antenna.

Directional Antennas. For certain types of radio applications, such as point-to-point service, it is necessary to radiate the maximum amount of energy in a definite direction. Energy will be radiated equally well in all directions from a vertical antenna. A horizontal antenna will radiate

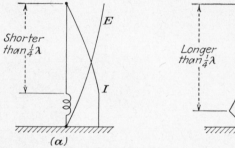

Fig. 13-32.—Methods of loading a Marconi antenna. (*a*) Loading a short antenna with a series-connected inductor, (*b*) loading a long antenna with a series-connected capacitor.

the greatest amount of energy in a direction at right angles to the wire. One of the first types of directional transmitting antennas used this principle. A more efficient and effective method is to use antenna arrays. An *antenna array* consists of two or more half-wave antennas, or quarter-wave antennas, or a combination of both. These antennas should be correctly spaced and their currents properly phased in order to produce a strong radiation in a desired direction. The subject of antenna arrays is quite complex and is beyond the scope of this text.

13-14. Transmission Lines. *Long and Short Lines.* Any wire or system of wires used to transmit energy from one point to another may be termed a transmission line. Electrically, transmission lines may be classed as either short lines or long lines. The electrical length of a line is not based on its physical length but depends upon its physical length in comparison to the wavelength of the energy to be transmitted. For example, a 300-mile, 60-cycle power line is not considered a long line because the wavelength of a 60-cycle current is approximately 3000 miles and therefore the physical length of the line is only approximately one-tenth of the wavelength. A 50-foot line operated at 50 mc would be considered a long line, since its physical length is approximately double the wavelength of the excitation voltage.   Low-frequency and direct-current power lines are classed as short lines and the calculations concerning these lines follow Ohm's law rules.   Because high-frequency lines are subject to the effects of standing waves the characteristics of these lines require special attention.   High-frequency transmission lines are generally made of a definite length that is some multiple of a quarter wavelength in order to obtain a resonant line and to provide the maximum transfer of energy.   Transmission lines whose lengths are other than some multiple of a quarter wavelength may be used in order to match the line to a reactive load.

Standing Waves.   Standing waves may be produced on transmission lines operating at high frequencies.   As an antenna may be considered as an open-ended transmission line, the standing-wave theory presented here will also apply to antennas.   When r-f energy is applied to an open-ended conductor, an electrical impulse travels along its length until the end of the conductor is reached where the impulse is reflected so that it travels back along the conductor to its source.   Because of the high frequency of the r-f current, a new impulse will periodically flow toward the open end and thus cause reflections to occur periodically.   The electrical impulse does not reach the end of the conductor instantaneously but travels at a finite rate.   The wave produced by the original electrical impulse is called the *incident wave* and the wave produced by the reflected current is called the *reflected wave*.   A reflected current wave will always be 180 degrees out of phase with its incident wave.   The sum of the instantaneous values of the incident and reflected currents produces a resultant current that varies in magnitude along the length of the conductor from zero to a maximum value.   This resultant current is called a *standing wave.*

Formation of a Standing Current Wave on a $\frac{5}{4}$ Wavelength Open-ended Transmission Line.   The instantaneous current conditions existing along an open-ended conductor whose physical length is equal to $\frac{5}{4}$ the wavelength of the applied current is shown in Fig. 13-33 for four different instants of the input cycle.   The instantaneous current conditions at the instant that the applied current is at its maximum positive value is shown in Fig. 13-33d.   At a point $\frac{1}{4}\lambda$ from the power source the current will be zero, since the current at this point on the conductor was sent out 90 degrees before.   In a similar manner the current along the conductor will also be zero at $\frac{3}{4}\lambda$ and $\frac{5}{4}\lambda$, and at its maximum negative value at $\frac{1}{2}\lambda$, and at its maximum positive value at λ.   Since the reflected wave is 180 degrees out of phase with its incident wave, the value of the reflected current at the end of the conductor will be the same as the value at $450 - 180$ or 270 degrees ($\frac{3}{4}\lambda$); at λ it will be the same as $540 - 180$ or

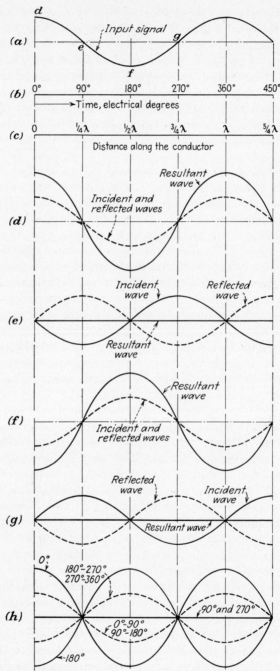

FIG. 13-33.—Curves showing the instantaneous current conditions existing along an open-ended conductor whose physical length is $\frac{5}{4}$ the wavelength of the applied current.

360 degrees (λ); etc. At this instant of time the incident and reflected waves are in phase with each other. The instantaneous current conditions along the length of the conductor at an instant 90 degrees later than in (d) is shown in Fig. 13-33e, 180 degrees later than in (d) in Fig. 13-33f, and 270 degrees later than in (d) in Fig. 13-33g. From these four diagrams it can be seen that the resultant current is always zero at odd quarter wavelengths, $\frac{1}{4}\lambda$, $\frac{3}{4}\lambda$, $\frac{5}{4}\lambda$; and varies sinusoidally between these points from a maximum positive value of twice the maximum positive value of the incident wave to a maximum negative value of twice the maximum negative value of the incident wave, as shown in Fig. 13-33h.

A standing wave will also be produced by the voltage with its distribution being just opposite to the current, that is, the voltage will be maximum when the current is at a minimum and minimum when the current is maximum.

Feeding the Antenna. In order for the antenna to radiate its maximum amount of energy, it must be connected to the transmitter with the minimum amount of loss in the coupling. Because a transmission line is an efficient means of transferring energy from a power source to a load, it is the method generally used to connect the output of the transmitter to the antenna. Energy may be fed to the antenna at either a current or voltage loop. An antenna that is fed at a current loop is referred to as being *current fed* and one fed at a voltage loop is referred to as being *voltage fed.* When feeding the energy into an antenna, maximum transfer of energy is obtained when the impedance of the line matches the impedance to which it is connected. If the impedance of the transmission line at the antenna end is of a low value the antenna should be current fed, and if it is of a high value it should be voltage fed.

Impedance of Resonant Transmission Lines. In the application of resonant lines the impedance of the load is never made equal to the characteristic impedance of the line, hence reflections are always present in these type lines. A resonant line may act as either a high resistive or low resistive impedance. In order to act in this manner the output end of a resonant line is either open circuited or short circuited, and its physical length is made equal to a multiple of a quarter wavelength. For physical lengths other than multiples of a quarter wavelength the line will act in the same manner as either a capacitor or inductor.

Because the magnitude and phase relation of the current and voltage varies along the length of a resonant line, the impedance along the length of the line will also vary. At the odd quarter wavelengths of an open-end line the current is at a maximum and the voltage at a minimum. There is also a rise in voltage from the odd quarter wavelength points toward the output end. Thus at all the odd quarter wavelength points the open-

TABLE XIII-I

Wavelength	Open-end line				Closed-end line			
	I	E	Circuit equivalent	Z	Circuit equivalent	E	I	Z
Less than $\frac{1}{4}$			Capacitor and resistor	$X_C + R$	Inductor and resistor			$X_L + R$
$\frac{1}{8}$			Capacitor	$X_C = Z_o$	Inductor			$X_L = Z_o$
$\frac{1}{4}$	Max	Min	Series resonant circuit	Low; R	Parallel resonant circuit	Max	Min	High; R
$\frac{1}{4}$ to $\frac{1}{2}$			Inductor and resistor	$X_L + R$	Capacitor and resistor			$X_C + R$
$\frac{3}{8}$			Inductor	$X_L = Z_o$	Capacitor			$X_C = Z_o$
$\frac{1}{2}$	Min	Max	Parallel resonant circuit	High; R	Series resonant circuit	Min	Max	Low; R
$\frac{1}{2}$ to $\frac{3}{4}$			Capacitor and resistor	$X_C + R$	Inductor and resistor			$X_L + R$
$\frac{5}{8}$			Capacitor	$X_C = Z_o$	Inductor			$X_L = Z_o$
$\frac{3}{4}$	Max	Min	Series resonant circuit	Low; R	Parallel resonant circuit	Max	Min	High; R
$\frac{3}{4}$ to 1			Inductor and resistor	$X_L + R$	Capacitor and resistor			$X_C + R$
$\frac{7}{8}$			Inductor	$X_L = Z_o$	Capacitor			$X_C = Z_o$
1	Min	Max	Parallel resonant circuit	High; R	Series resonant circuit	Min	Max	Low; R

end transmission line acts as a series resonant circuit.   At all even quarter wavelengths of an open-end line the voltage is at a maximum and the current at a minimum.   At these points the open-end transmission line acts in the same manner as a parallel resonant circuit.   Between zero and one-quarter wavelength, or between any even and odd quarter wavelength, the impedance of the open-end line is capacitive and resistive. Maximum capacitive reactance is obtained at each midpoint, $\frac{1}{8}\lambda$, $\frac{5}{8}\lambda$, etc., where $X_C \cong Z_0$.   Between any odd and even quarter wavelengths the impedance of the open-end line is inductive and resistive.   Maximum inductive reactance is obtained at each mid-point, $\frac{3}{8}\lambda$, $\frac{7}{8}\lambda$, etc., where $X_L \cong Z_0$.   The circuit equivalent, voltage, current, and impedance relations at various points along an open-end transmission line are listed in Table XIII-I.

When a line is short circuited at its end, this point will correspond to zero impedance.   The current at the short-circuited end of a closed-end transmission line will thus be at a maximum and the voltage will be at a minimum.   Since the current and voltage relationship in a short-circuited line are opposite to those of an open-end line, the impedance at any point on a closed-circuit line will also be opposite to an equivalent point on an open-end line.   For example, at the odd quarter wavelengths of the closed-end line the line acts similar to a parallel resonant circuit and at the even quarter wavelengths it acts as a series resonant circuit.   The circuit equivalent, voltage, current, and impedance relations at various points along a closed-end transmission line are listed in Table XIII-I.

Types of Transmission Lines.   The purpose of a transmission line is to transfer energy from a power source to a load with a minimum amount of loss.   In a radio transmitter, the last stage of the transmitter is the power source and the antenna is the load.   Any wire carrying an r-f current will radiate some amount of energy.   The energy loss due to radiation can be reduced to a minimum by (1) using a low value of line current, (2) using a specially designed transmission line.   The types of transmission lines generally used to connect a transmitter to the antenna are (1) the two conductor open-wire line, (2) the twisted-pair line, (3) the coaxial line, (4) the single-wire system.   A diagram illustrating each of these four types of transmission lines is shown in Fig. 13-34.   Transmission lines may also be classified as being tuned or resonant, and untuned or nonresonant.

Two Conductor Open-wire Line.   The type of transmission line most commonly used to transfer energy from the transmitter to the antenna is the two conductor open-wire line.   The radiation from the two wires is reduced to practically zero by having the electromagnetic field about each wire cancel the other.   This is accomplished by having the currents in the two wires equal in magnitude but opposite in phase. This action is obtained by placing the two wires parallel to each other and relatively close together. An insulator, commonly called a *spreader*, is used to maintain the distance between the two wires at a fixed value; the spacing is generally in the order of two to six inches.

Cancellation of the electromagnetic fields is obtained when the two lines are perfectly balanced. Any unbalance in the lines can be overcome

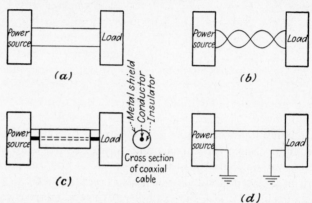

Fig. 13-34.—Four types of transmission lines. (a) Two-conductor open-wire line, (b) twisted-pair line, (c) coaxial line, (d) single-wire system.

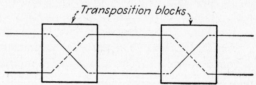

Fig. 13-35.—A two-conductor open-wire line using transposition blocks.

by reversing the positions of the two wires at regular intervals. A type of spreader called a *transposition block* is used for this purpose (see Fig. 13-35).

The two conductor open-wire line is ordinarily operated as a resonant line. In order for a transmission line to resonate, its length can be determined in the same manner as was explained for the antenna. A transmission line can be considered as a half-wave antenna that is folded back upon itself (see Fig. 13-36). The length of a transmission line refers to the length of one wire. The length of a resonant transmission line can therefore be made approximately equal to any whole multiple of a quarter wavelength. The current distribution on a quarter-wave transmission line for both current and voltage feed is shown in Fig. 13-36. From this figure it can be seen that the standing wave on each wire of the transmission line is 180 degrees out of phase with the other. The electromagnetic field set up about each wire will cancel the other and hence the net radiation of the transmission line will be zero.

Twisted-pair Line. Another method of reducing the radiation from a transmission line is to twist the two wires so that the electromagnetic fields about the two conductors cancel each other. This principle is used

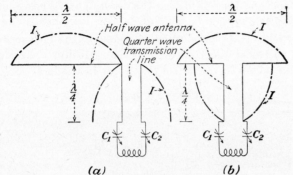

FIG. 13-36.—A half-wave antenna fed by a quarter-wave two-wire line. (*a*) Voltage-fed, (*b*) current-fed.

with the twisted-pair line, which consists of two insulated wires that are twisted together to form a flexible line. The impedance of a twisted-pair line is approximately 72 ohms, which is the same as the impedance at the center of a half-wave antenna. The twisted-pair line is therefore a convenient method to use with a half-wave antenna for obtaining maximum transfer of energy.

A twisted-pair line is usually operated as a nonresonant line. One advantage of an untuned line is that because its line current is low its losses will also be low. A disadvantage of the nonresonant line is that it can only be operated at one frequency and therefore cannot be used for harmonic operation of the fundamental frequency.

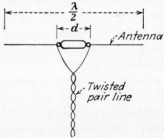

FIG. 13-37.—A half-wave antenna center-fed by a twisted-pair line.

In order to match the impedance of the line to the impedance of the antenna, a more complex adjustment is required with the nonresonant line than with the resonant line. Impedance matching can be accomplished by (1) using a line with an impedance equal to the impedance at the center of the antenna, (2) connecting the line at the proper point on the antenna, (3) connecting an impedance between the antenna and the line.

When using a twisted-pair line to center-feed a half-wave antenna, any difference in impedance between the line and the antenna can be adjusted by spreading the ends of the feeder wires at the antenna. The amount of spread, represented by d in Fig. 13-37, will vary with the size of the wire used for the feeder. This distance is normally between 6 and 18 inches. The correct distance can be obtained by connecting an r-f ammeter in each section of the antenna at the point where it connects with the feeder, and then adjusting this position until maximum current indication is obtained.

· *Coaxial Line.* Another method of reducing the energy loss due to radiation is to shield the transmission line. However, because of the eddy currents set up in the shield the losses in the line are too high to

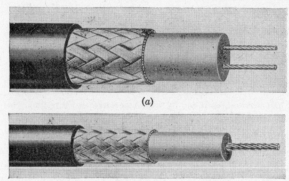

(a)

(b)

Fig. 13-38.—Coaxial cable. (a) Two-conductor Twinax cable, (b) single-condutor **Coax** cable. (*Courtesy of American Phenolic Corporation.*)

make this method practical. An efficient method of shielding is obtained by use of a concentric line.

The concentric line, generally referred to as a *coaxial line*, consists of a wire or metal rod inside a metal tube. The wire is separated from the walls of the tube by means of insulating spacers that are placed at regular intervals along the length of the line. Another form of the concentric line is the *coaxial cable*, in which a solid insulating material is used between the outer and inner conductors. The outer conductor is usually in the form of a braid, so that the cable will be more flexible.

The coaxial line may be operated as either a resonant or a nonresonant line. As a nonresonant line the outer conductor is operated at ground potential. Therefore the radiation from the line will be practically zero. The impedance of a coaxial line varies between 50 and 150 ohms, the exact value being dependent upon its physical dimensions and the dielectric constant of the insulating material.

When a coaxial line is operated as a resonant line, a standing electromagnetic wave is set up between the two conductors. The radiation from this field is absorbed by the outer conductor. The eddy currents that are set up in this conductor produce an electromagnetic field, which returns the energy to the line. The eddy currents produce an energy loss; however, this loss of energy is appreciably less than that in a two conductor open-wire line.

Single-wire System. Another method of reducing the energy loss due to radiation is to use a single conductor to feed the antenna. In this system the earth or ground is used as the return circuit and it is therefore essential that a good ground connection be used. The single-wire system operates as a nonresonant line. No standing waves will appear on the line when its characteristic impedance is matched by the impedance of the antenna at the point of connection. The distance from the center of the antenna to the point where the line connects to the antenna, represented by d in Fig. 13-39, is approximately 14 per cent of the length of the antenna. The distance d is dependent upon the size of the conductor used for the feeder and the

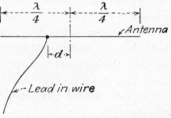

FIG. 13-39.—A single-wire antenna feed.

height of the antenna. Proper matching of the impedances is best obtained by use of an r-f ammeter and adjusting the position of the feeder on the antenna for maximum current flow.

13-15. Wave Propagation. *Radio Waves.* Radio waves are electromagnetic waves that travel through space at essentially the same speed as light. The radio wave radiated from an antenna is composed of two parts. One of these parts travels along the earth's surface and hence is called the *ground wave.* The other part travels through the atmosphere and hence is called the *sky wave.*

The Ground Wave. The ground wave suffers losses in energy that are caused by dispersion and absorption. The range of communication by means of the ground wave is limited to comparatively short distances, as the radio wave must supply these losses and hence the strength of the signal is attenuated. The energy loss due to dispersion is caused by the spreading out of the radio waves along the surface of the earth. The amount of energy that is dissipated in the ground will depend upon the resistance of the surface of the earth that the ground wave must travel through. The greater this resistance, the greater will be the absorption loss and also the greater the attenuation of the radio wave. Sea water and moist soil are good conductors, hence the range of communication is much greater for a signal traveling over these surfaces than for a signal traveling over dry land. The losses of the ground wave vary directly with the frequency and therefore the higher the frequency the greater will be the attenuation of the radio signal. The rate of attenuation is so high for signals above two megacycles that the range of communication by means of the ground wave at these frequencies is too small to be of any practical use.

As any horizontal component of the electric field will be short-circuited by the earth, it is essential that a vertical antenna be used for ground-wave communication. The antenna will then be polarized vertically and the electric field will be at right angles to the earth.

The Sky Wave. The sky wave leaves the antenna at an angle to the horizontal and travels upward until it strikes a layer of ionized air that causes it to be bent downward so that it strikes the earth's surface at some distance from the transmitting antenna. The sky wave upon reaching the earth may be reflected upward toward the ionized layer of air and the cycle is repeated until the sky wave is completely absorbed (see Fig. 13-40). The losses due to dispersion and the losses due to absorption within the ionized layer are comparatively small and hence the strength of the signal at a point where the sky wave strikes the earth's surface may be much stronger than a ground-wave signal that is much closer to the transmitting antenna. Because of this characteristic, long-distance communication is accomplished by use of the sky waves.

The bending of the sky wave by the ionized layer of air is called *refraction* and is caused by the wave passing at an angle from one medium to another. The degree of refraction is dependent upon the frequency of the sky wave and the intensity of ionization of the reflecting layer. The theory of refraction of the sky wave by an ionized layer of air was developed simultaneously by two men, an American named Kennelly and an Englishman named Heaviside, who worked independently of each other. The Kennelly-Heaviside layer is only one of a series of layers of ionized air, each one outside the other, which comprise the upper portion of the earth's atmosphere. This series of layers of ionized air is called the *ionosphere* and extends from approximately 30 miles above the earth's surface to approximately 200 miles above the earth's surface. Maximum intensity of the ionosphere is generally in the region of 70 miles above the earth's surface. Ionization of the air is caused to a large degree by the sun's rays and thus the intensity of ionization within the ionosphere will vary with the time of day and the season of the year. Radio communication by means of the sky wave, which is dependent upon the degree of ionization, will therefore also vary with the time of day and the season of the year.

The angle between a sky wave and the surface of the earth is called the *angle of radiation.* The distance between the point where the sky wave leaves the earth and the point where it returns is called the *skip distance.* This distance increases as the angle of radiation is decreased.

The smaller the angle of radiation the smaller will be the degree of refraction required to return the wave to the earth.   For each frequency and degree of refraction there is an angle of radiation, called the *critical angle*, above which there is no refraction.   No part of a sky wave that enters the ionosphere above the critical angle returns to the earth, as that portion of the sky wave that is not absorbed by the ionosphere continues on into space.   The value of the critical angle decreases with an increase of frequency.   The sky wave cannot be used for uhf (ultrahigh-fre-

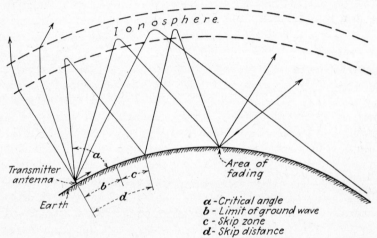

Fig. 13-40.—The propagation of ground waves and sky waves from an antenna.

quency) communication, as at these frequencies the critical angle is so low that no portion of the sky wave is refracted.

The distance between the transmitter and the point on the earth's surface where the sky wave first returns to the earth, or between any two successive points on the earth's surface where the sky wave returns, is called the *skip distance*.   The value of this distance is dependent upon the angle of radiation, the frequency, and the intensity of the ionosphere. With too small an angle of radiation the skip distance may become so large that the sky wave skips beyond the earth's surface.   The portion of the earth's surface not reached by either the sky wave or the ground wave is called the *skip zone*.

The variation in the signal intensity at a definite point of reception is called *fading*.   When two or more portions of a wave arrive at a point of reception along different paths their phase relations may not be the same.   The paths through the ionosphere are subject to change hence a signal from this type of communication is subject to fading.

Propagation of Ultrahigh Frequencies.   The sky wave sent out by a transmitter whose output frequency is greater than 30 mc will not be reflected back to the earth by the ionosphere. The ground wave at these frequencies, whether polarized vertically or horizontally, will be short-circuited by the earth. Because of these transmitting characteristics at the ultrahigh frequencies, communication at these frequencies is carried on by use of straight-line propagation of radio waves from the transmitter to the receiver. Because of the curvature of the earth the

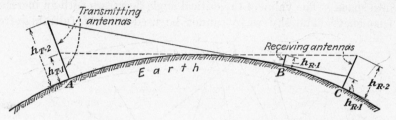

Fig. 13-41.—Direct-wave propagation at the ultrahigh frequencies.

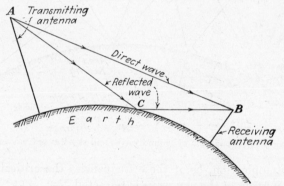

Fig. 13-42.—Direct and reflected waves at ultrahigh frequencies.

maximum distance over which ultrahigh-frequency communication can be accomplished is dependent upon the line-of-sight distance (see Fig. 13-41). The maximum distance of communication at the ultrahigh frequencies will therefore be determined by the height of the transmitting and receiving antennas. The maximum distance of communication between a transmitting antenna whose height is $h_{T.1}$ and a receiving antenna whose height is $h_{R.1}$ is obtained when the line-of-sight just clears the earth's surface as indicated by the distance A to B on Fig. 13-41. Increasing the height of the transmitting antenna to $h_{T.2}$ increases the distance of communication to point C. This same increase in the distance of communication can also be accomplished with a transmitting antenna of height $h_{T.1}$ by increasing the height of the receiving antenna to $h_{R.2}$.

Some of the radio waves sent out by the transmitting antenna are reflected by the earth. The signal at the receiving antenna will therefore be the resultant of the reflected wave ACB and the direct wave AB, as shown in Fig. 13-42.   Whether these two waves aid or oppose each other will depend upon their phase relation.   The reflected wave has its phase reversed when it is reflected.   Thus, when the length of the path of the two waves, *ACB*, and *AB*, are equal or approximately equal they will be out of phase when they arrive at the receiving antenna.   However, if the length of the path of the reflected wave is any odd number of half wavelengths longer than the direct wave the two waves will be in phase when they arrive at the receiving antenna.

BIBLIOGRAPHY

EASTMAN, A. V., *Fundamentals of Vacuum Tubes*, McGraw-Hill Book Company, Inc., New York.

HENNEY, K., *Principles of Radio*, John Wiley & Sons, Inc., New York.

HOAG, J. B., *Basic Radio*, D. Van Nostrand Company, Inc., New York.

MARCHAND, N., Frequency Modulation, *Communications*, January, 1946, to September, 1946.

NILSON, A. R., and HORNUNG, J. L., *Practical Radio Communication*, McGraw-Hill Book Company, Inc., New York.

REICH, H. J., *Theory and Application of Electron Tubes*, McGraw-Hill Book Company, Inc., New York.

TERMAN, F. E., *Fundamentals of Radio*, McGraw-Hill Book Company, Inc., New York.

TERMAN, F. E., *Radio Engineers' Handbook*, McGraw-Hill Book Company, Inc., New York.

The Radio Amateur's Handbook, The American Radio Relay League, Inc., West Hartford, Conn.

QUESTIONS

1. Name the essential parts of a simple transmitting circuit.

2. Explain why it is impractical to feed a-f signals directly into an antenna.

3. Define the following terms: (*a*) signal, (*b*) signal wave, (*c*) carrier wave, (*d*) modulation, (*e*) modulated wave, (*f*) modulating wave, (*g*) side band, (*h*) modulation envelope.

4. Name and define three methods of modulation.

5. (*a*) What is meant by per cent of modulation?   (*b*) Why is it desirable to operate an a-m transmitter with 100 per cent modulation?

6. (*a*) Explain why a 10-kc channel is required by an a-m transmitter whose modulating frequency has an upper limit of 5000 cycles.   (*b*) If the upper limit of the modulating frequency is increased to 10,000 cycles, why must the operating channel of the transmitter be increased to 20 kc?   (*c*) What would be the effect if the transmitter in (*b*) were operated with a channel of less than 20 kc?

7. What are the essential characteristics of a frequency-modulated wave?

8. Define the following terms: (*a*) center frequency, (*b*) resting frequency, (*c*) frequency deviation, (*d*) carrier swing, (*e*) deviation ratio.

9. (*a*) Name the factors that determine the channel width of an f-m transmitter. (*b*) Explain how each factor affects the channel width.

10. What is meant by (*a*) plate-supply keying?   (*b*) Blocked-grid keying?   (*c*) Cathode keying?

11. (*a*) What is meant by a master oscillator power amplifier?   (*b*) What are the functions of the buffer amplifier?   (*c*) What are the advantages of the master oscillator power amplifier?

12. Why is it desirable to use frequency multiplication to produce r-f outputs above 10 mc?

13. Draw a block diagram illustrating the essential components of an a-m transmitter for (a) low power output and medium radio frequencies, (b) high power output and frequencies greater than 10 mc.

14. Draw a block diagram illustrating the essential components of an f-m transmitter using (a) the reactance-tube system of modulation, (b) the Armstrong system of modulation.

15. Why is the efficiency with Class C operation of amplifiers higher than for Class A or Class B operation?

16. In order to obtain maximum efficiency from a Class C r-f power amplifier what should be the approximate relation between the input signal and the grid bias?

17. Explain how an undistorted output is obtained from Class C r-f power amplifier circuits.

18. How does the construction of Class C power amplifier tubes compare with low-power-output vacuum tubes?

19. What are the advantages and disadvantages of (a) low-level modulation? (b) High-level modulation?

20. (a) What is meant by grid modulation? (b) Describe the operation of a grid modulation circuit. (c) What are the advantages and disadvantages of grid modulation?

21. (a) What is meant by plate modulation? (b) Describe the operation of the Heising system of plate modulation. (c) Why is the Heising system of plate modulation also called the constant-current system? (d) What are the advantages and disadvantages of plate modulation?

22. (a) Name three types of interstage coupling used in transmitters. (b) What three requirements should a coupling unit fulfill in order to obtain maximum efficiency?

23. Explain the operation of each of the following types of coupling as used in transmitting circuits: (a) capacitive coupling, (b) impedance coupling, (c) link coupling.

24. Explain the operation of a simple a-m transmitting circuit.

25. (a) What is the purpose of a reactance modulator in an f-m transmitter circuit? (b) Describe the operation of a reactance-tube modulator circuit. (c) What are the advantages of this method of producing frequency modulation?

26. (a) What is the purpose of a balanced modulator in an f-m transmitter circuit? (b) Describe the operation of a balanced modulator circuit. (c) What are the advantages and disadvantages of this method of producing frequency modulation?

27. With the aid of a block diagram, describe the operation of an f-m transmitter employing the Crosby system of modulation.

28. With the aid of a block diagram, describe the operation of an f-m transmitter employing the Armstrong system of modulation.

29. (a) What is an antenna? (b) What is the purpose of an antenna? (c) Describe the principle of operation of an antenna. (d) Why is it necessary to have a high current flowing in a transmitting antenna?

30. Explain the following terms: (a) radiation field, (b) induction field.

31. In order to obtain the most effective transmission, why should the current fed into an antenna be of a high r-f value?

32. Describe a simple experiment that can be used to illustrate that the radiation resistance is greatest when the ends of a conductor (antenna) are diametrically opposite to each other.

33. Explain the characteristics of the fundamental antenna that enable it to be considered as a parallel resonant circuit.

34. Draw a diagram illustrating the voltage and current distribution along a fundamental antenna that is operated at (a) its fundamental frequency, (b) a harmonic of the fundamental frequency.

35. (a) What is the relation between the impedance at the center of the fundamental antenna and the impedance at the ends? (b) Explain the reason for this relation.

36. Why is the resistance at the center of the fundamental antenna considered to be approximately 72 ohms?

37. Explain why the efficiency of transmission is greater at the higher frequencies than at the low frequencies.

38. (a) Describe the construction and operating characteristics of a Hertz antenna. (b) What are the advantages and disadvantages of the Hertz antenna?

39. (a) Describe the construction and operating characteristics of a Marconi antenna. (b) What are the advantages and disadvantages of the Marconi antenna?

40. What is meant by a polarized antenna?

41. What is the purpose of loading an antenna circuit with (a) a capacitor? (b) An inductor?

42. (a) What is meant by an antenna array? (b) What is the purpose of the antenna array?

43. Explain what is meant by (a) a long transmission line, (b) a short transmission line.

44. Explain the following terms: (a) incident wave, (b) reflected wave, (c) standing wave.

45. With the aid of diagrams, explain how a standing wave is formed on an open-ended transmission line.

46. What is meant by (a) a current-fed antenna? (b) A voltage-fed antenna?

47. What must the physical length of a resonant line whose output ends are open-circuited be in order for it to act as (a) a series resonant circuit? (b) A parallel resonant circuit? (c) An inductor? (d) A capacitor?

48. What must the physical length of a resonant line whose output ends are short-circuited be in order for it to act as (a) a low resistance? (b) A high resistance? (c) An inductor? (d) A capacitor?

49. (a) What are the operating characteristics of a two conductor open-wire transmission line? (b) Explain how the net radiation of this type of line is reduced to practically zero.

50. Describe the purpose of (a) a spreader, (b) a transposition block.

51. Explain why the twisted-pair transmission line is convenient for use with a half-wave antenna.

52. What adjustments should be made with a twisted-pair transmission line when it is operated as a nonresonant line to center-feed a half-wave antenna?

53. Explain the operation of a coaxial line as: (a) a nonresonant line, (b) a resonant line.

54. Explain how a single wire may be used as a nonresonant line to feed an antenna.

55. (a) Describe the communication characteristics of the ground wave. (b) Why is it necessary to use a vertical antenna for ground wave communication?

56. Explain the following terms: (a) ionosphere, (b) refraction, (c) angle of radiation, (d) skip distance, (e) critical angle, (f) skip zone.

57. Why is the sky wave used for long-distance communication?

58. (a) Why must straight-line propagation of radio waves from the transmitter to the receiver be used for radio frequencies greater than 30 mc? (b) What factors determine the maximum distance of communication at the ultrahigh frequencies?

CHAPTER XIV

RECEIVING CIRCUITS

The operation of simple receiving circuits that do not require the use of vacuum tubes was presented in Chap. III. While these simple circuits do not have much practical value, they were presented to acquaint the reader with the fundamental functions of a receiving system before introducing the theory of vacuum tubes and their associated circuits. In the chapters following the simple receiving circuits, a detailed study of vacuum tubes and their uses as amplifiers, detectors, oscillators, and rectifiers was presented. With this knowledge of vacuum-tube applications, it is now possible to understand the purpose and operation of all the components in the average receiver.

14-1. Characteristics of Receivers. *Definitions.* A radio receiver may be defined as a device for converting radio waves into perceptible signals. How well a receiver accomplishes its purpose is generally determined by investigation of its characteristics, the most important of which are the sensitivity, selectivity, fidelity, stability, and signal-to-noise ratio.

Sensitivity. The IRE definition states that the sensitivity of a radio receiver is that characteristic which determines the minimum strength of signal input capable of causing a desired value of signal output. This characteristic is further described in Art. 6-1.

Selectivity. The IRE definition states that the selectivity of a radio receiver is that characteristic which determines the extent to which it is capable of differentiating between the desired signal and disturbances of other frequencies. It is also further explained in Art. 6-1.

Fidelity. The IRE definition states that fidelity is the degree with which a system, or a portion of a system, accurately reproduces at its output the essential characteristics of the signal which is impressed upon its input. This characteristic is also further explained in Art. 6-1.

Stability. Stability may be defined as a measure of the ability of a radio receiver to deliver a constant amount of output for a given period of time when the receiver is supplied with a signal of constant amplitude and frequency. Factors affecting the stability of a receiver are the variations in output voltage of the power supply unit, temperature variations, and occasionally features of mechanical construction. Instability of a receiver, in addition to affecting its fidelity, may also cause it to break into oscillations that produce a whistle or a howling noise at the loudspeaker.

Signal-to-noise Ratio.   The signal-to-noise ratio of a radio receiver is one of the important operating characteristics of the receiver.   Various definitions have been presented, depending upon the source of noise to be considered.   In terms of the receiver itself, a fair definition is that the signal-to-noise ratio is the ratio of the signal power output to the noise power output at a specified value of modulated carrier voltage applied to the input terminals.

Kinds and Sources of Noise.   The source of noise may be in the receiver itself or may be due to external causes such as static, background noises from other stations, or noises originating in the transmitter.   The noises produced within the receiver may be divided into four classifications, namely (1) thermal agitation, (2) shot effect, (3) microphonics, (4) hum from the a-c power source.   *Thermal agitation* may be defined as an irregular random movement of the free electrons in a conductor that is carrying a normal flow of electron current.   The random motion of the free electrons produces minute currents, which upon being amplified result in noise at the loudspeaker.   The magnitude of these minute currents increases with the temperature.   *Shot effect* is caused by the small irregularities in plate current, which normally exist due to the individual electrons striking the plate, and produces noise at the loudspeaker.   It is generally present only in high gain amplifiers operated with a low input signal.   *Microphonics* is the name generally applied to the noise present in the loudspeaker due to mechanical vibration at one or more points in a radio receiver, which causes corresponding variations in the a-f currents.   Although microphonic noises are most generally due to vibration of the elements of amplifier tubes, they may also be caused by the vibration of other circuit elements such as capacitors and coils.   *Hum from the a-c power source* is usually picked up in the a-f section of the receiver, although it may also be picked up at other points.   Among the causes of hum are (1) operating the heaters or filament circuits of the tubes on a-c, (2) insufficient filtering of cathode bias resistors, (3) insufficient filtering in the B power supply unit, (4) stray magnetic and electrostatic fields near the circuit elements of the receiver.

14-2. Frequency-modulation vs. Amplitude-modulation Reception. *Noise Reduction.*   The outstanding advantage of f-m over a-m reception is the great reduction in undesired external noises.   Numerous types of external and internal noises may be present in the sounds produced by the conventional a-m receiver.   External noises, generally called *static*, may be caused by nature, as in the case of lightning, northern lights, sunspots, etc., or it may be man-made static as produced by vacuum cleaners, neon signs, electric elevators and trolleys, electric vibrator mechanisms, etc. As these disturbances affect the amplitude of the received signal, they introduce undesired noises in the output of a-m receivers. In some instances the noise produced is so severe that it completely ruins the reception of the desired program.

In f-m reception, amplitude disturbances due to static do not affect the transmitted signal frequencies. The variations in amplitude are smoothed out by the limiter circuits (see Art. 14-17) in the f-m receiver, and hence the output of the receiver is practically free from noises due to static.

Fidelity. Potentially, the f-m receiver is superior to the a-m receiver in the fidelity of reproduction. It has been shown in Art. 13-3 that with f-m it is possible to reproduce sounds at frequencies up to 15,000 cycles. If this is compared with the 5,000-cycle range for the average a-m system, it should readily be understood that an f-m receiver, particularly as in the case of a symphonic musical program, will provide a more nearly exact reproduction of the original sounds than an a-m receiver.

Interstation Interference. With a-m reception, it is possible to be tuned to a desired station and to have another station interfering in the background. In some instances the interference may be sufficiently disturbing to spoil the program of the desired station, even though the interference is many times weaker than the desired program. With f-m reception, it is possible to receive only one of two stations operating at the same frequency if the relative signal strength exceeds a 2 to 1 ratio. Thus, it is unlikely to have a distant station interfere with a local station even though they may be operating on the same frequency.

Distance and Fading. With a-m reception, it is possible to receive programs from stations located considerable distances from the receiver but this reception is often accompanied by fading. Furthermore, the ability to receive distant stations varies with the time of the day and the time of year. The normal distance for f-m transmission is generally considered as *line-of-sight distance*, or approximately 40 miles, although greater distances can and have been achieved. However, f-m reception is equally good for day or night and any time of the year.

Disadvantages of Frequency-modulation. There are a number of disadvantages of f-m over a-m, although they are generally considered to be outweighed by the advantages. Among the disadvantages are: (1) higher cost of receivers; (2) generally requires a special antenna, which adds to the cost; (3) may be subject to static from auto ignitions, etc.; (4) tuning is unstable; (5) difficult to tune.

The f-m system of broadcasting is still in its infancy and there are comparatively few f-m transmitters in operation and the programs available are limited. However, there is every indication that the number of f-m transmitters will soon equal and perhaps surpass the number of a-m transmitters.

Use of Amplitude-modulation. The preceding discussion infers that f-m is so far superior to a-m reception that it raises the question of why a-m is used. This may be answered by the fact that early radio development employed only the a-m system of modulation and it became so firmly entrenched that it will take many years before the millions of a-m receivers now in use will be replaced by the newer f-m receivers.

Although the f-m system is superior to the a-m system, it is possible to obtain quite satisfactory reception from a-m receivers except in the case of severe electrical disturbances such as occurs during a thunderstorm.

14-3. Fundamental Principles of Amplitude-modulation Receivers. *Essential Functions.* The minimum essential functions of a radio receiver are: (1) reception, (2) selection, (3) detection, (4) reproduction. The order in which these functions are performed is indicated by the block diagram of Fig. 14-1. A simple discussion of these functions was presented in Chap. III and a simple receiving circuit is shown in Fig. 3-2.

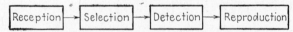

FIG. 14-1.—Block diagram showing the essential functions of a receiver.

The simple receiving circuit of Fig. 3-2 has many disadvantages such as poor sensitivity, poor selectivity, and possible loss of the signal when the crystal is jarred. Some of these disadvantages may be lessened or overcome by substituting a vacuum tube for the crystal detector. Two single-tube receiving circuits are shown in Fig. 14-2. Both of these circuits will provide increased signal strength, as has been explained in Arts. 5-5 and 5-8. However, the signal strength is still only sufficient to operate earphones.

Addition of Audio-frequency Amplification. In order to obtain sufficient signal strength to operate a loudspeaker, it is necessary to add one or more stages of a-f amplification as indicated in the block diagram of Fig. 14-3. The a-f amplifier stages are generally either of the transformer-coupled or the resistance-capacitance-coupled type, the operation of which has been presented in Chaps. VIII and IX. Figure 14-4a illustrates the addition of one stage of a-f amplification to the simple regenerative receiver of Fig. 14-2b. The circuit of Fig. 14-4b illustrates the addition of two stages of a-f amplification to the single-tube receiving circuit of Fig. 14-2a. In the circuit of Fig. 14-4b the first amplifier stage is used for obtaining voltage amplification and the second stage for obtaining power amplification.

The circuits of Fig. 14-4 do not have very great practical value because of the poor selectivity of the circuit. The a-f amplifier stages increase the strength of all signals passed on to them from the detector and consequently the interstation background noises are amplified to

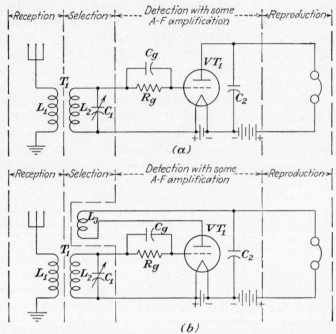

Fig. 14-2.—Two single-tube receiver circuits. (a) Simple receiver circuit with a grid-leak detector, (b) simple receiver circuit with a regenerative detector.

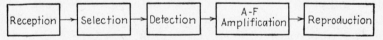

Fig. 14-3.—Block diagram of a simple receiver with the addition of a-f amplification.

the same degree as the signal of the desired station. This usually results in poor overall operation of the receiving circuit.

Addition of Radio-frequency Amplification. One method of improving the selectivity of a receiver is to introduce one or more additional tuning stages. As an additional tube is required for each stage added, amplification also takes place with the introduction of each new stage. As both tuning and amplification take place within each added stage, the process is commonly referred to as *tuned-radio-frequency amplification*, or it is said that one or more trf stages have been added. The block

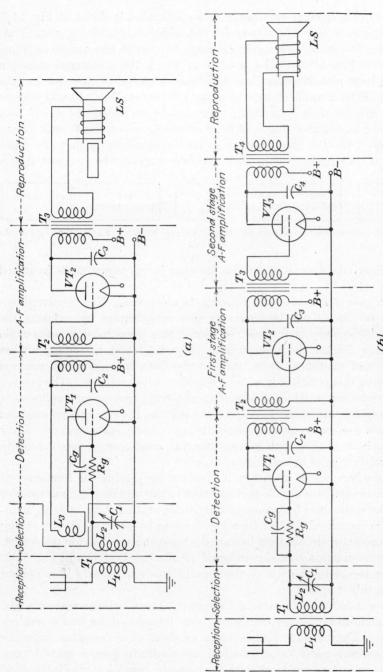

Fig. 14-4.—Two simple receiver circuits with a-f amplification. (a) Regenerative receiver with one stage of a-f amplification, (b) receiver with grid-leak detector and two stages of a-f amplification.

diagram of a receiver employing trf amplification is shown in Fig. 14-5. The circuit of Fig. 14-6 illustrates the addition of a single stage of trf amplification and one stage of a-f amplification to the simple receiving circuit of Fig. 14-2a. The manner in which the additional stages of tuning improves the selectivity has been discussed in Art. 6-6 and the matter of trf amplification was presented in Art. 7-5. It was pointed out in Art. 6-6 that, if too many tuned stages are added, the circuit may become too selective and will then adversely affect the fidelity of the receiver. Another disadvantage of trf amplification is that the selectivity of the circuit varies with the frequency of the received signal.

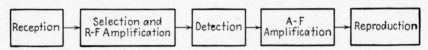

FIG. 14-5.—Block diagram of a simple receiver with the addition of both r-f and a-f amplification.

The selectivity decreases with an increase in frequency, as is indicated by Fig. 14-7.

Addition of Intermediate-frequency Amplification. The disadvantages of the trf circuit can be overcome to a large extent by reducing the received frequency of the selected station to a lower fixed value of radio frequency (called the intermediate frequency) and providing further tuning and amplification at this intermediate frequency. A receiver employing this principle is called a *superheterodyne receiver*. The portion of the receiver in which this tuning and fixed frequency amplification takes place is called the *i-f amplifier*. Because the i-f amplifier operates at a fixed frequency, greater selectivity, sensitivity, stability, and fidelity can be obtained than with an amplifier that must operate over the entire frequency range of the receiver.

The intermediate frequency is obtained by beating the frequency of a separate oscillator circuit that is added to the superheterodyne receiver with the modulated frequency of the desired station. In order to maintain a constant value of i-f for all stations to be received, the frequency of the oscillator circuit must be varied whenever a new station is selected. The block diagram of a superheterodyne receiver is shown in Fig. 14-8. A more complete analysis of the superheterodyne receiver is presented later in this chapter.

Other Additions to Receiving Circuits. Numerous improvements and additional operating features have been introduced for radio receiver circuits. They include such features as short-wave reception, all-wave reception, automatic volume control, automatic frequency control, tone control, noise suppression circuits, push-button control, tuning indicators, band switching, bandspread tuning, and preselection. These are described in various portions of this text. In general, the purpose of each is indicated by its name.

14-4. The Tuned-radio-frequency (TRF) Receiver. *The TRF Circuit.* A trf receiver may be defined as one in which the incoming signal is passed through one or more stages of tuned-radio-frequency amplification and then applied to the detector with the same frequency and wave form at which it was received. The trf receiver was used extensively in the early days of radio, but owing to its disadvantages, described in the preceding article, its use has decreased considerably with the introduction of the superheterodyne receiver. However, this circuit is still used to some extent, especially in some of the small low-cost receivers.

The circuit diagram of a five-tube, a-c operated, trf receiver is shown in Fig. 14-9. The circuit uses two stages of tuned r-f amplification, a biased detector, one stage of a-f voltage amplification, and one stage of a-f power amplification. It is designed to provide (1) sufficient selectivity for the reception of all local stations and some distant stations, (2) ample volume for average home use, (3) good fidelity, (4) high signal-to-noise ratio. A list of the various circuit elements together with their names and functions is presented in Table XIV-I. Also provided in the table are (1) figure references that illustrate the particular parts, (2) reference article and chapter numbers in which the parts

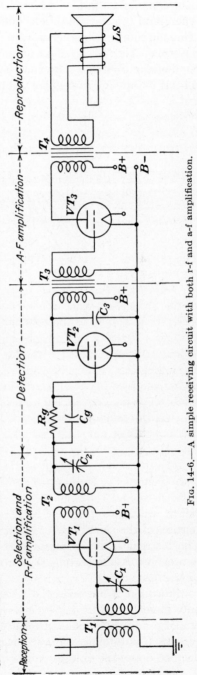

Fig. 14-6.—A simple receiving circuit with both r-f and a-f amplification.

and the explanation of their operation was presented, (3) approximate values of the various circuit elements for one specific receiver design. The function of those few parts not previously described in detail are given in the following discussion.

Volume Control. The control of the volume for the circuit of Fig. 14-9 is obtained by means of the potentiometer R_1. Examination of the

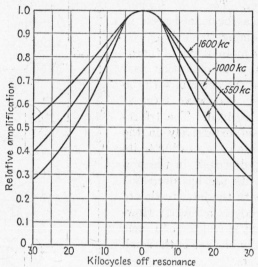

Fig. 14-7.—Curves showing the effect of frequency upon the selectivity of a typical trf amplifier stage.

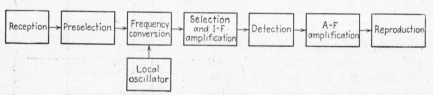

Fig. 14-8.—Block diagram of a simple superheterodyne receiver.

circuit will show that as the movable arm C approaches A a greater portion of the signal input is shunted to ground, thereby decreasing the signal strength in the primary of the antenna coil T_1. As the arm C approaches B less current is shunted to ground and the signal strength in the primary of T_1 increases. Also, advancing the movable arm C toward point A increases the cathode bias resistance (R_2 plus the resistance in section B-C of R_1), thereby reducing the amplification produced at VT_1 and VT_2, thus decreasing the volume. When the movable contact C is advanced toward B, the cathode bias of VT_1 and VT_2 is decreased and the volume will be increased.

Table XIV-I

Part No.	Name	Function	Described in	Illustrated in Fig. No.	Approximate value
T_1	Antenna coil	Reception and tuning	2-8, 6-2, Chap. VII	2-17, 6-5	
T_2, T_3	R-f transformer	Tuning	2-8, 6-2, Chap. VII	2-17, 6-5	
T_4	Output transformer	Impedance matching	2-8, 9-19	2-12	
T_5	Power transformer	Voltage transformation	2-8, 11-2	2-15	
VT_1, VT_2	Pentode	R-f amplification	4-14, Chap. VII	4-25	6K7
VT_3	Pentode	Biased detection and a-f amplification	4-14, Chaps. V, VIII	4-25	6J7
VT_4	Pentode	A-f power amplification	Chap. IX	4-25	6F6
VT_5	Duo-diode	Full-wave rectification	11-3, 11-4	4-15	5Y4-G
C_1, C_2, C_3	Three-gang variable capacitor	Tuning	6-2, 6-7	6-15	365 μμf (each)
C_4, C_5, C_6	Trimmer capacitors	Alignment	6-5, 6-8, 14-15	2-25, 6-15	
C_7	Paper capacitor	Cathode bias by-pass	5-4, 7-2	2-21	0.1 μf, 200 volts
C_8	Paper capacitor	R-f by-pass, decoupling	8-18, 14-4	2-21	0.1 μf, 200 volts
C_9	Paper capacitor	Cathode bias by-pass	5-4	2-21	0.1 μf, 200 volts
C_{10}	Paper capacitor	Screen-grid r-f by-pass	14-4	2-21	0.1 μf, 400 volts
C_{11}	Mica capacitor	R-f by-pass	5-3	2-21	200 to 500 μμf
C_{12}	Paper capacitor	Blocking	8-5	2-21	0.05 μf, 400 volts
C_{13}	Electrolytic capacitor	Cathode bias by-pass	5-4, 7-2	2-23	10 μf, 25 volts
C_{14}	Paper capacitor	Tone control	14-4	2-21	0.05 to 0.1 μf, 400 volts
C_{15}	Paper capacitor	High a-f attenuation	8-11, 8-12	2-21	0.005 to 0.01 μf, 400 to 600 volts
C_{16}, C_{17}	Electrolytic capacitor	B supply filter	11-7, 11-8	2-23	8 to 16 μf, 450 volts
C_{18}	Paper capacitor	Line filter	14-4	2-21	0.01 to 0.05 μf, 400 volts
R_1	Potentiometer	Volume control	2-2, 14-4	2-1	10,000 ohms
R_2	Carbon resistor	Provides cathode bias	5-4, 7-2	2-1	200 to 300 ohms

TABLE XIV-I.—(*Continued*)

Part No.	Name	Function	Described in	Illustrated in Fig. No.	Approximate value
R_3	Carbon resistor	To reduce voltage	14-4	2-1	40,000 to 60,000 ohms, 1 watt
R_4	Carbon resistor	Decoupling	8-18, 14-4	2-1	50,000 to 75,000 ohms, 1 watt
R_5	Carbon resistor	Provides cathode bias	5-4	2-1	10,000 to 50,000 ohms, $\frac{1}{4}$ watt
R_6	Carbon resistor	To reduce voltage	14-4	2-1	1 to 2 megohms, $\frac{1}{2}$ watt
R_7	Carbon resistor	Coupling	8-5	2-1	$\frac{1}{4}$ megohm, $\frac{1}{4}$ watt
R_8	Carbon resistor	Grid leak	8-5	2-1	$\frac{1}{4}$ to $\frac{1}{2}$ megohm, $\frac{1}{4}$ watt
R_9	Carbon resistor	Provides cathode bias	5-4, 7-2	2-1	400 ohms, 1 watt
R_{10}	Potentiometer	Tone control	2-2, 14-4	2-1	25,000 to 100,000 ohms
S_1	SPST switch	"On" and "Off" control	14-4		
LS	Loudspeaker	Reproduction of sound	12-10	12-13	
L_1	Field winding	Provides magnetic field, serves as filter choke	11-7, 11-8, 12-10	12-13	

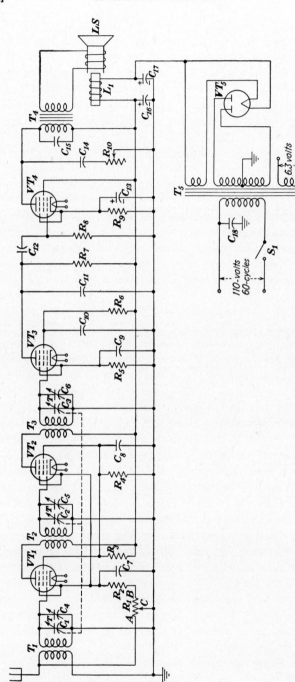

Fig. 14-9.—Circuit diagram of a five-tube, a-c operated, trf receiver.

Screen-grid Voltage-dropping Resistor. In the operation of pentode tubes, particularly in r-f amplifiers and in detector applications, it is common practice to operate the screen grids at a lower voltage than the plates. In order to avoid the use of high wattage resistors necessary at a voltage divider network, the screen grids are usually fed through a comparatively low-wattage carbon resistor directly from the high-voltage B power supply source. Resistors R_3 and R_6 of Fig. 14-9 are used for this purpose.

Screen-grid R-f By-pass Capacitors. Capacitors C_8 and C_{10} of Fig. 14-9 are sometimes referred to as the *screen-grid r-f by-pass capacitors* because they by-pass the r-f currents to ground instead of permitting these currents to flow through the screen-grid voltage-dropping resistors and on through the B power supply. Since the power supply acts as a common coupling impedance for all plate and screen-grid currents, any r-f currents flowing through the power source may cause trouble. Capacitors C_8 and C_{10} may therefore also be called *decoupling capacitors;* in fact the combination of R_4 and C_8 is often referred to as a *decoupling circuit.*

Tone Control. The potentiometer R_{10} and the capacitor C_{14} in Fig. 14-9 serve as a tone-control circuit. It should be observed that these two circuit elements are connected in series and that they provide a path to ground for a portion of the a-f current. The value of C_{14} is such that only the higher values of the audio frequencies are shunted to ground. The value of R_{10} determines the percentage of the a-f current that is shunted to ground instead of being permitted to flow through the primary of the output transformer. Thus, when the value of R_{10} is made very low, only the currents of the low and medium audio frequencies will pass through the output transformer and hence the loudspeaker accentuates the bass notes. By increasing the value of R_{10}, the higher frequency notes approach their normal strength and the bass is no longer accentuated.

Line Filter Capacitor. In receivers operated from power lines, it is common practice to connect a capacitor from one input line wire to ground as indicated by capacitor C_{18} in Fig. 14-9. The purpose of this capacitor is to by-pass any line voltage disturbances to ground, so that they will have little or no effect upon the operation of the receiver.

Receiver Power Switch. In many receivers, the control of the power source is obtained by use of a spst switch. This switch is connected in series with the power source. The switch is generally mounted on the back of the volume control and is operated by the same shaft and knob used to control the volume.

14-5. The Superheterodyne Receiver. *Definitions.* From the IRE definitions of terms: (1) *superheterodyne reception* is a form of heterodyne reception in which one or more frequency changes take place before detection, (2) *heterodyne reception* (beat reception) is the process of operation on radio waves to obtain similarly modulated waves of different frequency; in general, this process includes the use of a locally generated wave, which determines the change of frequency.

A *superheterodyne receiver* may thus be defined as one in which one or more changes of frequency are produced before the a-f signal is extracted from the modulated wave. However, the name superheterodyne is generally applied to receivers in which only one frequency change is made before a-f detection takes place, while a receiver using two intermediate frequencies is usually called a *double superheterodyne receiver*. As the average a-m broadcast receiver is required to operate at only comparatively low frequencies (550 to 1600 kc), there is no advantage of practical value in having two or more r-f frequency changes. The following discussion will be limited to a-m broadcast receiver circuits and therefore only the single superheterodyne circuit will be presented.

Advantages of the Superheterodyne Receiver. In the development of radio receivers, two types of receiving circuits have had outstanding use. They are the tuned-radio-frequency receiver (Art. 14-4) and the superheterodyne receiver. While both of these types have found considerable use, the superheterodyne has a number of advantages that have resulted in almost universal use of the superheterodyne circuit for average broadcast receivers. Its advantages over the trf receiver are (1) improved selectivity in terms of stations on adjacent channels, (2) more uniform selectivity over the broadcast band, (3) improved stability of operation, (4) the fact that a large portion of its amplification is obtained at a single (i-f) frequency instead of over the entire r-f range of the receiver, (5) higher gain per stage due to obtaining the amplification at the lower frequency value of the i-f stages.

The fundamental principle of the superheterodyne receiver has already been stated in Art. 14-3. The block diagram of Fig. 14-8 shows the various functions performed in the receiver. As some of these functions have not been discussed in the previous portions of the text they will now be studied.

14-6. Reception and Preselection. *Reception.* The function of reception is performed at the antenna, as is indicated in the various preceding block diagrams. For broadcast reception the antenna may be of the simple outdoor type, as shown in Fig. 3-4, or a loop antenna, as shown in Fig. 3-5. Because superheterodyne receivers are very sensitive and can thus operate with weak signals, it is possible to obtain satisfactory reception of all local stations and some distant stations with a loop antenna. In modern receivers, the loop antenna is made small enough to fit inside the receiver cabinet even with the smallest portable receivers.

There are several types of loop-antenna designs. In one type, the loop antenna contains both primary and secondary windings, which are connected in the same manner as an ordinary r-f antenna coil. The primary winding consists of a low number of turns and is made as large as the cabinet of the receiver will permit. The secondary has a greater number of turns, usually of a smaller size of wire, and may or may not be of the same overall dimensions as the primary. In most cases only the secondary circuit is tuned by use of a variable capacitor. Another type of loop antenna has only a single coil, which is connected in a manner similar to that of the secondary winding of the ordinary r-f antenna transformer. This circuit is tuned by use of a variable capacitor and if a fairly large size of wire is used the coil resistance can be kept low, thereby producing a high value of Q and obtaining a reasonably high value of signal voltage from the desired station.

The disadvantages of the loop antenna are: (1) the signal voltage applied to the grid of the first tube will be lower than if an outdoor antenna had been used; (2) the strength of the signal will be affected by the position of the loop antenna. The advantages of the loop antenna are: (1) unsightly, and sometimes dangerous, outdoor antennas can be eliminated; (2) the directional effect may be used to advantage in reducing or eliminating noises from local sources.

Preselection. In superheterodyne receivers, any tuning circuits located before frequency conversion takes place are generally referred to as *preselectors.* In Fig. 14-10, preselection takes place at the tuned circuit formed by the secondary of T_1 and capacitor C_1. It is general practice to have at least one preselection stage as just indicated. In the more expensive broadcast receivers, and in some short-wave (high-frequency) receivers, additional preselection stages are used (see Fig. 14-13). These additional stages are transformer-coupled r-f amplifiers and have been previously discussed. As in the previous cases, these r-f amplifiers are generally operated with untuned primaries and tuned secondaries and usually employ pentode tubes. The advantages derived by the use of preselection are (1) improved selectivity, (2) improved image suppression (see Art. 14-11), (3) improved signal-to-noise ratio.

14-7. Frequency Conversion. *Need for the Frequency Converter.* It is often said that the frequency converter is the heart of the superheterodyne receiver. This is readily understandable, since the advantages of the superheterodyne receiver are gained by reducing the frequency of the various r-f input signals to a constant i-f signal. This change in frequency is accomplished at the *frequency converter,* sometimes called the *mixer* or *first detector.*

Methods of Obtaining Frequency Conversion. The process of obtaining frequency conversion requires three fundamental functions, namely, oscillation, mixing, and detection. An oscillator circuit, generally called the *local oscillator*, is required to set up a frequency differing in value from the signal frequency in order to produce a heterodyne action. A *mixer* is required to obtain a new frequency by combining the signal frequency with that of the local oscillator through heterodyne action. As detector action is required to extract the beat frequencies obtained by the heterodyne action, the mixer is also called the *first detector*.

Explanation of the Fundamental Functions. The local oscillator circuits are either similar to or are merely variations of the fundamental oscillators presented in Chap. X. The oscillator may employ a separate vacuum tube or it may use a portion of the converter tube. Two important considerations in the oscillator circuit are (1) to sustain oscillation over the entire frequency range, (2) to avoid having the increase in the oscillator output voltage (as the oscillator frequency is increased) drive the grid of the mixer tube positive. If the feedback of the oscillator drops too low at the lower values of oscillator frequency, the tube may stop oscillating at the lower end of the frequency range. This may be corrected by increasing the coupling between the oscillator plate and grid circuits, but care should be exercised so that the corresponding increase in voltage at the higher frequencies does not adversely affect the operation of the mixer tube.

The function of mixing is accomplished by applying both the modulated r-f signal and the unmodulated local oscillator output to the mixer tube. There are a number of methods of feeding these two voltages to the mixer and several of these are presented in the following discussion. In general, when two signal voltages of different frequencies are applied to the mixer, the current in the plate circuit will contain many frequencies, namely, (1) the original signal frequency, (2) the local oscillator frequency, (3) the sum of the signal and oscillator frequencies, (4) the difference of the signal and oscillator frequencies, (5) numerous other frequencies produced by combinations of the fundamentals and harmonics of the signal and oscillator frequencies. Of these, the signal, the local oscillator, and the sum and difference frequencies will be the strongest. The sum and difference frequencies are the result of heterodyne action and of these only the difference frequency is used in a-m broadcast band superheterodyne receivers. The theory of the heterodyne action was presented in Art. 5-7 and the manner in which the difference frequency is obtained is illustrated by Fig. 5-16.

Applying the r-f signal and the local oscillator output voltages to a tube does not necessarily result in a beat frequency output. Although only the two original frequencies are applied, the envelopes formed by combining these frequencies will be of new values equal to the sum and difference of the two. The detector action of the converter tube makes it possible to obtain the envelope frequencies in the output circuit. The first detector tube is usually operated on a nonlinear portion of its characteristic curve and operates as a plate detector (see Art. 5-3). The output of the detector will contain the same a-f signal modulation that was present in the original r-f signal input.

Conversion Gain. In addition to the functions of mixing and detection, a certain amount of i-f amplification also takes place during the process of frequency conversion. The ratio of the i-f voltage developed in the output of the converter to the r-f signal input voltage is called the *conversion gain,* or *conversion efficiency.* The voltage amplification obtained at the converter varies from about 0.3 to 0.5 times the value which would be obtained with a similar tube operated as an i-f amplifier. For example, a tube that could produce a voltage amplification of 100 when operated as an i-f amplifier will only provide a voltage amplification of from 30 to 50 when operated as a frequency converter.

14-8. Frequency Converter Circuits. In the development of superheterodyne receivers, numerous circuits designed to obtain frequency conversion have been introduced. Some circuits require the use of two tubes, while others accomplish the purpose with a single tube. As the variety of circuits is vast, only the fundamental and the commonly used circuits will be presented. A more extensive treatment of frequency converters can be obtained from the references listed at the end of this chapter.

Simple Converter Circuits. The first superheterodyne receivers used separate tubes for the oscillator and the mixer or first detector as shown in Fig. 14-10. Although the tubes illustrated in Fig. 14-10 are triodes, tetrodes and pentodes may also be used. The circuits in both figures are identical except for the manner in which the oscillator output is coupled to the mixer. In Fig. 14-10a the oscillator output is inductively coupled to the mixer at T_4 and in Fig. 14-10b the output is capacitively coupled by means of capacitor C_7.

It should be observed that both the r-f signal and the oscillator output are applied to the control grid. The electron stream flowing from the cathode to the plate will thus be affected by both voltages. With the proper amount of grid bias, VT_1 can be operated as a plate detector. As the current in the plate circuit of VT_1 contains numerous frequencies and as only the difference frequency is desired, the double-tuned transformer T_3 is tuned to the desired i-f value. Because of the excellent selectivity of the double-tuned i-f transformer (see Art. 7-6), only the desired frequency is passed on to the succeeding circuits, all other fre-

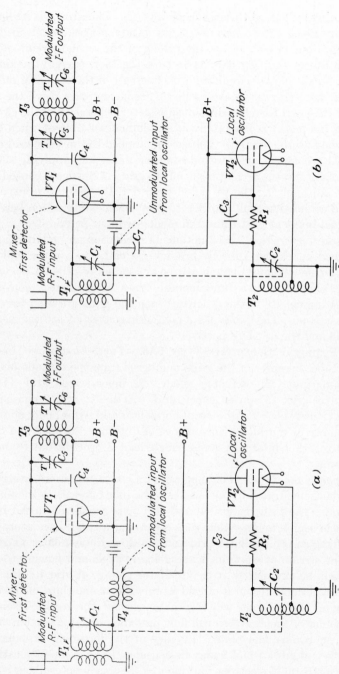

Fig. 14-10.—Simple frequency converter circuits. (a) Oscillator output inductively coupled, (b) oscillator output capacitively coupled.

quencies being by-passed through capacitor C_4. This circuit is no longer used to any great extent because of its disadvantages, which are: (1) the tuning of one circuit affects the tuning of the second circuit, which sometimes causes the two circuits to lock together, thereby making it difficult to track the two circuits; (2) the increase of the oscillator output voltage with an increase in the oscillator frequency may drive the grid of VT_1 positive and thereby cause unsatisfactory operation of the circuit.

Among the methods used to avoid the difficulties present when both the r-f signal and the oscillator voltage are applied to the same grid as in Fig. 14-10, are (1) using a tetrode for the mixer and applying the r-f signal to grid 1 and the oscillator output to grid 2; (2) using a pentode for the mixer and applying the r-f signal to grid 1, the oscillator output to grid 3, and connecting grid 2 to B+ to provide shielding action between the r-f signal input at grid 1 and the oscillator input at grid 3.

Pentagrid Converters. The functions of oscillation and mixing can be accomplished in a single tube by providing a cathode, a plate, and five grids in a single envelope. Such a tube is commonly called a *pentagrid converter.* There are two fundamental types of pentagrid converter tubes, differing chiefly in the order in which the grids are used for their various functions. The two types of pentagrid converters are represented by the 6A8 and the 6SA7 respectively.

14-9. Pentagrid Converter—Type 6A8. *Tube Electrodes.* In the type 6A8 tube the order of the grids numbered from the cathode out are (1) oscillator grid, (2) oscillator anode, (3) inner screen grid, (4) r-f signal control grid, (5) outer screen grid. Actually, grid 2 consists of only two vertical side rods, the usual horizontal grid wires being omitted, but it is shown as a grid for convenience of drawing. Grids 3 and 5 are connected together internally and a single lead is brought out to one of the base pins.

Operation of the Tube. The diagram of a converter circuit using this type of tube is illustrated in Fig. 14-11. The tube operates in the following manner. The cathode, grid 1, and grid 2 are connected to the external circuit in such a manner that they operate as a triode oscillator, with grid 1 serving as the oscillator grid and grid 2 as the oscillator anode or plate. The stream of electrons leaving the cathode and flowing toward the plate will be modulated by the oscillator voltage at grid 1. Because of the constructional features of grid 2, only about one-third of the electrons leaving the cathode will return by way of the oscillator anode. The remainder of the electrons will flow past the oscillator portion of the tube and on toward the plate. In view of the foregoing explanation, the cathode and grids 1 and 2 may be considered as a composite cathode supplying a stream of electrons varying at a frequency determined by the

tuned circuit of the oscillator.   Grid 3 is connected to B+ and its function is to accelerate the flow of electrons.   Grid 4 serves as a control grid
and is connected to the r-f signal source, thereby producing an additional
control on the electron stream flowing from the cathode to the plate.
Grid 5 is connected to B+ and its function is to accelerate the flow of
electrons.   As the screen grids 3 and 5 are operated at a lower voltage
than the plate, they serve chiefly as an accelerating force, the higher
plate potential causing the majority of the electrons to flow through the

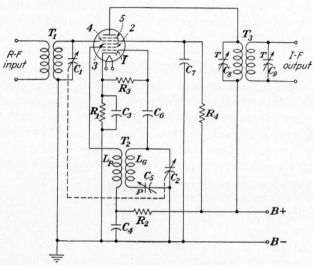

FIG. 14-11.—Frequency converter circuit using a pentagrid converter tube similar to the
type 6A8.

plate circuit.   Grids 3 and 5 serve the additional function of shielding
grid 4 from the other electrodes of the tube.   This method of coupling
the r-f signal and oscillator output is referred to as *electron coupling.*

Operation of the Circuit.   The circuit of Fig. 14-11 operates in the
following manner.   The r-f signals are received at the primary of the
r-f transformer T_1, and selection of the desired station is made by means
of the tuning circuit consisting of the secondary of T_1 and capacitor C_1.
The r-f signal voltage of the selected station is applied to grid 4, where it
modulates the electron stream flowing from the cathode to the plate of
the tube.   The local oscillator employs a simple tuned-grid feedback
oscillator circuit.   The oscillator frequency is controlled by the grid
tank circuit, consisting of the coil L_G and capacitor C_2; capacitor C_5 is a
padder used for aligning the oscillator circuit as described in Art. 14-16.
The feedback necessary to produce and sustain oscillations is obtained
from the coil L_P in the oscillator plate circuit.   Resistor R_3 and capacitor

C_6 provide the bias for the oscillator portion of the converter. Resistor R_1 and capacitor C_3 provide the bias for the tetrode mixer portion of the converter. Resistor R_2 is a voltage-dropping resistor used to obtain the proper voltage at the oscillator anode, and together with capacitor C_4 also acts as a filter circuit. Resistor R_4 is a screen-grid voltage-dropping resistor and together with capacitor C_7 also serves as a screen-grid filter circuit. The plate current, from which the output of the converter is obtained, is fed through the primary of the doubly tuned i-f transformer T_3. Because of the band-pass tuning characteristics of the i-f transformer, only the desired frequency appears at the output terminals of T_3.

Characteristics of the Circuit. Three minor disadvantages of this type of frequency converter circuit are: (1) the oscillator frequency will vary slightly with variations in the bias of the tetrode section; (2) some oscillator-frequency current may flow in the r-f signal circuit, thereby overloading the r-f signal grid and reducing the conversion efficiency; (3) the low transconductance of the oscillator section affects the operation of the oscillator at high frequencies. These effects can be minimized by modifying the construction of the tube, as is done in the type 6SA7.

Other pentagrid converter tubes of the 6A8 type are the 1A6, 1A7-G, 1C6, 1C7-G, 1D7-G, 2A7, 6A7, 6D8-G, 7B8, and 12A8-GT.

14-10. Pentagrid Converter—Type 6SA7. *Tube Electrodes.* In the type 6SA7 tube the order of the grids numbered from the cathode out are (1) oscillator grid, (2) inner screen grid, (3) r-f signal control grid, (4) outer screen grid, (5) suppressor grid. (Grids 2 and 4 combined serve as a composite anode of the oscillator triode.) In addition, a pair of collector plates are mounted on the side rods of grid 2. Grids 2 and 4 are connected together internally and a single lead is brought out to one of the base pins.

Operation of the Tube. The diagram of a converter circuit using this type of tube is illustrated in Fig. 14-12. The tube operates in the following manner. The cathode, grid 1, and grids 2 and 4 are connected to the external circuit in such a manner that they operate as a triode oscillator, with grid 1 serving as the oscillator grid and grids 2 and 4 serving as a composite anode for the oscillator. The stream of electrons leaving the cathode and flowing toward the plate will be modulated by the oscillator voltage at grid 1. Some of the electrons upon passing grid 1 will return to the cathode by way of grid 2. The remainder of the electrons will be drawn on toward grid 4 because of their acceleration and because of the positive potential of grid 4. However, before reaching grid 4 the electron stream will be further modulated by the r-f signal voltage at grid 3. As grid 3 is generally biased negatively, some electrons will be driven back toward the cathode. If these electrons succeed in reaching the space charge area about the cathode they will cause a change in the amount of cathode current.   However, before reaching the space charge area these electrons are attracted to the positive collector plates mounted on the side rods of grid 2 and are returned to the cathode through the B power supply.   Thus the collector plates help to maintain the cathode current practically constant, which is one of the important advantages of this type of converter tube.   Thus far it has been shown that the electron stream in its travel from the cathode toward grid 4 has been modulated by both the oscillator and r-f signal voltages.   Of those electrons which

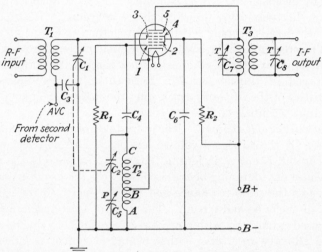

Fig. 14-12.—Frequency converter circuit using a pentagrid converter tube similar to the type 6SA7.

pass grid 3, some will return to the cathode by way of grid 4 and the remainder by way of the plate circuit.   The r-f signal voltage at grid 3 produces variations in the plate current, which is of course essential to the operation of the converter circuit.   As the signal voltage at grid 3 also produces an approximately equal change in the current of grid 4 but opposite in direction to the plate current change, the cathode current will not be affected to any appreciable extent by changes in the r-f signal voltage.   Grid 5 acts as a suppressor grid and may be connected directly to the cathode or to ground.   Its function is similar to the suppressor grid in a pentode.

Operation of the Circuit.   The circuit of Fig. 14-12 operates in the following manner.   The r-f signals are received at the primary of the r-f transformer T_1 and selection of the desired station is made by means of the tuning circuit consisting of the secondary of T_1 and capacitor C_1.

The r-f signal voltage of the selected station is applied to grid 3, where it modulates the electron stream flowing from the cathode to the plate of the tube.   The local oscillator is a variation of the Hartley circuit.   The oscillator coil T_2 is an autotransformer connected so that any variations in the cathode current flowing through section AB will induce a voltage in section BC.   This induced voltage is applied to the oscillator grid and provides the feedback necessary to produce and sustain oscillations.   The oscillator frequency is determined by the tuned circuit formed by the oscillator coil T_2 and capacitors C_2 and C_5.   The oscillator grid bias is obtained by means of resistor R_1 and capacitor C_4.   Capacitor C_3 is used to prevent short-circuiting the avc voltage to ground.   Resistor R_2 is a screen-grid voltage-dropping resistor and together with capacitor C_6 also serves as a screen-grid filter circuit.   The plate current, from which the output of the converter is obtained, is fed through the primary of the doubly tuned i-f transformer T_3.   Because of the band-pass tuning characteristics of the i-f transformer, only the desired frequency appears at the output terminals of T_3.

Characteristics of the Circuit.   The advantages of this type of converter circuit are: (1) the r-f signal voltage has practically no effect upon the cathode current, hence variations in the avc bias applied to the r-f input will not cause any detuning of the oscillator; (2) the use of a suppressor grid increases the plate resistance and thereby increases the conversion efficiency of the tube and circuit.   This type of tube and its associated circuit is used extensively with a-c/d-c receivers for both single broadcast band and all-wave receivers.   Other pentagrid converter tubes of the 6SA7 type are the 1R5, 12SA7, 7Q7, and 14Q7.

14-11. The Intermediate-frequency Characteristics.   *Frequencies Present at the Converter.*   When the r-f signal and the oscillator output are combined, the output current of the first detector will contain (1) the r-f signal frequency, (2) the oscillator frequency, (3) the sum of the r-f signal and oscillator frequencies, (4) the difference of the r-f signal and oscillator frequencies, (5) numerous other frequencies produced by combinations of the fundamentals and harmonics of the r-f signal and oscillator frequencies.   For example, if a receiver has its r-f circuit tuned to 550 kc and its oscillator is tuned to 1015 kc, the frequencies appearing at the first detector output will be 550, 1015, 1565, and 465 kc and harmonics of these frequencies.   Of these, only the difference frequency of 465 kc is desired; the reason for using the difference frequency will soon become apparent.   As the output of the first detector is fed directly to the highly selective i-f amplifier, tuning this amplifier to 465 kc will result in acceptance of the 465-kc currents and rejection of the currents of all other frequencies.

Image-frequency Signals. It is possible that with a certain value of oscillator frequency the desired value of i-f can be obtained from two different carrier frequencies at the same time. For example, an r-f signal of 550 kc and an oscillator frequency of 1015 kc will produce an i-f signal of 465 kc. It is also possible to obtain a 465-kc i-f signal with the same oscillator frequency if an r-f signal of 1480 kc reaches the first detector. Of these two 465-kc i-f signals only one is desired; the undesired signal is called the *image-frequency signal.* The effect of image-frequency signals may be minimized or eliminated by providing one or more stages of r-f tuning or preselection. The ratio of the output from the desired r-f signal to that from the undesired r-f signal is called the *signal-to-image ratio* or simply the *image ratio.* The effect of image frequency signals is present mostly in short-wave receivers operating at high frequencies and in receivers designed to operate at a low i-f value.

Choice of the Intermediate-frequency Value. Throughout the development of superheterodyne receivers a wide range of values have been used for the intermediate frequency. At the start, values as low as 50 kc were used, and in short-wave receivers values of several megacycles may be used. In receivers intended for use on the broadcast band only, the i-f values range from approximately 130 to 485 kc the value varying with the manufacturer and the design of the receiver. Among the values of i-f used for broadcast receivers are, 130, 175, 262, 345, 450, 455, 456, 460, 465, 470, and 485 kc. The majority of home receivers use either 455, 456, or 465 kc, while many receivers designed for use in automobiles employ an i-f value of either 175 or 262 kc.

The choice of frequency for the i-f is affected by a number of factors. Two important factors are (1) the tuning ratio, (2) selectivity.

Tuning Ratio. The purpose of the converter is to combine the variable r-f signal input with the variable oscillator frequency and thereby obtain a constant frequency output from the converter. This can best be accomplished by increasing the oscillator frequency by the same amount that the frequency of the preselector circuit is increased. Under this condition the difference in frequency between the r-f input and the oscillator can be maintained practically constant. The intermediate frequency can be obtained by making the oscillator frequency either higher or lower than the r-f signal by the amount of the i-f desired. In broadcast receivers it is almost universal practice to make the oscillator frequency higher than the r-f signal. In short-wave receivers the oscillator frequency may be made either higher or lower than the r-f signal. By making the oscillator frequency of a broadcast receiver higher than the r-f signal it becomes possible to obtain a more desirable frequency range for the oscillator, as is illustrated by the following example. If it is desired to have a receiver operate over an r-f range of 550 to 1600 kc and maintain a 465-kc intermediate frequency, the oscillator will have to be tuned from 85 to 1135 kc if the oscillator frequency is to be lower than the r-f signal or from 1015 to 2065 kc if the oscillator frequency is to be higher than the r-f signal. With the lower oscillator frequency the required tuning ratio is approximately 13 to 1 while for the high frequency the ratio is approximately only 2 to 1. It is thus obvious why broadcast receivers are designed to have the oscillator frequency higher than the r-f signal input.

Selectivity. The use of low i-f values, that is, in the order of 130, 175, and 262 kc, has the advantage of improved selectivity of stations on adjacent broadcast channels. This becomes apparent when the difference in frequency between stations on adjacent channels is expressed as a percentage of the frequency at which tuning and amplification take place. As adjacent broadcast transmitter frequencies may be as little as 10 kc apart, this percentage for an i-f of 175 kc is 5.7 per cent, for 262 kc it is 3.8 per cent, and for 465 kc it is 2.1 per cent. Incidentally, this provides an excellent means of showing one advantage of the superheterodyne over the trf receiver where the percentage is 1.8 at the lower frequency limit of 550 kc and only 0.625 per cent at the upper frequency limit of 1600 kc. Use of low i-f values, however, results in greater possibility of image-frequency interference because the image frequency gets closer to the desired station frequency as the i-f value is reduced. Accordingly, most manufacturers of broadcast receivers now use i-f values of approximately 450 to 470 kc. It is interesting to note that most i-f values are odd numbers such as 456, 465, 472.5, etc., in preference to such values as 450, 460, and 470. Use of the odd-number values reduces the possibility of two transmitter carrier frequencies heterodyning with one another and producing a signal of the same value as the intermediate frequency, which, of course, would cause interference with the signal of the desired carrier wave.

Spurious Responses. There are some additional sources of interference sometimes present in superheterodyne receivers. These are usually due to the effects of harmonics generated in some portion of the receiver, which find their way to the i-f input. These interferences are generally referred to as *spurious responses.* Among the possible causes of spurious responses are: (1) harmonics of the intermediate frequency generated by the a-f detector (sometimes called the second detector) that may find their way back to the r-f circuit or to the i-f input through stray coupling or feedback; (2) harmonics of an r-f signal generated by the first detector, particularly the second harmonics of stations with carrier frequencies of from 550 to 800 kc; (3) harmonics of the oscillator, which may beat with

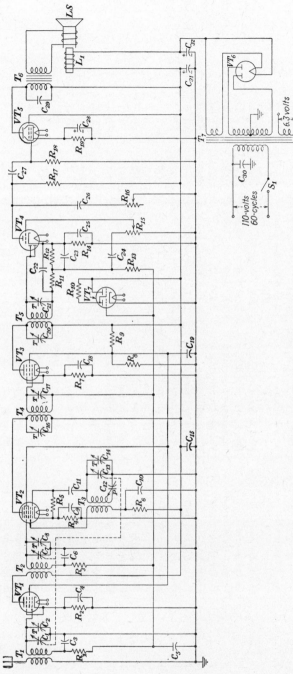

FIG. 14-13.—Circuit diagram of a seven-tube, a-c operated, superheterodyne receiver.

TABLE XIV-II

Part No.	Name	Function	Described in	Illustrated in Fig. No.	Approximate value
T_1	Antenna coil	Reception and preselection	2-8, 6-2, 14-6 Chap. VII	2-17, 6-5	
T_2	R-f transformer	Preselection	2-8, 6-2, 14-6 Chap. VII	2-17, 6-5	
T_3	Oscillator coil	Part of local oscillator	14-9, Chap. X	2-17	
T_4, T_5	I-f transformer	Band-pass tuning	2-30, 7-6	2-17	
T_6	Output transformer	Impedance matching	2-8, 9-19	2-12	
T_7	Power transformer	Voltage transformation	2-8, 11-2	2-15	
VT_1	Pentode	R-f amplification	4-14, Chap. VII	4-25	6K7
VT_2	Pentagrid converter	Frequency conversion	14-7, 14-8, 14-9	4-25	6A8
VT_3	Pentode	I-f amplification	4-14, 7-6	4-25	6K7
VT_4	Duo-diode—triode	Detection and a-f voltage amplification	Chaps. V, VIII	4-25	6Q7
VT_5	Beam power tube	A-f power amplification	4-16, Chap. IX	4-25	6V6
VT_6	Full-wave rectifier	Full-wave rectification	11-3, 11-4	4-15	5Y4-G
VT_7	Electron-ray tube	Tuning indicator	14-13	14-15	6U5/6G5
C_1, C_7, C_{13}	3-gang variable capacitor	Tuning	6-2, 6-7, 14-12	6-15	365 $\mu\mu$f (each)
C_2, C_8, C_{14}	Trimmer capacitor	Alignment	6-8, 14-16	2-25, 6-15	
C_3, C_6	Paper capacitor	Coupling and blocking	2-26, 2-27, 2-28	2-21	0.05 μf, 200 volts
C_4, C_9	Paper capacitor	Cathode bias by-pass	5-4, 7-2	2-21	0.1 μf, 200 volts
C_5	Paper capacitor	AVC by-pass	5-11	2-21	0.05 μf, 200 volts
C_{10}	Paper capacitor	Oscillator by-pass	2-26, 2-27	2-21	0.05 μf, 400 volts
C_{11}	Mica capacitor	Oscillator bias	10-5, 10-6	2-21	250 $\mu\mu$f
C_{12}	Padder capacitor	Tracking	14-16	2-25	
C_{15}	Paper capacitor	Decoupling	2-26, 2-27, 8-18	2-21	0.1 μf, 400 volts
C_{16}, C_{17}, C_{20}, C_{21}	Adjustable capacitor	Band-pass adjustment	14-16	2-17, 2-25	
C_{18}	Paper capacitor	Cathode bias by-pass	5-4, 7-2	2-21	0.05 μf, 200 volts

C_{19}	Paper capacitor	Decoupling	8-18, 14-4	2-21	0.1 μf, 200 volts
C_{22}	Mica capacitor	I-f by-pass	5-2	2-21	250 μμf
C_{23}	Mica capacitor	I-f filter	5-2	2-21	250 μμf
C_{24}	Paper capacitor	A-f coupling	5-2	2-21	0.05 μf, 200 volts
C_{25}, C_{28}	Electrolytic capacitor	Cathode bias by-pass	5-4, 7-2	2-23	10 μf, 25 volts
C_{26}	Paper capacitor	Tone control	14-4	2-21	0.05 μf, 400 volts
C_{27}	Paper capacitor	Blocking	8-5	2-21	0.05 μf, 400 volts
C_{29}	Paper capacitor	High a-f attenuation	8-11, 8-12	2-21	0.006 μf, 600 volts
C_{30}	Paper capacitor	Line filter	14-4	2-21	0.05 μf, 600 volts
C_{31}, C_{32}	Electrolytic capacitor	B supply filter	11-7, 11-8	2-23	15 μf, 450 volts
R_1, R_3	Carbon resistor	AVC filter	2-26, 2-27, 2-28	2-1	100,000 ohms, $\frac{1}{4}$ watt
R_2	Carbon resistor	Provides cathode bias	5-4, 7-2	2-1	800 ohms, $\frac{1}{4}$ watt
R_4	Carbon resistor	Provides cathode bias	5-4, 7-2	2-1	400 ohms, $\frac{1}{4}$ watt
R_5	Carbon resistor	Provides oscillator bias	10-5, 10-6	2-1	50,000 ohms, $\frac{1}{4}$ watt
R_6	Carbon resistor	To reduce voltage	2-1, 14-9	2-1	30,000 ohms, 1 watt
R_7	Carbon resistor	Provides cathode bias	5-4, 7-2	2-1	500 ohms, $\frac{1}{4}$ watt
R_8	Carbon resistor	Decoupling	8-18, 14-4	2-1	40,000 ohms, $\frac{1}{2}$ watt
R_9	Carbon resistor	To reduce voltage	14-4	2-1	30,000 ohms, 1 watt
R_{10}	Carbon resistor	To reduce voltage	14-13	2-1	1 megohm, $\frac{1}{4}$ watt
R_{11}	Carbon resistor	Portion of diode load	5-2	2-1	50,000 ohms, $\frac{1}{4}$ watt
R_{12}	Carbon resistor	Portion of diode load	5-2	2-1	250,000 ohms, $\frac{1}{4}$ watt
R_{13}	Carbon resistor	AVC filter	5-11	2-1	500,000 ohms, $\frac{1}{4}$ watts
R_{14}	Carbon resistor	Provides cathode bias	5-4, 7-2	2-1	2000 ohms, $\frac{1}{2}$ watt
R_{15}	Potentiometer	Volume control	2-2	2-1	500,000 ohms
R_{16}	Potentiometer	Tone control	14-4	2-1	50,000 ohms
R_{17}	Carbon resistor	Coupling	8-5	2-1	250,000 ohms, $\frac{1}{4}$ watt
R_{18}	Carbon resistor	Grid leak	8-5	2-1	500,000 ohms, $\frac{1}{4}$ watt
R_{19}	Carbon resistor	Provides cathode bias	5-4, 7-2	2-1	300 ohms, 1 watt
S_1	SPST switch	"On and Off" control	14-4		
LS	Loudspeaker	Reproduction of sound	12-10	12-13	
L_1	Field winding	Provides magnetic field, serves as filter choke	11-7, 11-8, 12-10	12-13	

the signal from a short-wave station and thus be received by the broadcast receiver; (4) interference caused by the beat frequency of two r-f signals differing in frequency by an amount equal to the i-f value; (5) reception of the r-f signal of a transmitter operating on a frequency equal to that of the i-f of the receiver. These various interferences are not present in a well-designed and carefully adjusted receiver, since they can be avoided by providing sufficient preselection and by shielding of wires, coils, and tubes to eliminate stray pickup of any undesired frequencies.

14-12. A Typical Superheterodyne Receiver Circuit. The circuit diagram of a seven-tube, a-c operated superheterodyne receiver is shown in Fig. 14-13. This circuit has one stage of r-f amplification before the first detector and consequently has two preselection circuits. The first detector or frequency converter employs a tube of the 6A8 type, and the oscillator and mixer functions are performed in the one tube. A three-gang variable capacitor represented by C_1, C_7, and C_{13} is used to tune the two r-f preselector circuits and the oscillator simultaneously. Capacitors C_2, C_8, C_{14} are trimmer capacitors for aligning the receiver and are usually mounted on the variable gang-capacitor assembly. Inclusion of the padder capacitor C_{12} in the oscillator tuning circuit is an indication that the three units of the three-gang tuning capacitor are of equal size (see Art. 14-16). The first detector is followed by one stage of i-f amplification, which in turn is followed by a diode detector circuit. Simple avc is obtained from the diode second detector circuit, the avc voltage being fed back to the grids of VT_1, VT_2, and VT_3. The a-f output of the diode detector VT_4 is fed to the triode a-f amplifier section of VT_4 and at this point volume control is obtained by means of the potentiometer R_{15}. Tone control is also obtained at this point by means of resistor R_{16} and capacitor C_{26}. One stage of resistance-capacitance-coupled a-f amplification is provided and the a-f signal is then passed through the power amplifier tube VT_5. An output transformer T_6 couples the a-f output to the loudspeaker. The plate and screen-grid voltage supplies are obtained by stepping up the supply voltage at the power transformer T_7 and rectifying it by means of a full-wave rectifier tube VT_6. The capacitor-input type of filter consists of capacitors C_{31} and C_{32} together with the loudspeaker field L_1, which is made to serve as the filter choke. Vacuum tube VT_7 is a tuning indicator and is the only part of this circuit which has not previously been described. Its purpose and function is presented in the following article. The fact that the receiver uses a power transformer limits its operation to a-c power circuits of the proper rated voltage and frequency. A list of the parts and their functions is given in Table XIV-II.

In some receivers the power transformer is eliminated and the receiver may be operated from either an a-c or a d-c power line of the proper voltage. Figure 14-14 illustrates the circuit diagram of such a receiver. The tubes used in this receiver have higher heater-voltage ratings than the tubes used in receivers employing power transformers. The tubes of this circuit have identical current ratings and their heater-voltage ratings add up to approximately 117 volts. It is therefore possible to connect the heaters in series and operate the circuit directly from the power line. The plate circuit of the rectifier tube is also operated directly

TABLE XIV-III.—VALUES OF THE CIRCUIT ELEMENTS OF FIG. 14-14

R_1 = 470 ohms	R_2 = 10 megohms	R_3 = 22,000 ohms
R_4 = 470,000 ohms	R_5 = 470 ohms	R_6 = 47,000 ohms
R_7 = 220,000 ohms	R_8 = 2.2 megohms	R_9 = 2 megohms
R_{10} = 1000 ohms	R_{11} = 5.6 megohms	R_{12} = 470,000 ohms
R_{13} = 470,000 ohms	R_{14} = 150 ohms	R_{15} = 39 ohms
R_{16} = 1200 ohms	R_{17} = 18 ohms	

C_1 = 0.01 µf	C_2 = 6–426 µµf	C_3 = 1.5–15 µµf
C_4 = 13–139 µµf	C_5 = 3–30 µµf	C_6 = 0.1 µf
C_7 = 47 µµf	C_8 = 130–170 µµf	C_9 = 130–170 µµf
C_{10} = 130–170 µµf	C_{11} = 130–170 µµf	C_{12} = 0.05 µf
C_{13} = 0.05 µf	C_{14} = 330 µµf	C_{15} = 100 µµf
C_{16} = 0.005 µf	C_{17} = 0.01 µf	C_{18} = 150 µµf
C_{19} = 0.01 µf	C_{20} = 0.01 µf	C_{21} = 0.1 µf
C_{22} = 40 µf	C_{23} = 50 µf	C_{24} = 50 µf

VT_1 = 12SA7	VT_2 = 12SG7	VT_3 = 12SQ7
VT_4 = 50L6-GT	VT_5 = 35Z5-GT/G	PL = 47 pilot lamp

from the power line and the power transformer may therefore be eliminated. Such circuits generally operate equally well on a-c or d-c power lines and are called *a-c/d-c receivers*. The fundamentals of superheterodyne principles and operation as explained for the circuit of Fig. 14-13 also apply to the remainder of this receiver circuit.

14-13. Tuning Indicators. *Need for Tuning Indicators.* In the operation of a highly selective receiver, such as that of Fig. 14-13, it should be carefully tuned so that the carrier frequency of the desired station is at the center of the response band (see Fig. 13-3). If the receiver is not properly tuned the output at the loudspeaker may be badly distorted. Various devices have been introduced for indicating when a receiver is properly tuned. The *electron-ray tube*, also called a *magic eye* or a *cathode-ray indicator tube*, is commonly used to indicate whether a receiver is properly tuned to the desired station.

Electron-ray Tube. One type of electron-ray tuning indicator is shown in Fig. 14-15. The tube illustrated contains two sections: (1) a triode consisting of the cathode, a control grid, and a plate which together

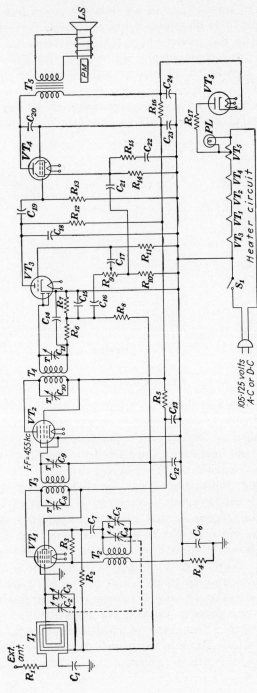

Fig. 14-14.—Circuit diagram of a five-tube a-c/d-c superheterodyne receiver.

function as a d-c amplifier; (2) the fluorescent-coated target and the ray-control electrode. The circuit connections for this type tube are illustrated in Figs. 14-13 and 14-15d. Electrons from the cathode have two paths, one to the triode plate and the other to the fluorescent target. The triode plate current is controlled by the voltage of the triode grid, and the target current is controlled by the voltage of the ray-control electrode. When electrons from the cathode strike the target they cause the coating on the target to fluoresce and give off a faint green light. When the voltage of the ray-control electrode and the target are of

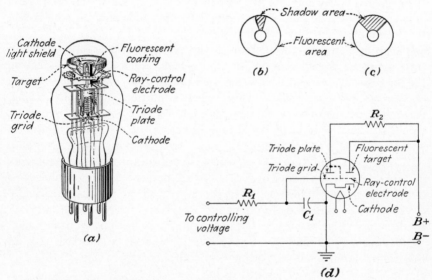

FIG. 14-15.—The tuning indicator. (a) Construction of the electron-ray tube, (b) indication when the receiver is properly tuned, (c) indication when the receiver is improperly tuned, (d) circuit connections. (*Photograph courtesy of RCA Manufacturing Co., Inc.*)

approximately equal value, the target will be illuminated evenly or may have only a very small shaded area, as indicated in Fig. 14-15b. When the voltage of the ray-control electrode is less than the target voltage, so that it is negative with respect to the target, fewer electrons reach the target and the fluorescent area decreases as indicated by Fig. 14-15c.

The tuning indicator tube is mounted in the receiver in such a manner that the fluorescent-coated target is visible to the person tuning the receiver. When the receiver is being tuned to a station the operator should observe the action taking place at this tube. The receiver is properly tuned to a station when the shadow appearing on the target covers a minimum amount of area (Fig. 14-15b). Improper tuning causes the shadow to cover a greater area, as is indicated in Fig. 14-15c.

Electron-ray Indicator Circuit. In analyzing the action of the tuning indicator in the circuit of Fig. 14-13, it should be observed that the triode grid is connected to the avc line. When the receiver is not tuned to a station, the avc voltage will be at its minimum value and the plate current of the triode section of the tuning indicator will be at its highest value. An appreciable voltage drop will be present at the one megohm resistor R_{10} and the ray-control electrode voltage will be considerably lower than the voltage at the fluorescent target. This will result in the target having a large shaded area. As the receiver tunes in a station, the negative voltage at the avc line increases. This negative voltage is applied to the triode grid of the tuning indicator and causes a reduction in the triode-plate current, which in turn reduces the voltage drop at R_{10} and thereby increases the voltage at the ray-control electrode. This in turn increases the current in the fluorescent target, thereby increasing the fluorescent area and decreasing the shaded area. As the avc voltage reaches its highest negative value when a station is properly tuned, because the diode-detector current through R_{12} will then be at its highest value, the shaded area of the tuning indicator will be at its minimum value when the receiver is properly tuned to a desired station.

Electron-ray tubes of the type just described are represented by the 6U5/6G5, 6AB5/6N5, and 6E5. There are numerous other applications of the electron-ray indicator tubes, especially in the field of measurements.

14-14. Tracking and Alignment of Receivers. *Need for Alignment.* Modern receivers are constructed so that station selection can be obtained by turning a single dial (see Art. 6-7). In order to accomplish this, all the tuning circuits must be adjusted simultaneously. This is ordinarily accomplished by use of ganged capacitors. In the trf receiver of Fig. 14-9, there are three tuning circuits and thus a three-gang variable capacitor is used to obtain single-dial tuning. In the superheterodyne receiver of Fig. 14-13, two preselector circuits and the oscillator are tuned simultaneously by means of a three-gang capacitor. In order to have a receiver properly tuned to a station, each of its tuned circuits must be adjusted so that they are resonant to the proper value of frequency. When ganged tuning is employed, it is difficult to have two or more tuned circuits have their correct resonant frequencies at all points of the dial, even with modern precision manufacturing methods. It thus becomes necessary that the tuning circuits be provided with means of adjustment so that alignment of the circuits will be as nearly uniform as is practically possible over the entire frequency range of the receiver. When this is accomplished the circuits are said to be tracking each other. The fundamental principles of equalizing the tuning circuits was presented in Art. 6-8.

There are two reasons why a receiver should be carefully aligned. First, correct alignment is necessary in order to obtain the best possible performance of the receiver. Second, proper alignment is required in order to calibrate the receiver dial, that is, to have it receive a desired station at its designated position on the dial.

Method of Aligning a Receiver. Accurate alignment can best be accomplished by use of a signal generator and a meter or other device that will indicate the strength of the output signal of the receiver. The signal generator should have a calibrated variable r-f output of sufficient frequency range to check all the frequencies at which the receiver is to operate. The signal generator should also be provided with a means of modulating its r-f output with an a-f signal of constant value, preferably in the order of 400 cycles. As the procedure in aligning a receiver is based on obtaining the maximum output for a given setting of the receiver, the device for indicating the output need only indicate whether maximum output is being obtained. Among the devices used for obtaining an indication of the relative value of the output are (1) an output meter, (2) a magic-eye tuning indicator, especially if it is already a part of the receiver circuit, (3) a vacuum-tube voltmeter, (4) a cathode-ray oscilloscope.

When the output of a signal generator is applied to the antenna and ground terminals of a receiver for the purpose of aligning the receiver, it is usually desirable to connect a small capacitor between the high-side terminal of the signal generator and the antenna terminal of the receiver. This capacitor is used to make allowance for the antenna that is normally connected to the receiver and is therefore called a *dummy antenna;* for broadcast receivers a 200-$\mu\mu$f capacitor is recommended. If the receiver has a loop antenna, the signal generator output may be coupled to the receiver by connecting a piece of wire about two feet in length to the high-side terminal of the signal generator. This wire is not connected to the receiver but acts as an antenna and should be kept about two feet from the receiver's loop antenna.

In general, the procedure in aligning a receiver is to apply the modulated r-f output of a signal generator to the receiver through a dummy antenna and to connect an output meter at the loudspeaker. With the receiver and the signal generator tuned to the same frequency, the tuning circuits are adjusted so that maximum output is obtained. Specific alignment procedure is given in the two following articles.

14-15. Aligning the TRF Receiver. Aligning the trf receiver is a relatively simple task because all its tuning circuits are to be adjusted to the same frequency. Thus in the circuit of Fig. 14-9, the inductance of each of the tuned circuits is of the same value and identical tuning capacitors are used. The adjustments need then only compensate for minor variations in capacitance and inductance.

A convenient procedure in aligning the receiver of Fig. 14-9 is to connect the output of a signal generator (through a dummy antenna) to the antenna and ground terminals of the receiver. An output meter is also connected across the secondary side of the output transformer T_4. With power applied to both the signal generator and the radio receiver, set the receiver dial to about 90 per cent of its maximum frequency

Fig. 14-16.—Top view showing the parts used in a radio receiver. (*Courtesy of Philco Corporation.*)

range, for example, 1400 kc, and turn the receiver's volume control on full. Then adjust the frequency of the signal generator to 1400 kc and increase its signal strength until an indication appears on the output meter. With this setting, adjust each of the trimmer capacitors (C_4, C_5, and C_6) in turn until maximum output is indicated on the output meter. As the receiver becomes more sensitive and its output increases in amplitude, the strength of the output of the signal generator should be reduced. The adjustment of the trimmer capacitors should be made at the high-frequency end of the receiver dial because the capacitance of the circuit is lowest at this frequency and the trimmer adjustment will thus be most sensitive at the high-frequency end of the dial.

If the end rotor plates of the variable capacitors are slotted (see Art.

6-8 and Fig. 6-16), alignment may be made at several other points on the dial by changing the frequency setting of both the receiver and the signal generator and adjusting for maximum output by bending the slotted rotor plates.

14-16. Aligning the Superheterodyne Receiver. *Procedure.* Aligning a superheterodyne receiver is more difficult than aligning a trf receiver because the tuned circuits of the superheterodyne receiver do not all

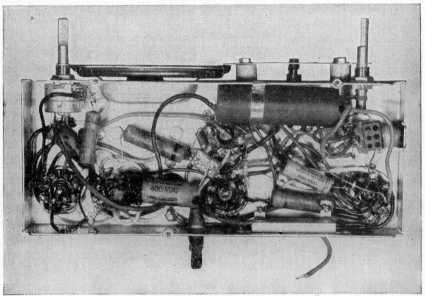

Fig. 14-17.—Bottom view showing the parts used in a radio receiver. (*Courtesy of Philco Corporation.*)

operate at the same value of frequency. Instead, three tuned circuits, namely, the i-f, oscillator, and r-f circuits, must each be adjusted to a different value of frequency.

In aligning superheterodyne receivers, the following procedure may be used. First adjust the tuned circuit nearest the a-f output of the receiver and then work back toward the antenna. In the average superheterodyne receiver, the order in which the circuits are aligned is (1) the i-f amplifier circuit, (2) the oscillator circuit, (3) the r-f or preselector circuits.

Aligning the Intermediate-frequency Amplifier Circuits. When tuning the i-f circuits, the local oscillator and the avc should be made inoperative. In the circuit of Fig. 14-13 this may be done by (1) short-circuiting the oscillator tuning capacitor C_{13}, (2) short-circuiting the avc capacitor C_5. The output meter is connected across the secondary terminals of the output transformer T_6 and can remain there throughout the entire alignment and tracking procedure. The signal generator is connected with its ground terminal to the chassis of the receiver and its high-side terminal connected through a 0.01-μf capacitor to the control grid of VT_3. The receiver volume control should be turned on full, the signal generator frequency set to correspond with the i-f value recommended for the receiver, and the signal generator output turned up just enough to produce an indication on the output meter. The trimmer capacitors C_{20} and C_{21} are then adjusted to obtain maximum indication on the output meter. When the i-f transformer T_5 is properly adjusted, the next step is to adjust i-f transformer T_4. This may be done by applying the output of the signal generator to the r-f control grid of VT_2 and then proceeding to adjust the trimmer capacitors C_{16} and C_{17} until maximum indication is obtained on the output meter. If the output indication becomes too high for the meter, it should be reduced by decreasing the amplitude of the output of the signal generator. It cannot be too strongly emphasized that, in order to obtain satisfactory tracking and overall operation of the receiver, the frequency to which the i-f circuits are adjusted must correspond exactly with the value recommended by the manufacturer of the receiver. The correct i-f value for a receiver may be obtained from some markings or diagram supplied with the receiver or from a service manual.

Aligning the Oscillator and Radio-frequency Circuits. In order to align the oscillator it is necessary to remove the short circuit at the oscillator tuning capacitor C_{13}, which had been placed there when adjusting the i-f circuits. With the signal generator still connected to the r-f control grid of VT_2, set the receiver dial and the signal generator frequency each to a value near 1400 kc, but not to a point at which a station is received, and adjust the oscillator trimmer capacitor C_{14} to obtain maximum indication on the output meter. With the tuning dial of the receiver and the signal generator frequency at the same setting, apply the signal generator output to the antenna terminal of the receiver through a 200-$\mu\mu$f capacitor and adjust trimmer capacitors C_8 and C_2 until maximum indication is obtained on the output meter. It would also have been possible to adjust the local oscillator and the two preselector circuits with the signal generator output connected to the antenna terminal through a 200-$\mu\mu$f capacitor and, with the receiver and signal generator set near 1400 kc, then progressively adjust the trimmer capacitors C_{14}, C_8, and C_2 to obtain maximum indication on the output meter.

The local oscillator must also be adjusted for some value at the low-frequency end of the dial. It is generally desirable to make the low-frequency adjustment at about 10 per cent above the minimum frequency of the receiver; in fact, most manufacturers recommend a specific value at which the low-frequency range tracking should be adjusted. This information is usually obtained from a service manual. As no specific value is given for the circuit of Fig. 14-13, 600 kc will be a convenient value. Accordingly, the low-frequency alignment may be made by setting the receiver dial and the signal generator frequency at 600 kc. The oscillator padding capacitor C_{12} is then adjusted to obtain maximum indication on the output meter, while gently rocking the ganged capacitor back and forth to keep the signal tuned in. The low-frequency adjustment should be made only at the padder capacitor and no adjusting is to be done at the trimmer capacitors.

It is considered good practice to recheck the high-frequency setting after completing the low-frequency adjustments and make any corrections necessary. Although the use of tuning capacitors with slotted rotor plates makes it possible to make an additional adjustment at about the middle of the frequency range, most superheterodyne receivers will be found to track satisfactorily if they are carefully aligned at the high- and low-frequency ends.

Methods of Aligning the Oscillator and Radio-frequency Circuits. There are two commonly used methods of making the oscillator circuit of the superheterodyne receiver track with the preselector circuits. One method is to use a padder capacitor as in the circuit of Fig. 14-13. In the second method, sometimes called the *cut-plate method*, the variable capacitor used to tune the oscillator circuit has a lower value of capacitance than the capacitor used in the r-f tuning circuits.

In the method that employs a padder capacitor, all the ganged tuning capacitors are of the same construction. Because the oscillator is tuned to a higher frequency, but over an identical span in kilocycles, the ratio of high- to low-frequency values is less for the oscillator than for the r-f circuits. For example, to cover the broadcast band of from 550 to 1600 kc the frequency range of the r-f circuits is almost 3 to 1. With an intermediate frequency of 465 kc the oscillator frequency range is from 1015 to 2065 kc or approximately 2 to 1. It should be apparent that the capacitors used to tune the r-f circuits must have a greater range than the capacitor used to tune the oscillator. In order to use identical capacitors for all the tuning circuits, something must be done to reduce the range of the capacitor used to tune the oscillator circuit. Connecting another capacitor, called a *padder capacitor*, in series with the original tuning capacitor will reduce the ratio of the maximum to minimum values of the series combination. This may readily be verified by reference to Examples 6-9 and 6-10 in Art. 6-5. Radio receivers may be designed so that exact tracking will be obtained at three frequencies in the band and will also provide satisfactory tracking over the remainder of the band. In order to provide a means of making tracking adjustments the padding capacitor is made adjustable. The capacitance required for the padder is in the order of 350 $\mu\mu$f for a 465-kc i-f, and nearly 1000 $\mu\mu$f for an i-f of 175 kc. When a high value of capacitance is required for the padder and only a small amount of variation is needed, some receivers use a fixed capacitor shunted by a suitable small trimmer for this purpose.

In the cut-plate method, the shape of the rotor plates of the oscillator tuning capacitor is different from those of the r-f tuning capacitors. By properly designing the shapes of the rotor plates it is possible to achieve proper tracking of the oscillator circuit without the need of a padding capacitor. The disadvantages of this method are: (1) cost of

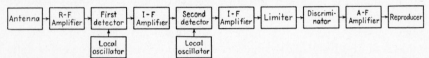

FIG. 14-18.—Block diagram of a frequency-modulation receiver.

manufacture is higher; (2) it is not satisfactory for use in multiband receivers; (3) the capacitors can usually only be used for receivers with the same i-f value; (4) in some instances the capacitors can only be used for one circuit design; (5) it is more difficult to make service adjustments than with the padder-capacitor method.

14-17. Fundamental Principles of Frequency-modulation Receivers. *Essential Functions.* In general, the f-m receiver is similar in many respects to the a-m superheterodyne receiver but its circuits are more complex. In addition to performing the same functions as the a-m receiver, it has two additional functions, namely, amplitude limiting and frequency discrimination. The limiter circuit is largely responsible for the noise-free reception obtained with the f-m receiver, and the discriminator serves as the detector which converts the frequency modulations into the audio signal. The block diagram of an f-m receiver is illustrated in Fig. 14-18.

Specifically, the f-m receiver differs from the a-m superheterodyne receiver in the following respects: (1) the antenna must be well designed, carefully constructed, and adjusted at the receiver location; (2) the r-f amplifier is usually designed to provide as much gain as possible in addition to performing the function of preselection; (3) the frequency converter operates at a much higher value of frequency than in an a-m receiver, the r-f input being in the order of 100 mc and the i-f in the order of 3 to 8 mc; (4) some f-m receivers employ two stages of frequency conversion and two values of i-f in order to obtain better amplification; (5) the i-f amplifier is designed to pass a wider band of frequencies (approximately 200 kc); (6) a voltage limiter circuit is provided between the i-f amplifier and the discriminator; (7) the discriminator or a-f detector is of different design from the a-f or second detector in an a-m superheterodyne receiver; (8) the a-f amplifier is designed to provide a wider range of frequency response; (9) a loudspeaker that is capable of producing high-fidelity production should be provided.

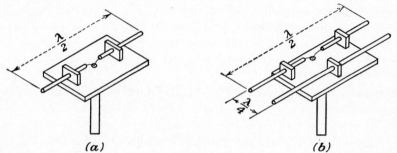

(a)   *(b)*

Fig. 14-19.—Antenna system for an f-m receiver.   (*a*) Dipole antenna, (*b*) dipole antenna and reflector.

The Antenna.   For the best operation of an f-m receiver, a special antenna should be provided.   Modern practice is to use a dipole antenna of approximately one-half the wavelength of the r-f signals to be received. For frequencies in the order of 100 mc, the length of the dipole should be approximately $4\frac{3}{4}$ feet.   The line connecting the antenna to the receiver should be either a twisted-pair transmission line or a coaxial cable.   The strength of the signal picked up by the antenna will be greatest when the position of the antenna is at right angles to the direction of the transmitting station.   It is therefore advisable to consider the location of the transmitting stations when installing the antenna.   If most of the transmitters are in one general direction, a reflector is sometimes added to the antenna installation to increase the strength of the input signal.   The reflector is merely a rod of one-half wavelength that is placed parallel to the dipole antenna and one-quarter wavelength in back of it.   A dipole antenna and reflector are illustrated in Fig. 14-19.

Some f-m receivers have a folded dipole antenna, which is mounted in the cabinet of the receiver.   If such a receiver is used in an area close to the majority of the transmitters the antenna will provide satisfactory results, but if the receiver is used in a remote area it may become necessary to install the conventional outdoor dipole antenna.   Furthermore, as f-m reception is limited to practically line-of-sight distances the height of the antenna becomes important for receivers located considerable distances from the transmitters.

The Radio-frequency Section. The combination of the r-f amplifier, converter, and i-f amplifier is commonly referred to as the *r-f section* of the receiver. The important overall function of this portion of the receiver is to provide sufficient amplification so that the signal voltage available at the input of the limiter is high enough to provide satisfactory performance of the limiter.

In general, the r-f amplifier of an f-m receiver is similar to the r-f amplifier in an a-m receiver except that it must operate at a much higher value of frequency. Vacuum tubes designed for high-frequency operation should be used in these circuits. Tubes having a high mutual conductance are generally used in the r-f amplifier in order to obtain as much gain as possible in the r-f stage. A higher gain in the r-f amplifier reduces the amount of gain required in the i-f stage, thereby improving the stability of the receiver.

The converter may be of the conventional single-tube type or it may use a pentode mixer and a separate triode oscillator. The use of a separate mixer and oscillator has the advantage of high sensitivity and good frequency stability. In order to obtain the high gain desired in the i-f stages, some receivers use two converters and the i-f stages have two different frequency values. In such receivers, the first converter produces a new frequency in between the r-f and final i-f values, and some amplification is provided at this frequency. The signal is then passed through a second converter, which reduces the frequency to the final i-f value, and additional amplification is provided at this frequency. The output is then passed on to the limiter and discriminator. Circuits employing two steps of frequency conversion are sometimes called *double superheterodyne circuits* or *triple detector circuits*. The oscillator circuits are generally provided with a means of compensation for frequency drift in order to reduce the frequency variation due to the increase in the temperature of the oscillator circuit components as the receiver warms up.

The i-f amplifier differs from that in an a-m receiver in that it must pass a much wider band of frequencies and also that it operates at a higher frequency. It was explained in Art. 13-3 that in the f-m system the frequency deviation is 75 kc above and below the center frequency, hence the i-f stage of an f-m receiver operates with a frequency variation of 150 kc as compared with only 10 kc in the a-m receiver. The band width of the i-f amplifier is generally made 200 kc. In order to obtain good i-f performance with this wide pass band, the i-f value is made in the order of 3 to 12 mc. A 200-kc band width at 4 mc corresponds to about a 23-kc band width at 465 kc. As one of the simple ways of increasing the width of the pass band of a tuned circuit is to increase the resistance of the circuit, it is not uncommon in f-m circuits to connect a resistor across the tuned i-f amplifier circuits.

The Limiter.   An important factor in the noise-free operation of the f-m system is the fact that the transmitted f-m waves are of constant amplitude.   However, even though the transmitter provides an output wave train of constant amplitude, the wave form that the output of the i-f amplifier of the receiver presents to the discriminator contains variations in amplitude.   These variations may have been picked up in transmission from the transmitter's antenna to the receiver's antenna or may be caused by various circuits in the receiver.   In order to eliminate any amplitude variations, a limiter circuit is placed between the i-f output and the final detector.

The limiter is essentially an i-f amplifier operated with such values of voltage at its electrodes that the tube reaches saturation before the input

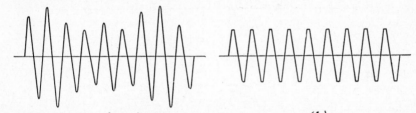

(a)   *(b)*

Fig. 14-20.—Effect of the limiter circuit on the wave form of the signal.   (*a*) Signal input to the limiter, (*b*) signal output of the limiter.

wave reaches its maximum value.   Under this condition, the portion of each input cycle above a certain value is cut off and hence the amplitude of each cycle is limited to a fixed amount.   The i-f output should be of sufficient strength so that even its weakest signal will cause the limiter tube to saturate.   The wave shapes of the signal at the input and output side of the limiter are shown in Fig. 14-20.   By passing the output of the limiter through a transformer, the harmonics due to the flat-topped waves are reduced to a negligible value.

Figure 14-21 illustrates the circuit diagrams of single-and two-stage limiters.   In the circuit of Fig. 14-21*a*, a pentode having a sharp cutoff characteristic is used.   A grid bias is developed at R_2, but the time constant of the R_2C_3 combination is such as to permit the signal to drive the grid positive for just a small portion of each input cycle.   With the proper choice of R_2, C_3, screen-grid voltage, and plate voltage the circuit will perform the limiting action indicated by Fig. 14-20 for a given input signal condition.   In the two-stage limiter of Fig. 14-21*b*, the second stage is resistance coupled to the first stage and serves the purpose of eliminating any residual variations in amplitude.

The Discriminator.   The discriminator or f-m detector takes the place of the ordinary detector in an a-m receiver.   Its function is to convert the frequency modulations of the i-f signal to a-f voltages of amplitudes and frequencies that will be replicas of those produced in the microphone circuit at the transmitting station.

Two discriminator circuits are shown in Fig. 14-22. In the circuit of Fig. 14-22a, the output of the limiter tube is applied to the primary winding P of the transformer T_1 and is tuned to the center value of the intermediate frequency by means of capacitor C_3. The secondary winding is split into two sections S_1 and S_2. Section S_1 is tuned by means of capacitor C_1 to a frequency slightly above the center i-f value, and

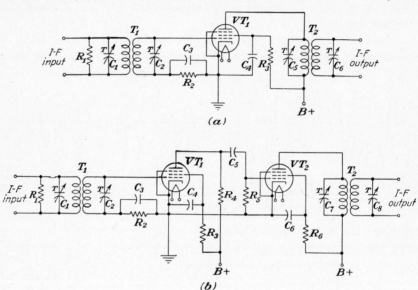

Fig. 14-21.—Limiter circuits. (a) Single-stage limiter, (b) two-stage limiter.

section S_2 is tuned by means of capacitor C_2 to a frequency slightly below the center i-f value. When the input signal is unmodulated, that is, operating at its center frequency, the voltage across each of the two secondary sections will be equal. Under this condition, the current in each section of the diode VT_1 will be equal and the voltage drops across R_1 and R_2 will be equal. From the polarities of the voltages indicated on the diagram, it becomes obvious that under these conditions the output voltage of the discriminator will be zero. When the input signal is frequency-modulated, the voltage at the plates of each section of the diode will vary. For an increase in frequency above the center i-f value the voltage at one diode plate will increase and at the other it will decrease. For a decrease in frequency the voltage at the diode plates will change in the direction opposite that for an increase in frequency. As changes in plate voltage will produce similar changes in the plate currents it should be apparent that the voltage drops at R_1 and R_2 will vary.   When the voltage drop at R_1 is greater than that at R_2 the output voltage will be positive, and when the voltage drop at R_2 exceeds that at R_1 the output voltage will be negative.   The net result is that the output of the discriminator will be an a-f voltage whose magnitude and frequency are determined by the frequency modulations at the input of the discriminator.

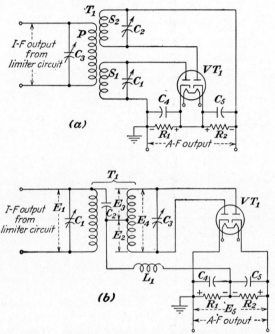

FIG. 14-22.—Discriminator circuits.   (*a*) Split-secondary discriminator circuit, (*b*) phase-shift discriminator circuit.

The discriminator circuit of Fig. 14-22*b* is the one most commonly used.   In this circuit both the primary and secondary of T_1 are tuned to a frequency equal to the center value of the intermediate frequency.   At this resonant frequency the voltages E_2 and E_3 are 90 degrees out of phase with the primary voltage E_1, and E_2 is equal to E_3.   Under this condition the currents in the two sections of the diode VT_1 are equal, the voltage drops at R_1 and R_2 are equal, and the output voltage E_5 is zero. When the frequency of the input is other than the center frequency value, the phase angle between E_2 and E_1 will change either increasing or decreasing from the 90 degree relation depending upon whether the frequency increases or decreases.   A change in the phase relationship of E_2 and E_1 will produce a change in the voltage at the plates of the diode

VT_1. Changes in plate voltages will produce changes in the plate currents, voltage drops at R_1 and R_2, and the resultant output voltage E_5. Thus this circuit will produce the same kind of variations in the voltage across the load resistors R_1 and R_2 as the circuit of Fig. 14-22a.

In order to provide an undistorted a-f output signal the discriminator should have a linear characteristic. The curve of Fig. 14-23 illustrates the desired output characteristics of a discriminator circuit. It should be observed that the characteristic is a straight line for ±75 kc and that little curvature is present until after ±100 kc. The circuit therefore

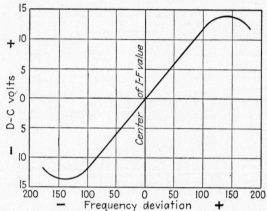

Fig. 14-23.—Operating characteristics of a discriminator circuit.

provides excellent reproduction over the 200-kc pass band normally used with f-m receivers.

The Audio-frequency Circuits. The a-f section is very similar to that of an a-m receiver. The main difference is that the f-m receiver can reproduce audio frequencies up to 15,000 cycles, which is about three times as high as the a-f range of ordinary a-m broadcast receivers. In order to utilize this high-fidelity reproduction the a-f circuits should be designed to provide satisfactory response over the high-frequency range (see Chap. VIII). This also requires the use of a high-quality loudspeaker.

BIBLIOGRAPHY

CUNNINGHAM, J. E., Alignment of Radio Receivers, *Radio News*, October, 1946.

GHIRARDI, A. A., Practical Radio Course, *Radio News*, August, 1944, to October, 1946.

HICKS, H. J., *Principles and Practice of Radio Servicing*, McGraw-Hill Book Company, Inc., New York.

HOAG, J. B., *Basic Radio*, D. Van Nostrand Company, Inc., New York.

MEISSNER Instruction Manual, *How to Build Radio Receivers*, Meissner Manufacturing Division Maguire Industries, Inc., Mt. Carmel, Ill.

MYE Technical Manual, *Superheterodyne First Detectors and Oscillators*, P. R. Mallory & Co., Inc., Indianapolis, Ind.

MYE Technical Manual, *Frequency Modulation*, P. R. Mallory & Co., Inc., Indianapolis, Ind.

NILSON, A. R., and HORNUNG, J L., *Practical Radio Communication*, McGraw-Hill Book Company, Inc., New York.

TERMAN, F. E., *Fundamentals of Radio*, McGraw-Hill Book Company, Inc., New York.

TERMAN, F. E., *Radio Engineers' Handbook*, McGraw-Hill Book Company, Inc., New York.

The Radio Amateur's Handbook, The American Radio Relay League, Inc., West Hartford, Conn.

QUESTIONS

1. Define the following terms: (a) sensitivity, (b) selectivity, (c) fidelity, (d) stability, (e) signal-to-noise ratio.

2. Name and describe four types of noise that may occur in a radio receiver.

3. (a) What are the advantages of f-m receivers?   (b) What are the disadvantages of f-m receivers?

4. Name four essential functions of a radio receiver.

5. Why is it generally undesirable to have more than two stages of a-f amplification in a radio receiver?

6. (a) What is meant by a tuned-radio-frequency stage of amplification?   (b) Describe two advantages of trf amplification.

7. (a) What is meant by an i-f amplifier?   (b) What is the purpose of an i-f amplifier?   (c) What advantages are gained in using i-f amplification?

8. With the aid of a block diagram explain the operation of a trf receiver.

9. (a) Draw a circuit diagram of a five-tube trf receiver.   (b) Explain the operation of this circuit.

10. Draw a circuit diagram and explain the operation of (a) a volume control circuit, (b) a tone control circuit.

11. With the aid of circuit diagrams explain the operation of: (a) a voltage-dropping resistor, (b) an r-f by-pass capacitor, (c) a decoupling network.

12. Define: (a) superheterodyne receiver, (b) double superheterodyne receiver.

13. Explain five advantages of the superheterodyne receiver.

14. With the aid of a block diagram explain the operation of a superheterodyne receiver.

15. (a) Describe several types of loop antennas.   (b) What are the advantages of the loop antenna?   (c) What are the disadvantages of the loop antenna?

16. (a) What is meant by a preselector?   (b) Describe the operation of a preselector circuit.   (c) What advantages are obtained by the use of preselection?

17. (a) Name the three essential functions required to obtain frequency conversion.   (b) Explain the purpose of each of these functions.

18. Explain two factors that must be taken into consideration in the design of a local oscillator that is to be used with a superheterodyne receiver.

19. (a) What five frequencies are present in the output circuit of a mixer tube when two signal voltages of different frequencies are applied to its input circuits?   (b) Which of these frequencies is used in a-m broadcast band superheterodyne receivers?

20. (a) What is meant by conversion gain?   (b) How does the voltage amplification of a tube used as a converter compare with the voltage amplification of the same tube when used as an i-f amplifier?

21. (a) Describe the operation of a converter circuit that uses separate tubes for the oscillator and mixer.   (b) What are the advantages of this type of circuit?

22. (*a*) Describe the operation of a pentagrid converter tube of the 6A8 type. (*b*) Describe the operation of a converter circuit using a pentagrid converter tube of the 6A8 type. (*c*) What are the characteristics of this type of converter circuit?

23. (*a*) Describe the operation of a pentagrid converter tube of the 6SA7 type. (*b*) Describe the operation of a converter circuit using a pentagrid converter tube of the 6SA7 type. (*c*) What are the characteristics of this type of converter circuit?

24. What is meant by (*a*) image-frequency signal? (*b*) Image ratio?

25. (*a*) Explain the relation between the tuning ratio, the oscillator frequency, and the intermediate frequency. (*b*) In broadcast receivers, why is it desirable to have the oscillator frequency higher than the r-f signal input?

26. (*a*) Explain the relation between the value of the intermediate frequency and the selectivity of a receiver. (*b*) Why are odd number values of intermediate frequency generally used?

27. (*a*) What is meant by spurious responses? (*b*) Name five possible causes of spurious responses. (*c*) What precautions are used in superheterodyne receivers to minimize the interference caused by spurious responses?

28. (*a*) Draw a circuit diagram of a superheterodyne receiver to be operated from an a-c power line. (*b*) Explain the operation of this circuit.

29. (*a*) Draw a circuit diagram of a superheterodyne receiver that may be operated from either an a-c or a d-c power line. (*b*) Explain the operation of this circuit.

30. (*a*) Describe the principle of operation of an electron-ray indicator tube. (*b*) Describe the operation of an electron-ray indicator circuit.

31. (*a*) Explain two reasons why a radio receiver should be properly aligned. (*b*) What instruments should be used to properly align a receiver?

32. Describe a method of aligning a trf receiver.

33. Explain the order in which the various tuned circuits in a superheterodyne receiver should be aligned.

34. Describe the procedure for aligning an i-f amplifier circuit.

35. Describe the procedure for aligning an oscillator circuit.

36. Describe the procedure for aligning an r-f tuned circuit.

37. How does the f-m receiver differ from an a-m superheterodyne receiver?

38. (*a*) Why is a dipole antenna generally used with f-m receivers? (*b*) What is the purpose of a reflector? (*c*) Describe the construction of a reflector.

39. What factors must be taken into consideration in constructing the antenna for an f-m receiver?

40. Describe the operation of the r-f section of an f-m receiver.

41. (*a*) How does the band width of the i-f amplifier used with f-m receivers compare with those used with a-m receivers? (*b*) How does the value of the intermediate frequencies of f-m receivers compare with those used in a-m receivers?

42. (*a*) What is the purpose of the limiter in an f-m reciever? (*b*) Describe the operation of a single-stage limiter circuit.

43. (*a*) What is the purpose of the discriminator in an f-m receiver? (*b*) Describe the operation of a discriminator circuit in which only the primary winding of the coupling transformer between the limiter and discriminator is tuned to the center value of the intermediate frequency.

44. Describe the operation of a discriminator circuit in which both the primary and secondary windings of the coupling transformer between the limiter and discriminator are tuned to the center value of the intermediate frequency.

45. What is the main difference between the a-f section of an f-m receiver and an a-m receiver?

CHAPTER XV

TEST EQUIPMENT

Modern radio and electronic equipment consists of a large number and variety of circuit elements having a wide range of values. The circuit elements are connected to one another, either directly or indirectly, to form a complex circuit. The testing of such circuits can best be accomplished by the use of definite test procedures and adequate test equipment. As a detailed discussion of all types of test instruments and their various applications is beyond the scope of this text, only a brief description of the more common types of test instruments and an outline description of three basic systems of testing will be given in this chapter.

15-1. Systems of Testing. *Purpose of Testing.* There are two fundamental reasons for testing radio or electronic equipment: (1) to check the operation of a complete unit, or any of its sections, against a set of recommended operating values; (2) to locate a faulty section or part. Although there are numerous methods for testing radio and electronic equipment only three basic systems of testing will be considered in this text, namely, (1) point-to-point resistance measurement, (2) measurement of voltage and current for each individual circuit, (3) signal tracing. The procedure to be followed in testing radio and electronic equipment may be based upon one or more of these three systems of testing.

The ultimate aim of all systems of testing is to locate as quickly as possible the portion of a circuit that is not functioning properly. This is best accomplished by testing individually each section of the complete circuit. When used to test a particular circuit, each system of testing has certain characteristics and advantages that are not common to the other systems. Because of this, the best system to use will depend upon the circuit to be tested and the operating characteristics that are to be checked. A complete test procedure may be a combination of any two systems or all three systems of testing.

Point-to-point Resistance Measurement. In this system of testing, the resistance between the various elements of a tube are measured while the tube is in its socket but with the power turned off. The values obtained are checked for any variation from the known correct values. The only instrument required for this system of testing is an ohmmeter. The

677

point-to-point resistance measurement method of testing has a number of disadvantages, among which are: (1) a source of reference containing the known correct values of resistance between certain points is required for every make and model of radio and electronic equipment that is to be tested; (2) care must be exercised when measuring the resistance between two points that all elements in the circuit are taken into consideration; (3) this is only a static test and cannot be used for determining the dynamic characteristics of the circuit; (4) a circuit element may appear satisfactory under static conditions but may be faulty under dynamic conditions. An advantage of this system of testing is that, when the fault has been traced to a definite circuit, this system provides a convenient method for quickly locating a shorted or open-circuited element.

Voltage and Current Measurement. In this system of testing, voltage and current measurements are taken at the prongs of each tube. The values obtained are checked for any variation from the known correct values. The instruments used for this system of testing may include one or more of the following: (1) a multirange d-c voltmeter, (2) a multirange a-c voltmeter, (3) a multirange d-c ammeter, (4) a vacuum-tube voltmeter, (5) a set analyzer. The voltage-current measurement system of testing also has a number of disadvantages, among which are: (1) a source of reference indicating the correct operating values of voltage and current is required for each make and model of radio and electronic equipment to be tested; (2) care must be exercised when taking voltage and current measurements so that the resistance of the instrument used does not affect the circuit. An advantage of this system of testing is that it provides a quick method of checking the operating voltages on a tube's electrodes with the values recommended by the tube manufacturer for that type of tube. The only reference then required is a tube manual. Any major variation from the recommended values will ordinarily localize the faulty circuit. However, vacuum tubes are not always operated at the control voltages recommended by the tube manufacturer and this fact must be taken into consideration before declaring a circuit to be faulty.

Signal Tracing. In this system of testing, the progress of a signal is traced through each stage of the equipment. With signal tracing it is possible to analyze the signal at each stage of a radio receiver for both its quality and strength. The circuit for each stage can then be adjusted so that the strength and quality of its output signal are at their optimum value. As the signal is the ultimate factor in a radio receiver, the signal-tracing system of testing is the most effective method of checking and aligning a receiver. There are various methods of signal tracing and the equipment required will depend upon the method used. In general, the following equipment is required: (1) a source of signal input, such as an r-f signal generator, that is capable of producing an r-f, a-f, and modulated r-f signal output; (2) an output indicating device such as an output meter, electron-ray indicator tube, or cathode-ray oscilloscope.

One method of signal tracing is to test each stage individually by applying the proper signal to its input circuit and checking the strength and quality of its output signal. Another method is to apply a modulated r-f signal to the input circuit of the first r-f stage and to check the output from each succeeding stage. There are many variations of these two methods.

The signal-tracing method of radio circuit testing has many advantages, among which are: (1) a radio receiver may be tested under actual operating conditions; (2) the intermittent faulty operation of a circuit element can quite readily be located; (3) variation in the amount of gain, by-passing, and coupling (above or below the optimum value) can be detected.

15-2. Combination Meters. *Requirements.* In testing radio or electronic equipment a wide range of voltage, current, and resistance measurements may be required. If individual meters having only one range were to be used for these tests, the number of instruments required would be too large and the cost too great to be practical. One method of reducing the number of instruments needed is to use a multirange meter for each type of indication that is required. A more practical method is to combine a multirange voltmeter, ammeter, and ohmmeter into one instrument having an adequate switching arrangement that permits only one range of one type of measurement to be used for each of its settings. This type instrument is called a *combination meter* and is also known as a *multimeter, multitester, multipurpose tester,* and *volt-ohm-milliammeter.*

Since a combination meter consists of a voltmeter, ammeter, and ohmmeter its principles of operation and use can best be understood by first studying the principles of operation and use of each individual type of meter. Only a brief description of the individual meters and the combination meter will be given in this text. For a detailed description of the principles of operation, construction, and use of these instruments the reader is referred to the chapter on Meters in the authors' text *Electrical Essentials of Radio.*

Ammeters. An ammeter is an instrument used for measuring electric currents. It is always connected in series with that part of a circuit whose current is to be measured. In Fig. 15-1, ammeter 1 is connected in series with the line to indicate the line current, and ammeters 2 and 3 are connected in series with the lamp and fixed resistor, respectively, to obtain their individual currents. Being connected in series, an ammeter must carry the current passing through that part of the circuit in which it is connected. In Fig. 15-1, if ammeter 1 has a resistance of 1 ohm and the line current is 10 amperes, it follows that there would be a 10-volt drop across the ammeter. This would cause the appliance and lamp to operate on a voltage of 10 volts less than intended, thus giving incorrect indications of the currents flowing in the circuit under normal conditions (that is, without the ammeters). The voltage drop across the meter is decreased by making the resistance of the meter as low as possible. The value of this drop varies with the type of meter and the manufacturer. Most ammeters are designed for 50-mv drop at full rated current.

Since the resistance of an ammeter is very low the current that would flow through the ammeter if through error it was connected directly

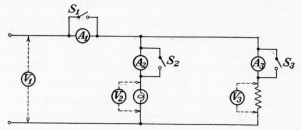

Fig. 15-1.—Correct method of connecting ammeters and voltmeters.

across a source of power would be excessively large and the meter would be damaged. *An ammeter should therefore never be connected across any source of power.* The current due to an unforeseen short circuit or overload may be large enough to injure an ammeter if it is left connected in a circuit. To prevent damage due to factors that cannot be foreseen, *the ammeter should always be protected by connecting a short-circuiting switch across it*, as illustrated by S_1, S_2, and S_3 in Fig. 15-1. The switch is always kept closed except when a reading is to be taken. If, upon opening the switch, the needle swings backward or completely across the meter scale, it should be closed instantly to prevent damaging the meter. The necessary changes to the circuit should then be made before the switch is again opened.

Voltmeters. A voltmeter is an instrument used for measuring voltage. It is always connected across that part of the circuit whose voltage is to be measured. Figure 15-1 shows the correct way to connect voltmeters in a parallel circuit. Voltmeter 1 indicates the line voltage; voltmeter 2 shows the voltage across the lamp; and voltmeter 3 shows the voltage across the fixed resistance.

As a voltmeter is connected directly across the line it is desirable that it take as little current as is practicable.   Because of its comparatively low resistance, approximately 20 ohms, the moving element of a voltmeter cannot be connected directly across the line.   It is therefore necessary to connect a high resistance in series with it.   The value of this resistance depends on the resistance of the coil, or moving element, and the full-scale voltage desired.

Voltmeters do not form a definite part of a circuit as do ammeters. It is therefore not necessary to connect voltmeters permanently in the circuit.   If a voltmeter is connected only when a reading is to be taken, a single meter can be used to take readings at various points in a circuit. A voltmeter may be damaged by excessive voltage, but as it is connected only when a reading is to be taken it may therefore be disconnected instantly if any overvoltage condition is apparent.

Voltmeters are often rated in terms of their sensitivity in ohms per volt, which is obtained by dividing the resistance in ohms for any range by the full-scale voltage rating of that particular range.   In testing radio and electronic equipment, it is generally desirable and in many cases necessary to use a voltmeter with a very high sensitivity.   Although a voltmeter with a sensitivity of 100 ohms per volt may be excellent for industrial power circuits, it would prove very unsatisfactory for testing radio and electronic circuits.   For testing these circuits it is recommended that the voltmeters have a sensitivity of 20,000 ohms per volt or higher.

Alternating- and Direct-current Instruments.   Ammeters and voltmeters are usually designed to measure either direct or alternating currents or voltages and in order to obtain accurate readings an ammeter or voltmeter should only be used to measure the type of current or voltage for which it is designed.   The ordinary a-c ammeter cannot be used to measure accurately currents whose frequencies are greatly in excess of 500 cycles.   Thermal-type instruments measure the effective value of the current flowing and therefore can be used on direct, a-f, and r-f currents.   Instruments giving accurate readings at frequencies up to 100 mc can be obtained.

Rectifier-type meters are used for measuring alternating currents of small magnitude such as milliamperes and microamperes, and voltages ranging from values in millivolts up to 1000 volts.   A rectifier-type meter consists of a copper oxide rectifier and a permanent-magnet moving-coil instrument.   Rectifier-type meters can be used to measure alternating currents of frequencies up to 20,000 cycles per second.

Shunts.   The current that may safely be led into an ammeter movement is limited by the current-carrying capacity of the moving element, which must necessarily be small.   To increase the range of such instruments, shunts and current transformers are used, the former with direct currents and the latter with alternating currents.   It has previously been stated that the movement's current must be very small, generally about one ma.   This is accomplished by connecting a low resistance in parallel

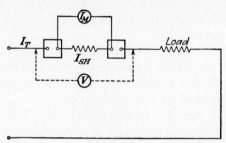

Fig. 15-2.—Proper connections for the use of a shunt with a millivoltmeter.

with the meter.   The ammeter is in reality now a voltmeter (see Fig. 15-2) indicating the voltage drop across a resistance.   This resistance is called a *shunt* and forms a definite part of all ammeters.   The resistance of the shunt may be calculated by use of the following equation.

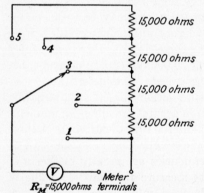

Fig. 15-3.—Circuit showing the application of a rotary switch and resistors to increase the voltmeter range by multiples of 2, 3, 4, or 5.

$$R_{SH} = \frac{I_M \times R_M}{I_{SH}} \qquad (15\text{-}1)$$

where R_{SH} = shunt resistance, ohms
R_M = meter resistance, ohms
I_{SH} = shunt current, amperes
I_M = meter current, amperes

When the shunt is connected permanently inside an ammeter, it is called an *internal shunt*.   When it is desired to increase the range of an ammeter an *external shunt* may be used.   Multirange ammeters use a series of shunts and a rotary switch for connecting the proper shunt across the ammeter in order to obtain a desired range.

Multipliers.   The range of a voltmeter having its resistance incorporated within the instrument may be increased by the use of an external resistance connected in series with the instrument.   External resistances used in this manner are called *multipliers*.   Multirange voltmeters use a series of resistors and a rotary switch for connecting the proper value of resistance in series with the voltmeter in order to obtain a desired range (see Fig. 15-3).   The multiplying power of a resistor may be calculated by use of the following equation.

$$M = \frac{R_{EX} + R_M}{R_M} \qquad (15\text{-}2)$$

where M = multiplying power

R_{EX} = resistance of the multiplier, ohms

R_M = resistance of the meter, ohms

Multipliers may be used for alternating voltages up to 1000 volts as well as for direct voltages. For all alternating voltages higher than this, it is advisable to use potential transformers.

Ohmmeters. An ohmmeter is an instrument that indicates the resistance of a circuit directly in ohms without any need for calculations. Figure 15-4 is a schematic diagram of the circuit of a simple ohmmeter.

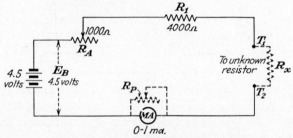

Fig. 15-4.—Circuit of a simple ohmmeter.

In this instrument, unit cells are used as the power source. The milliammeter scale is calibrated to indicate the resistance in ohms directly. When terminals T_1 and T_2 are short circuited and the battery cells are new, so that $E_B = 4.5$ volts, then $R_1 + R_A$ must be equal to 4500 ohms in order to have the milliammeter indicate its full-scale deflection, which will occur when the current in the circuit is one ma. Inserting an unknown resistance R_X between terminals T_1 and T_2 will decrease the indication on the meter. For example, if the value of R_X is 4500 ohms, the reading on the milliammeter will decrease to one-half of its full-scale deflection. As the meter scale is calibrated to indicate the value in ohms of the unknown resistor R_X, the point at the center of the meter scale is marked 4500 ohms. The remainder of the points on the meter scale may be calibrated in the same manner.

As the voltage of the unit cells decreases with age, the resistor R_A is made adjustable to compensate for variations in the voltage of the battery. Resistance values obtained with an ohmmeter using this method of compensation for decreases in battery voltage will not be accurate when the voltage drops because of the aging of the cells   A more accurate method is to connect an adjustable resistor in parallel with the milliammeter as indicated by the dotted lines in Fig. 15-4. The resistor R_P is used in place of resistor R_A, which had been connected in series with the meter and the fixed resistor R_1.

By using different values of resistance and battery voltage, an ohm-meter can be made to indicate any value of resistance. In Fig. 15-5, resistors R_1, R_2, R_3, and R_4 are whole-number multiples of one another, therefore it is only necessary to have a single scale marked to indicate the values of the lowest range and to use a multiplying factor for each of the other ranges. A rotary switch SR is used to connect or disconnect these resistors into the circuit.

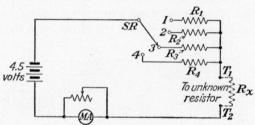

Fig. 15-5.—Diagram showing the use of resistors and a switch to select the range of a multirange ohmmeter.

Combination Meters. The construction of a voltmeter, ammeter, or ohmmeter does not differ materially from one another as far as the move-ments and magnets are concerned. With the proper switching and circuit arrangements it is therefore possible to use a single d-c milliammeter as a multirange d-c voltmeter, d-c ammeter, or ohmmeter. A meter used in this manner is called a *combination meter*. The values of the multipliers, shunts, and ohmmeter resistors can be calculated by using the methods explained under multipliers, shunts, and ohmmeters. By using a copper oxide rectifier, the d-c milliammeter can also be used to measure alter-nating currents and voltages. In radio test and service work, combina-tion meters are very useful, since one instrument is made to take the place of several meters.

Figure 15-7 shows the circuit diagram of a combination meter. This instrument has five ranges of a-c and d-c voltages, 2.5, 10, 50, 250, and 1000 volts; four ranges of resistance, 3000 ohms, 30,000 ohms, 3 megohms, and 30 megohms; and eight d-c current ranges, 0.05 ma, 0.1 ma, 1 ma, 10 ma, 50 ma, 250 ma, 1 amp, and 10 amp. It can also be used to measure capacitance or to indicate the output of an amplifier stage in volts or decibels.

In using combination meters, care should be taken to see that all switches and dial settings are in their correct positions before the instrument is connected into the circuit.　If this is not done, the instrument may be damaged, as it might be set for use on direct current and be used on alternating current, or set to be used as an ammeter and connected for use as a voltmeter, or set in some other incorrect fashion.

15-3. Special Purpose Voltmeters　*Output Meter.*　The power level of radio or speech equipment is usually measured by means of an output

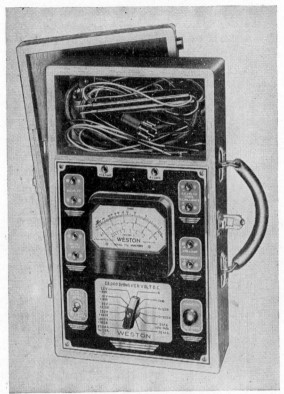

FIG. 15-6.—A combination ohmmeter, a-c/d-c voltmeter, and d-c ammeter.　(*Courtesy of Weston Electrical Instrument Corporation.*)

meter.　This instrument consists of two parts: (1) a device for rectifying the a-f current, (2) a meter that is calibrated to indicate the strength of the rectified current in volts, decibels, or both.　Commercial instruments, such as the one shown in Fig. 15-8, generally use a copper oxide rectifier; however, a vacuum-tube rectifier can also be used.　It can thus be seen that an output meter is essentially the same as a rectifier-type a-c voltmeter.　Comdination meters that employ a rectifier-type instrument generally make provision for using this instrument as an output meter.

The most convenient place to connect an output meter is across the

voice coil leads of the loudspeaker.   However, for very weak signals it is
generally necessary to connect the output meter between the plate of the
output tube and the chassis.   Because of the high direct voltage between
these two points, a capacitor should always be connected in series with an
output meter used in this manner in order to prevent damage to the

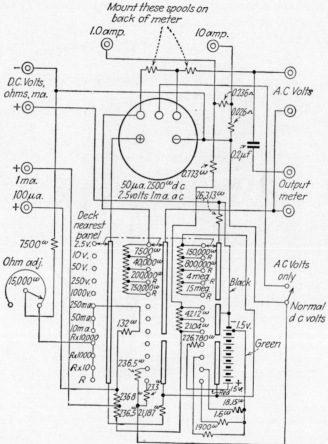

Fig. 15-7.—Schematic diagram of a combination meter.   (*Courtesy of Weston Electrical
Instrument Corporation.*)

instrument.   If the output stage consists of two tubes connected in
push-pull, the output meter may be connected from the plate of either
tube to the chassis.

Electronic D-C Voltmeter.   Because of its comparatively low internal
resistance, the ordinary voltmeter cannot be used to measure the direct
voltage at a number of points in radio or electronic circuits without
affecting the operation of the unit.   Some of the points in a radio circuit

at which the use of an ordinary d-c voltmeter (low sensitivity) affects the circuit operation are grid or plate terminal of a vacuum tube, oscillator circuits, avc and afc circuits, and high-fidelity audio amplifier circuits. To overcome this difficulty, the electronic d-c voltmeter has been developed. With this instrument, it is possible to measure the control or operating voltage at any point in a circuit where a signal is present without affecting the operation of the circuit.

Fig. 15-8.—Output or power-level meter. (*Courtesy of Weston Electrical Instrument Corporation.*)

Fig. 15-9.—A Voltohmyst. (*Courtesy of RCA Manufacturing Co., Inc.*)

A popular type of electronic d-c voltmeter is the Voltohmyst illustrated in Fig. 15-9. A Voltohmyst can be used as a d-c voltmeter, a-c voltmeter for low-frequency power circuits, a-f voltmeter, ohmmeter, power level meter, or f-m discriminator-balance indicator. The model of the Voltohmyst shown in Fig. 15-9 has six ranges of a-c and d-c voltages, namely 5, 10, 50, 100, 500, and 1000 volts. There is practically no loading of a circuit when taking direct voltage readings, as the instrument has a constant input resistance of 10 megohms for all direct voltage ranges. A one-megohm isolating resistor is connected in the sleeve of the d-c lead for dynamic voltage checking. The electronic ohmmeter uses a shielded cable and by proper use of its six ranges resistance measurements of from 0.1 ohm to 1000 megohms can be obtained. A three-volt source of power is used for all ohmmeter ranges and it is only necessary to adjust for zero

indication once as this setting is common for all ranges. Because of the
many advantages outlined, the Voltohmyst is one of the most useful of
all voltage testing instruments.

The Vacuum-tube Voltmeter.   Another form of electronic voltmeter is
the vacuum-tube voltmeter, commonly abbreviated vtvm.   This instrument utilizes the characteristics of a vacuum tube for measuring voltages

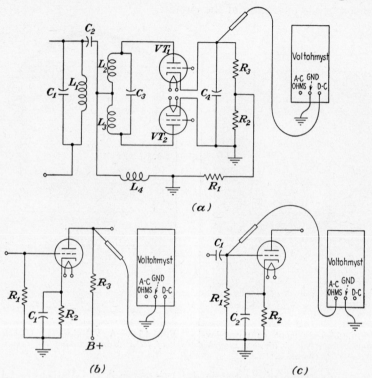

Fig. 15-10.—Methods of connecting the Voltohmyst for making radio circuit measurements.   (a) F-m balance, (b) plate voltage, (c) a-f signal voltage.

with minimum effect on the circuit to which it is connected.   Some types
of vacuum-tube voltmeters can be used to obtain the peak, trough,
effective, or average values of voltage.   By using a known value of capacitance as a shunt, the vtvm can also be used to measure small values of
current in high-frequency circuits.

There are various types of vtvm circuits, the choice of circuit used
being determined by the type of measurements for which it is to be used.
A simple form of vacuum-tube voltmeter circuit using plate rectification
is shown in Fig. 15-11.   The principle of operation of this type of vtvm
is as follows.   When an alternating voltage is applied to the grid circuit
of the tube, the alternating voltage will be rectified by the tube.   The

d-c component of the rectified output is indicated on the d-c meter, which is calibrated to indicate the proper voltage. The value of the tube's operating voltages are determined by the value of the alternating voltage input and the range of voltage to be indicated. The grid bias should be

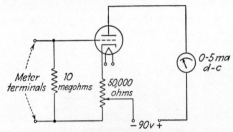

FIG. 15-11.—A simple vacuum-tube voltmeter circuit.

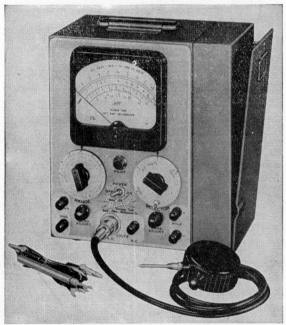

FIG. 15-12.—A vacuum-tube voltmeter. (*Courtesy of The Hickok Electrical Instrument Company.*)

greater than the peak value of the input voltage in order that the grid be maintained at a negative value throughout the entire cycle. The value of the plate voltage is determined by the range of the voltage that is to be indicated by the instrument. The plate voltage should be of such a value that it will produce a maximum deflection of the instrument for the prescribed input voltage.

A commercial vtvm that also measures current and resistance is shown in Fig. 15-12. This instrument is capable of measuring voltages having frequencies up to 150 megacycles. When using a vtvm for r-f measurements, care should be exercised to keep the input capacitance of the instrument and its leads at a minimum. For extreme accuracy, the input capacitance should be approximately 1 $\mu\mu$f and under no circumstances should it exceed 6 $\mu\mu$f. In order to obtain this low input capacitance,

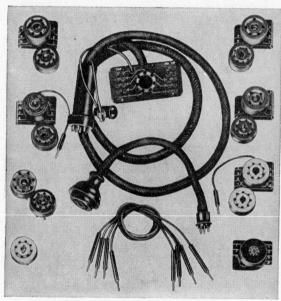

Fig. 15-13.—A socket selector set. (*Courtesy of Weston Electrical Instrument Corporation.*)

some vacuum-tube voltmeters make provisions for connecting the control grid of the vtvm tube directly to the point in the circuit being investigated. In order to prevent the circuit under test from being affected when the vtvm is connected to the circuit, the input impedance of the instrument should be very high. The meter illustrated in Fig. 15-12 has an input impedance of 15 megohms shunted by 6 $\mu\mu$f. In order to obtain greater accuracy, some vacuum-tube voltmeters employ a voltage-regulator tube to isolate any fluctuations in the line voltage from the instrument circuit.

15-4. Set Analyzer. *Socket Selector Unit.* The measurement of voltage, current, or resistance at the electrodes of a tube is greatly facilitated by the use of a set of socket adaptors and a selector block similar to the selector unit shown in Fig. 15-13. By using a selector unit in conjunction with the proper testing instrument, it is possible to make all tube voltage, current, and resistance measurements of a radio receiver from the top of each tube socket. This method of circuit analysis eliminates the necessity for probing among the wires of a receiver with the possibility of causing a short circuit and also eliminates the necessity of opening any soldered connections in order to take current readings.

The selector unit shown in Fig. 15-13 consists of three parts: (1) a selector block; (2) a cable, one end of which is permanently connected to the selector block, the other end being connected to an adaptor plug; (3) a set of adaptors. This unit is designed to be used with the combination meter shown in Fig. 15-6. To obtain readings it is necessary to select the adaptor unit that has a base corresponding to that of the tube under test. Each adaptor unit consists of two parts: (1) a skirted adaptor, which is inserted in the selector block; (2) a plug adaptor, which is inserted in the cable plug. The tube on which measurements are to be made is removed from its socket and the cable plug, to which the proper adaptor has been connected, is inserted in the tube socket. The tube is then placed in the adaptor that has been inserted in the selector block. The skirt on each adaptor extends over to a set of pin jacks numbered to correspond with the tube pin numbering system on each type base in accordance with the RMA standards. With the aid of a socket connection chart as in Appendix XV, or a tube manual, readings of voltage, current, or resistance may be obtained by connecting the instrument leads to the proper pin jacks.

Operation of the Selector Block.   The selector block contains two sets of pin jacks, which are connected in a manner similar to the circuit shown in Fig. 15-14a. Voltage and resistance measurements are obtained by using only the inner set of pin jacks. Current measurements are obtained by inserting the test leads in the two pin jacks that are connected in the electrode circuit whose current is to be measured. The outer set of pin jacks are closed-circuit jacks. Inserting a pin in this type of jack opens the contacts, thus permitting a current reading to be taken.

Set Analyzer.   The combination of a socket selector unit and a multipurpose meter is called a *set analyzer*. Some manufacturers mount both units in a single instrument. The comparative ease with which measurements can be taken with a set analyzer can best be illustrated by the following example.

The socket connections of a type 6K6-G tube are shown in Fig. 15-14b. Some of the measurements that can be taken on this tube by inserting the meter leads to the pin jacks noted are (1) heater voltage 2v to 7v, (2) plate voltage 3v to 8v, (3) screen-grid voltage 4v to 8v, (4) control-grid voltage 5v to 8v, (5) plate current 3v to 3a, (6) screen-grid current 4v to 4a, (7) external plate circuit resistance 3v to 8v. It can thus be seen that a set analyzer provides a convenient means of obtaining either static or dynamic measurements of a radio receiver.

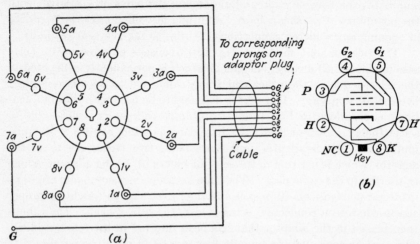

Fig. 15-14.—Socket connections of a socket selector-set unit. (a) Schematic wiring diagram of a socket selector block, (b) socket connections of a type 6K6-G tube.

15-5. Signal Generators. *Audio Oscillator.* An audio-frequency oscillator is an instrument employing vacuum-tube circuits that can be adjusted to generate a low voltage signal having any desired value of audio frequency. This instrument is commonly called an *audio oscillator*. Commercial audio oscillators may be divided into two classes: (1) the beat-frequency type (see Art. 10-2), (2) the resistance-capacitance type. A simple a-f oscillator circuit of the resistance-capacitance type is shown in Fig. 15-15. The output of this oscillator circuit has a constant amplitude and constant frequency. However, by the proper connection of additional circuit elements to this simple circuit a variable amplitude and variable frequency output can be obtained. The resistance-capacitance type a-f oscillator has two advantages over the beat-frequency type: (1) it has higher frequency stability, (2) its circuit is much simpler.

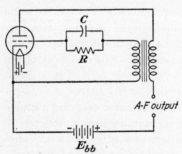

Fig. 15-15.—A simple a-f oscillator circuit.

Although an a-f oscillator may be obtained as a separate unit, it is generally combined with an r-f oscillator into a single unit. Such an instrument is called a *signal generator, all-wave generator,* or a *test oscillator*.

A commercial signal generator is shown in Fig. 15-16. This instrument has two a-f oscillator circuits, one provides a fixed a-f output of 400 cycles and the other a variable a-f output of from 50 to 15,000 cycles. The output voltage can be varied from zero to one volt. The r-f signal may be modulated by the output of either a-f oscillator.

The a-f oscillator has many uses in testing radio parts and equipment and may be used to test (1) the amplifying characteristics at various frequencies of all forms of a-f coupling such as transformers, chokes, resistor-capacitor networks, etc., (2) the tone-reproducing qualities of all forms of loudspeakers, (3) the gain per stage and the overall gain of an a-f amplifier. When an a-f oscillator is used for these tests the oscillator supplies the a-f signal and a vacuum-tube voltmeter, Voltohmyst, or cathode-ray oscilloscope is used to determine the output characteristics of the unit being tested. The a-f oscillator may also be used for the following purposes: (1) to supply a sound signal for a-c bridge measurements, (2) to trace open and grounded circuits with the aid of a pair of earphones, (3) for modulating an r-f oscillator, (4) for locating loose mechanical connections in a radio receiver.

Radio-frequency Test Oscillator. An r-f test oscillator is an instrument capable of generating the various r-f voltages required for alignment and servicing of radio equipment. The circuit of this type of instrument is based on the principles of oscillator circuits, as was explained in Chap. X. Since an r-f oscillator is generally designed for a particular type of service, its output requirements will determine the circuit arrangement and the values of the circuit elements. The general requirements of a test oscillator are: (1) good frequency and amplitude stability; (2) a wide range of frequency output, which can readily be adjusted and whose frequency value can be easily read; (3) an attenuator for adjusting the amplitude of the output signal from zero to its maximum value without affecting the frequency; (4) provision for modulating the r-f signal.

The r-f test oscillator can be obtained as either a separate unit or combined with an a-f oscillator. However, as many tests require a modulated r-f signal, an audio oscillator is usually combined with an r-f oscillator to form a single test instrument, as shown in Fig. 15-16. This instrument has seven r-f ranges, which makes it possible to obtain a continuous variable radio frequency from 100 kc to 133 mc. The r-f output may be used as unmodulated, amplitude modulated, or frequency modulated. For amplitude modulation, the r-f output may be modulated with either a constant 60-cycle or 400-cycle signal, or with a variable 50-15,000 cycle signal. For frequency modulation, band widths of 30, 150, or 750 kc can be obtained. The r-f output is modulated with either the 60-cycle, 400-cycle, or 50-15,000 cycle signal, depending upon which range and band width is being used.   In addition to the r-f output, this instrument can also provide the following: (1) a-f outputs of 60 cycles, 400 cycles, or 50-15,000 cycles, (2) a synchronized sweep voltage for oscilloscope use, (3) a power level meter having three ranges that are capable of indicating outputs from −10 db to +38 db.   This instrument is very useful for testing and aligning all types of a-m radio equipment, f-m radio equipment, television equipment, and various types of electronic equipment.

FIG. 15-16.—A commercial universal crystal-controlled signal generator.   (*Courtesy of The Hickok Electrical Instrument Company.*)

Uses of the Signal Generator.   A signal generator is required for accurate alignment and measurements of all tuned circuits in electronic equipment.   In general, the output of the signal generator may be applied to the input circuit of the unit being tested or to any one of its individual stages.   The signal generator should first be adjusted to produce a signal output of the desired frequency and amplitude.   It is then possible to align each stage, measure the gain per stage, or the overall gain, by connecting an output meter or electronic voltmeter in the proper circuit. The distortion characteristics of each stage can be observed by using a signal generator to supply an input signal and a cathode-ray oscilloscope for observing the wave form of the output from each stage.   Four

oscilloscope patterns illustrating the frequency-response characteristics
of an i-f amplifier stage are shown in Fig. 15-17.

For proper alignment or testing of a radio receiver, the following procedure is suggested: (1) ascertain the proper operation, applications, and
limitations of the test equipment from the manufacturer's instructions;
(2) much time can be saved in the aligning of each stage or the localizing
of a fault or faults by referring to the circuit diagram of the equipment
being tested; (3) the output of the test oscillator should be maintained
at a low level; (4) when aligning the i-f stage, short-circuit the local
oscillator or in some other manner prevent any part of the oscillator
output from entering the i-f stage; (5) the output of the signal generator

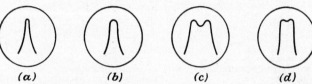

(a)   *(b)*   *(c)*   *(d)*

Fig. 15-17.—Oscilloscope patterns illustrating the frequency characteristics of an i-f
amplifier. (*a*) Single peak which is too narrow, (*b*) single peak of the proper width, (*c*)
double peak which is too broad and whose depression is too deep, (*d*) double peak of the
proper width and depth.

should be fed through a dummy antenna as specified by the manufacturer
of the receiver; (6) follow the instructions for alignment suggested by the
manufacturer of the receiver; (7) after the complete unit has been aligned,
recheck the alignment of each stage and make any readjustment that may
be required due to the reaction from the alignment of the other stages.

15-6. Cathode-ray Tubes. *General Principles.* The cathode-ray
tube forms an essential part of the cathode-ray oscilloscope, and it is
therefore best to understand the principles of operation of this tube before
studying the operation of the oscilloscope. In a cathode-ray tube, the
electrons emitted by the cathode are attracted by a high positive potential
anode. The structure of this anode is such that the electrons are formed
into a narrow beam and their velocity is so great that they continue a
forward motion until they strike the screen. This beam follows a straight
line unless it is diverted by either an electrostatic or electromagnetic
field. An electron beam consists of a moving stream of electrons and
hence has the following important characteristics: (1) it is attracted to
positive charged objects and is repelled by negative charged objects;
(2) like any other form of electric current it is subject to forces from a
magnetic field. Because of these two characteristics it is possible to
focus or deflect an electron beam by using either magnetic or electric
fields. Electron beams are not visible to the naked eye and in order to
follow their movements it is necessary to direct the beam at a specially

treated screen, which fluoresces when it is hit by the electron beam. The spot where an electron beam strikes such a screen is indicated by a point of light.

Construction. The general construction of most cathode-ray tubes is practically the same. The tube consists of a highly evacuated glass

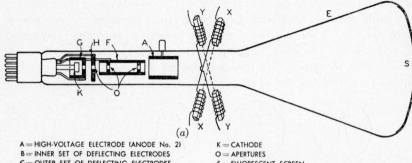

(a)

A = HIGH-VOLTAGE ELECTRODE (ANODE No. 2)   K = CATHODE
B = INNER SET OF DEFLECTING ELECTRODES   O = APERTURES
C = OUTER SET OF DEFLECTING ELECTRODES   S = FLUORESCENT SCREEN
E = GLASS ENVELOPE   XX = PAIR OF COILS FOR PRODUCING MAGNETIC FIELD
F = FOCUSING ELECTRODE (ANODE No. 1)   YY = PAIR OF COILS FOR PRODUCING MAGNETIC FIELD
G = CONTROL ELECTRODE (GRID No. 1)   AT RIGHT ANGLES TO THAT PRODUCED BY THE PAIR
H = ACCELERATING ELECTRODE (GRID No. 2)   OF COILS XX

NOTE: ELECTRODES K, G, H, F, AND A CONSTITUTE AN "ELECTRON GUN".

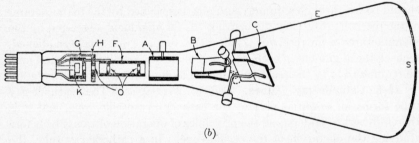

(b)

Fig. 15-18.—Schematic arrangement of the electrodes in a cathode-ray tube. (a) Electromagnetic deflection, electrostatic-focus type, (b) electrostatic deflection, electrostatic-focus type. (*Courtesy of RCA Manufacturing Co., Inc.*)

envelope containing an electron gun at one end, a fluorescent screen at the other end, and in between these two somes means of deflecting the electron beam. The arrangement of the various parts of the cathode-ray tube is shown in Figs. 15-18 and 15-20.

Operation of the Electron Gun. A typical electron gun is shown in Fig. 15-19. The *heater H* consists of a tungsten filament coated with an insulating material. The heater is mounted inside a small metal cylinder *K* called the *cathode.* The front end of this cylinder is concave and is chemically treated to make this portion of the cathode a good emitter of electrons. A *heat shield HS* is placed outside the cathode to aid in concentrating the electrons into a beam.

The control electrode *CG* performs the same function as the control grid in an ordinary vacuum tube. This electrode consists of a metal cylinder having a metal diaphragm with a small aperture that is placed directly in front of the electron-emitting surface of the cathode. The potential on the control electrode is made negative with respect to the cathode, and as a result the electrons, which are themselves negative, are prevented from diverging from the cathode and are bent inward along the axis of the tube. The number of electrons in the beam is thus controlled by the control-grid potential.

A cylinder containing several diaphragms, each with an aperture, is placed in front of the control electrode. This cylinder *AE* is called the

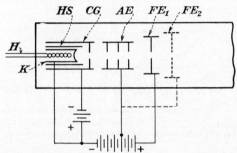

FIG. 15-19.—The electron gun of a cathode-ray tube.

first anode or *accelerating electrode*. The apertures within the cylinder serve to remove from the beam any strongly divergent electrons that would otherwise produce a fuzzy spot. In order to accelerate the electron beam, this electrode has a positive charge of several hundred volts with respect to the cathode.

Following the first anode is the *second anode* or *focusing electrode*. This anode FE_1 is of a larger diameter than the first anode and is also much shorter in length. It generally has only one diaphragm. The second anode is charged to a much higher potential than the first anode. In some instances this voltage may be several thousand volts. Variations in the construction of the electron gun can be seen by observation of Figs. 15-18 and 15-20.

Focusing. The principal focusing action occurs in the electrostatic field between the accelerating and focusing electrodes. The beam is focused by changing the voltage on the focusing electrode, just as the intensity of the electron beam is controlled by varying the potential on the control grid. These two control actions are not wholly independent, for example, changing the beam intensity affects the focus and vice versa.

In order to increase the brilliance and fineness of the trace, an extra element is sometimes placed in the tube. In some tubes this electrode

FE_2 takes the form of a screen grid and is connected to the accelerating electrode AE.

Greater speed of the electrons results in lower sensitivity of deflection. In some tubes an extra element, called an *intensifier*, is used to speed up the electrons after they have passed the deflecting source. In this way, higher sensitivity can be obtained. This element is located close to the fluorescent screen and may be maintained at the potential of the second anode or increased to several thousand volts.

Fluorescent Screen. The fluorescent screen consists of certain chemicals deposited on the inside surface of the flat end of the tube. The chemicals may be willemite, zinc oxide, calcium tungstate, zinc sulphide, zinc silicate, etc. When these chemicals are hit by fast-moving

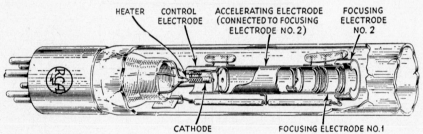

FIG. 15-20.—Structure of the electron gun in a cathode-ray tube. (*Courtesy of RCA Manufacturing Co., Inc.*)

electrons they fluoresce, the color depending upon the particular chemical used. The color may be green, blue, violet, yellow, orange, red, or white. Green is most useful for visual observation because the eye is most sensitive to this color.

After the electron beam strikes the fluorescent screen, the emission of light persists for a short time interval. The length of this time interval varies with the nature of the screen material and is usually only a small fraction of a second. Cathode-ray tubes are usually referred to as having a screen material with a long, medium, or short persistence.

The viewing screen of standard-type tubes ranges in size from one to twelve inches in diameter. Increasing the size of the screen requires an increase in the length of the tube. Screen sizes ranging from one to five inches are generally used for laboratory oscilloscopes.

Electrostatic Deflection. The electron beam may be deflected by using either electrostatic or electromagnetic means. In the electrostatic system, the electron beam is made to pass between two sets of parallel plates (see Fig. 15-18). Since an electron possesses a negative charge, as well as inertia, it will be attracted by a positive charge and repelled by a negative one. When a voltage is applied to either set of plates, the force caused by the charges on these plates will deflect the electron beam toward the positive plate. This force is only effective during the period of time that the electron beam is passing between the plates and the longer the plates the greater will be the final displacement of the beam.

One set of parallel plates, the set that is mechanically vertical, will cause the beam to be deflected in a horizontal direction. The other set of plates, mounted mechanically horizontal, will cause the beam to be deflected in a vertical direction. The deflection of the electron beam is directly proportional to the voltage applied to the plates. Since negligible power is required by the deflecting plates, they can be connected across practically any circuit to observe its voltage variations. Cathode-ray oscilloscopes generally use the electrostatic deflection type of tube.

Electromagnetic Deflection. The electron beam consists of electrons moving in one general direction at a high velocity. This beam therefore has the same characteristics as an electric current and as a result in the presence of a magnetic field the beam follows the laws of magnetism.

In the electromagnetic type of deflection two pairs of coils are mounted around the neck of the tube. These coils are arranged with their respective axis perpendicular to each other and perpendicular to the axis of the tube (see Fig. 15-18). The two coils Y-Y have a common vertical axis and any current applied to them will cause a horizontal deflection of the electron beam. The two coils X-X have a common horizontal axis and any current flowing through these coils will cause vertical deflection of the beam.

The advantages of the electromagnetic type of deflection are: (1) the length of the tube is decreased; (2) control of the deflection of the beam is accomplished outside the tube; (3) elimination of the deflection plates makes the tube more rugged and cheaper to construct.

Type Numbers. Originally each manufacturer assigned his own type numbers for cathode-ray tubes, but now the RMA has standardized the numbering system. In the RMA system the first number indicates the diameter of the screen in inches and the last two characters indicate the persistence and color of the trace. P_1 indicates green, P_2 blue, P_3 yellow, P_4 white, and P_5 light blue. Thus, a $5AP_1$ is a tube having a green trace on a screen whose outside diameter is five inches.

15-7. Cathode-ray Oscilloscope. *General Principle.* The oscilloscope is an instrument for indicating the wave form of a variable voltage or current. The oscilloscope is based on the principle that a moving fluorescent spot can be made to appear as a stationary figure by properly adjusting the frequencies of the voltages across the two sets of deflection plates.

Cathode-ray oscilloscopes are designed to produce on the screen of its cathode-ray tube an instantaneous visible curve of one electrical quantity as a function of another electrical quantity. If the quantities vary recurrently, the trace of the electron beam will appear on the fluorescent screen as a continuous curve, owing to the persistence of vision of the human eye. The voltage whose wave form is to be investigated is applied to the vertical deflection plates. A voltage that acts as a timing wave is applied to the horizontal deflection plates. The resultant deflection of the electron beam produces a pattern on the fluorescent screen which is a visible indication of the manner that the voltage being investigated varies with respect to time. Generally, one or more circuits are incorporated within the oscilloscope to generate a timing wave. Usually a saw-tooth-shaped voltage wave is applied to the horizontal deflection plates so that the voltage being investigated will vary as a linear function of time.

Oscilloscopes are designed primarily for the analysis of electrical circuits by studying the wave form of voltage and current at various points in the network. However, such an instrument may be applied to the study of any variable quantity which may be translated into electrical voltages by such means as a vibrator pickup unit, pressure pickup, etc.

The cathode-ray tube may be considered as an indicating device with a pointer of negligible inertia and for this reason its frequency range is practically unlimited. However, the frequency range of an oscilloscope is limited by the frequency-response characteristics of the vacuum-tube amplifiers that are incorporated within the instrument.

Sweep. Applying a voltage that has a constant time rate of change to the horizontal deflection plates will cause the beam to move straight across the face of the oscilloscope. Applying a varying voltage to the vertical deflection plates will then cause the electron beam to trace the wave form of the applied voltage on the fluorescent screen. The circuit that supplies the timing voltage to the horizontal deflection plates is arranged so that as soon as the timing voltage moves the beam all the way across the screen the beam is returned to the starting point and the process is repeated. This movement is called the *sweep* and the number of times it is repeated per second is referred to as the *sweep frequency*. Although the horizontal sweep is used practically universally for radio applications, a horizontal, vertical, or radial sweep may be used for electronic applications.

Sweep Oscillator. The sweep oscillator is used to generate a voltage having a wave form suitable for application to a set of deflecting plates in a cathode-ray tube in order to make the electron beam sweep back and forth across the fluorescent screen. For ideal conditions, the voltage produced by the sweep oscillator should have a linear time base. A saw-tooth wave, as shown in Fig. 15-21, produces a linear time base. The interval from A to C constitutes one period. The interval A-B is the go or *sweep time* and the interval B-C is the *flyback time*. For ideal conditions, the sweep portion A-D should be perfectly linear and the flyback

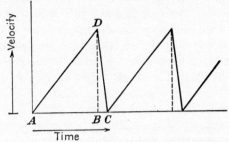

Fig. 15-21.—A saw-tooth linear time base.

time should be of a very short duration. To prevent the return trace from affecting the pattern on the screen, the electron beam is cut off during each flyback period. This can be accomplished by applying sufficient negative voltage to the control grid of the cathode-ray tube to cut off the electron beam during each of these intervals.

Sweep Generator Circuits. The most common method of obtaining a saw-tooth wave is by charging a capacitor through a resistor from a high direct voltage source and using only the linear portion of the varying voltage (see Art. 2-31). As only a relatively small portion of the charging curve is linear the capacitor should be allowed to charge for only this

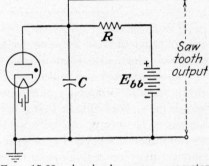

Fig. 15-22.—A simple sweep generator circuit.

small interval of time. This can be accomplished by connecting the capacitor across the plate and cathode of a gas diode or triode. When the voltage charge on the capacitor reaches an amount equal to the breakdown voltage of the tube, the tube will start to conduct. Because of its low internal resistance while conducting, the tube will practically short-circuit the capacitor, thereby causing it to discharge almost instantaneously. The interval of time during which the capacitor is charging will be determined by the breakdown voltage of the gas tube and the values of the capacitor and resistor. A simple sweep generator circuit using these principles is shown in Fig. 15-22.

The useful frequency range of a sweep generator circuit using a gas tube is limited by the deionization time of the tube. At frequencies above 50 kc, the deionization time of gas tubes becomes an appreciable portion of the total cycle, thus prohibiting their use at high frequencies. A number of vacuum-tube circuits have been developed that employ the trigger characteristic of a triode or pentode. The trigger action is produced by causing a slight change in a circuit constant to change suddenly the plate or screen-grid current. This sudden change in current is used to charge or discharge a capacitor. A simple multivibrator circuit using this principle is shown in Fig. 15-23. Linear time bases having a fre-

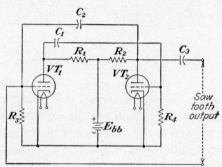

Fig. 15-23.—A simple multivibrator circuit.

quency range of from 2 cycles per second to 1,000,000 cycles per second can be obtained with vacuum-tube sweep generator circuits.

Synchronization. A stationary pattern is obtained on the fluorescent screen when the frequency of the sweep voltage is synchronized with the frequency of the voltage being investigated. With proper apparatus, the sweep frequency can be adjusted from a few cycles per second to several hundred thousand cycles per second. Figure 15-24 illustrates the manner in which a single sine-wave pattern is produced on the screen when the frequency of the sine-wave input signal and the sweep frequency are equal. Figure 15-25 illustrates the manner in which a double sine-wave pattern is produced on the screen when the frequency of the sine-wave input signal is twice the value of the sweep frequency.

Operation of an Oscilloscope. The operation of an oscilloscope will vary with the manufacturer and model. However, the following general instructions will apply to most oscilloscopes. The arrangement of the various controls of a commercial cathode-ray oscilloscope is shown in Fig. 15-26.

All normal operating controls and terminals for most oscilloscopes are located on the front panel. Direct connection to the deflecting plates can generally be made by proper connection to terminals located on the back or side of most oscilloscopes.

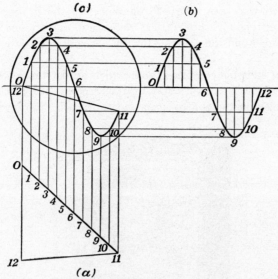

Fig. 15-24.—Pattern produced on the oscilloscope screen when the frequencies of the input voltage and the time base are equal and in phase. (a) Linear time base, (b) sine-wave input voltage, (c) pattern on the oscilloscope screen.

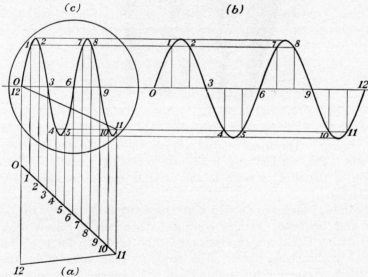

Fig. 15-25.—Pattern produced on the oscilloscope screen when the frequency of the input voltage is twice the frequency of the time base and both frequencies are in phase. (a) Linear time base, (b) sine-wave input voltage, (c) pattern on the oscilloscope screen.

Related controls are grouped together and the groups are plainly marked. Controls for the vertical deflection are on one side of the instrument panel and the controls for the horizontal deflection are on the other side.

The beam controls comprise those which adjust the intensity, focus, and position of the fluorescent spot on the screen. The intensity control adjusts the bias on the control grid and thus varies the intensity of the

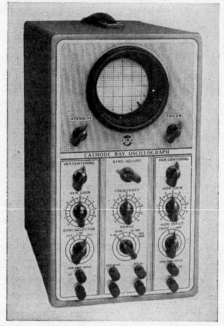

Fig. 15-26.—A cathode-ray oscilloscope. (*Courtesy of RCA Manufacturing Co., Inc.*)

beam current. The focus control adjusts the voltage on the focusing electrode. The vertical and horizontal centering controls adjust the location of the spot or trace in the vertical and horizontal directions respectively.

The linear time base or sweep generator controls include the frequency range and frequency vernier controls, synchronizing signal selector, synchronizing signal amplitude control, and provision for applying an external synchronizing signal. The frequency-range selector determines the frequency range of the timing base. The frequency vernier control adjusts the frequency to any value within the range of a particular frequency-range-selector setting. The position of the synchronizing selector switch determines whether the signal is to be synchronized internally, externally, or from the 60-cycle power line. A synchronizing adjustment for varying the amplitude of the synchronizing voltage is also usually provided. The resultant signal, as seen on the screen, may be amplified either vertically or horizontally by adjusting their respective gain controls.

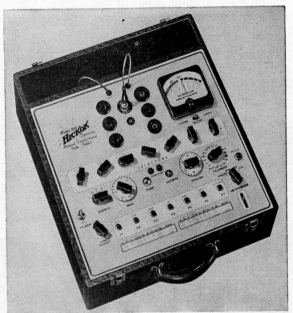

Fig. 15-27.—A commercial tube tester. (*Courtesy of The Hickok Electrical Instrument Company.*)

Uses of the Oscilloscope. The uses of the cathode-ray oscilloscope are many and varied. It is beyond the scope of this text to give a detailed discussion of each application. A few of the many uses as applied to radio receivers are (1) to align the i-f stages of a radio receiver when used in conjunction with a signal generator, (2) to align the r-f stages of a radio receiver when used in conjunction with a signal generator, (3) to determine the quality of the a-f signal by examination of its wave form at various points in the audio section of the receiver.

15-8. Tube Testers. Since vacuum tubes form an essential part of radio and electronic equipment it is necessary to have a test instrument that is capable of indicating the condition of a tube. There are a number of types of commercial tube testers and a good instrument should have provisions for checking (1) the emission of grid-type tubes, (2) the transconductance of grid-type tubes, (3) the plate current of rectifiers and diodes, (4) interelectrode short circuits in all types of tubes. For a quick appraisal of the condition of a tube, most tube testers provide an emission test with the results indicated on a scale marked *Bad-Fair-Good* or *Replace-Doubtful-Good*. Some instruments have provision for testing the power output of power amplifier tubes. A tube tester may measure either the static or dynamic transconductance of a tube or both. The dynamic mutual conductance test is more indicative of a tube's operating characteristics than the static test, and hence is the type that is preferred.

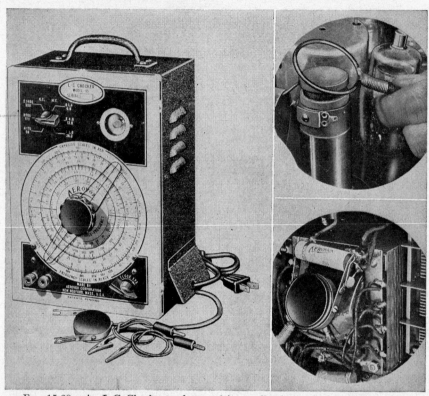

Fig. 15-28.—An L-C Checker and two of its applications. Left, the L-C Checker; upper right, checking the inductance of a coil; lower right, checking the capacitance of a capacitor in a receiver. (*Courtesy of Aerovox Corporation.*)

The operation of a tube tester will vary with the manufacturer and model and for best results should be operated in accordance with the instructions accompanying the instrument. A commercial tube tester illustrating the arrangement of the various controls and tube sockets is shown in Fig. 15-27. In addition to providing means for testing all types of vacuum tubes, this instrument also provides means of testing gas tubes, ballast tubes, and electron-ray indicator tubes. The dynamic mutual conductance is indicated directly in micromhos, and this test can be taken simultaneously with the emission test. The gas content of a tube can be measured and the condition of the tube indicated directly on the meter.

15-9. L-C Checker. There are various types of commercial test instruments designed for checking inductors and capacitors. One of these instruments is the *L-C Checker* shown in Fig. 15-28. An outstanding feature of this instrument is that it can be used for checking the characteristics of circuit elements without removing them from the circuit. This instrument thus provides a means for measuring the effective r-f

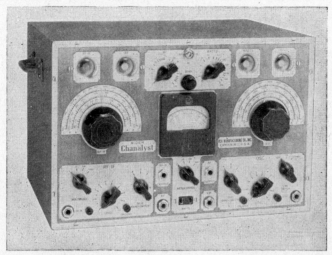

Fig. 15-29.—RCA Chanalyst. (*Courtesy of RCA Manufacturing Co., Inc.*)

capacitance of a capacitor and the effective r-f inductance of an inductor under actual operating conditions (see Fig. 15-28). Another feature of this instrument is that it provides a means of checking the resonant frequency of tuned circuits such as r-f and i-f stages, antennas, transmission lines, wave traps, choke coils, etc.

15-10. Chanalyst. One of the many test instruments that have been developed for effectively checking a radio receiver in a minimum amount of time is the *Chanalyst*. The Chanalyst is essentially an instrument that is designed to permit tracing the progress of a signal through each part of radio equipment. The Chanalyst shown in Fig. 15-29 is used chiefly for locating faults in radio receivers. This instrument has an r-f/i-f channel, an oscillator channel, an audio channel, a separate cathode-ray tuning indicator for each channel, an electronic voltmeter, and a power indicator. The operation of this instrument varies with the type of test for which it is to be used. The Chanalyst is used for checking radio equipment while it is in operation and hence this instrument has many different types of applications. In general, the testing procedure is to substitute one of the channels of the Chanalyst for the section of the receiver to be tested (see Fig. 15-30). However, for the proper use of the

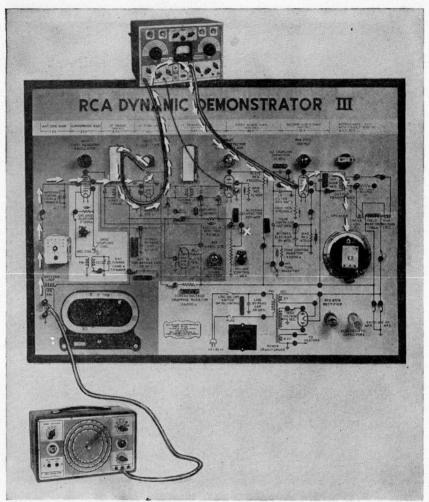

Fig. 15-30.—Illustration of signal-tracing technique. The arrows indicate the path of the signal from the antenna through the RCA Chanalyst to the loudspeaker, thus bridging the artificial defect at point *x*. (*Courtesy of RCA Manufacturing Co., Inc.*)

Chanalyst it is essential to follow rigidly the manufacturer's instructions for each test.

BIBLIOGRAPHY

Hicks, H. J., *Principles and Practice of Radio Servicing*, McGraw-Hill Book Company, Inc., New York.

Hoag, J. B., *Basic Radio*, D. Van Nostrand Company, Inc., New York.

Rider, J. F., *Perpetual Troubleshooters' Manual*, John F. Rider Publisher, Inc., New York.

Sams, H. W., *Radio Engineer's Service*, H. W. Sams & Co., Inc., Indianapolis, Ind.

Slurzberg, M., and Osterheld, W., *Electrical Essentials of Radio*, McGraw-Hill Book Company, Inc., New York.

Technical, Descriptive, and Instructional Data; distributed by manufacturers of radio and electronic test equipment.

Technical Service Data; distributed by manufacturers of radio receivers.

The Radio Amateur's Handbook, The American Radio Relay League, Inc., West Hartford, Conn.

QUESTIONS

1. (*a*) State two reasons for testing radio and electronic equipment. (*b*) Name three systems of testing radio and electronic equipment.

2. (*a*) Describe the point-to-point resistance measurement system of testing. (*b*) What are the advantages and disadvantages of this system?

3. (*a*) Describe the voltage and current measurement system of testing. (*b*) What are the advantages and disadvantages of this system?

4. (*a*) Describe the signal-tracing system of testing. (*b*) What are the advantages and disadvantages of this system?

5. (*a*) What is meant by a combination meter? (*b*) What are four other names for a combination meter? (*c*) What are the advantages of combination meters?

6. (*a*) What is an ammeter? (*b*) What is a milliammeter? (*c*) How is an ammeter connected in a circuit? (*d*) How should an ammeter be protected when readings are not being taken?

7. (*a*) What is a voltmeter? (*b*) How is a voltmeter connected in a circuit? (*c*) How should a voltmeter be protected when readings are not being taken?

8. (*a*) How is the sensitivity of a voltmeter usually expressed? (*b*) What sensitivity is considered desirable for a voltmeter used in testing electronic circuits?

9. (*a*) Name a few applications of thermal-type instruments. (*b*) Name a few applications of rectifier-type instruments.

10. (*a*) What is the purpose of a shunt? (*b*) What is the difference between an internal and external shunt?

11. (*a*) What is the purpose of a multiplier? (*b*) Can multipliers be used with alternating current and direct current instruments?

12. (*a*) What is an ohmmeter? (*b*) Explain its basic principle of operation.

13. (*a*) How does a decrease in battery voltage affect the reading of an ohmmeter? (*b*) What provision may be made to compensate for decreases in the battery voltage?

14. (*a*) Describe the basic construction of a combination meter designed to measure a-c and d-c voltages, d-c currents, and resistance. (*b*) What precautions are necessary in using combination meters?

15. (*a*) What is an output meter? (*b*) Describe the basic construction of an output meter.

16. (*a*) How is the output meter connected to a radio receiver? (*b*) What is the purpose of using a capacitor with an output meter?

17. (*a*) What are some applications of the electronic d-c voltmeter? (*b*) What are the advantages of the electronic d-c voltmeter?

18. Describe the principle of operation of a vacuum-tube voltmeter using plate rectification.

19. (*a*) What are some applications of the vacuum-tube voltmeter? (*b*) What are the advantages of the vtvm? (*c*) What precautions are necessary in using a vacuum-tube voltmeter?

20. Describe the construction and principle of operation of a socket-selector unit.

21. (*a*) What is a set analyzer? (*b*) What are its advantages?

22. (*a*) What is an audio oscillator? (*b*) Name two types of circuits used in commercial audio oscillators. (*c*) What are the advantages of the resistance-capacitance type of audio oscillator?

23. Describe seven uses of the audio oscillator.

24. (*a*) What is an r-f test oscillator? (*b*) What are the requirements of a good r-f test oscillator?

25. (*a*) What is a signal generator? (*b*) What are two other names for a signal generator?

26. Describe some applications of the signal generator.

27. What procedure is suggested for aligning a radio receiver?

28. Describe the two characteristics of an electron beam that enables the beam to be deflected or focused by use of electric or magnetic fields.

29. Describe the general construction of a cathode-ray tube.

30. Explain the operation of an electron gun.

31. (*a*) Explain the electrostatic field method of focusing the electron beam. (*b*) What is an intensifier?

32. (*a*) What materials are used in making a fluorescent screen? (*b*) What seven colors are used for the fluorescence of the screen? (*c*) Which color of fluorescence is generally used?

33. Explain the operation of the electrostatic deflection of an electron beam.

34. Explain the operation of the electromagnetic deflection of an electron beam.

35. Describe the RMA numbering system used for cathode-ray tubes.

36. (*a*) What is an oscilloscope? (*b*) What is the basic principle of the oscilloscope? (*c*) Describe the operation of an oscilloscope.

37. Define: (*a*) sweep, (*b*) sweep frequency, (*c*) sweep time, (*d*) flyback time.

38. (*a*) What is a sweep oscillator? (*b*) What is the advantage of a saw-tooth wave?

39. Describe the operation of a simple sweep generator circuit that is capable of producing a saw-tooth wave.

40. (*a*) What is the disadvantage in using a gas tube in sweep generator circuits? (*b*) What is meant by a trigger circuit? (*c*) What is the advantage of trigger circuits?

41. How is a stationary pattern obtained on the fluorescent screen of an oscilloscope?

42. Describe the operation of a commercial cathode-ray oscilloscope.

43. Describe several applications of the oscilloscope.

44. (*a*) State four requirements of a good commercial tube tester. (*b*) What is the advantage of a dynamic mutual conductance test?

45. Describe several applications of the L-C Checker.

46. (*a*) What is a Chanalyst? (*b*) What are the uses of a Chanalyst? (*c*) Describe the general testing procedure when using a Chanalyst.

APPENDIX I

DRAWING SYMBOLS USED IN ELECTRONICS

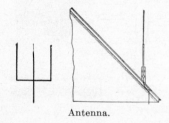

Antenna.

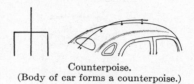

Counterpoise.
(Body of car forms a counterpoise.)

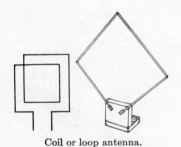

Coil or loop antenna.

Battery cell.
(Positive terminal indicated by a long line.)

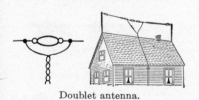

Doublet antenna.

Battery.

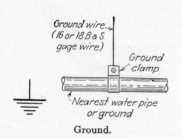

Ground.

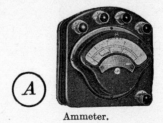

Ammeter.

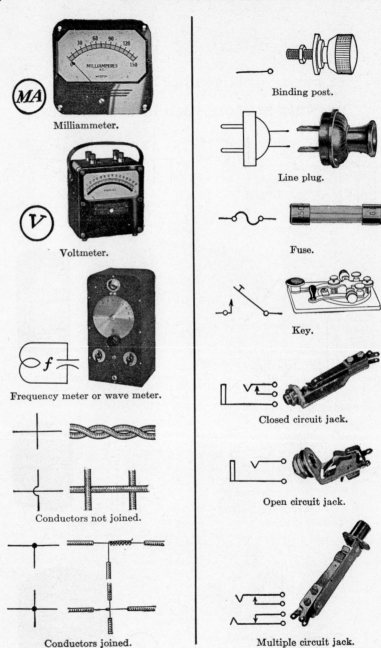

Milliammeter.

Voltmeter.

Frequency meter or wave meter.

Conductors not joined.

Conductors joined.

Binding post.

Line plug.

Fuse.

Key.

Closed circuit jack.

Open circuit jack.

Multiple circuit jack.

Single-pole single-throw switch.

Multiple-deck circuit-selector switch.

Single-pole double-throw switch.

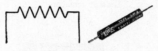

Fixed resistor.

Double-pole single-throw switch.

Adjustable resistor.

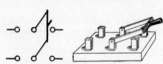

Double-pole double-throw switch.

Tapped resistor.

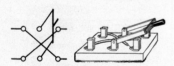

Double-pole double-throw
reversing switch.

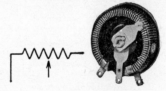

Rheostat.

Single-deck circuit-selector switch.

Potentiometer.

Ballast resistor.

Thermo element.

Inductor, air-core.

Inductor, iron-core.

Adjustable inductor.

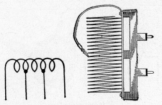

Tapped inductor.

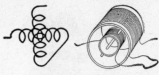

Variable inductor.
(Variometer.)

Transformer, air-core.

Transformer with variable coupling.
(Variocoupler with the moving coil
indicated.)

Three-circuit tuner.

Transformer, iron-core.

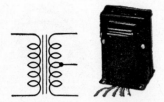

Push-pull transformer.

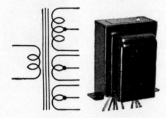

Power transformer.

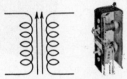

Variable-core transformer.

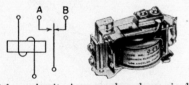

Relay; circuit A open when deenergized.

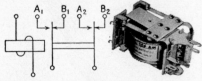

Relay; circuits B₁ and B₂ closed when deenergized.

Fixed capacitor.
(Paper, mica, or oil.)

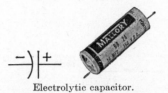

Electrolytic capacitor.

Variable capacitor.

Adjustable capacitor.
(Trimmer.)

Adjustable capacitor.
(Padder.)

Split-stator variable capacitor.

Ganged variable capacitors.
Mechanical linkage.

Coaxial cable.

Twin coaxial cable.

Shielded cable.

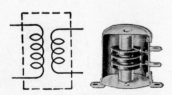

Shielded coil.

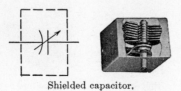

Shielded capacitor.

Earphones.

Permanent-magnet dynamic speaker.

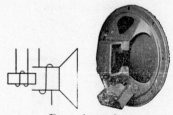

Dynamic speaker.

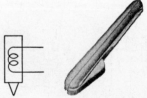

Magnetic phonograph-pickup.

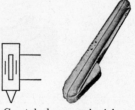

Crystal phonograph-pickup.

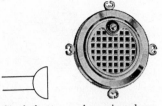

Single-button carbon microphone.

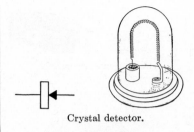

Crystal detector.

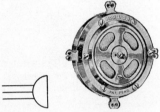

Double-button carbon microphone.

Crystal.

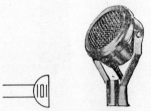

Crystal microphone.

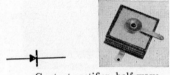

Contact rectifier, half-wave.

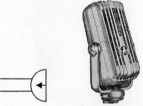

Velocity microphone.
(Ribbon.)

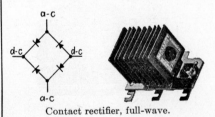

Contact rectifier, full-wave.

Dynamic microphone.
(Moving coil.)

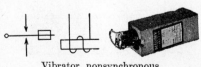

Vibrator, nonsynchronous.

Vibrator, synchronous.

Pilot lamp.

DC motor or generator.

Neon lamp.

AC motor or generator.
(Single phase.)

Photo tube.

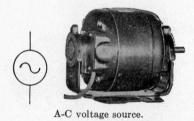

A-C voltage source.

Cold cathode triode.
(Gaseous.)

Link coupling.

Voltage regulator, cold cathode.
(Gaseous.)

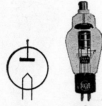

Half-wave rectifier,
directly heated cathode.

Triode, indirectly heated cathode.

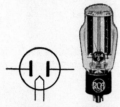

Full-wave rectifier,
directly heated cathode.

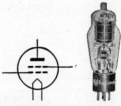

Tetrode, directly heated cathode.

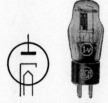

Half-wave rectifier,
indirectly heated cathode.

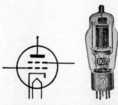

Tetrode, indirectly heated cathode.

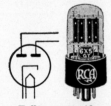

Full-wave rectifier,
indirectly heated cathode.

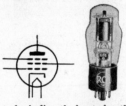

Pentode, indirectly heated cathode.

Duplex-diode triode.

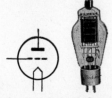

Triode, directly heated cathode.

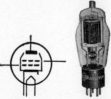

Beam-power amplifier.

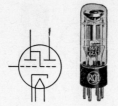

Electron-ray indicator tube.

Cathode-ray tube,
electromagnetic-deflection type.

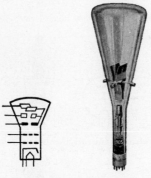

Cathode-ray tube,
electrostatic-deflection type.

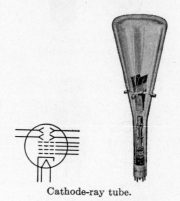

Cathode-ray tube.

LETTER SYMBOLS AND ABBREVIATIONS USED IN ELECTRONICS

Term	Symbol	Abbreviation
Alternating current		a-c
Alternating current or direct current		a-c/d-c
American Standards Association		ASA
Ampere (unit of current flow)	I	a or amp
Milliampere		ma
Microampere		μa
Ampere-turn	NI	A-T
American Wire Gauge		AWG
Antenna		ant
Apparent power (see also Volt-amperes)	VA	A-P
Area		A
Circular mils		cm or cir mils
Square centimeters		sq cm
Square inches		sq in
Automatic frequency control		afc
Automatic volume control		avc
Capacitance	C	
Capacitor	C	
Cathode ray		c-r
Cathode-ray tube		crt
Cathode-ray oscilloscope		cro
Centimeter-gram-second		cgs
Conductance	G	
Constant	K	
Continuous wave		c-w
Interrupted continuous wave		icw
Modulated continuous wave		mcw
Coulomb (unit of charge)	q	
Coupling, coefficient of	K	
Current	I	
Alternating		a-c
Average value	I_{ave}	
Direct		d-c
Effective value (also rms value)	I	
Instantaneous value	i_θ	
Maximum value	I_{max}	
Signal	i	
Cycles	$\sim$	c

Term	Symbol	Abbreviation
Per second (see also Frequency)................	$\sim$	cps or c/sec
Kilocycles...........................		kc
Megacycles..........................		mc
Decibel..............................		db
Density, flux........................	B	
Diameter............................	d	d or diam
Direct current.......................		d-c
Distance............................	d	
Efficiency...........................		eff
Electromotive force..................		emf
Counter electromotive force..........		cemf
Energy..............................	W	en
Equivalent..........................		eq
Farad (unit of capacitance)..........		f
Microfarad..........................		μf
Micromicrofarad.....................		$\mu\mu$f
Flux, magnetic......................	ϕ	
Density.............................	B	
Force...............................	F	
Frequency...........................	f	
Audio...............................		a-f
Intermediate........................		i-f
Modulation..........................		f-m
Radio...............................		r-f
Resonance...........................	f_r	
Superhigh...........................		shf
Ultrahigh...........................		uhf
Very high...........................		vhf
Gausses (magnetic induction)........	B	
Gilbert (unit of magnetomotive force)......	F	

Term	Capital	Lower case
Greek alphabet		
Alpha..............................	A	α
Beta...............................	B	β
Gamma.............................	Γ	γ
Delta..............................	Δ	δ
Epsilon............................	E	ϵ
Zeta...............................	Z	ζ
Eta................................	H	η
Theta..............................	Θ	θ
Iota...............................	I	ι
Kappa.............................	K	κ
Lambda............................	Λ	λ
Mu................................	M	μ
Nu................................	N	ν
Xi.................................	Ξ	ξ
Omicron............................	O	o

Term	Symbol		Abbreviation
Pi..	Π	π	
Rho...	P	ρ	
Sigma.......................................	Σ	σ	
Tau...	T	τ	
Upsilon.....................................	Υ	υ	
Phi...	Φ	φ	
Chi...	X	χ	
Psi...	Ψ	ψ	
Omega.......................................	Ω	ω	
Ground......................................			gnd
Henry (unit of inductance)..................	L		h
Millihenry...............................			mh
Microhenry...............................			μh
Impedance...................................	Z		
Inch..			in.
Inductance, self-...........................	L		
Mutual...................................	M		
Institute of Radio Engineers................			IRE
Intensity, magnetic field...................	H		
Joule.......................................	j		j
Kilo..			k
Length......................................	l		
Loudspeaker.................................	LS		
Magnetomotive force.........................			mmf
Master oscillator power amplifier...........			mopa or MOPA
Mathematical symbols			
Equals...................................	=		
Is approximately equal to................	≅		
Does not equal...........................	≠		
Is greater than..........................	>		
Is much greater than.....................	≫		
Is less than.............................	<		
Is much less than........................	≪		
Therefore................................	∴		
Multiplied by............................	x or ·		
Divided by...............................	÷ or :		
Positive, or plus........................	+		
Negative, or minus.......................	−		
Plus or minus............................	±		
Angle....................................	∠		
Sine..			sin
Cosine......................................			cos
Tangent.....................................			tan
Common logarithm............................			log
Antilogarithm...............................			antilog
Cologarithm.................................			colog
Maximum.....................................			max

Term	Symbol	Abbreviation
Maxwell	ϕ	
Meter (measure of length)		m
Centimeter		cm
Millimeter		mm
Minimum		min
Modulation, amplitude		a-m
Factor	m	
Frequency		f-m
Per cent of	M	
Phase		p-m
Oersted (unit of magnetic intensity)	H	
Ohm (unit of resistance)	Ω or ω	
Megohm	$M\Omega$	meg
Permanent magnet (loudspeaker)	PM	pm
Permeability	μ	
Permeance	$\mathcal{P}$	
Pi	$\pi(3.1416)$	
Phase angle	θ	
Pole, north seeking	N	
South seeking	S	
Power		p
Power, output	P_o	
Power, output maximum	$P_{o\cdot m}$	
Power, output maximum undistorted	$P_{o\cdot m\cdot u}$	
Power amplification		PA
Power factor		p-f
Primary	P	p or pri
Q-Factor (also Ratio of X_L to R)	Q	
Reactance	X	
Inductive	X_L	
Capacitive	X_C	
Radio Manufacturers Association		RMA
Reluctance	$\mathcal{R}$	
Resistance	R or r	resis
Root mean square		rms
Secondary	S	sec
Switch	S	sw
Single pole, single throw		spst
Single pole, double throw		spdt
Double pole, single throw		dpst
Double pole, double throw		dpdt
Three deck, four circuit, eight positions		3d-4c-8p
Temperature, coefficient	T_c	
Degrees centigrade	$°C$	
Degrees Fahrenheit	$°F$	
Thickness	t	
Time	t or T	

Term	Symbol	Abbreviation
Seconds.....................................		sec
Microseconds...............................		μsec
Minutes....................................		min
Hour.......................................		hr
Time constant..............................	t	
Transformer................................	T	
Tuned radio frequency......................		trf
Turns, number of...........................	N	
Vacuum tube................................	VT	
Vacuum-tube symbols		
Cathode.................................	K	
Heater..................................	H	
Plate (or anode)........................	P	
Control grid in a triode................	G	
Control grid in a multigrid tube........	G_1	
Screen grid.............................	G_2	
Suppressor grid.........................	G_3	
Plate supply voltage....................	E_{bb}	
Control-grid supply voltage.............	E_{cc1}	
Screen-grid supply voltage..............	E_{cc2}	
Filament or heater supply voltage.......	E_{ff}	
Instantaneous total grid voltage........	e_c	
Instantaneous total plate voltage.......	e_b	
Instantaneous total grid current........	i_c	
Instantaneous total plate current.......	i_b	
Average or quiescent value of grid voltage........	E_c	
Average or quiescent value of plate voltage.......	E_b	
Average or quiescent value of grid current........	I_c	
Average or quiescent value of plate current.......	I_b	
Instantaneous value of the varying component of the grid voltage...........................	e_g	
Instantaneous value of the varying component of the plate voltage...........................	e_p	
Instantaneous value of the varying component of the grid current...........................	i_g	
Instantaneous value of the varying component of the plate current...........................	i_p	
Effective or maximum value of the varying component of the grid voltage..................	E_g	
Effective or maximum value of the varying component of the plate voltage.................	E_p	
Effective or maximum value of the varying component of the grid current..................	I_g	
Effective or maximum value of the varying component of the plate current.................	I_p	
Filament or heater terminal voltage.............	E_f	
Filament or heater current.....................	I_f	

Term	Symbol	Abbreviation
Plate resistance.............................	r_p	
Grid-plate transconductance (mutual conductance)	g_m	
Amplification factor..........................	μ	
Grid-plate capacitance.......................	C_{gp}	
Grid-cathode capacitance.....................	C_{gk}	
Plate-cathode capacitance....................	C_{pk}	
Grid-heater capacitance......................	C_{gh}	
Plate-heater capacitance.....................	C_{ph}	
Power output................................	P_o	
Power input.................................	P_i	
Plate dissipation............................	P_p	
Vacuum-tube voltmeter.......................		vtvm
Volt (unit of electrical pressure)...................	E	v
Kilovolt.......................................		kv
Millivolt......................................		mv
Microvolt.....................................		μv
Voltage......................................	E	
Average value...............................	E_{ave}	
Effective value (also rms value)................	E	
Instantaneous value..........................	e_θ	
Maximum value..............................	E_{max}	
Signal......................................	e	
Volt-amperes................................	VA	v-a
Kilovolt-amperes............................	KVA	kva
Voltage amplification.........................		VA
Voltage amplification at medium values of audio frequencies................................		VA_M
Voltage amplification at low values of audio frequencies.....................................		VA_L
Voltage amplification at high values of audio frequencies.....................................		VA_H
Voltage regulation............................		VR
Volume unit.................................		v-u
Watt (unit of electrical power)...................	W or P	w
Kilowatt......................................		kw
Kilowatt-hour................................		kwhr
Milliwatt.....................................		mw
Microwatt....................................		μw
Wavelength..................................	λ	
Wire, single cotton covered....................		scc
Double cotton covered........................		dcc
Single silk covered...........................		ssc
Double silk covered...........................		dsc
Enamel single cotton covered..................		escc
Enamel double silk covered...................		edsc

APPENDIX III

CONVERSION FACTORS

Given	To obtain	Multiply by	Divide by
Amperes	Milliamperes	1000	
Amperes	Microamperes	1,000,000	
Ampere turns	Gilberts	1.257	
Bars	Dynes per sq cm	1	
Centimeters	Feet	....	30.48
Centimeters	Inches	....	2.54
Centimeters	Meters	....	100
Centimeters	Millimeters	10	
Centimeters	Mils	393.7	
Circular mils	Square centimeters	....	197,300
Circular mils	Square inches	....	1,273,000
Circular mils	Square mils	....	1.273
Cycles per second	Kilocycles per second	....	1000
Cycles per second	Megacycles per second	....	1,000,000
Degrees (angle)	Minutes	60	
Degrees (angle)	Seconds	3600	
Degrees (angle)	Radians	....	57.3
Dynes	Grams	....	980.7
Dynes	Kilograms	....	980,665
Dynes	Ounces	....	27,800
Dynes	Pounds	....	444,823
Dynes per square centimeter	Bars	1	
Farads	Microfarads	1,000,000	
Farads	Micromicrofarads	10^{12}	
Feet	Centimeters	30.48	
Feet	Inches	12	
Feet	Meters	....	3.281
Feet	Miles	....	5280
Foot-pounds per minute	Horsepower	....	33,000
Foot-pounds per second	Horsepower	....	550
Frequency in kilocycles	Wavelength in meters	(See Appendix XIV)	
Gausses	Lines per square centimeter	1	
Gausses	Lines per square inch	6.452	
Gilberts	Ampere-turns	....	1.257
Grams	Dynes	980.7	
Grams	Kilograms	....	1000

Given	To obtain	Multiply by	Divide by
Grams	Ounces	. . . .	28.35
Grams	Pounds	. . . .	453.6
Henries	Millihenries	1000	
Henries	Microhenries	1,000,000	
Horsepower	Foot-pounds per minute	33,000	
Horsepower	Foot-pounds per second	550	
Horsepower	Kilowatts	. . . .	1.341
Horsepower	Watts	746	
Inches	Centimeters	2.54	
Inches	Feet	. . . .	12
Inches	Meters	. . . .	39.37
Inches	Mils	1000	
Joules	Kilowatt-hours	. . . .	3,600,000
Joules	Watt-hours	. . . .	3600
Joules	Watt-seconds	1	
Kilo-units	Units	1000	
Kilocycles per second	Cycles per second	1000	
Kilocycles per second	Megacycles per second	. . . .	1000
Kilocycles per second	Wavelength in meters	(See Appendix XIV)	
Kilograms	Dynes	980,665	
Kilograms	Grams	1000	
Kilograms	Pounds	2.205	
Kilometers	Meters	1000	
Kilometers	Miles	. . . .	1.609
Kilovolts	Volts	1000	
Kilovolt amperes	Volt-amperes	1000	
Kilowatts	Horsepower	1.341	
Kilowatts	Watts	1000	
Kilowatt-hours	Joules	3,600,000	
Lines per square centimeter	Gausses	1	
Lines per square centimeter	Lines per square inch	6.452	
Lines per square inch	Gausses	. . . .	6.452
Lines per square inch	Lines per square centimeter	. . . .	6.452
Megacycles per second	Cycles per second	1,000,000	
Megacycles per second	Kilocycles per second	1000	
Mega-units	Units	1,000,000	
Megohms	Ohms	1,000,000	
Meters	Centimeters	100	
Meters	Feet	3.281	
Meters	Inches	39.37	
Meters	Millimeters	1000	
Mhos	Micromhos	1,000,000	
Microamperes	Amperes	. . . .	1,000,000
Microamperes	Milliamperes	. . . .	1000
Microfarads	Farads	. . . .	1,000,000
Microfarads	Micromicrofarads	1,000,000	

Given	To obtain	Multiply by	Divide by
Microhenries	Henries	....	1,000,000
Microhenries	Millihenries	....	1000
Micromhos	Mhos	....	1,000,000
Micromicrofarads	Farads	....	10^{12}
Micromicrofarads	Microfarads	....	1,000,000
Micromicro-units	Units	....	10^{12}
Microseconds	Seconds	....	1,000,000
Micro-units	Units	....	1,000,000
Microvolts	Volts	....	1,000,000
Microvolts	Millivolts	....	1000
Microwatts	Watts	....	1,000,000
Microwatts	Milliwatts	....	1000
Miles	Feet	5280	
Miles	Kilometers	1.609	
Milliamperes	Amperes	....	1000
Milliamperes	Microamperes	1000	
Millihenries	Henries	....	1000
Millihenries	Microhenries	1000	
Millimeters	Centimeters	....	10
Millimeters	Meters	....	1000
Milli-units	Units	....	1000
Millivolts	Volts	....	1000
Millivolts	Microvolts	1000	
Milliwatts	Watts	....	1000
Milliwatts	Microwatts	1000	
Mils	Centimeters	....	393.7
Mils	Inches	....	1000
Minutes	Seconds	60	
Minutes	Degrees	....	60
Ohms	Megohms	....	1,000,000
Ounces	Dynes	27,800	
Ounces	Grams	28.35	
Ounces	Pounds	....	16
Pounds	Dynes	444,823	
Pounds	Grams	453.6	
Pounds	Kilograms	....	2.205
Pounds	Ounces	16	
Radians	Degrees	57.3	
Seconds	Degrees	....	3600
Seconds	Microseconds	1,000,000	
Seconds	Minutes	....	60
Square centimeters	Circular mils	197,300	
Square centimeters	Square inches	....	6.452
Square inches	Circular mils	1,273,000	
Square inches	Square centimeters	6.452	
Square mils	Circular mils	1.273	
Units	Mega-units	....	1,000,000

Given	To obtain	Multiply by	Divide by
Units	Kilo-units	. . . .	1000
Units	Milli-units	1000	
Units	Micro-units	1,000,000	
Units	Micromicro-units	10^{12}	
Volt-amperes	Kilovolt-amperes	. . . .	1000
Volts	Kilovolts	. . . .	1000
Volts	Millivolts	1000	
Volts	Microvolts	1,000,000	
Wavelength (meters)	Frequency (kc)	(See Appendix XIV)	
Watt-hours	Joules	3600	
Watt-seconds	Joules	1	
Watts	Horsepower	. . . .	746
Watts	Kilowatts	. . . .	1000
Watts	Milliwatts	1000	
Watts	Microwatts	1,000,000	

APPENDIX IV

EXPONENTS AND THEIR USE

When circuit or problem calculations involve the use of very large or very small numbers, the method of expressing these numbers and performing arithmetic operations can be simplified by the use of exponents. This is really a shorthand method of mathematics.

The following table shows a list of numbers and the corresponding representations by the exponent method.

Number	Exponent method	Number	Exponent method
100,000,000	10^8	1	10^0
10,000,000	10^7	$0.1 \quad = \frac{1}{10}$	10^{-1}
1,000,000	10^6	$0.01 \quad = \frac{1}{100}$	10^{-2}
100,000	10^5	$0.001 = \frac{1}{1000}$	10^{-3}
10,000	10^4	0.0001	10^{-4}
1,000	10^3	0.00001	10^{-5}
100	10^2	0.000001	10^{-6}
10	10^1	0.0000001	10^{-7}
1	10^0	0.00000001	10^{-8}

The following examples illustrate the use of the exponent method of expressing common numbers.

1. $5 \text{ ma} = 0.005 \text{ amp} = 5 \times 10^{-3} \text{ amp}$
2. $25 \mu a = 0.000025 \text{ amp} = 25 \times 10^{-6} \text{ amp}$
3. $3.9 \text{ mc} = 3,900,000 \text{ cycles} = 3.9 \times 10^6 \text{ cycles}$
4. $8,500,000 = 8.5 \times 10^6$
5. $0.0035 = 3.5 \times 10^{-3}$
6. $6.28 \times 10^{18} = 6,280,000,000,000,000,000$

Note.—This is the number of electrons corresponding to one ampere.

Numbers that have similar exponent characteristics may be added or subtracted as indicated by the following illustrations.

7. $(4.5 \times 10^6) + (8.25 \times 10^6) + (0.25 \times 10^6) = 13 \times 10^6$
8. $(8.5 \times 10^3) - (3.5 \times 10^3) = 5 \times 10^3$

When numbers are multiplied, the exponents are added. The exponents do not have to be the same.

9. $650,000 \times 3,000 = (6.5 \times 10^5) \times (3 \times 10^3) = 19.5 \times 10^8$
10. $2,500,000 \times 0.005 = (2.5 \times 10^6) \times (5 \times 10^{-3}) = 12.5 \times 10^3$
11. $0.015 \times 0.0006 = (1.5 \times 10^{-2}) \times (6 \times 10^{-4}) = 9 \times 10^{-6}$

When numbers are divided, the exponents are subtracted. The exponents do not have to be the same.

12. $750,000 \div 150 = (7.5 \times 10^5) \div (1.5 \times 10^2) = 5 \times 10^3$

13. $2,500 \div 50,000 = (25 \times 10^2) \div (5 \times 10^4) = 5 \times 10^{-2}$

14. $5,000 \div 0.025 = (5 \times 10^3) \div (2.5 \times 10^{-2}) = 2 \times 10^5$

When a number set up in its exponent form is increased by a power such as a square, cube, etc., the number is increased by the power and the exponent factor is multiplied by the power as is indicated by the following illustrations.

15. $15,000^2 = (15 \times 10^3)^2 = 225 \times 10^6$

16. $300^3 = (3 \times 10^2)^3 = 27 \times 10^6$

17. $2000^4 = (2 \times 10^3)^4 = 16 \times 10^{12}$

When it is desired to obtain the root of a number, the exponent method may sometimes facilitate the work. This does not apply to every number and root but requires keen observation to detect when it may be used. The procedure is to extract the root of the number and divide the exponent factor by the root. This is illustrated by the following examples.

18. $\sqrt{64 \times 10^8} = 8 \times 10^4$

19. $\sqrt{64 \times 10^9} =$ not solvable by the short method

20. $\sqrt[3]{64 \times 10^9} = 4 \times 10^3$

21. $\sqrt[4]{16 \times 10^8} = 2 \times 10^2$

By using combinations of the preceding procedures it is often possible to shorten much of the tedious work of arithmetic and to increase the speed and accuracy of electrical circuit calculations. The method of solution in the following illustrations may not be apparent immediately, but upon careful inspection it should be detected.

22. $\dfrac{26,000 + 14,000 + 2000}{1400 - 800} = \dfrac{(26 + 14 + 2)10^3}{(14 - 8)10^2} = \dfrac{42 \times 10^3}{6 \times 10^2} = 7 \times 10^1$

23. $\dfrac{2500 \times 500 \times 2000}{80 \times 12,500} = \dfrac{25 \times 10^2 \times 5 \times 10^2 \times 2 \times 10^3}{8 \times 10^1 \times 1.25 \times 10^4} = \dfrac{250 \times 10^7}{10 \times 10^5}$

$$= 25 \times 10^2$$

24. $\dfrac{650 \times 2000 \times 400}{0.02 \times 0.013} = \dfrac{6.5 \times 10^2 \times 2 \times 10^3 \times 4 \times 10^2}{2 \times 10^{-2} \times 13 \times 10^{-3}} = \dfrac{52 \times 10^7}{26 \times 10^{-5}}$

$$= 2 \times 10^{12}$$

APPENDIX V

FORMULAS COMMONLY USED IN RADIO AND ELECTRONICS

NOTE.—The numbers appearing opposite the equations correspond to the numbers of the same equations in the text or to the equations from which they were derived. These numbers are included to facilitate reference to figures, text, and nomenclature when such reference is desirable.

DIRECT CURRENT

Ohm's Law

$$\text{Voltage} = IR = \frac{P}{I} = \sqrt{RP} \qquad \text{(2-26), (2-27)}$$

$$\text{Current} = \frac{E}{R} = \frac{P}{E} = \sqrt{\frac{P}{R}} \qquad \text{(2-26), (2-27)}$$

$$\text{Resistance} = \frac{E}{I} = \frac{P}{I^2} = \frac{E^2}{P} \qquad \text{(2-26), (2-27)}$$

$$\text{Power} = EI = I^2R = \frac{E^2}{R} \qquad \text{(2-27)}$$

Series Circuit

$$R = r_1 + r_2 + r_3 \cdots \qquad \text{(2-28)}$$
$$E = e_1 + e_2 + e_3 \cdots \qquad \text{(2-29)}$$
$$I = i_1 = i_2 = i_3 \cdots \qquad \text{(2-30)}$$
$$P = p_1 + p_2 + p_3 \cdots \qquad \text{(2-31)}$$

Parallel Circuits

Two resistors in parallel

$$R = \frac{r_1 r_2}{r_1 + r_2} \qquad \text{(2-32a)}$$

$$r_2 = \frac{R r_1}{r_1 - R} \qquad \text{(2-32b)}$$

Any number of resistors in parallel

$$R = \frac{1}{\dfrac{1}{r_1} + \dfrac{1}{r_2} + \dfrac{1}{r_3} \cdots} \qquad \text{(2-32)}$$

$$E = e_1 = e_2 = e_3 \cdots \qquad \text{(2-33)}$$
$$I = i_1 + i_2 + i_3 \cdots \qquad \text{(2-34)}$$
$$P = p_1 + p_2 + p_3 \cdots \qquad \text{(2-31)}$$

ALTERNATING CURRENT

Maximum, Effective, and Average Values of Sine Wave Currents and Voltages

$$\text{Maximum value} = \sqrt{2} \text{ effective value} = 1.414 \text{ effective value}$$
$$= \frac{\text{effective value}}{0.707} = 1.57 \text{ average value}$$
$$\text{Effective value} = \frac{\text{maximum value}}{\sqrt{2}} = \frac{\text{maximum value}}{1.414}$$

Effective value = 0.707 maximum value = 1.11 average value
Average value = 0.637 maximum value = 0.9009 effective value

Ohm's Law

$$\text{Voltage} = IZ = \frac{P}{I \times \text{P-F}} \qquad\qquad (2\text{-}35),\ (2\text{-}36)$$

$$\text{Current} = \frac{E}{Z} = \frac{P}{E \times \text{P-F}} \qquad\qquad (2\text{-}35),\ (2\text{-}36)$$

$$\text{Impedance} = \frac{E}{I} = \frac{R}{\text{P-F}} = \sqrt{R^2 + (X_L - X_C)^2} \quad (2\text{-}35),\ (2\text{-}37a),\ (2\text{-}41)$$

$$\text{Power} = I^2 R = E \times I \times \text{P-F} \qquad\qquad (2\text{-}1),\ (2\text{-}36)$$

$$\text{Power factor} = \frac{P}{EI} = \frac{R}{Z} = \cos\theta \qquad\qquad (2\text{-}37),\ (2\text{-}37a),\ (2\text{-}37b)$$

Series Circuit

Resistance and inductance

$$Z = \sqrt{R^2 + X_L{}^2} \qquad\qquad (2\text{-}10)$$
$$R = \sqrt{Z^2 - X_L{}^2} \qquad\qquad (2\text{-}10)$$
$$X_L = \sqrt{Z^2 - R^2} \qquad\qquad (2\text{-}10)$$

Resistance and capacitance

$$Z = \sqrt{R^2 + X_C{}^2} \qquad\qquad (2\text{-}22)$$
$$R = \sqrt{Z^2 - X_C{}^2} \qquad\qquad (2\text{-}22)$$
$$X_C = \sqrt{Z^2 - R^2} \qquad\qquad (2\text{-}22)$$

Inductance and capacitance

$$Z = X_L - X_C \qquad\qquad (2\text{-}41)$$
$$X_L = Z + X_C \qquad\qquad (2\text{-}41)$$
$$X_C = Z + X_L \qquad\qquad (2\text{-}41)$$

Resistance, inductance, and capacitance

$$Z = \sqrt{R^2 + (X_L - X_C)^2} \qquad\qquad (2\text{-}41)$$
$$R = \sqrt{Z^2 - (X_L - X_C)^2} \qquad\qquad (2\text{-}41)$$
$$X_L = \sqrt{Z^2 - R^2} + X_C \qquad\qquad (2\text{-}41)$$
$$X_C = X_L - \sqrt{Z^2 - R^2} \qquad\qquad (2\text{-}41)$$

Any number of resistors, inductors, and capacitors in series (Fig. 2-33)

$$Z = \sqrt{(r_1 + r_2 + r_3 \cdots)^2 + (x_{L1} + x_{L2} + x_{L3} \cdots - x_{C1} - x_{C2} - x_{C3} \cdots)^2}$$
$$(2\text{-}28),\ (2\text{-}39),\ (2\text{-}40),\ (2\text{-}41)$$
$$E = e_1 + e_2 + e_3 \cdots \quad \text{(added vectorially)} \qquad (2\text{-}42)$$
$$I = i_1 = i_2 = i_3 \cdots \qquad\qquad (2\text{-}30)$$
$$P = p_1 + p_2 + p_3 \cdots \qquad\qquad (2\text{-}31)$$
$$\text{P-F} = \frac{P}{EI} \qquad\qquad (2\text{-}37)$$

Parallel Circuits

Two circuits in parallel

$$Z = \frac{Z_1 Z_2}{Z_1 + Z_2} \qquad\qquad (2\text{-}54)$$

Resistance and inductance

$$Z = \frac{R X_L}{\sqrt{R^2 + X_L{}^2}} \qquad\qquad (2\text{-}54)$$

Resistance and capacitance

$$Z = \frac{R X_C}{\sqrt{R^2 + X_C{}^2}} \qquad\qquad (2\text{-}54)$$

Inductance and capacitance

$$Z = \frac{X_L X_C}{X_L - X_C} \qquad (2\text{-}54)$$

Resistance, inductance, and capacitance

$$Z = \frac{R X_L X_C}{\sqrt{(X_L X_C)^2 + R^2(X_L - X_C)^2}} \qquad (2\text{-}54)$$

For parallel circuits listed above

$$E = e_1 = e_2 = e_3 \cdots \qquad (2\text{-}33)$$
$$I = i_1 + i_2 + i_3 \cdots \quad \text{(added vectorially)} \qquad (2\text{-}43)$$
$$P = p_1 + p_2 + p_3 \cdots \qquad (2\text{-}31)$$
$$\text{P-F} = \frac{P}{EI} \qquad (2\text{-}37)$$

Combination Parallel-series Circuit

Also see equations listed under Parallel Resonant Circuit. No single equation is available for this type of circuit. For solution see Art. 10-9 of the authors' *Electrical Essentials of Radio.*

INDUCTORS
Inductance of a Coil
Multilayer coil

$$L = \frac{0.8a^2 N^2}{6a + 9b + 10c} \qquad (2\text{-}5)$$

Flat or pancake coil

$$L = \frac{a^2 N^2}{8a + 11c} \qquad (2\text{-}5a)$$

Solenoid

$$L = \frac{a^2 N^2}{9a + 10b} \qquad (2\text{-}5b)$$

Inductive Reactance

$$X_L = 2\pi f L \qquad (2\text{-}8)$$

Impedance of a Coil

$$Z = \sqrt{R_L{}^2 + X_L{}^2} \qquad (2\text{-}10)$$

Power Factor

$$\cos \theta_L = \frac{R_L}{Z_L} = \frac{R_L}{\sqrt{R_L{}^2 + X_L{}^2}} \qquad (2\text{-}12),\ (2\text{-}12a)$$

Coil Q

$$Q = \frac{X_L}{R} = \frac{2\pi f L}{R} \qquad (2\text{-}8),\ (2\text{-}58)$$

Inductors in Series

$$L_T = L_1 + L_2 + L_3 \cdots \quad \text{(no flux linkage between coils)} \qquad (2\text{-}13)$$
$$X_{LT} = x_{L1} + x_{L2} + x_{L3} \cdots \quad \text{(no flux linkage between coils)} \qquad (2\text{-}39)$$
$$L_T = L_1 + L_2 \pm 2K\sqrt{L_1 L_2} \quad \text{(flux linking the coils)} \qquad (2\text{-}15)$$
$$X_{LT} = 2\pi f L_T \qquad (2\text{-}8)$$

Inductors in Parallel

$$L_T = \frac{1}{\dfrac{1}{L_1} + \dfrac{1}{L_2} + \dfrac{1}{L_3} \cdots} \quad \text{(no flux linkage between coils)} \qquad (2\text{-}14)$$

$$X_{LT} = \frac{1}{\dfrac{1}{x_{L1}} + \dfrac{1}{x_{L2}} + \dfrac{1}{x_{L3}} \cdots} \quad \text{(no flux linkage between coils)} \qquad (2\text{-}45)$$

Mutual Inductance

$$M = K \sqrt{L_1 L_2} \tag{2-6}$$

$$L_1 = \frac{M^2}{K^2 L_2} \tag{2-6}$$

Coefficient of Coupling

$$K = \frac{M}{\sqrt{L_1 L_2}} \tag{2-6}$$

Energy Stored

$$W = \frac{L I^2}{2} \tag{2-3}$$

CAPACITORS

Capacitance

$$C = \frac{22.45 K A (N-1)}{10^8 t} \tag{2-19}$$

Capacitive Reactance

$$X_C = \frac{10^6}{2\pi f C} = \frac{159{,}000}{f C} \quad (C \text{ in microfarads}) \tag{2-20), (2-20a}$$

Impedance of a Capacitor

$$Z = \sqrt{R_C^2 + X_C^2} \tag{2-22}$$

Power Factor

$$\cos \theta_C = \frac{R_C}{Z_C} = \frac{R_C}{\sqrt{R_C^2 + X_C^2}} \tag{2-23), (2-23a}$$

Capacitors in Series

Two capacitors

$$C_T = \frac{C_1 C_2}{C_1 + C_2} \tag{2-24a}$$

$$C_2 = \frac{C_T C_1}{C_1 - C_T} \tag{2-24b}$$

Any number of capacitors

$$C_T = \frac{1}{\dfrac{1}{C_1} + \dfrac{1}{C_2} + \dfrac{1}{C_3} \cdots} \tag{2-24}$$

$$X_{CT} = x_{C1} + x_{C2} + x_{C3} \cdots = \frac{10^6}{2\pi f C_T} \tag{2-40), (2-20}$$

Capacitors in Parallel

$$C_T = C_1 + C_2 + C_3 \cdots \tag{2-25}$$

$$X_{CT} = \frac{1}{\dfrac{1}{x_{C1}} + \dfrac{1}{x_{C2}} + \dfrac{1}{x_{C3}} \cdots} = \frac{10^6}{2\pi f C_T} \tag{2-46), (2-20}$$

Energy Stored

$$W = \frac{C E^2}{2} \tag{2-18}$$

RESONANCE

Resonant Frequency, Inductance, and Capacitance

(Applies to both series and parallel resonant circuits)
Frequency of resonance

$$f_r = \frac{10^3}{2\pi \sqrt{LC}} = \frac{159}{\sqrt{LC}} \tag{2-48}$$

Inductance required for resonance

$$L = \frac{25,300}{f_r^2 C} \tag{2-49}$$

Capacitance required for resonance

$$C = \frac{25,300}{f_r^2 L} \tag{2-50}$$

Series Resonant Circuit (Fig. 2-36a)

At any frequency

$$Z = \sqrt{R^2 + (X_L - X_C)^2} \tag{2-41}$$

At resonant frequency

$$Z = R \quad \text{(minimum value possible)}$$

$$I = \frac{E}{R} \quad \text{(maximum value possible)}$$

$$E_L = E_C = EQ \tag{2-53}$$

Parallel Resonant Circuit (Fig. 2-36b)

At any frequency

$$Z_T = \frac{Z_1 Z_2}{Z_1 + Z_2} \tag{2-54}$$

$$Z_T = X_C \sqrt{\frac{R^2 + X_L^2}{R^2 + (X_L - X_C)^2}} \tag{2-54}$$

when R is much smaller than X_L,

$$Z_T \cong \frac{X_C X_L}{\sqrt{R^2 + (X_L - X_C)^2}} \tag{2-55}$$

At resonant frequency

$$Z_T = QX_L = \frac{X_L^2}{R} \quad \text{(maximum possible value)} \tag{2-56}$$

$$I_L = I_C = IQ \tag{2-57}$$

$$I = \frac{E}{QX_L} \quad \text{(minimum possible value)} \tag{2-35}$$

Width of Frequency Band for a Single Resonant Circuit at 0.707 of the Maximum Response

$$f_2 - f_1 = \frac{f_r}{Q} = \frac{R}{2\pi L} \tag{2-59}$$

COUPLED RESONANT CIRCUITS

Width of Band Pass

$$f_2 - f_1 = Kf_r \tag{2-84}$$

Critical Coupling

$$K_c = \frac{1.5}{\sqrt{Q_P Q_S}} \tag{2-86}$$

$$Q_P Q_S = \frac{2.25}{K_c^2} \tag{2-87}$$

TANK CIRCUIT

Energy Stored

$$W_t = \frac{L i_t^2}{2} + \frac{C e_t^2}{2} \tag{10-6}$$

$$W_t = C E_t^2 \tag{10-13c}$$

$$W_t = L I_t^2 \tag{10-14}$$

TRANSFORMERS

Ratio

$$n = \frac{N_S}{N_P} = \sqrt{\frac{L_S}{L_P}} = \sqrt{\frac{R_S}{R_P}} \qquad \text{(2-72), (2-72}a\text{)}$$

Secondary Voltage

$$E_S = nE_P \qquad \text{(2-16)}$$

Reflected Impedance

$$Z_{P-S'} = \frac{Z_S}{n^2} \qquad \text{(2-73)}$$

$$Z_{S-P'} = n^2 Z_P \qquad \text{(2-74)}$$

Reflected Resistance

$$R_{P-S'} = \frac{R_S}{n^2} \qquad \text{(2-76)}$$

$$R_{S-P'} = n^2 R_P \qquad \text{(2-77)}$$

Reflected Reactance

$$X_{P-S'} = \frac{X_S}{n^2} \qquad \text{(2-78)}$$

$$X_{S-P'} = n^2 X_P \qquad \text{(2-79)}$$

Reflected Inductance

$$L_{P-S'} = \frac{L_S}{n^2} \qquad \text{(2-80)}$$

$$L_{S-P'} = n^2 L_P \qquad \text{(2-81)}$$

Reflected Capacitance

$$C_{P-S'} = n^2 C_S \qquad \text{(2-82)}$$

$$C_{S-P'} = \frac{C_P}{n^2} \qquad \text{(2-83)}$$

TIME CONSTANT

Resistance-inductance Circuit

$$t = \frac{L}{R} \qquad \text{(2-88)}$$

Resistance-capacitance Circuit

$$t = CR \qquad \text{(2-89)}$$

DECIBELS

In Terms of Power

$$db = 10 \log \frac{P_1}{P_2} \qquad \text{(8-1)}$$

In Terms of Voltage and Resistance

$$db = 20 \log \frac{E_1 \sqrt{R_2}}{E_2 \sqrt{R_1}} \qquad \text{(8-2}c\text{)}$$

In Terms of Voltage

$$db = 20 \log \frac{E_1}{E_2} \qquad \text{(8-4)}$$

In Terms of Current and Resistance

$$db = 20 \log \frac{I_1 \sqrt{R_1}}{I_2 \sqrt{R_2}} \qquad \text{(8-3}c\text{)}$$

In Terms of Current

$$db = 20 \log \frac{I_1}{I_2} \qquad \text{(8-5)}$$

In Terms of Pressure Levels

$$db = 20 \log \frac{F}{F_R} \qquad (12\text{-}1)$$

VACUUM-TUBE CONSTANTS

Amplification Factor

$$\mu = \frac{de_b}{de_c} \; (i_b - \text{constant}) \qquad (4\text{-}1)$$

$$\mu = g_m r_p \qquad (4\text{-}5)$$

Dynamic Plate Resistance

$$r_p = \frac{de_b}{di_b} \; (e_c - \text{constant}) \qquad (4\text{-}2)$$

$$r_p = \frac{\mu}{g_m} \qquad (4\text{-}5b)$$

Grid-plate Transconductance (Mutual Conductance)

$$g_m = \frac{di_b}{de_c} \; (e_b - \text{constant}) \qquad (4\text{-}3)$$

$$g_m = \frac{\mu}{r_p} \qquad (4\text{-}5a)$$

VOLTAGE AMPLIFICATION

Triode with Resistance Load

$$VA = \frac{\mu R_o}{R_o + r_p} \qquad (4\text{-}10)$$

Triode with Reactance Load

$$VA = \frac{\mu Z_o}{Z_o + r_p} \qquad (7\text{-}5)$$

Pentode with Reactance Load

$$VA = g_m \frac{r_p Z_o}{Z_o + r_p} \qquad (7\text{-}8)$$

when $r_p >> Z_o$

$$VA \cong g_m Z_o \qquad (7\text{-}11)$$

Multistage Amplifier Circuit

$$VA_T = VA_1 \times VA_2 \times VA_3, \; \cdots \qquad (8\text{-}33)$$
$$db_T = db_1 + db_2 + db_3, \; \cdots \qquad (8\text{-}34)$$

VOLTAGE AMPLIFICATION OF R-F AMPLIFIERS

Tuned Impedance

$$VA \cong g_m 2\pi f L Q \qquad (7\text{-}13)$$

$$VA \cong g_m \frac{(2\pi f L)^2}{R_L} \qquad (7\text{-}14)$$

Transformer with Untuned Primary and Tuned Secondary

$$VA \cong g_m 2\pi f M Q \qquad (7\text{-}17)$$

Transformer with Tuned Primary and Tuned Secondary (Band-pass Amplifier)

$$VA = g_m K \frac{2\pi f_r \sqrt{L_P L_S}}{K^2 + \dfrac{1}{Q_P Q_S}} \qquad (7\text{-}18)$$

VOLTAGE AMPLIFICATION OF A-F AMPLIFIERS

Resistance-capacitance Coupling

Medium frequencies
Triodes

$$\text{VA}_M = \frac{\mu Z_o}{Z_o + r_p} \tag{7-5}$$

Pentodes

$$\text{VA}_M = g_m R_{eq} \tag{8-10b}$$

Low frequencies

$$\text{VA}_L = K_L \text{VA}_M \tag{8-12}$$

Triodes, $r_p < R_c$ and R_g

$$K_L \cong \frac{R_g}{\sqrt{R_g{}^2 + \left(\dfrac{1}{2\pi f C_b}\right)^2}} \tag{8-11c}$$

Pentodes

$$K_L = \frac{1}{\sqrt{1 + \left(\dfrac{1}{2\pi f C_b R}\right)^2}} \tag{8-11}$$

High frequencies

$$\text{VA}_H = K_H \text{VA}_M \tag{8-15}$$

$$K_H = \frac{1}{\sqrt{1 + (2\pi f C_T R_{eq})^2}} \tag{8-14a}$$

Transformer Coupling

$$\text{VA} = \mu n \frac{Z_P}{Z_P + r_p} \tag{8-27}$$

Medium frequencies

$$\text{VA}_M = \mu n = \frac{X_{LP}}{\sqrt{R_1{}^2 + X_{LP}{}^2}} \tag{8-29}$$

Low frequencies

$$\text{VA}_L = K_L \text{VA}_M \tag{8-12}$$

$$K_L = \frac{X_{LP}}{\sqrt{R_1{}^2 + X_{LP}{}^2}} \tag{8-31}$$

High frequencies

$$\text{VA}_H = K_H \text{VA}_M \tag{8-15}$$

$$K_H = \frac{X_T}{\sqrt{R_{1-2}{}^2 + (X_P{}'' - X_T)^2}} \tag{8-32}$$

FEEDBACK AMPLIFIERS

Output Voltage

$$e_o{}' = e_s \frac{A}{1 - A\beta} \tag{8-40}$$

Distortion Voltage

$$D' = e_o{}' \frac{d}{1 - A\beta} \tag{8-41}$$

Negative Feedback
Voltage amplification

$$\text{VA}' = \frac{e_o{}'}{e_s} = \frac{A}{1 - A\beta} = -\frac{1}{\beta}\left(\frac{1}{1 - \dfrac{1}{A\beta}}\right) \tag{8-43, 8-43a}$$

when $A\beta > 1$

$$\text{VA}' \cong -\frac{1}{\beta} \tag{8-44}$$

Feedback factor

$$A\beta = \frac{e_f}{e_s - e_f} \tag{8-42}$$

Per cent output voltage being fed back

$$\beta \cong \frac{R_f}{R_f + R_2} \tag{8-47a}$$

POWER AMPLIFIERS

Single-tube Triodes, Class A

Power output

$$P_o = R_o \frac{(\mu e_g)^2}{(R_o + r_p)^2} \tag{9-2b}$$

Maximum power output

$$P_{o \cdot m} = \frac{(\mu E_g)^2}{4r_p} = \frac{(\mu E_{g \cdot m})^2}{8r_p} \tag{9-4}, (9-4a)$$

Maximum undistorted power output

$$P_{o \cdot m \cdot u} = \frac{2(\mu E_g)^2}{9r_p} = \frac{(\mu E_{g \cdot m})^2}{9r_p} \tag{9-6}, (9-6a)$$

Power Output, Pentodes, and Beam Power Tubes

$$P_o = \frac{[i_{b \cdot \max} - i_{b \cdot \min} + 1.41(I_x - I_y)]^2 R_o'}{32} \tag{9-15}$$

Push-pull Operation, Triodes, Class A

Power output

$$P_o = \frac{4(\mu E_g)^2 R_o'}{(2r_p + R_o')^2} \tag{9-18}$$

Maximum power output

$$P_{o \cdot m} = \frac{(\mu E_{g \cdot m})^2}{4r_p} \tag{9-19}$$

POWER SUPPLY

Output Voltage, without Filter, Resistance Load

Full-wave

$$E_o = 0.9E_{a-c} \tag{11-1}$$

Half-wave

$$E_o = 0.45E_{a-c} \tag{11-2}$$

Per Cent of Ripple Voltage

General equation

$$\text{Per cent } E_r = \frac{E_r}{E_{d \cdot c}} \times 100 \tag{11-4}$$

Capacitor input filter circuit
At the output of first capacitor

$$\text{Per cent } E_{r \cdot 1} \cong \frac{2245 \times 10^4}{f_r R_o C_1} \tag{11-5}$$

At the output of second capacitor
Using a filter choke

$$\text{Per cent } E_{r \cdot 2} \cong \frac{\text{Per cent } E_{r \cdot 1}}{[10^{-6}(2\pi f_r)^2 L_1 C_2] - 1} \tag{11-6}$$

Using a filter resistor

$$\text{Per cent } E_{r \cdot 2} \cong \frac{\text{Per cent } E_{r \cdot 1} \times 10^6}{2\pi f_r C_2 R_1} \tag{11-7}$$

Choke input filter circuit, $f_r = 120$ cycles
At the output of first capacitor

$$\text{Per cent } E_{r \cdot 1} \cong \frac{100}{L_1 C_1} \qquad (11\text{-}9a)$$

At the output of second capacitor

$$\text{Per cent } E_{r \cdot 2} \cong \frac{650}{L_1 L_2 (C_1 + C_2)^2} \qquad (11\text{-}10a)$$

Voltage Regulation

$$\text{VR} = \frac{E_{NL} - E_L}{E_L} \times 100 \qquad (11\text{-}8)$$

Critical Inductance of Input Choke

$$L_c = \frac{R_o}{1000} \qquad (11\text{-}11)$$

RELATION BETWEEN WAVELENGTH AND FREQUENCY

Wavelength

$$\lambda = \frac{300,000}{f} \qquad (1\text{-}2)$$

Frequency

$$f = \frac{300,000}{\lambda} \qquad (1\text{-}3)$$

AMPLITUDE MODULATION

Per Cent of Amplitude Modulation

$$M = \frac{\text{maximum voltage of the modulating wave}}{\text{maximum voltage of the carrier wave}} \times 100 \qquad (13\text{-}3)$$

FREQUENCY MODULATION

Frequency Deviation

f_d = variation of the radio frequency away from the center or resting frequency

Deviation Ratio or Frequency Modulation Index

$$M_f = \frac{\text{variation of the r-f away from the center frequency}}{\text{modulating (audio) frequency}}$$

ANTENNAS

Length of Half-wave, Fundamental, or Hertz Antenna

$$l = \frac{492 \times k}{f} \qquad (13\text{-}9)$$

Length of Quarter-wave, Grounded, or Marconi Antenna

$$l \cong \frac{\lambda}{4.2}$$

CRYSTALS

Resonant Frequency

$$f_r = \frac{k}{t} \qquad (10\text{-}17)$$

APPENDIX VI

BARE ANNEALED COPPER WIRE TABLE

American Wire Gauge (formerly Brown & Sharpe Gauge)
Resistance values at 20 degrees centigrade, 68 degrees Fahrenheit

AWG (B & S) gauge	Diameter in mils	Area in circular mils	Ohms per 1000 feet	Feet per pound
0000	460	211,600	0.0490	1.561
000	409.6	167,800	0.0618	1.968
00	364.8	133,100	0.0779	2.482
0	324.9	105,500	0.0983	3.130
1	289.3	83,690	0.1239	3.947
2	257.6	66,370	0.1563	4.977
3	229.4	52,640	0.1970	6.276
4	204.3	41,740	0.2485	7.914
5	181.9	33,100	0.3133	9.980
6	162.0	26,250	0.3951	12.58
7	144.3	20,820	0.4982	15.87
8	128.5	16,510	0.6282	20.01
9	114.4	13,090	0.7921	25.23
10	101.9	10,380	0.9989	31.82
11	90.74	8234	1.260	40.12
12	80.81	6530	1.588	50.59
13	71.96	5178	2.003	63.80
14	64.08	4107	2.525	80.44
15	57.07	3257	3.184	101.4
16	50.82	2583	4.016	127.9
17	45.26	2048	5.064	161.3
18	40.30	1624	6.385	203.4
19	35.89	1288	8.051	256.5
20	31.96	1022	10.15	323.4
21	28.46	810.1	12.80	407.8
22	25.35	642.4	16.14	514.2
23	22.57	509.5	20.36	648.4
24	20.10	404.0	25.67	817.7
25	17.90	320.4	32.37	1031
26	15.94	254.1	40.81	1300
27	14.20	201.5	51.47	1639
28	12.64	159.8	64.90	2067
29	11.26	126.7	81.83	2607

AWG (B & S) gauge	Diameter in mils	Area in circular mils	Ohms per 1000 feet	Feet per pound
30	10.03	100.5	103.2	3287
31	8.928	79.70	130.1	4145
32	7.950	63.21	164.1	5227
33	7.080	50.13	206.9	6591
34	6.305	39.75	260.9	8310
35	5.615	31.52	329.0	10,480
36	5.000	25.00	414.8	13,210
37	4.453	19.83	523.1	16,660
38	3.965	15.72	659.6	21,010
39	3.531	12.47	831.8	26,500
40	3.145	9.888	1049	33,410
41	2.80	7.8400	1323	42,140
42	2.49	6.2001	1673	53,270
43	2.22	4.9284	2104	67,020
44	1.97	3.8809	2672	85,100
45	1.76	3.0976	3348	106,600
46	1.57	2.4649	4207	134,040

APPENDIX VII

DIELECTRIC CONSTANT (K) AND DIELECTRIC STRENGTH (VOLTS PER 0.001 IN.) OF VARIOUS MATERIALS

Material	Dielectric constant, K	Dielectric strength, volts per 0.001 in.
Air	1	80
Aluminum oxide layer	10	
Bakelite	6	500
Cambric, varnished	4.5	1200
Cotton	....	300
Fiber	6.5	50
Glass, common	4.2	200
Isolantite	3.5	
Mica	5.5	2000
Oil, castor	4.7	380
Pyranol	4.2	350
Transformer	2.4	250
Paper, beeswaxed	3.1	1800
Paraffined	2.2	1200
Shellacked	3.4	
Porcelain	5.5	750
Quartz	4.5	
Resin	2.5	
Tantalum oxide layer	11.5	
Water, pure	81	

NOTE.—The values given in the above table may vary considerably, depending upon the quality and manufacture of the material. The values in the table are average values; for greater accuracy, values should be obtained from the manufacturer of the materials used.

APPENDIX VIII

STANDARD COLOR CODING FOR RESISTORS

For the identification of resistance values of small carbon-type resistors, numbers are represented by the following colors:

0—Black	5—Green
1—Brown	6—Blue
2—Red	7—Violet
3—Orange	8—Gray
4—Yellow	9—White

Three colors are used on each resistor or capacitor to identify its value.

There are two methods of placing the color identification on a resistor. In the first method, illustrated by Fig. A-1, the body color A represents the first figure of the resistance value; one end or tip B is colored to represent the second figure; a colored band or dot C near the center of the resistor represents the number of zeros following the first two figures. By this system, a 150,000-ohm resistor would be colored as follows:

Body, brown   Tip, green   Dot or band, yellow

In the second method, illustrated by Fig. A-2, the colors are indicated by a series of bands or dots generally placed at one end of the resistor. In order to obtain the value of a resistor, with this method, the colors are read starting from the end or tip and going toward the center. With this system, a 750,000-ohm resistor would be colored as follows:

Band A, violet   Band B, green   Band C, yellow

An auxiliary color code has been established, covering the tolerances of resistors. The tolerances are indicated by the following colors, which appear as a fourth band or dot placed on one end of the resistor:

Gold, 5%   Silver, 10%   None, 20%

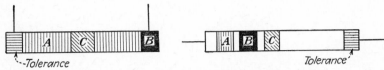

FIG. A-1.   FIG. A-2.

APPLICATION OF COLOR CODE

Resistance, ohms	A	B	C	Resistance, ohms	A	B	C
50	Green	Black	Black	25,000	Red	Green	Orange
75	Violet	Green	Black	30,000	Orange	Black	Orange
100	Brown	Black	Brown	40,000	Yellow	Black	Orange
150	Brown	Green	Brown	50,000	Green	Black	Orange
200	Red	Black	Brown	60,000	Blue	Black	Orange
250	Red	Green	Brown	75,000	Violet	Green	Orange
300	Orange	Black	Brown	100,000	Brown	Black	Yellow
350	Orange	Green	Brown	120,000	Brown	Red	Yellow
400	Yellow	Black	Brown	150,000	Brown	Green	Yellow
450	Yellow	Green	Brown	200,000	Red	Black	Yellow
500	Green	Black	Brown	250,000	Red	Green	Yellow
600	Blue	Black	Brown	300,000	Orange	Black	Yellow
750	Violet	Green	Brown	400,000	Yellow	Black	Yellow
1,000	Brown	Black	Red	500,000	Green	Black	Yellow
1,200	Brown	Red	Red	600,000	Blue	Black	Yellow
1,500	Brown	Green	Red	750,000	Violet	Green	Yellow
2,000	Red	Black	Red	$1M\Omega$	Brown	Black	Green
2,500	Red	Green	Red	$1\frac{1}{2}M\Omega$	Brown	Green	Green
3,000	Orange	Black	Red	$2M\Omega$	Red	Black	Green
3,500	Orange	Green	Red	$3M\Omega$	Orange	Black	Green
4,000	Yellow	Black	Red	$4M\Omega$	Yellow	Black	Green
5,000	Green	Black	Red	$5M\Omega$	Green	Black	Green
7,500	Violet	Green	Red	$6M\Omega$	Blue	Black	Green
10,000	Brown	Black	Orange	$7M\Omega$	Violet	Black	Green
12,000	Brown	Red	Orange	$8M\Omega$	Gray	Black	Green
15,000	Brown	Green	Orange	$9M\Omega$	White	Black	Green
20,000	Red	Black	Orange	$10M\Omega$	Brown	Black	Blue

APPENDIX IX

STANDARD COLOR CODING FOR MICA CAPACITORS

Mica capacitors that are not stamped with their capacitance values usually are marked with three or more colored dots and with an arrow or other symbol indicating the sequence in which the dots are to be read. The capacitance values are in micro-microfarads, and the color code is the same as the one used for resistors. The three-dot RMA color code, shown in Fig. A-3a, is used for capacitors whose working voltage is 500 volts and for which one or more of the following conditions apply: (1) the tolerance is greater than 10 per cent, (2) the capacitance rating is less than 10 $\mu\mu$f, (3) the capacitance rating has only one or two significant figures. In this system, the color of the first dot indicates the value of the first significant figure of the capacitance; the second dot indicates the second figure; and the third dot indicates the value of the multiplying factor. For indicating the capacitance of capacitors having three significant figures the five- and six-dot systems, shown in Figs. A-3c, A-3d, and A-3e, are used. The systems using more than three dots provide a dot to indicate the capacitance tolerance. The six-dot system also provides a dot to indicate the d-c working voltage. The use of the capacitor color code can best be understood by reference to the following table, the examples listed in the accompanying table of applications of the color code, and the diagrams of the various systems shown in Fig. A-3.

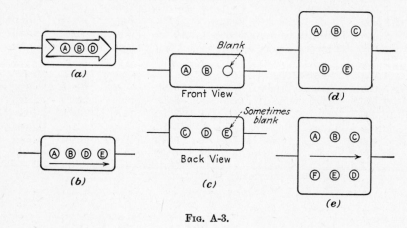

Fig. A-3.

748

CAPACITANCE IN MICROMICROFARADS ($\mu\mu$f)

Color of dot	Significant figures			Multiplying factor	Per cent tolerance	D-c working voltage
	A	B	C	D	E	F
Black	0	0	0	1		
Brown	1	1	1	10	1	100
Red	2	2	2	100	2	200
Orange	3	3	3	1000	3	300
Yellow	4	4	4	10,000	4	400
Green	5	5	5	100,000	5	500
Blue	6	6	6	1,000,000	6	600
Violet	7	7	7	10,000,000	7	700
Gray	8	8	8	100,000,000	8	800
White	9	9	9	1,000,000,000	9	900
Gold	..	..	..	0.1	5	1000
Silver	..	..	..	0.01	10	2000
No Color	..	..	..	....	20	500

APPLICATION OF COLOR CODE

System, Fig. A-3	Capacitance, μf	Capacitance, $\mu\mu$f	Per cent of tolerance	D-c working voltage	A	B	C	D	E	F
(a)	0.000005	5			Black	Green		Black		
(a)	0.000012	12			Brown	Red		Black		
(a)	0.00035	350			Orange	Green		Brown		
(a)	0.0004	400			Yellow	Black		Brown		
(b)	0.000025	25	2		Red	Green		Black	Red	
(b)	0.00075	750	5		Violet	Green		Brown	Green	
(b)	0.006	6000	10		Blue	Black		Red	Silver	
(c), (d)	0.0003	300	1		Orange	Black	Black	Black	Brown	
(c), (d)	0.000125	125	3		Brown	Red	Green	Black	Orange	
(c), (d)	0.008	8000	20		Gray	Black	Black	Brown	No color	
(e)	0.000002	2	4	1000	Red	Black	Black	Silver	Yellow	Gold
(e)	0.000025	25	10	500	Red	Green	Black	Gold	Silver	No color
(e)	0.0003	300	20	300	Orange	Black	Black	Black	No color	Orange
(e)	0.0075	7500	5	600	Violet	Green	Black	Brown	Gold	Blue

APPENDIX X

STANDARD COLOR CODING FOR LOUDSPEAKER AND TRANSFORMER LEADS

In order to identify the various leads of loudspeakers and transformers used in radio equipment, the Radio Manufacturers' Association has adopted a set of standards that are used by most manufacturers. The following diagrams indicate the color of the leads for six types of electrodynamic loudspeakers and three types of transformers generally used.

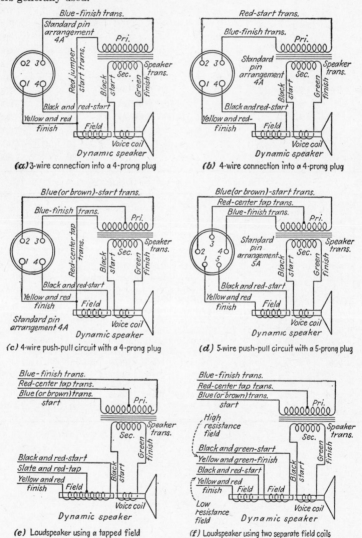

Fig. A-4.—Identification of electrodynamic loudspeaker leads. (*Courtesy of P. R. Mallory & Co., Inc.*)

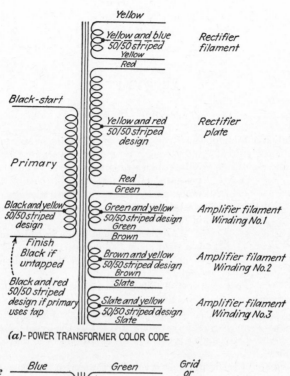

Yellow

Yellow and blue
50/50 striped
Yellow

Red

Rectifier
filament

Black-start

Primary

Yellow and red
50/50 striped
design

Rectifier
plate

Red
Green

Black and yellow
50/50 striped
design

Green and yellow
50/50 striped design
Green

Amplifier filament
Winding No.1

Finish
Black if
untapped

Brown

Brown and yellow
50/50 striped design
Brown

Amplifier filament
Winding No.2

Black and red
50/50 striped
design if primary
uses tap

Slate

Slate and yellow
50/50 striped design
Slate

Amplifier filament
Winding No.3

(a)- POWER TRANSFORMER COLOR CODE

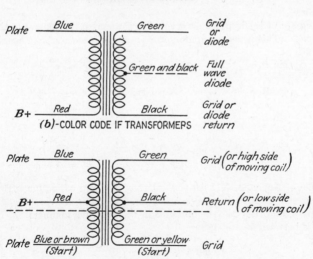

Plate — Blue ———————— Green — Grid
or
diode

Green and black — Full
wave
diode

B+ — Red ———————— Black — Grid or
diode
(b)-COLOR CODE IF TRANSFORMERS return

Plate — Blue ———————— Green — Grid (or high side
of moving coil)

B+ — Red ———————— Black — Return (or low side
of moving coil)

Plate — Blue or brown ———— Green or yellow — Grid
(Start) (Start)

The upper portion (that code above the dotted line)
for single primary and/or secondary transformers

(c)-COLOR CODE-AUDIO TRANSFORMERS

FIG. A-5.—Identification of transformer leads. *(Courtesy of P. R. Mallory & Co., Inc.)*

APPENDIX XI

TRIGONOMETRY

The solution of a-c problems frequently involves adding or subtracting quantities such as voltages, currents, and ohmages by means of vectors. The mathematical solution of these problems requires the use of trigonometry. The method of solution presented in the text makes it possible to solve all such problems by the use of right triangles. The following statements apply to any right triangle and are illustrated in Fig. A-6.

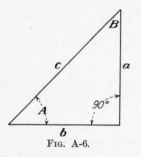

FIG. A-6.

1. A right triangle is one in which one of the angles is a right angle (90 degrees).

2. The hypotenuse is the side opposite the right angle.

3. The legs of a right triangle are the two sides that form the right angle.

4. The sine of any angle θ is equal to the side opposite that angle divided by the hypotenuse.

5. The cosine of any angle θ is equal to the side adjacent to that angle divided by the hypotenuse.

6. The square of the hypotenuse is equal to the sum of the squares of the two legs of the triangle. (This is also commonly known as the *theorem of Pythagoras*.)

$$\sin A = \frac{a}{c}; \qquad a = c \sin A; \qquad c = \frac{a}{\sin A}$$

$$\cos A = \frac{b}{c}; \qquad b = c \cos A; \qquad c = \frac{b}{\cos A}$$

$$\sin B = \frac{b}{c}; \qquad b = c \sin B; \qquad c = \frac{b}{\sin B}$$

$$\cos B = \frac{a}{c}; \qquad a = c \cos B; \qquad c = \frac{a}{\cos B}$$

$$c^2 = a^2 + b^2; \qquad a^2 = c^2 - b^2; \qquad b^2 = c^2 - a^2$$

The tables of Appendix XII list the values of sine and cosine for angles between 0 and 90 degrees. In some instances, it is desired to obtain the sine of angles greater than 90 degrees, and they may be obtained in the following manner:

When θ is between 90 and 180°

$$\sin \theta = \cos (\theta - 90)$$

Example: What is the sine of 137°?

$$\begin{aligned} \sin 137° &= \cos (137 - 90) \\ &= \cos 47° \\ &= 0.682 \end{aligned}$$

When θ is between 180 and 270°

$$\sin \theta = - \sin (\theta - 180)$$

Example: What is the sine of 218°?

$$\begin{aligned} \sin 218° &= - \sin (218 - 180) \\ &= - \sin 38° \\ &= - 0.616 \end{aligned}$$

When θ is between 270 and 360°

$$\sin \theta = - \cos (\theta - 270)$$

Example: What is the sine of 336°?

$$\begin{aligned} \sin 336° &= - \cos (336 - 270) \\ &= - \cos 66° \\ &= - 0.407 \end{aligned}$$

APPENDIX XII

SINE AND COSINE TABLES

Degrees	sin	cos	Degrees	sin	cos
0.0	0.000	1.000	21.5	0.366	0.930
0.5	0.009	1.000	22.0	0.374	0.927
1.0	0.017	0.999	22.5	0.383	0.924
1.5	0.026	0.999	23.0	0.391	0.920
2.0	0.035	0.999	23.5	0.399	0.917
2.5	0.043	0.999	24.0	0.407	0.913
3.0	0.052	0.998	24.5	0.415	0.910
3.5	0.061	0.998	25.0	0.422	0.906
4.0	0.070	0.997	25.5	0.430	0.902
4.5	0.078	0.997	26.0	0.438	0.899
5.0	0.087	0.996	26.5	0.446	0.895
5.5	0.096	0.995	27.0	0.454	0.891
6.0	0.104	0.994	27.5	0.462	0.887
6.5	0.113	0.993	28.0	0.469	0.883
7.0	0.122	0.992	28.5	0.477	0.879
7.5	0.130	0.991	29.0	0.485	0.875
8.0	0.139	0.990	29.5	0.492	0.870
8.5	0.148	0.989	30.0	0.500	0.866
9.0	0.156	0.988	30.5	0.507	0.862
9.5	0.165	0.986	31.0	0.515	0.857
10.0	0.173	0.985	31.5	0.522	0.853
10.5	0.182	0.983	32.0	0.530	0.848
11.0	0.191	0.981	32.5	0.537	0.843
11.5	0.199	0.980	33.0	0.544	0.839
12.0	0.208	0.978	33.5	0.552	0.834
12.5	0.216	0.976	34.0	0.559	0.829
13.0	0.225	0.974	34.5	0.566	0.824
13.5	0.233	0.972	35.0	0.574	0.819
14.0	0.242	0.970	35.5	0.581	0.814
14.5	0.250	0.968	36.0	0.588	0.809
15.0	0.259	0.966	36.5	0.595	0.804
15.5	0.267	0.963	37.0	0.602	0.798
16.0	0.275	0.961	37.5	0.609	0.793
16.5	0.284	0.959	38.0	0.616	0.788
17.0	0.292	0.956	38.5	0.622	0.783
17.5	0.301	0.954	39.0	0.629	0.777
18.0	0.309	0.951	39.5	0.636	0.772
18.5	0.317	0.948	40.0	0.643	0.766
19.0	0.325	0.945	40.5	0.649	0.760
19.5	0.334	0.942	41.0	0.656	0.755
20.0	0.342	0.940	41.5	0.663	0.749
20.5	0.350	0.937	42.0	0.669	0.743
21.0	0.358	0.933	42.5	0.675	0.737

Degrees	sin	cos	Degrees	sin	cos
43.0	0.682	0.731	67.0	0.920	0.391
43.5	0.688	0.725	67.5	0.924	0.383
44.0	0.695	0.719	68.0	0.927	0.375
44.5	0.701	0.713	68.5	0.930	0.366
45.0	0.707	0.707	69.0	0.934	0.358
45.5	0.713	0.701	69.5	0.937	0.350
46.0	0.719	0.695	70.0	0.940	0.342
46.5	0.725	0.688	70.5	0.943	0.334
47.0	0.731	0.682	71.0	0.945	0.326
47.5	0.737	0.675	71.5	0.948	0.317
48.0	0.743	0.669	72.0	0.951	0.309
48.5	0.749	0.663	72.5	0.954	0.301
49.0	0.755	0.656	73.0	0.956	0.292
49.5	0.760	0.649	73.5	0.959	0.284
50.0	0.766	0.643	74.0	0.961	0.276
50.5	0.772	0.636	74.5	0.964	0.267
51.0	0.777	0.629	75.0	0.966	0.259
51.5	0.783	0.622	75.5	0.968	0.250
52.0	0.788	0.616	76.0	0.970	0.242
52.5	0.793	0.609	76.5	0.972	0.233
53.0	0.798	0.602	77.0	0.974	0.225
53.5	0.804	0.595	77.5	0.976	0.216
54.0	0.809	0.588	78.0	0.978	0.208
54.5	0.814	0.581	78.5	0.980	0.199
55.0	0.819	0.574	79.0	0.982	0.191
55.5	0.824	0.566	79.5	0.983	0.182
56.0	0.829	0.559	80.0	0.985	0.174
56.5	0.834	0.552	80.5	0.986	0.165
57.0	0.839	0.544	81.0	0.988	0.156
57.5	0.843	0.537	81.5	0.989	0.148
58.0	0.848	0.530	82.0	0.990	0.139
58.5	0.853	0.522	82.5	0.991	0.130
59.0	0.857	0.515	83.0	0.992	0.122
59.5	0.862	0.507	83.5	0.994	0.113
60.0	0.866	0.500	84.0	0.994	0.104
60.5	0.870	0.492	84.5	0.995	0.096
61.0	0.875	0.485	85.0	0.996	0.087
61.5	0.879	0.477	85.5	0.997	0.078
62.0	0.883	0.469	86.0	0.997	0.070
62.5	0.887	0.462	86.5	0.998	0.061
63.0	0.891	0.454	87.0	0.998	0.052
63.5	0.895	0.446	87.5	0.999	0.043
64.0	0.899	0.438	88.0	0.999	0.035
64.5	0.903	0.430	88.5	0.999	0.026
65.0	0.906	0.423	89.0	0.999	0.017
65.5	0.910	0.415	89.5	1.000	0.009
66.0	0.913	0.407	90.0	1.000	0.000
66.5	0.917	0.399			

APPENDIX XIII

COMMON LOGARITHMS OF NUMBERS

Logarithms of Numbers

N	0	1	2	3	4	5	6	7	8	9
10	0000	0043	0086	0128	0170	0212	0253	0294	0334	0374
11	0414	0453	0492	0531	0569	0607	0645	0682	0719	0755
12	0792	0828	0864	0899	0934	0969	1004	1038	1072	1106
13	1139	1173	1206	1239	1271	1303	1335	1367	1399	1430
14	1461	1492	1523	1553	1584	1614	1644	1673	1703	1732
15	1761	1790	1818	1847	1875	1903	1931	1959	1987	2014
16	2041	2068	2095	2122	2148	2175	2201	2227	2253	2279
17	2304	2330	2355	2380	2405	2430	2455	2480	2504	2529
18	2553	2577	2601	2625	2648	2672	2695	2718	2742	2765
19	2788	2810	2833	2856	2878	2900	2923	2945	2967	2989
20	3010	3032	3054	3075	3096	3118	3139	3160	3181	3201
21	3222	3243	3263	3284	3304	3324	3345	3365	3385	3404
22	3424	3444	3464	3483	3502	3522	3541	3560	3579	3598
23	3617	3636	3655	3674	3692	3711	3729	3747	3766	3784
24	3802	3820	3838	3856	3874	3892	3909	3927	3945	3962
25	3979	3997	4014	4031	4048	4065	4082	4099	4116	4133
26	4150	4166	4183	4200	4216	4232	4249	4265	4281	4298
27	4314	4330	4346	4362	4378	4393	4409	4425	4440	4456
28	4472	4487	4502	4518	4533	4548	4564	4579	4594	4609
29	4624	4639	4654	4669	4683	4698	4713	4728	4742	4757
30	4771	4786	4800	4814	4829	4843	4857	4871	4886	4900
31	4914	4928	4942	4955	4969	4983	4997	5011	5024	5038
32	5051	5065	5079	5092	5105	5119	5132	5145	5159	5172
33	5185	5198	5211	5224	5237	5250	5263	5276	5289	5302
34	5315	5328	5340	5353	5366	5378	5391	5403	5416	5428
35	5441	5453	5465	5478	5490	5502	5514	5527	5539	5551
36	5563	5575	5587	5599	5611	5623	5635	5647	5658	5670
37	5682	5694	5705	5717	5729	5740	5752	5763	5775	5786
38	5798	5809	5821	5832	5843	5855	5866	5877	5888	5899
39	5911	5922	5933	5944	5955	5966	5977	5988	5999	6010
40	6021	6031	6042	6053	6064	6075	6085	6096	6107	6117
41	6128	6138	6149	6160	6170	6180	6191	6201	6212	6222
42	6232	6243	6253	6263	6274	6284	6294	6304	6314	6325
43	6335	6345	6355	6365	6375	6385	6395	6405	6415	6425
44	6435	6444	6454	6464	6474	6484	6493	6503	6513	6522
45	6532	6542	6551	6561	6571	6580	6590	6599	6609	6618
46	6628	6637	6646	6656	6665	6675	6684	6693	6702	6712
47	6721	6730	6739	6749	6758	6767	6776	6785	6794	6803
48	6812	6821	6830	6839	6848	6857	6866	6875	6884	6893
49	6902	6911	6920	6928	6937	6946	6955	6964	6972	6981
50	6990	6998	7007	7016	7024	7033	7042	7050	7059	7067
51	7076	7084	7093	7101	7110	7118	7126	7135	7143	7152
52	7160	7168	7177	7185	7193	7202	7210	7218	7226	7235
53	7243	7251	7259	7267	7275	7284	7292	7300	7308	7316
54	7324	7332	7340	7348	7356	7364	7372	7380	7388	7396

756

N	0	1	2	3	4	5	6	7	8	9
55	7404	7412	7419	7427	7435	7443	7451	7459	7466	7474
56	7482	7490	7497	7505	7513	7520	7528	7536	7543	7551
57	7559	7566	7574	7582	7589	7597	7604	7612	7619	7627
58	7634	7642	7649	7657	7664	7672	7679	7686	7694	7701
59	7709	7716	7723	7731	7738	7745	7752	7760	7767	7774
60	7782	7789	7796	7803	7810	7818	7825	7832	7839	7846
61	7853	7860	7868	7875	7882	7889	7896	7903	7910	7917
62	7924	7931	7938	7945	7952	7959	7966	7973	7980	7987
63	7993	8000	8007	8014	8021	8028	8035	8041	8048	8055
64	8062	8069	8075	8082	8089	8096	8102	8109	8116	8122
65	8129	8136	8142	8149	8156	8162	8169	8176	8182	8189
66	8195	8202	8209	8215	8222	8228	8235	8241	8248	8254
67	8261	8267	8274	8280	8287	8293	8299	8306	8312	8319
68	8325	8331	8338	8344	8351	8357	8363	8370	8376	8382
69	8388	8395	8401	8407	8414	8420	8426	8432	8439	8445
70	8451	8457	8463	8470	8476	8482	8488	8494	8500	8506
71	8513	8519	8525	8531	8537	8543	8549	8555	8561	8567
72	8573	8579	8585	8591	8597	8603	8609	8615	8621	8627
73	8633	8639	8645	8651	8657	8663	8669	8675	8681	8686
74	8692	8698	8704	8710	8716	8722	8727	8733	8739	8745
75	8751	8456	8762	8768	8774	8779	8785	8791	8797	8802
76	8808	8814	8820	8825	8831	8837	8842	8848	8854	8859
77	8865	8871	8876	8882	8887	8893	8899	8904	8910	8915
78	8921	8927	8932	8938	8943	8949	8954	8960	8965	8971
79	8976	8982	8987	8993	8998	9004	9009	9015	9020	9025
80	9031	9036	9042	9047	9053	9058	9063	9069	9074	9079
81	9085	9090	9096	9101	9106	9112	9117	9122	9128	9133
82	9138	9143	9149	9154	9159	9165	9170	9175	9180	9186
83	9191	9196	9201	9206	9212	9217	9222	9227	9232	9238
84	9243	9248	9253	9258	9263	9269	9274	9279	9284	9289
85	9294	9299	9304	9309	9315	9320	9325	9330	9335	9340
86	9345	9350	9355	9360	9365	9370	9375	9380	9385	9390
87	9395	9400	9405	9410	9415	9420	9425	9430	9435	9440
88	9445	9450	9455	9460	9465	9469	9474	9479	9484	9489
89	9494	9499	9504	9509	9513	9518	9523	9528	9533	9538
90	9542	9547	9552	9557	9562	9566	9571	9576	9581	9586
91	9590	9595	9600	9605	9609	9614	9619	9624	9628	9633
92	9638	9643	9647	9652	9657	9661	9666	9671	9675	9680
93	9685	9689	9694	9699	9703	9708	9713	9717	9722	9727
94	9731	9736	9741	9745	9750	9754	9759	9763	9768	9773
95	9777	9782	9786	9791	9795	9800	9805	9809	9814	9818
96	9823	9827	9832	9836	9841	9845	9850	9854	9859	9863
97	9868	9872	9877	9881	9886	9890	9894	9899	9903	9908
98	9912	9917	9921	9926	9930	9934	9939	9943	9948	9952
99	9956	9961	9965	9969	9974	9978	9983	9987	9991	9996

APPENDIX XIV

TABLE OF FREQUENCY, WAVELENGTH, AND THE *LC* PRODUCT REQUIRED TO PRODUCE RESONANCE AT THE CORRESPONDING FREQUENCIES

The frequency is expressed in kilocycles, the wavelength in meters, the inductance in microhenries, and the capacitance in microfarads.

Equations used to calculate values for the table:

$$\text{Wavelength} = \frac{300,000}{f}$$

$$LC \text{ product} = \frac{25,300}{f^2}$$

Frequency in kc	Wavelength in meters	$L \times C$	Frequency in kc	Wavelength in meters	$L \times C$
600,000	0.5	0.00000007028	10,000	30	0.0002530
500,000	0.6	0.0000001012	9000	33.33	0.0003123
400,000	0.75	0.0000001581	8000	37.5	0.0003953
300,000	1	0.0000002811	7000	42.85	0.0005163
250,000	1.2	0.0000004048	6000	50	0.0007028
200,000	1.5	0.0000006325	5000	60	0.001012
150,000	2	0.000001124	4500	66.66	0.001249
100,000	3	0.000002530	4000	75	0.001581
90,000	3.333	0.000003123	3500	85.71	0.002065
80,000	3.75	0.000003953	3000	100	0.002811
70,000	4.285	0.000005163	2500	120	0.004048
60,000	5	0.000007028	2400	125	0.004392
55,000	5.454	0.000008363	2300	130.4	0.004782
50,000	6	0.00001012	2200	136.3	0.005227
45,000	6.666	0.00001249	2100	142.8	0.005737
40,000	7.5	0.00001581	2000	150	0.006325
35,000	8.571	0.00002065	1950	153.8	0.006653
30,000	10	0.00002811	1900	157.8	0.007008
25,000	12	0.00004048	1850	162.1	0.007392
20,000	15	0.00006325	1800	166.6	0.007808
15,000	20	0.0001124	1750	171.4	0.008261

Frequency in kc	Wavelength in meters	$L \times C$	Frequency in kc	Wavelength in meters	$L \times C$
1700	176.4	0.008754	980	306.1	0.02634
1650	181.5	0.009292	960	312.5	0.02745
1600	187.5	0.009882	940	319.1	0.02863
1550	193.5	0.01053	920	326	0.02989
1500	200	0.01124	900	333.3	0.03123
1475	203.3	0.01162	880	340.9	0.03267
1450	206.8	0.01203	860	348.8	0.03420
1425	210.5	0.01245	840	357.1	0.02585
1400	214.2	0.01290	820	365.8	0.03762
1380	217.3	0.01328	800	375	0.03953
1360	220.5	0.01367	780	384.6	0.04158
1340	223.8	0.01409	760	394.7	0.04380
1320	227.2	0.01452	740	405.4	0.04620
1300	230.7	0.01497	720	416.6	0.04880
1280	234.8	0.01544	700	428.5	0.05163
1260	238	0.01593	680	441.1	0.05471
1240	241.9	0.01645	660	454.5	0.05808
1220	245.9	0.01699	640	468.7	0.06176
1200	250	0.01757	620	483.8	0.06581
1180	254.2	0.01817	600	500	0.07028
1160	258.6	0.01880	580	517.2	0.07520
1140	263.1	0.01946	560	535.7	0.08067
1120	267.8	0.02016	540	555.5	0.08676
1100	272.7	0.02090	520	576.9	0.09356
1080	277.7	0.02169	500	600	0.1012
1060	283	0.02251	450	666.6	0.1249
1040	288.4	0.02339	400	750	0.1581
1020	294.1	0.02431	350	857.1	0.2065
1000	300	0.02530	300	1000	0.2811

APPENDIX XV

RECEIVING-TUBE CHARACTERISTICS AND SOCKET CONNECTIONS

The purpose of this appendix is to provide a source of reference for the tube characteristics and socket connections of those tubes referred to throughout the text, questions, and problems. A more complete listing of tubes may be found in the tube manuals of the various manufacturers.

RECEIVING-TUBE CHARACTERISTICS CHART

Key to Symbol Designations

a For grid-leak detection—plate volts 45, grid return to + filament or to cathode.

b Either A.C. or D.C. may be used on filament or heater, except as specifically noted. For use of D.C. on A.C. filament types, decrease stated grid volts by ½ (approx.) of filament voltage.

c Supply voltage applied through 20,000-ohm voltage-dropping resistor.

d Grids #3 and #5 are screen. Grid #4 is signal-input control grid.

e Grids #2 and #4 are screen. Grid #1 is signal-input control grid.

f For grid of following tube.

g Both grids connected together; likewise, both plates.

h Power output is for two tubes at stated plate-to-plate load.

i For two tubes.

j This diagram is like the one having the same designation without the prefix G, except that Pin No. 1 has no connection.

k Obtained preferably by using 70,000-ohm voltage-dropping resistor in series with a 90-volt supply.

l This diagram is like the one having the same designation with the prefix G, except that base sleeve is connected to Pin No. 1.

m Grids #2 and #3 tied to plate.

n For signal-input control-grid (#1); control-grid #3 bias, −3 volts.

o Applied through plate resistor of 250,000 ohms or 500-henry choke shunted by 0.25-megohm resistor.

p Applied through plate resistor of 100,000 ohms.

q Applied through plate resistor of 250,000 ohms.

r 50,000 ohms.

s Maximum.

t Megohms.

w Grid #2 tied to plate.

x Grids #2 and #4 are screen. Grid #3 is signal input-control grid.

760

KEY TO TERMINAL DESIGNATIONS OF SOCKETS

Alphabetical subscripts B, D, P, T, HP, and HX indicate, respectively, beam unit, diode unit, pentode unit, triode unit, heptode unit, and hexode unit in multi-unit types.

BP = Bayonet Pin	FM = Filament Mid-Tap	HL = Heater Tap for	SL = Base Sleeve
BS = Base Shell	G = Grid	Panel Lamp	TA = Target
F = Filament	H = Heater	HM = Heater Mid-Tap	U = Unit

HL = Heater Tap for	K = Cathode	RC = Ray-Control Electrode
Panel Lamp	NC = No Connection	S = Shell
HM = Heater Mid-Tap	P = Plate (Anode)	SI = Interlead Shield
	● = Gas-Type Tube	

SOCKET CONNECTIONS—BOTTOM VIEWS

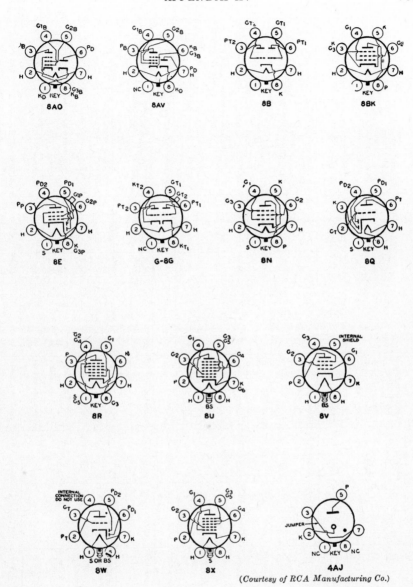

(Courtesy of RCA Manufacturing Co.)

RCA type	Name	Socket connections	Cathode type and rating — C.T.	Volts	Amp	Use — Values to right give operating conditions and characteristics for indicated typical use	Plate supply, volts	Grid bias, volts	Screen supply, volts	Screen current, ma	Plate current, ma	A-c plate resistance, ohms	Transconductance (grid-plate), μmhos	Amplification factor	Load for stated power output, ohms	Power output, watts
1A4-P	Super-control R-F amplifier pentode	4M	D.C. F	2.0	0.06	Amplifier	For other characteristics, refer to Type 1D5-GP.									
1A6	Pentagrid converter[d]	6L	D.C. F	2.0	0.06	Converter	135 / 180	{ −3.0 min. }	67.5 / 67.5	2.5 / 2.4	1.2 / 1.3	400,000 / 500,000	Anode-grid (#2): 180[c] max. volts, 2.3 ma. Oscillator-grid (#1) Resistor.[r] Conversion transcond., 300 micromhos.			
1A7-G	Pentagrid converter[d]	G-7Z	D.C. F	1.4	0.05	Converter	For other characteristics, refer to Type 1A7-GT.									
1A7-GT	Pentagrid converter[d]	GT-7Z[i]	D.C. F	1.4	0.05	Converter	90	0	45[k]	0.7	0.6	600,000	Anode-grid (#2): 90 max. volts, 1.2 ma. Oscillator-grid (#1) resistor, 0.2 meg. Conversion transcond., 250 micromhos.			
1B5/25S	Duplex-diode triode	6M	D.C. F	2.0	0.06	Triode unit as amplifier	135	−3.0	—	—	0.8	35,000	575	20	—	—
1C6	Pentagrid converter[d]	6L	D.C. F	2.0	0.12	Converter	For other characteristics, refer to Type 1C7-G.									
1C7-G	Pentagrid converter[d]	G-7Z	D.C. F	2.0	0.12	Converter	135 / 180	−3.0 / −3.0	67.5 / 67.5	2.5 / 2.0	1.3 / 1.5	600,000 / 700,000	Anode-grid (#2): 180[c] max. volts, 4.0 ma. Oscillator-grid (#1) Resistor.[r] Conversion transcond., 325 micromhos.			
1D5-GP	Super-control R-F amplifier pentode	G-5Y	D.C. F	2.0	0.06	Class A amplifier	90 / 180	{ −3.0 min. }	67.5 / 67.5	0.9 / 0.8	2.2 / 2.3	600,000 / 1,000,000	720 / 750	—	—	—
1D5-GT	Super-control R-F amplifier tetrode	G-5R	D.C. F	2.0	0.06	Class A amplifier	180	−3.0	67.5	0.7	2.2	600,000	650	—	—	—
1D8-GT	Diode-triode-power amplifier pentode	G-8AJ	D.C. F	1.4	0.1	Pentode unit as class A amplifier	45 / 90	−4.5 / −9.0	45 / 90	0.3 / 1.0	1.6 / 5.0	300,000 / 200,000	650 / 925	—	20,000 / 12,000	0.035 / 0.200
						Triode unit as class A amplifier	45 / 90	0 / 0	—	—	0.3 / 1.1	77,000 / 43,500	325 / 575	25 / 25	—	—
1E5-GP	R-F amplifier pentode	G-5Y	D.C. F	2.0	0.06	Class A amplifier	90 / 180	−3.0 / −3.0	67.5 / 67.5	0.7 / 0.6	1.6 / 1.7	1,000,000 / 1,500,000	600 / 650	—	—	—

Type	Name		Heater	Volts	Amps	Service	Plate Volts	Grid Volts	Screen Volts		Plate ma.	Plate Resistance	Transconductance	Amp. Factor	Load	Power Output
1G4-GT/G	Detector amplifier triode	G-5S₁	D.C. F	1.4	0.05	Class A amplifier	90	− 6.0	—	—	2.3	10,700	825	8.8	—	—
1H4-G	Detector amplifier[a]	G-5S₁	D.C. F	2.0	0.06	Class A amplifier	90 135 180	− 4.5 − 9.0 −13.5	—	—	2.5 3.0 3.1	11,000 10,300 10,300	850 900 900	9.3 9.3 9.3	—	—
						Class B amplifier	157.5	−15.0	—	—	1.0[i]	—	—	—	8,000	2.1[h]
1H5-G	Diode high-mu triode	G-5Z	D.C. F	1.4	0.05	Triode unit as amplifier	For other characteristics, refer to Type 1H5-GT.									
1H5-GT	Diode high-mu triode	GT-5Z[f]	D.C. F	1.4	0.05	Triode unit as class A amplifier	90	0	—	—	0.15	240,000	275	65	—	—
1J5-G	Power amplifier pentode	G-6X	D.C. F	2.0	0.12	Class A amplifier	135	−16.5	135	2.0	7.0	105,000	950	—	135,000	0.45
1J6-G	Twin triode amplifier	G-7AB	D.C. F	2.0	0.24	Class B amplifier	135 135	0 − 3.0	—	—	Power output is for one tube at stated plate-to-plate load.				10,000 10,000	2.1 1.9
1L4	R-f amplifier pentode	6AR	D.C. F	1.4	0.05	Class A amplifier	90 90	0 0	67.5 90	1.2 2.0	2.9 4.5	600,000 350,000	925 1,025	—	—	—
1N5-G	R-f amplifier pentode	G-5Y	D.C. F	1.4	0.05	Amplifier	For other characteristics, refer to Type 1N5-GT.									
1N5-GT	R-f amplifier pentode	GT-5Y[f]	D.C. F	1.4	0.05	Class A amplifier	90	0	90	0.3	1.2	1,500,000	750	—	—	—
1T4	Super-control r-f amplifier pentode	6AR	D.C. F	1.4	0.05	Class A amplifier	45 90	0 0	45 67.5	0.7 1.4	1.7 3.5	350,000 500,000	700 900	—	—	—
1T5-GT	Beam power amplifier	G-6X	D.C. F	1.4	0.05	Class A amplifier	90	− 6.0	90	1.4	6.5	—	1,150	—	14,000	0.17
2A3	Power amplifier triode	4D	F	2.5	2.5	Class A amplifier	250	−45.0	—	—	60.0	800	5,250	4.2	2,500	3.5
						Push-pull class AB₁ amplifier	300 300	Cath. bias, 780 ohms[i] −62 volts, fixed bias	—	—	80.0[i] 80.0[i]	—	—	—	5,000 3,000	10.0[i] 15.0[i]
5T4	Full-wave rectifier	5T	F	5.0	2.0	With condenser-input filter	Max. a-c volts per plate (rms), 450 Max. peak inverse volts, 1,550				Max. d-c output ma., 225 Max. peak plate ma., 675					Min. total effect. supply Imped. per plate ma., 150 ohms
						With choke-input filter	Max. a-c volts per plate (rms), 550 Max. peak inverse volts, 1,550				Max. d-c output ma., 225 Max. peak plate ma., 675					Min. value of input choke, 3 henries
5W4	Full-wave rectifier	5T	F	5.0	1.5	For other ratings, refer to Type 5W4-GT/G.										

RCA type	Name	Socket connections	C.T.	Volts	Amp	Use — Values to right give operating conditions and characteristics for indicated typical use	Plate supply, volts	Grid bias,[b] volts	Screen supply, volts	Screen current, ma	Plate current, ma	A-c plate resistance, ohms	Transconductance (grid-plate), μmhos	Amplification factor	Load for stated power output, ohms	Power output, watts
5W4-GT/G	Full-wave rectifier	G-5Tj	F	5.0	1.5	With condenser-input filter		Max. a-c volts per plate (rms), 350 — Max. peak inverse volts, 1,400					Max. d-c output ma., 100 — Max. peak plate ma., 300			Min. total effect. supply imped. per plate, 50 ohms
						With choke-input filter		Max. a-c volts per plate (rms), 500 — Max. peak inverse volts, 1,400					Max. d-c output ma., 100 — Max. peak plate ma., 300			Min. value of input choke, 6 henries
5Y3-GT/G	Full-wave rectifier	G-5Tj	F	5.0	2.0	With condenser-input filter		Max. a-c volts per plate (rms), 350 — Max. peak inverse volts, 1,400					Max. d-c output ma., 125 — Max. peak plate ma., 375			Min. total effect. supply imped. per plate, 50 ohms
						With choke-input filter		Max. a-c volts per plate (rms), 500 — Max. peak inverse volts, 1,400					Max. d-c output ma., 125 — Max. peak plate ma., 375			Min. value of input choke, 5 henries
5Y4-G	Full-wave rectifier	G-5Q	F	5.0	2.0			For other ratings, refer to Type 5Y3-GT/G.								
6A3	Power amplifier triode	4D	F	6.3	1.0	Class A amplifier	250	−45.0			60.0	800	5,250	4.2	2,500	3.20
						Push-pull class AB₁ amplifier	325 — 325	Cath. bias, 850 ohms;[j] −68 volts, fixed bias			80.0[f] — 80.0[f]				5,000 — 3,000	10.0[h] — 15.0[h]
6A6	Twin triode amplifier	7B	H	6.3	0.8	Amplifier		For other characteristics, refer to Type 6N7-GT/G.								
6A7	Pentagrid converter[d]	7C	H	6.3	0.3	Converter		For other characteristics, refer to Type 6A8.								
6A8	Pentagrid converter[d]	8A	H	6.3	0.3	Converter	100 — 250	−1.5 — −3.0	50 — 100	1.3 — 2.7	1.1 — 3.5	600,000 — 360,000	Anode-grid (#2): 250[e] max. volts, 4.0 ma. Oscillator-grid (#1) resistor,[r] Conversion transcond., 550 micromhos.			
6B4-G	Power amplifier triode	G-5S₈	F	6.3	1.0	Amplifier		For other characteristics, refer to Type 6A3.								
6B7	Duplex-diode pentode	7D	H	6.3	0.3	Pentode unit as amplifier		For other characteristics, refer to Type 6B8-G.								
6B8-G	Duplex-diode pentode	G-8Ej	H	6.3	0.3	Pentode unit as r-f amplifier	100 — 250	−3.0 — −3.0	100 — 125	1.7 — 2.3	5.8 — 9.0	300,000 — 600,000	950 — 1,125			
						Pentode unit as a-f amplifier	90[p] — 300[p]	Cath. bias, 3,500 ohms. — Cath. bias, 1,600 ohms.	Screen resistor = 1.1 meg. — Screen resistor = 1.2 meg.			Grid resistor,[f] = 1.0 megohm. — 0.5 megohm.				Gain per stage = 55 — Gain per stage = 79
6C5	Detector[a] amplifier triode	6Q	H	6.3	0.3	Class A amplifier	250	−8.0			8.0	10,000	2,000	20		
							90[p] — 300[p]	Cath. bias, 6,400 ohms. — Cath. bias, 5,300 ohms.				Grid resistor,[f] 0.25 megohm.				Gain per stage = 11 — Gain per stage = 13
						Bias detector	250	−17.0 approx. Plate current to be adjusted to 0.2 milliampere with no signal.								

Tube	Name	Application	Type	Cath.	Heater V	Heater A	Plate V	Grid bias	Screen V	Screen I	Plate I	Plate res.	g_m	μ	Load	Power out
6C8-G	Twin triode amplifier	Each unit as amplifier	G-8G	H	6.3	0.3	250	−4.5	—	—	3.2	22,500	1,600	36	—	—
6D6	Triple-grid super-control amplifier	Amplifier mixer	6F	H	6.3	0.3	For other characteristics, refer to Type 6U7-G.									
6E5	Electron-ray tube	Visual indicator	6R	H	6.3	0.3	Plate and target supply = 100 volts. Triode plate resistor = 0.5 meg. Target current = 1.0 ma. Grid bias, −3.3 volts; shadow angle, 0°. Bias, 0 volts; angle, 90°; plate current, 0.19 ma. Plate and target supply = 250 volts. Triode plate resistor = 1.0 meg. Target current = 4.0 ma. Grid bias, −8.0 volts; shadow angle, 0°. Bias, 0 volts; angle, 90°; plate current, 0.24 ma.									
6F6	Power amplifier pentode	Amplifier	7S	H	6.3	0.7	For other characteristics, refer to Type 6F6-G.									
6F6-G	Power amplifier pentode	Pentode class A amplifier	G-7S[j]	H	6.3	0.7	250 / 285	−16.5 / −20.0	250 / 285	6.5 / 7.0	34.0 / 38.0	80,000 / 78,000	2,500 / 2,550	—	7,000 / 7,000	3.2 / 4.8
		Triode[w] class A amplifier					250	−20.0	—	—	31.0	2,600	2,600	6.8	4,000	0.85
		Pentode push-pull class A amplifier					315 / 315	Cath. bias −24.0	285 / 285	12.0[i] / 12.0[i]	62.0[i] / 62.0[i]	Cath. bias resistor = 320 ohms[i]			10,000 / 10,000	10.5[A] / 11.0[A]
		Pentode push-pull class AB2 amplifier					375 / 375	Cath. bias −26.0	250 / 250	8.0[i] / 5.0[i]	54.0[i] / 34.0[i]	Cath. bias resistor = 340 ohms[i]			10,000 / 10,000	19.0[A] / 18.5[A]
		Triode[w] push-pull class AB2 amplifier					350 / 350	Cath. bias −38.0	—	—	50.0[i] / 48.0[i]	Cath. bias resistor = 730 ohms[i]			10,000 / 6,000	9.0[A] / 13.0[A]
6G6-G	Power amplifier pentode	Pentode class A amplifier	G-7S[j]	H	6.3	0.15	135 / 180	−6.0 / −9.0	135 / 180	2.0 / 2.5	11.5 / 15.0	170,000 / 175,000	2,100 / 2,300	—	12,000 / 10,000	0.6 / 1.1
		Triode[w] class A amplifier					180	−12.0	—	—	11.0	4,750	2,000	9.5	12,000	0.25
6H6	Twin diode	Voltage doubler	7Q	H	6.3	0.3	Max. a-c supply volts per plate (rms), 150. Total effect. plate supply imped. per plate: half-wave, 30 ohms; full-wave, 15 ohms. Max. d-c output 8 ma.									
		Half-wave rectifier					Max. a-c plate volts (rms), 150. Max. d-c output ma., 8 per plate. Min. total effective plate-supply impedance: up to 117 volts, 15 ohms; at 150 volts, 40 ohms.									
6J5	Detector amplifier triode	Class A amplifier	6Q	H	6.3	0.3	90 / 250	− / −8.0	—	—	10.0 / 9.0	6,700 / 7,700	3,000 / 2,600	20 / 20	—	—

RCA type	Name	Socket connections	C.T.	Volts	Amp	Use: Values to right give operating conditions and characteristics for indicated typical use	Plate supply, volts	Grid bias, volts	Screen supply, volts	Screen current, ma	Plate current, ma	A-c plate resistance, ohms	Transconductance (grid-plate), μmhos	Amplification factor	Load for stated power output, ohms	Power output, watts
6J7	Triple-grid detector amplifier	7R	H	6.3	0.3	Pentode class A r-f amplifier	100	-3.0	100	0.5	2.0	1,000,000	1,185	Grid resistor = 1.2 meg.	—	—
							250	-3.0	100	0.5	2.0	1.0+[f]	1,225		—	—
						Pentode class A a-f amplifier	90[g]	Cath. bias, 2,600 ohms.	Screen resistor = 1.2 meg.					Grid resistor,[f] 0.5 megohm.		Gain per stage = 85
							300[g]	Cath. bias, 1,200 ohms.	Screen resistor = 1.2 meg.							Gain per stage = 140
						Pentode bias detector	250	-4.3	100	Cathode current 0.43 ma.						—
						Triode[m] class A amplifier	180	-5.3			5.3	11,000	1,800	20	Plate resistor, 500,000 ohms.	
							250	-8.0			6.5	10,500	1,900	20	Grid resistor,[f] 250,000 ohms.	
6K5-G	High-mu triode	G-5U	H	6.3	0.3	Class A amplifier	100	-1.5			0.35	78,000	900	70	—	—
							250	-3.0			1.1	50,000	1,400	70	—	—
6K6-GT/G	Power amplifier pentode	G-7S[j]	H	6.3	0.4	Single-tube class A amplifier	100	-7.0	100	1.6	9.0	104,000	1,500		12,000	0.35
							250	-18.0	250	5.5	32.0	68,000	2,300		7,600	3.40
							315	-21.0	250	4.0	25.5	75,000	2,100		9,000	4.50
						Push-pull class A amplifier	285	-25.5	285	9.0[c]	55.0[c]	Cath. bias resistor, 400 ohms.			12,000	10.5[A]
							285	Cath. bias	285	9.0[c]	55.0[c]				12,000	9.8[A]
6K7	Triple-grid super-control amplifier	7R	H	6.3	0.3	Class A amplifier	100	-1.0	100	2.7	9.5	150,000	1,650		—	—
							250	-3.0	125	2.6	10.5	600,000	1,650		—	—
						Mixer in super-heterodyne	250	-10.0	100					Oscillator peak volts = 7.0	—	—
6L5-G	Detector amplifier triode	G-6Q[j]	H	6.3	0.15	Class A amplifier	135	-5.0			3.5	11,300	1,500	17	—	—
							250	-9.0			8.0	9,000	1,900	17	—	—
6L6	Beam power amplifier	7AC	H	6.3	0.9	Single-tube class A amplifier	250	-14.0	250	5.0	72.0	Cath. bias resistor, 170 ohms.			2,500	6.5
							250	Cath. bias	250	5.4	75.0				2,500	6.5
						Push-pull class A amplifier	270	-17.5	270	11.0	134.0[c]	Cath. bias resistor, 125 ohms.			5,000	17.5[A]
							270	Cath. bias	270	11.0	134.0[c]				5,000	18.5[A]
						Push-pull class AB₁ amplifier	360	-22.5	270	5.0[c]	88.0[c]	Cath. bias resistor, 250 ohms.			6,600	26.5[A]
							360	Cath. bias	270	5.0[c]	88.0[c]				9,000	24.5[A]
						Push-pull class AB₂ amplifier	360	-18.0	225	3.5[j]	78.0[j]				6,000	31.0[A]
							360	-22.5	270	5.0[c]	88.0[c]				3,800	47.0[A]
						Single-triode[w] class A amplifier	250	-20.0			40.0	1,700	4,700	8.0	5,000	1.4
							250	Cath. bias			40.0	Cath. bias resistor, 490 ohms.			6,000	1.3

Type	Name	Base	Cath.	Heater Volts	Heater Amp.	Use	Plate Volts	Grid Volts	Screen Volts	Screen Current (ma)	Plate Current (ma)	Plate Resistance (ohms)	Transconductance (micromhos)	Amp. Factor	Load Resistance / Power Output / Remarks
6L7	Pentagrid mixer amplifier[a]	7T	H	6.3	0.3	Mixer in super-heterodyne	250	—3.0	100	7.1	2.4	600,000	1,100	—	Oscillator-grid (#3) bias, —10 volts. Grid #3 peak swing, 12 volts minimum. Conversion transcond., 375 micromhos.
6N7	Twin triode amplifier	8B	H	6.3	0.8	Class A amplifier	250	—3.0[a]	100	6.5	5.3	—	—	—	For other characteristics, refer to Type 6N7-GT/G.
6N7-GT/G	Twin triode amplifier	G-8B[j]	H	6.3	0.8	Class A amplifier (as driver)[j]	250 / 294	—5.0 / —6.0	—	—	6.0 / 7.0	11,300 / 11,000	3,100 / 3,200	35 / 35	20,000 or more; exceeds 0.4
						Class B amplifier	300	0	—	—	—	—	—	—	8,000; 10.0. Power output is for one tube at stated plate-to-plate load.
6P5-GT/G	Detector amplifier triode	G-6Q[j]	H	6.3	0.3	Class A amplifier	100 / 250	—5.0 / —13.5	—	—	2.5 / 5.0	12,000 / 9,500	1,150 / 1,450	13.8 / 13.8	Gain per stage = 9 / Gain per stage = 10. Grid resistor,[f] 0.25 megohm.
						Bias detector	250	{—20.0 approx.}	—	—	—	—	—	—	Plate current to be adjusted to 0.2 milliampere with no signal.
6Q7	Duplex-diode high-mu triode	7V	H	6.3	0.3	Triode unit as class A amplifier	100 / 250	—1.0 / —3.0	—	—	0.8 / 1.0	58,000 / 58,000	1,200 / 1,200	70 / 70	Gain per stage = 32 / Gain per stage = 45. Cath. bias, 6,500 ohms. / Cath. bias, 6,400 ohms. Grid resistor,[f] 0.5 megohm.
6R7	Duplex-diode triode	7V	H	6.3	0.3	Triode unit as class A amplifier	250	—9.0	—	—	9.5	8,500	1,900	16	Gain per stage = 10 / Gain per stage = 10. Cath. bias, 7,600 ohms. / Cath. bias, 3,000 ohms. Grid resistor,[f] 0.25 megohm.
6S7	Triple-grid super-control amplifier	7R	H	6.3	0.15	Class A amplifier	135 / 250	—3.0 / —3.0	67.5 / 100	0.9 / 2.0	3.7 / 8.5	1,000,000 / 1,000,000	1,250 / 1,750	—	—
6SA7	Pentagrid converter[z]	8R	H	6.3	0.3	Mixer	100 / 250	Self-excited	100 / 100	8.5 / 8.5	3.3 / 3.5	500,000 / 1,000,000	—	—	Grid #1 Resistor, 20,000 ohms. Conversion Transcond., 450 micromhos.
6SA7-GT/G	Pentagrid converter[z]	GT-8AD	H	6.3	0.3	Mixer	100 / 250	— 1.0 / — 1.0	100 / 100	—	—	—	—	—	For other characteristics, refer to Type 6SA7.
6SF5	High-mu triode	6AB	H	6.3	0.3	Class A amplifier	100 / 250	—1.0 / —2.0	—	—	0.4 / 0.9	85,000 / 66,000	1,150 / 1,500	100 / 100	—
6SF7	Diode super-control amplifier pentode	7AZ	H	6.3	0.3	Pentode unit as class A amplifier	100 / 250	Cath. bias, 8,800 ohms. / Cath. bias, 3,200 ohms.	100 / 100	3.4 / 3.3	12.0 / 12.4	200,000 / 700,000	1,975 / 2,050	—	Gain per stage = 43 / Gain per stage = 63. Grid resistor,[f] 0.5 megohm.

RCA type	Name	Socket connections	C. T.	Volts	Amp	Use — Values to right give operating conditions and characteristics for indicated typical use	Plate supply, volts	Grid bias,[b] volts	Screen supply, volts	Screen current, ma	Plate current, ma	A-c plate resistance, ohms	Transconductance (grid-plate), μmhos	Amplification factor	Load for stated power output, ohms	Power output, watts
6SG7	H-f amplifier pentode	8BK	H	6.3	0.3	Class A amplifier	10 250 250	−1.0 −1.0 −2.5	100 125 150	3.2 3.4	8.2 11.8 9.2	250,000 900,000 1.0+⁴	4,100 4,700 4,000	—	—	—
6SJ7	Triple-grid detector amplifier	8N	H	6.3	0.3	Class A amplifier	100 250	−3.0 −3.0	100 100	0.9 0.8	2.9 3.0	700,000 1.0+⁴	1,575 1,650	—	—	—
							90ᵃ 300ᵃ	Cath. bias, 1,700 ohms. Cath. bias, 800 ohms.	Grid resistor,ᶠ 0.5 megohms.						{ Gain per stage = 93 { Gain per stage = 167	
6SK7	Triple-grid super-control amplifier	8N	H	6.3	0.3	Class A amplifier	100 250	−1.0 −3.0	100 100	4.0 2.6	13*0 9.2	120,000 800,000	2,350 2,000	—	—	—
6SQ7	Duplex-diode high-mu triode	8Q	H	6.3	0.3	Triode unit as class A amplifier	100 250	−1.0 −2.0			0.4 0.9	110,000 91,000	900 1,100	100 100		
							90ᵃ 300ᵃ	Cath. bias, 11,000 ohms. Cath. bias, 3,900 ohms.				Grid resistor,ᶠ 0.5 megohm.			{ Gain per stage = 40 { Gain per stage = 53	
6T7-G	Duplex-diode high-mu triode	G-7Vi	H	6.3	0.15	Triode unit as class A amplifier	135 250	−1.5 −3.0			0.9 1.2	65,000 62,000	1,000 1,050	65 65		
							90ᵃ 300ᵃ	Cath. bias, 8,300 ohms. Cath. bias, 4,580 ohms.				Grid resistor,ᶠ 0.5 megohm.			{ Gain per stage = 30 { Gain per stage = 40	
6U5/6G5	Electron-ray tube	6R	H	6.3	0.3	Visual indicator	Plate and target supply = 100 volts. Triode plate resistor = 0.5 meg. Target current = 1.0 ma. Grid bias, −8 volts; angle, 0°. Bias, 0 volts; angle, 90°; plate current, 0.19 ma.									
							Plate and target supply = 250 volts. Triode plate resistor = 1.0 meg. Target current = 4.0 ma. Grid bias, −22 volts; shadow angle, 0°. Bias, 0 volts; angle, 90°; plate current, 0.24 ma.									
6U7-G	Triple-grid super-control amplifier	G-7Ri	H	6.3	0.3	Class A amplifier	100 250	−3.0 −3.0	100 100	2.2 2.0	8.0 8.2	250,000 800,000	1,500 1,600			
						Mixer in super-heterodyne	100 250	−10.0 −10.0	100 100	—	—	Grid resistor,ᶠ 0.5 megohm.			Oscillator peak volts = 7.0	
6V6	Beam power amplifier	7AC	H	6.3	0.45	Amplifier	For other characteristics, refer to Type 6V6-GT/G.									
6V6-GT/G	Beam power amplifier	G-7ACi	H	6.3	0.45	Single-tube class A amplifier	180 250 315	−8.5 −12.5 −13.0	180 250 225	3.0 4.5 2.2	29.0 45.0 34.0	58,000 52,000 77,000	3,700 4,100 3,750	—	5,500 5,000 8,500	2.0 4.5 5.5
						Push-pull class AB₁ amplifier	250 285	−15.0 −19.0	250 285	5.0ⁱ 4.0ⁱ	70.0ⁱ 70.0ⁱ	—	—	—	10,000 8,000	10.0ʰ 14.0ʰ

Type	Name	Base	Heater	Volts	Amp.	Use	Max. Plate Volts	Grid Volts	Screen Volts	Screen ma.	Plate ma.	Plate Resistance	Transconductance	Load Resistance	Power Output
7A5	Beam power amplifier	6AA	H	6.3	0.7	Class A amplifier	110 / 125	−7.5 / −9.0	110 / 125	3.0 / 3.3	40.0 / 44.0	14,000 / 17,000	5,800 / 6,000	2,500 / 2,700	1.5 / 2.2
7A7	Triple-grid super-control amplifier	8V	H	6.3	0.3	Class A amplifier	For other characteristics, refer to Type 6SK7.								
7A8	Octode converter	8U	H	6.3	0.15	Converter	100 / 250	−3.0 / −3.0	75 / 100	2.7 / 3.2	1.8 / 3.0	650,000 / 700,000	Anode-grid (#2): 250[e] max. volts, 4.2 ma. Oscillator-grid (#1) resistor.[f] Conversion transcond., 550 micromhos.		
7B5	Power amplifier pentode	6AE	H	6.3	0.4	Class A amplifier	For other characteristics, refer to Type 6K6-GT/G.								
7B6	Duplex-diode high-mu triode	8W	H	6.3	0.3	Triode unit as amplifier	For other characteristics, refer to Type 6SQ7.								
7B8	Pentagrid converter	8X	H	6.3	0.3	Converter	For other characteristics, refer to Type 6A8.								
7Y4	Full-wave rectifier	5AB	H	6.3	0.5	With condenser-input filter	Max. a-c volts per plate (rms), 325; Max. peak inverse volts, 1,250. Min. total effect. supply imped. per plate, 150 ohms.								
						With choke-input filter	Max. a-c volts per plate (rms), 450; Max. peak inverse volts, 1,250. Min. value of input choke, 10 henries.								
12SA7	Pentagrid converter[z]	8R	H	12.6	0.15	Mixer	For other characteristics, refer to Type 6SA7.								
12SG7	H-f amplifier pentode	8BK	H	12.6	0.15	Amplifier	For other characteristics, refer to Type 6SG7.								
12SK7	Triple-grid super-control amplifier	8N	H	12.6	0.15	Amplifier	For other characteristics, refer to Type 6SK7.								
12SQ7	Duplex-diode high-mu triode	8Q	H	12.6	0.15	Triode unit as amplifier	For other characteristics, refer to Type 6SQ7.								
12Z3	Half-wave rectifier	4G	H	12.6	0.3	With condenser-input filter	Max. a-c plate volts (rms), 235; Max. d-c output ma., 55. Min. total effective plate-supply impedance: up to 117 volts, 0 ohms; at 150 volts, 30 ohms; at 235 volts, 75 ohms.								
24-A	R-f amplifier tetrode	5E	H	2.5	1.75	Screen-grid r-f amplifier	180 / 250	−3.0 / −3.0	90 / 90	1.7[z] / 1.7[z]	4.0 / 4.0	400,000 / 600,000	1,000 / 1,050	— / —	— / —
						Bias detector	250[o]	{ −5.0 approx. }	20 to 45	—	Plate current to be adjusted to 0.1 milliampere with no signal.				
25A6-GT/G	Power amplifier pentode	G-7S[j]	H	25.0	0.3	Class A amplifier	95 / 160	−15.0 / −18.0	95 / 120	4.0 / 6.5	20.0 / 33.0	45,000 / 42,000	2,000 / 2,375	4,500 / 5,000	0.9 / 2.2
25L6-GT/G	Beam power amplifier	G-7AC[j]	H	25.0	0.3	Amplifier	For other characteristics, refer to Type 50L6-GT.								

RCA type	Name	Socket connections	Cathode type and rating			Use — Values to right give operating conditions and characteristics for indicated typical use	Plate supply, volts	Grid bias,[b] volts	Screen supply, volts	Screen current, ma	Plate current, ma	A-c plate resistance, ohms	Transconductance (grid-plate), μmhos	Amplification factor	Load for stated power output, ohms	Power output, watts
			C. T.	Volts	Amp											
25Z5	Rectifier-doubler	6E	H	25.0	0.3	Rectifier-doubler	For other ratings, refer to Type 25Z6.									
25Z6	Rectifier-doubler	7Q	H	25.0	0.3	Voltage doubler	Max. a-c volts per plate (rms), 117. Max. d-c output ma, 75. Min. total effective plate-supply impedance: half-wave, 30 ohms; full-wave, 15 ohms.									
						Half-wave rectifier	Max. a-c volts per plate (rms), 235. Max. d-c output ma. per plate, 75. Min. total effect. supply imped. per plate: up to 117 volts, 15 ohms; at 150 volts, 40 ohms; at 235 volts, 100 ohms.									
27	Detector[a] amplifier triode	5A	H	2.5	1.75	Class A amplifier	135 250	− 9.0 −21.0	—	—	4.5 5.2	9,000 9,250	1,000 975	9.0 9.0	— —	—
						Bias detector	250	{ −30.0 approx. }	—	—	Plate current to be adjusted to 0.2 milliampere with no signal.					
30	Detector[a] amplifier triode	4D	D.C. F	2.0	0.06	Amplifier	For other characteristics, refer to Type 1H4-G.									
35L6-GT/G	Beam power amplifier	G-7AC[i]	H	35.0	0.15	Single-tube class A amplifier	110 200	− 7.5 − 8.0	110 110	3.0 2.0	40.0 41.0	14,000 40,000	5,800 5,900	—	2,500 4,500	1.5 3.3
35Z3	Half-wave rectifier	4Z	H	35.0	0.15	With condenser-input filter	For other ratings, refer to Type 35Z4-GT.									
35Z4-GT	Half-wave rectifier	G-5AA	H	35.0	0.15	With condenser-input filter	Max. a-c plate volts (rms), 235. Max. d-c output ma., 100. Min. total effect. plate-supply impedance: up to 117 volts, 15 ohms; at 235 volts, 100 ohms.									
35Z5-GT/G	Half-wave rectifier, Heater tap for pilot	G-6AD	H	35.0	0.15	With condenser-input filter	Max. a-c plate volts (rms), 235. Max. d-c output ma.: with pilot, 90; without pilot, 100. Min. total effect. plate-supply imped.: up to 117 volts, 15 ohms; at 235 volts, 100 ohms. Max. d-c output ma.: with pilot and no shunt res., 60; with pilot and shunt res., 100.									
42	Power amplifier pentode	6B	H	6.3	0.7	Amplifier	For other characteristics, refer to Type 6F6-G.									
43	Power amplifier pentode	6B	H	25.0	0.3	Amplifier	For other characteristics, refer to Type 25A6-GT/G.									
45	Power amplifier triode	4D	F	2.5	1.5	Class A amplifier	180 275	−31.5 −56.0	—	—	31.0 36.0	1,650 1,700	2,125 2,050	3.5 3.5	2,700 4,600	0.82 2.00
						Push-pull class AB₂ amplifier	275 275	Cath. bias, 775 ohms[j] −68.0 volts, fixed bias			36.0[i] 28.0[i]				5,000 3,200	12.0[h] 18.0[h]

Type	Name	Base	Cathode	V	A	Use	Plate V	Grid V	Screen V	Screen ma	Plate ma	Plate res.	Transcond.		Load	Power out
5OL6-GT	Beam power amplifier	G-7AC	H	50.0	0.15	Single-tube class A amplifier	110 / 200	− 7.5 / − 8.0	110 / 110	4.0 / 2.0	49.0 / 50.0	13,000 / 30,000	9,000 / 9,500	—	2,000 / 3,000	2.1 / 4.3
75	Duplex-diode high-mu triode	6G	H	6.3	0.3	Amplifier	For other characteristics, refer to Type 6SQ7.									
77	Triple-grid detector amplifier	6F	H	6.3	0.3	Class A amplifier	100 / 250	− 1.5 / − 3.0	60 / 100	0.4 / 0.5	1.7 / 2.3	600,000 / 1.0-⁴	1,100 / 1,250	—	—	
						Bias detector	250	− 1.95	50	Cathode current 0.65 ma.		—	Plate resistor, 250,000 ohms. Grid resistor, 250,000 ohms.			
78	Triple-grid super-control amplifier	6F	H	6.3	0.3	Amplifier mixer	For other characteristics, refer to Type 6K7.									
80	Full-wave rectifier	4C	F	5.0	2.0								For other ratings, refer to Type 5Y3-GT/G.			
81	Half-wave rectifier	4B	F	7.5	1.25	With condenser-input filter	Max. a-c plate volts (rms), 700 Max. peak inverse volts, 2000				Max. d-c output ma., 85 Max. peak plate ma., 500					
117L/M7-GT	Rectifier-beam power amplifier	8AO	H	117	0.09	Amplifier unit as class A amplifier	105	− 5.2	105	4.0	43.0	17,000	5,300	—	4,000	0.85
						Half-wave rectifier	Max. a-c plate volts (rms), 117 Max. peak inverse volts, 350				Max. d-c output ma., 75 Max. peak plate ma., 450		Min. total effect. plate-supply imped., 15 ohms.			
117N7-GT	Rectifier-beam power amplifier	8AV	H	117	0.09	Amplifier unit as class A amplifier	100	− 6.0	100	5.0	51.0	16,000	7,000	—	3,000	1.2
						Half-wave rectifier	Max. a-c plate volts (rms), 117 Max. peak inverse volts, 350				Max. d-c output ma., 75 Max. peak plate ma., 450		Min. total effect. plate-supply impedance, 15 ohms.			
117Z6-GT/G	Rectifier-doubler	G-7Q	H	117	0.075	Voltage doubler	Max. a-c volts per plate (rms), 117 Max. d-c output ma., 60						Min. total effective plate-supply impedance per plate: half-wave, 30 ohms; full-wave, 15 ohms.			
						Half-wave rectifier	Max. a-c volts per plate (rms), 235 Max. d-c output ma. per plate, 60						Min. total effect. supply imped. per plate: up to 117 volts, 15 ohms; at 150 volts, 40 ohms; at 235 volts, 100 ohms.			
VR 75-30	Voltage regulator	4AJ	Cold	—	—	Regulator	Min. d-c starting supply volts, 75. D-c operating volts, 75.						D-c operating ma., 5-30.			
VR 105-30	Voltage regulator	4AJ	Cold	—	—	Regulator	Min. d-c starting supply volts, 127. D-c operating volts, 105.						D-c operating ma., 5-30.			
VR 150-30	Voltage regulator	4AJ	Cold	—	—	Regulator	Min. d-c starting supply volts, 180. D-c operating volts, 150.						D-c operating ma., 5-30.			

APPENDIX XVI

RESISTANCE-CAPACITANCE-COUPLED AMPLIFIER CHART

The purpose of this appendix is to provide the data required for resistance-capacitance-coupled amplifiers referred to in the text, questions, and problems. A more complete list may be found in a tube manual.

C_b = blocking capacitor, μf
C_k = cathode by-pass capacitor, μf
C_2 = screen-grid by-pass capacitor, μf
E_{bb} = plate-supply voltage, volts
E_o = voltage output, max. value

R_k = cathode resistor, ohms
R_2 = screen-grid resistor, megohms
R_g = grid resistor, megohms
R_c = plate resistor, megohms
VA = voltage amplification

6B7

E_{bb}	90			180					300		
R_c	0.1	0.25	0.5	0.1	0.25			0.5	0.1	0.25	0.5
R_g	0.25	0.5	1	0.25	0.25	0.5	1	1	0.25	0.5	1
R_2	0.5	1.1	2.8	0.5	1.18	1.2	1.5	2.8	0.55	1.2	2.9
R_k	2200	3500	6000	1200	1900	2100	2200	3500	1100	1600	2500
C_2	0.07	0.04	0.04	0.08	0.05	0.06	0.05	0.04	0.09	0.06	0.05
C_k	3	2.1	1.55	4.4	2.7	3.2	3	2	5	3.5	2.3
C_b	0.01	0.007	0.003	0.015	0.01	0.007	0.003	0.003	0.015	0.008	0.003
E_o	28	33	29	52	39	55	53	55	89	100	120
VA	33	55	85	41	55	69	83	115	47	79	150

6C5, 6C5-G (6J7, 6J7-G, 6J7-GT, 12J7-GT AS TRIODES)

E_{bb}	90			180					300		
R_c	0.05	0.1	0.25	0.05	0.1			0.25	0.05	0.1	0.25
R_g	0.1	0.25	0.5	0.1	0.1	0.25	0.5	0.5	0.1	0.25	0.5
R_k	3400	6400	14500	2700	3900	5300	6200	12300	2600	5300	12300
C_k	1.62	0.84	0.4	2.1	1.7	1.25	1.2	0.55	2.3	1.3	0.59
C_b	0.025	0.01	0.006	0.03	0.035	0.015	0.008	0.008	0.04	0.015	0.008
E_o	17	22	23	45	41	54	55	52	70	84	85
VA	9	11	12	11	12	12	13	13	11	13	14

6J5, 6J5-G, 6J5-GT, 12J5-GT

E_{bb}	90			180					300		
R_c	0.05	0.1	0.25	0.05	0.1			0.25	0.05	0.1	0.25
R_g	0.1	0.25	0.5	0.1	0.1	0.25	0.5	0.5	0.1	0.25	0.5
R_k	2070	3940	9760	1490	2330	2830	3230	7000	1270	2440	5770
C_k	2.66	1.29	0.55	2.86	2.19	1.35	1.15	0.62	2.96	1.42	0.64
C_b	0.029	0.012	0.007	0.032	0.038	0.012	0.006	0.007	0.034	0.0125	0.0075
E_o	14	17	18	30	26	34	38	36	51	56	57
VA	12	13	13	13	14	14	14	14	14	14	14

6J7, 6J7-G, 6J7-GT, 12J7-GT (AS TRIODES, SEE 6C5)

E_{bb}	90			180					300		
R_c	0.1	0.25	0.5	0.1	0.25			0.5	0.1	0.25	0.5
R_g	0.25	0.5	1	0.25	0.25	0.5	1	1	0.25	0.5	1
R_2	0.44	1.18	2.6	0.5	1.1	1.18	1.4	2.9	0.5	1.18	2.9
R_k	1100	2600	5500	750	1200	1600	2000	3100	450	1200	2200
C_2	0.05	0.03	0.05	0.05	0.04	0.04	0.04	0.025	0.07	0.04	0.04
C_k	5.3	3.2	2	6.7	5.2	4.3	3.8	2.5	8.3	5.4	4.1
C_b	0.01	0.005	0.0025	0.01	0.008	0.005	0.0035	0.0025	0.01	0.005	0.003
E_o	22	32	29	52	41	60	60	56	81	104	97
VA	55	85	120	69	93	118	140	165	82	140	350

6N7, 6N7-G

E_{bb}	90			180					300		
R_c	0.1	0.25	0.5	0.1	0.25			0.5	0.1	0.25	0.5
R_g	0.25	0.5	1	0.25	0.25	0.5	1	1	0.25	0.5	1
R_k	2250	4950	8500	1700	2950	3800	4300	6600	1500	3400	6100
C_b	0.01	0.006	0.003	0.015	0.015	0.007	0.0035	0.0035	0.015	0.0055	0.003
E_o	19	20	23	46	40	50	57	54	83	87	94
VA	19	22	23	21	23	24	24	25	22	24	24

6SJ7, 12SJ7

E_{bb}	90			180					300		
R_c	0.1	0.25	0.5	0.1	0.25			0.5	0.1	0.25	0.5
R_g	0.25	0.5	1	0.25	0.25	0.5	1	1	0.25	0.5	1
R_2	0.29	0.92	1.7	0.31	0.83	0.94	0.94	2.2	0.37	1.10	2.2
R_k	880	1700	3800	800	1050	1060	1100	2180	530	860	1410
C_2	0.085	0.045	0.03	0.09	0.06	0.06	0.07	0.04	0.09	0.06	0.05
C_k	7.4	4.5	2.4	8	6.8	6.6	6.1	3.8	10.9	7.4	5.8
C_b	0.016	0.005	0.002	0.015	0.001	0.004	0.003	0.002	0.016	0.004	0.002
E_o	23	18	22	60	38	47	54	44	96	88	79
VA	68	93	119	82	109	131	161	192	98	167	238

6SQ7, 12SQ7

E_{bb}	90			180					300		
R_c	0.1	0.25	0.5	0.1		0.25		0.5	0.1	0.25	0.5
R_g	0.25	0.5	1	0.25	0.25	0.5	1	1	0.25	0.5	1
R_k	6600	11000	16600	2900	4300	4800	5300	8000	2200	3900	6100
C_k	1.7	1.07	0.7	2.9	2.1	1.8	1.5	1.1	3.5	2	1.3
C_b	0.01	0.006	0.003	0.015	0.015	0.007	0.004	0.004	0.015	0.007	0.004
E_o	5	7	10	22	21	28	33	33	41	51	62
VA	29	40	44	36	43	50	53	57	39	53	60

6T7-G

E_{bb}	90			180					300		
R_c	0.1	0.25	0.5	0.1		0.25		0.5	0.1	0.25	0.5
R_g	0.25	0.5	1	0.25	0.25	0.5	1	1	0.25	0.5	1
R_k	4750	8300	14200	2830	4410	5220	5920	9440	2400	4580	8200
C_k	1.5	1	0.6	2.25	1.5	1.25	1.11	0.74	2.55	1.35	0.82
C_b	0.012	0.0075	0.0045	0.0135	0.012	0.008	0.005	0.0045	0.0135	0.0075	0.0055
E_o	7.8	10	12	29	27	34	39	39	58	69	77
VA	24	30	33	28	34	36	38	41	32	40	43

(Courtesy of RCA Manufacturing Co.)

APPENDIX XVII

BIBLIOGRAPHY

I. Compilation of the textbooks listed as references in the bibliographies at the end of each chapter.

ALBERT, A. L., *The Electrical Fundamentals of Communication*, McGraw-Hill Book Company, Inc., New York.

ALBERT, A. L., *Fundamental Electronics and Vacuum Tubes*, The Macmillan Company, New York.

BRAINERD, J. G., KOEHLER, G., REICH, H. J., and WOODRUFF, L. F., *Ultra-high-frequency Techniques*, D. Van Nostrand Company, Inc., New York.

COOKE, N. M., and MARKUS, J., *Electronics Dictionary*, McGraw-Hill Book Company, Inc., New York.

DAWES, C. L., *Course in Electrical Engineering*, Vols. I and II, McGraw-Hill Book Company, Inc., New York.

EASTMAN, A. V., *Fundamentals of Vacuum Tubes*, McGraw-Hill Book Company, Inc., New York.

Encyclopaedia Britannica, Encyclopaedia Britannica, Inc., New York.

FLETCHER, G. L., MOSBACHER, I., and LEHMAN, S., *Unified Physics*, McGraw-Hill Book Company, Inc., New York.

GHIRARDI, A. A., *Radio Physics Course*, Murray Hill Books, Inc., New York.

GILBERT, N. E., *Electricity and Magnetism*, The Macmillan Company, New York.

GLASGOW, R. S., *Principles of Radio Engineering*, McGraw-Hill Book Company, Inc., New York.

HENNEY, K., *Principles of Radio*, John Wiley & Sons, Inc., New York.

HICKS, H. J., *Principles and Practice of Radio Servicing*, McGraw-Hill Book Company, Inc., New York.

HOAG, J. B., *Basic Radio*, D. Van Nostrand Company, Inc., New York.

MAGNUSSON, C. E., *Electric Transients*, McGraw-Hill Book Company, Inc., New York.

MANLY, H. P., *Drake's Cyclopedia of Radio and Electronics*, Frederick J. Drake & Co., Chicago.

NILSON, A. R., and HORNUNG, J. L., *Practical Radio Communication*, McGraw-Hill Book Company, Inc., New York.

PREISMAN, A., *Graphical Constructions for Vacuum Tube Circuits*, McGraw-Hill Book Company, Inc., New York.

REICH, H. J., *Theory and Applications of Electron Tubes*, McGraw-Hill Book Company, Inc., New York.

RIDER, J. F., *The Oscillator at Work*, John F. Rider Publisher, Inc., New York.

SLURZBERG, M., and OSTERHELD, W., *Electrical Essentials of Radio*, McGraw-Hill Book Company, Inc., New York.

TERMAN, F. E., *Fundamentals of Radio*, McGraw-Hill Book Company, Inc., New York.

777

TERMAN, F. E., *Radio Engineers' Handbook*, McGraw-Hill Book Company, Inc. New York.

TIMBIE, W. H., *Elements of Electricity*, John Wiley & Sons, Inc., New York.

The Radio Amateur's Handbook, The American Radio Relay League, Inc., West Hartford, Conn.

WATSON, H. M., WELCH, H. E., and EBY, G. S., *Understanding Radio*, McGraw-Hill Book Company, Inc., New York.

II. Reference books that can be purchased from manufacturers of radio equipment.

DEELEY, P. M., *Electrolytic Capacitors*, The Cornell-Dubilier Electric Corp., South Plainfield, N.J.

Jensen Technical Monographs: (1) *Loudspeaker Frequency-Response Measurements;* (2) *Impedance Matching and Power Distribution;* (3) *Frequency Range and Power Considerations in Music Reproduction;* (4) *The Effective Reproduction of Speech;* (5) *Horn Type Loudspeakers.* Jensen Radio Manufacturing Company, Chicago.

Meissner Instruction Manual—*How to Build Radio Receivers*, Meissner Manufacturing, Division Maguire Industries, Inc., Mt. Carmel, Illinois.

MYE Technical Manual, P. R. Mallory & Co., Inc., Indianapolis, Ind.

Reference Data for Radio Engineers, Federal Telephone and Radio Corporation, New York.

SMITH, F. L., *The Radiotron Designer's Handbook*, The Wireless Press, Sydney, Australia: distributed in U.S.A. by RCA Manufacturing Company, Inc., Harrison, New Jersey.

Tube Manuals

Allen B. DuMont Laboratories, Inc., Passaic, New Jersey.
General Electric Company, Tube Division, Schenectady, N. Y.
National Union Radio Corporation, Newark, N.J.
RCA Manufacturing Company, Inc., Harrison, N.J.
Sylvania Electric Products, Inc., Emporium, Pa.

Wiring Diagrams and Service Data of Commercial Radio Receivers

Radio Diagrams and Servicing Information, Supreme Publications, Chicago.
Radio Photo Fact Service, Howard W. Sams & Co., Inc., Indianapolis, Ind.
Rider Perpetual Troubleshooters' Manuals, John F. Rider Publisher, Inc., New York.

III. Magazines

Communications, Bryan Davis Publishing Co., Inc., New York.
Electronics, McGraw-Hill Publishing Company, Inc., New York.
Electronic Industries, Caldwell-Clements, Inc., New York.
Radio, Radio Magazines, Inc., New York.
Radio and Television Retailing, Caldwell-Clements Inc., New York.
Radio-Craft, Radcraft Publications, Inc., New York.
Radio Maintenance, Radio Maintenance Magazine, Montclair, N.J.
Radio News, Ziff-Davis Publishing Company, Chicago.
Service, Bryan Davis Publishing Co., Inc., New York.

APPENDIX XVIII

ANSWERS TO PROBLEMS

NOTE 1: Answers are provided for approximately 50 per cent of the problems. Except in a few cases, answers are provided for the odd-numbered problems. Instructors using this text can purchase a complete answer book from the publisher.

NOTE 2: As far as is practicable, all answers are accurate to three significant figures.

NOTE 3: Answers to problems involving values obtained from curves are generally difficult to check accurately because of variations in reading the curves. In preparing the answer book, enlarged drawings of the curves were used to aid in obtaining greater accuracy. In most cases the values obtained from the curve for use in solving the problems have been included with the answers.

Chapter I

1. (a) 4.414 feet
   (b) 1.345 meters
3. (a) 0.177 second
   (b) 0.00268 second
   (c) The radio listener
5. 5.65 to 0.376 feet
7. 0.0941 foot
9. 570 kc
11. 4.89 to 4.56 meters
13. 7812 kc
15. (a) 3.02 meters
    (b) 9.89 feet
17. 9340
19. 11,000
21. 0.0134 second
23. 60.7 feet

Chapter II

1. (a) 2 watts
   (b) 1 watt
   (c) 1 watt
   (d) 50 watts
3. (a) I_{BC}—1.74 ma
      I_{AB}—7.74 ma
   (b) I_{BC}—2.22 ma
      I_{AB}—5.22 ma
5. (a) 12 mv
   (b) 12 volts

(c) 36 volts
(d) 720 volts
7. (a) 56.9 μh
   (b) 719 μh
   (c) 25,396 μh
9. (a) 0.237
   (b) 0.32
   (c) 0.04
11. (a) 8635 ohms
    (b) 15,700 ohms
    (c) 23,550 ohms
    (d) 66,725 ohms
13. (a) 1500 ohms
    (b) 250 ohms
    (c) 1479 ohms
    (d) 3.92 henries
15. (a) 10 turns
    (b) 25 turns
    (c) 20 turns
    (d) 3480 turns
    (e) 1740 turns
17. 6 plates
19. 494 $\mu\mu$f
21. 49.82 $\mu\mu$f
23. (a) 331.7 ohms
    (b) 331.8 ohms
    (c) 0.331 amp
    (d) 0.0301
    (e) 88.5 degrees
    (f) 1.095 watts
25. 1.93 μf

779

27. (a) 162.1 ohms
   (b) i_{500}—0.6 amp
      i_{400}—0.75 amp
      i_{600}—0.5 amp
   (c) I_{line}—1.85 amp
   (d) p_{500}—180 watts
      p_{400}—225 watts
      p_{600}—150 watts
   (e) P_{line}—555 watts

29. (a) Group 1—40 ohms
      Group 2—50 ohms
      Group 3—30 ohms
      Group 4—30 ohms
   (b) 150 ohms
   (c) 2 amp
   (d) 600 watts
   (e) e_1—80 volts
      e_2—80 volts
      e_3—80 volts
      e_4—100 volts
      e_5—100 volts
      e_6—60 volts
      e_7—60 volts
      e_8—60 volts
   (f) i_1—0.5 amp
      i_2—1 amp
      i_3—0.5 amp
      i_4—0.667 amp
      i_5—1.333 amp
      i_6—2 amp
      i_7—1 amp
      i_8—1 amp
   (g) p_1—40 watts
      p_2—80 watts
      p_3—40 watts
      p_4—66.7 watts
      p_5—133.3 watts
      p_6—120 watts
      p_7—60 watts
      p_8—60 watts

31. (a) 500 ohms
   (b) 5250 ohms
   (c) 7950 ohms
   (d) 2745 ohms
   (e) 36.4 ma
   (f) Z_1—3010 ohms
      Z_2—2650 ohms
      Z_3—2258 ohms
      Z_4—5300 ohms
   (g) e_1—109.5 volts
      e_2—96.4 volts

e_3—82.2 volts
e_4—192.9 volts
   (h) p_1—0.331 watt
      p_2—0.0265 watt
      p_3—0.265 watt
      p_4—0.0397 watt
   (i) 0.662 watt
   (j) p-f_1—0.0830
      p-f_2—0.0075
   (j) p-f_3—0.0885
      p-f_4—0.0056
   (k) θ_1—85-degree lag
      θ_2—89.5-degree lead
      θ_3—85-degree lag
      θ_4—89.5-degree lead
   (l) 0.182
   (m) 79.5-degree lead

33. (a) 139.5 $\mu\mu$f
   (b) 45 $\mu\mu$f
   (c) 13.6 $\mu\mu$f

35. (a) 289 μh
   (b) 2416 kc

37. (a) 15.86 $\mu\mu$f
   (b) 1.96 mc
   (c) 3.36 mc
   (d) 3.77 mc

39. (a) 1138 μh
   (b) 274
   (c) 900,638 ohms
   (d) 55.5 μa
   (e) 15.2 ma
   (f) 15.2 ma

41. (a) 199 μh
   (b) 1083
   (c) 1.2 kc

43. 10.48 kc

47. (a) 2000 ohms
   (b) 2000 ohms
   (c) 1998.8 ohms
   (d) 1990 ohms
   (e) 1872 ohms
   (f) 1043 ohms

49. (a) 7222 ohms
   (b) 25,120 ohms
   (c) 62,800 ohms
   (d) 235,500 ohms

51. 4.24 henries

53. (a) 63,600 ohms
   (b) 636 ohms
   (c) 628 ohms
   (d) 62,800 ohms

55. (a) 63.6 ohms
  (b) The capacitor circuit
57. (a) 79.5 ohms
  (b) The capacitor circuit
59. (a) 80 henries
  (b) 111 ohms
  (c) 800 ohms
  (d) 720 henries
  (e) 900 ohms
61. (a) 7.8 kc
  (b) 6.0384
  (c) 50
  (d) 39
63. (a) 0.0375
  (b) 261.7 to 271.7 kc
  (c) 59.2 $\mu\mu$f
65. (a) 500 ohms
  (b) 800 ohms (k—1.60)
67. (a) 0.00025 second
  (b) 0.0002 second
  (c) No

Chapter III

1. 1500 kc
3. 4.99 μh
5. 247 $\mu\mu$f
7. 9938 kc
8. 546 kc
11. 10 μh
13. (a) 334 $\mu\mu$f
  (b) 550 to 813 kc
15. (a) 389 μh
  (b) 43.3 μh
  (c) 6.08 μh
17. (a) 194.6 $\mu\mu$f
  (b) 194.6 $\mu\mu$f
19. 39.3 $\mu\mu$f

Chapter IV

1. (a) 153.6 ohms
  (b) 25 watts
3. (b) 1.51 ohms
  2 watts
5. (b) 21 ohms
  (c) 5 watts
7. (b) R_1—42 ohms
  R_2—724.6 ohms
  (c) R_1—2 watts
  R_2—30 watts

11. 20 (de_b—50 volts)
  (de_c—2.5 volts)
13. 20 (de_b—50 volts)
  (de_c—2.5 volts)
16. 8000 ohms
  (de_b—100 volts)
  (di_b—12.5 ma)
18. 14,000 ohms
  (de_b—100 volts)
  (di_b—7.15 ma)
21. (a) 2500 μmhos
  (di_b—2.5 ma)
  (de_c—1 volt)
  (b) 2500 μmhos
23. (a) 1400 μmhos
  (di_b—1.4 ma)
  (de_c—1 volt)
  (b) 1428 μmhos
25. 99
27. 8421 ohms
29. (a) 3.15
  (b) 15.7
  (c) 4.72 volts
  23.5 volts
31. (a) 1.81
  (b) 13.6
  (c) 2.71 volts
  20.4 volts
33. (a) 78,000 ohms
  (b) 140,400 ohms
35. 250,000 ohms

Chapter V

1. (a) 50×10^{-6} second
  (b) 0.667×10^{-6} second
  (c) 75
2. (a) 1060 ohms
  (b) R is 471 times greater than X_C
  (c) The capacitor path
  (d) 3,180,000 ohms
  (e) X_C is 6.36 times greater than R
  (f) The resistor path
5. (a) 3419 ohms
  (b) Path through C_1
  (c) Yes. A small amount
  (d) 3419 ohms
  (e) Additional i-f filtering
  (f) 80 per cent
7. (a) 1060 ohms
  (b) 282,600 ohms

(c) 3,180,000 ohms
(d) 94.2 ohms
(e) The capacitor path
(f) The inductor path
9. (a) −4 to −2 volts
(b) −6 to 0 volts
(c) −7 to 1 volt
11. (a) −4.3 volts
(b) 4.3 volts (max value)
13. (a) −30 volts
(b) 30 volts (max value)
15. (a) 120,000 ohms
(b) 48,000 ohms
(c) 30,000 ohms
17. (a) 100,000 ohms
(b) 0.004 watt
(c) ¼ watt
19. (a) 3000 ohms
(b) 0.00126 watt
(c) ¼ watt
21. (a) 0.318 μf
(b) 0 5-μf, 200-volt, paper capacitor
23. (a) 10 6 μf
(b) 10-μf, 25-volt, electrolytic capacitor
25. 270 volts
27. 251.95 volts
28. (a) 970 ohms (I_b—8.25 ma)
(b) 870 ohms (I_b—6 9 ma)
(c) 667 ohms (I_b—6 ma)
(d) 400 ohms (I_b—5 ma)
29. (a) 0.066 watt
(b) 0.041 watt
(c) 0.024 watt
(d) 0.010 watt
32. (a) 172 ohms (I_k—5.3 ma)
(b) 476 ohms (I_k—3.7 ma)
(c) 757 ohms (I_k—2.8 ma)
(d) 1200 ohms (I_k—2 ma)
33. (a) 0.0057 watt
0.0084 watt
0.0082 watt
0.0075 watt
(b) ¼ watt (each)
35. (a) 2000.5 or 1999.5 kc
(b) 2001 or 1999 kc
(c) 2001.5 or 1998.5 kc
37. (a) 0.1 second
(b) 18.1 per cent
(c) 5 cycles

Chapter VI

1. (a) 278 μh
(b) 2383 kc
2. (a) 540 to 1870 kc
(b) 533 to 1590 kc
5. (a) 258 μμf
(b) 4664 kc
7. 300 μh
37.4 μh
5.27 μh
0.697 μh
8. 2295 kc
6.50 mc
17.3 mc
47.6 mc
9. 517 to 1650 kc
1.46 to 4.67 mc
3.90 to 12.4 mc
10.7 to 34.2 mc
13. 42.7 μμf
14. 1500 to 2097 kc
15. 517 to 1300 kc
1272 to 1570 kc
19. (a) 5.4 μμf
(b) Reduced to 494 kc
21. (a) 2629 μμf
(b) 1784 kc
22. (a) 5744 μμf
(b) 2252 kc

Chapter VII

1. (a) 2 volts
(b) 4 volts
(c) 4 volts
3. (a) 1000 ohms (I_b—8 ma)
0.064 watt
(b) 480 ohms (I_b—12.5 ma)
0.075 watt
(c) 228 ohms (I_b—17.5 ma)
0.07 watt
5. (a) −3 volts
(b) 8.2 ma
2.0 ma
(c) 294 ohms
(d) 0.03 watt
7. (a) 35
(b) −3 volts
(c) 105 volts (max)
(d) 2.1 ma
9. 27,777 ohms

11. (*a*) 70.5
    (*b*) 56.4 volts (max)
    (*c*) 1.41 ma
13. 177
15. (*a*) 91.5 (*Q*—145)
    (*b*) 144 (*Q*—143)
    (*c*) 148 (*Q*—98)
    (*d*) 90.8 (*Q*—45)
17. (*a*) 12.9
    (*b*) 35.1
    (*c*) 42.1
19. 181
21. (*a*) 226
    (*b*) 228
    (*c*) 226
23. (*a*) 72.9 per cent
    (*b*) 21.6 per cent
26. 122
27. (*a*) 0.0119
    (*b*) 138
30. (*a*) 85.7
    (*b*) 61.8
    (*c*) 5296

Chapter VIII

1. (*a*) 2.2553
    (*c*) 0.942
    (*e*) 0.699
    (*g*) 4.5441
    (*i*) 1.2625
2. (*a*) 1.2730
    (*c*) 0.9935
    (*e*) 3.57608
3. (*a*) 300
    (*c*) 6
    (*e*) 218
    (*g*) 9.625
    (*i*) 2082.5
5. 9.87 db
7. (*a*) 31.2 db
    (*c*) 37 db
9. (*a*) 40 db
    (*b*) 20 db
    (*c*) 30 db
    (*d*) 22.2 db
    (*e*) 30 vu
11. (*a*) 0.9 db (loss)
    (*b*) 6.02 db (loss)
13. (*a*) 47.3

    (*b*) 43.9
    (*c*) 46.1
14. (*a*) 0.64 db (loss)
    (*b*) 0.22 db (loss)
17. (*a*) 284
    (*b*) 262
    (*c*) 236
19. (*a*) 16.1
    (*b*) 17.5
21. (*a*) 81.7
    (*b*) 74
    (*c*) 81
    (*d*) 81.7
       74
       81
23. (*a*) 6674
    (*b*) 5476
    (*c*) 6561
26. (*a*) R_g—500,000 ohms
       R_1—1200 ohms
       R_2—1,180,000 ohms
       R_3—1200 ohms
       R_4—1,180,000 ohms
       C_b—0.005 μf
       C_1—5.4 μf
       C_2—0.04 μf
       C_3—5.4 μf
       C_4—0.04 μf
26. (*b*) 175
       159
       169
    (*c*) 89.7 db
       88.0 db
       89.1 db
27. 91 cycles
29. (*a*) R_g—250,000 ohms
       C_b—0.016 μf
       R_1—530 ohms
       C_1—10.9 μf
       R_2—370,000 ohms
       C_2—0.09 μf
    (*b*) 110
       105.6
       109.4
    (*c*) 40.8 db
       40.4 db
       40.7 db
30. 39 cycles (min)
    76,300 cycles (max)

31. (a) 304 volts
(b) 15.1
19.7
19.4
(c) 2.3 db
33. (a) 50 volts
(b) 300 volts
(c) 188,400 ohms
1,884,000 ohms
9,420,000 ohms
(d) 189,500 ohms (inductive)
4,623,000 ohms (inductive)
682,000 ohms (capacitive)
35. (a) 0.0079 μf
(b) 79 μμf
(c) 3.16 μμf
37. (a) 250.64 volts
(b) 39
50
59.7
(c) 23,900 cycles
(d) 148
(e) 2.1 db (loss)
(f) 1.5 db (gain)
39. (a) 40 volts
(b) 0.8
(c) 22.2 volts
(d) 4.5 volts
41. (a) 0.1
(b) 9.4
(c) 10
43. (a) 0.424
(b) 0.179

Chapter IX

1. −2 to −10 volts
78 to 185 volts
0.35 to 3.05 ma
3. 0 to −8 volts
48 to 160 volts
1 to 3.75 ma
5. (a) 60 ma
(b) 0 to −90 volts
(c) 104 to 372 volts
(d) 11 to 118 ma
6. (a) 58 ma
(b) 49 ma
(c) 146 volts
(d) 122 volts
7. (a) 57.2 ma
(b) 143 volts

(d) 40.4 ma
101 volts
(e) 4.08 watts
9. (a) 1650 ohms
(b) 0.920 watt
(c) 0.818 watt
11. 4.20 per cent
13. (a) 3300 ohms
(b) 0.818 watt
14. (a) 16.6 per cent
(b) 26.6 per cent
16. 11 watts
18. 3950 μmhos
21. (a) 3.96 watts
(b) 19 per cent
(c) 26.4 per cent
(d) 11.04 watts
(e) 5.76 watts
23. 1.7 watts
7.5 per cent
24. (a) 81 ma
(b) 5 ma
(c) 35.5 ma
(d) 68.5 ma
(e) 10.5 ma
(f) 315 volts
25. (a) 9.5 per cent
(b) 3.66 per cent
(c) 10.1 per cent
(d) 3.88 watts
(e) 28.1 per cent
28. (a) 3.4 watts
(b) 13.6 watts
(c) 33.5 db
30. (a) 16 watts
(b) 34.2 db
32. (a) 260 ma
136 ma
(b) 15.6 watts
(c) 1846 ohms
(d) 1.5 per cent
34. 23.4 watts
37. (a) 100,000 ohms
(b) 22
(c) 11,363 ohms
(d) 238,637 ohms
39. (a) 35.3
(c) 17.6
41. R_1—90,000 ohms
R_2—10,000 ohms

Chapter X

1. 877 to 2833 kc
3. 997 to 2400 kc
5. (a) 2.5 μsec
   (b) 0.227 μsec
   (c) Long
7. (a) X_L—34,540 ohms
      X_C—14.5 ohms
   (b) 2380
   (c) X_L—15,700 ohms
      X_C—31.8 ohms
   (d) 494
9. 1227 kc
11. 15
13. (a) 112 μμf
    (b) 15.9 ma
    (c) 7.96 mw
    (d) 0.0252 mw per cycle
    (e) 4.77
15. (a) 11.4 μh
    (b) 88.7 μμf
    (c) 4.16 amp
    (d) 0.332 amp
    (e) 199 μ watts per cycle
17. (a) 41.6 μh
    (b) 5.94 μh
    (c) 236 μμf
    (d) 4.62 μ watts per cycle
19. (a) 750 cycles (decrease)
    (b) 375 cycles (increase)
    (c) 750 cycles (increase)
21. 4239
23. (a) 0.45 inch
    (b) 0.045 inch
    (c) 0.01126 inch
25. (a) 400 kc
    (b) 2200 kc
    (c) 4000 kc

Chapter XI

1. (a) 135 volts
   (c) 90 volts
   (d) 423 volts
3. (a) 405 volts
   (c) 330 volts
   (d) 634.5 volts
5. (a) 169 volts
   (b) 338 volts
   (c) 338 volts
   (d) 338 volts

7. (b) 200 volts for C_1
      350 volts for C_2
      500 volts for C_3
   (c) 250 volts for C_1
      450 volts for C_2
      600 volts for C_3
   (d) 330 volts at each tube
9. 400 ma
11. (a) 117 volts
    (b) 111 per cent
    (c) 60 cycles per sec
13. (a) 53.1 volts
    (b) 180 cycles per sec
15. 0.09 volt
17. 3.74 per cent
19. (a) 1500 ohms
    (b) 998 μf
    (c) 2.66 ohms
    (d) 62 amp
    (e) Burn it out
    (f) No
21. (a) 9.97 per cent
    (b) 0.24 per cent
23. (a) 12.4 per cent
    (b) 0.452 per cent
    (c) 0.022 per cent
25. (a) 7.8 per cent
    (b) 0.517 per cent
28. 50 per cent
30. 96 volts
31. 2.5 per cent
33. (a) 1.25 per cent
    (b) 0.025 per cent
35. 14.4 per cent
37. (a) 1.80 per cent
    (b) 0.052 per cent
38. 4.8 henries
40. R_1—3344 ohms
    R_2—1886 ohms
    R_3—5555 ohms
    R_4—24.7 ohms
    R_5—6.2 ohms
    R_6—191 ohms
41. (a) 144 watts
    (b) 5.97 watts
       2.63 watts
       3.6 watts
       0.324 watt
       0.081 watt
       2.5 watts
44. (a) Reduces the voltage for the
       second grid of VT_1

(b) Reduces the voltage for the screen grids of VT_1, VT_2, and VT_3

(c) 180 volts

(d) 0.48 watt

(e) 105 volts

(f) 1.26 watts

45. 343 volts

Chapter XII

1. (a) 378 μw
   (b) 3.78 μw
   (c) 3.78 μw
   (d) 1.51 mw
3. 0.316 volt
5. (a) 0.0025 μw
   (b) 0.062 μw
7. (a) 50 μv
   (b) 2 mv
9. (a) 3.98 mv
   (b) 39.8 mv

11.

Feet	Volts	Per cent
7	2.23 mv	100
50	1.26 mv	56
100	0.84 mv	36
200	0.50 mv	22

13. 24.5
15. (a) 44.7
    (b) 22.3
    (c) 14.1
17. (a) 50
    (b) 100
19. (a) 0.00632 μf
    (b) 100 ohms
    (c) 5385 ohms
    (d) 3434 ohms
21. 109.6 db
23. (a) 79 db below 6 mw
    (b) 38 db below 6 mw

INDEX

A